ABSORPTION SPECTROSCOPY

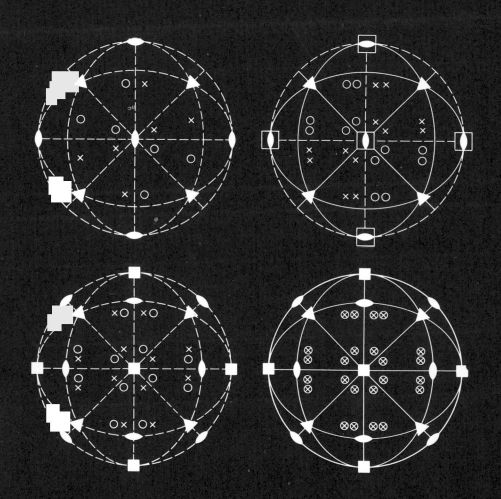

ABSORPTION SPECTROSCOPY

ROBERT P. BAUMAN, Assistant Professor of Physical Chemistry,
Polytechnic Institute of Brooklyn

John Wiley & Sons, Inc., New York · London

Library of Congress Catalog Card Number: 61–17353
Printed in the United States of America

to Edith

Preface

The need for an introductory textbook on absorption spectroscopy has become increasingly apparent in recent years. Rapid expansion of the field has created a severe shortage of personnel capable of operating the instruments and interpreting the results. At the same time there has been a growing recognition, both in universities and in industry, that the most effective utilization of these techniques is possible only when the individual chemist understands enough of the theory and practice to know how his samples should be prepared for analysis, to know which technique will be most likely to yield the specific information required, and to be able to interpret many features of the spectrum himself and consult intelligently with the specialist in spectroscopy on the interpretation of the remainder. This is increasingly true as the availability of low-cost spectrometers has moved such instruments onto the chemist's bench in rapidly increasing numbers.

Three distinct types of educational programs are required to meet the needs in this area. There must be courses aimed at developing specialists in valence theory and molecular dynamics, but there must also be courses with strong emphasis on applications of spectroscopy for qualitative identification and quantitative analysis. In addition, the industrial analyst with little or no formal training in spectroscopy must have available a guide to the field that can fill in the background material necessarily omitted from current research publications and from specialized monographs.

In view of this wide variation in goals and in academic and practical backgrounds, the choice of topics and of depth of coverage is not easy, but it has been shaped by experience gained in teaching courses corresponding roughly to the classifications described above. These have included a course in molecular spectroscopy, for physical chemistry majors and others with theoretical inclinations, a course in analytical absorption spectroscopy, with emphasis on techniques and applications, and an intensive, one-week summer course for those from industry who require sufficient understanding to begin effective laboratory work in applied infrared spectroscopy or who wish to fill in and supplement the working knowledge recently acquired.

Since it is, unfortunately, not possible to assume that students have had a course in optics or any acquaintance with matrices or with the theory of groups, these topics have been treated to the extent that an understanding of them seems important to the specific problems of spectroscopy. A brief review of certain features of classical mechanics and quantum mechanics is given in chapter V, but a conscious effort has been made to avoid the temptation to write a quantum mechanics text. Much of the development of quantum mechanical principles has been relegated to the problems. Several omissions and limitations will be readily apparent to the reader. Electronics is de-emphasized. Measurement and specification of color and the chemistry of producing absorbing species for colorimetric analysis have been excluded. There is no pretense of making the discussions of characteristic infrared frequencies or the description of electronic spectra of large molecules as comprehensive as the monographs already published on these topics. Only a brief venture into molecular spectroscopy is included, with emphasis placed on acquainting the student with the nomenclature and fundamental ideas involved in order to open up the extensive literature on this topic. Subjects requiring extended calculations—in particular, normal coordinate analysis, interpretations of absolute intensities, and molecular orbital calculations—have been intentionally slighted. This is not a reflection on their importance but rather a conviction that at our present state of knowledge the methods, the results, and the interpretation of these results depend heavily on the type of computer available. These topics are therefore better discussed in the current literature or monographs than in this introduction to the field.

Special thanks are due to Professor Howard Stidham for his helpful criticism of early versions of the manuscript, and to Mrs. Mary Caldera Caulfield and Mr. Stanley Abramowitz for assistance in running spectra. The contributions of Professor Joseph Steigman, Dr. Abraham Savitzky, Professor Ernest Loebl, and Mr. James Considine are also gratefully acknowledged, as well as the patient efforts of Mrs. Mary Sefferien who typed and retyped the many pages of stencils and manuscript.

It is a pleasure, also, to recognize the indispensable contributions by the many students whose questions and puzzled faces have been a guide to the elimination of many early difficulties and whose accomplishments of understanding have provided the encouragement so often required.

ROBERT P. BAUMAN

January, 1962

Contents

Introduction

Absorption spectroscopy is among the oldest of the fields of scientific specialization. Newton presented the optical principles required for spectroscopic investigations in the first years of the eighteenth century,[1] and a few years later Bouguer published his observations on the change in intensity of a beam as it passes through various thicknesses of absorbing material.[2] By the middle of the nineteenth century, Bunsen and Kirchhoff had developed the simple spectroscope in Fig. I-1 and had shown that the emission and absorption (Fraunhofer) lines of the elements are characteristic and can serve for the identification of the elements.[3] About the same time, Beer published his observations on the dependence of transmitted intensity on the concentration of the absorbing species in a solution.[4]

During the second half of the nineteenth century the discoveries of spectroscopists, working with both emission and absorption techniques, laid the groundwork for the early twentieth-century theories of atomic and molecular structure, and recent refinements of these theories have been based primarily upon modern spectroscopic measurements. By substitution of silica for glass these investigations have included the ultraviolet region, discovered by Ritter in 1801, as well as the visible. The infrared region, first recognized by Herschel in 1800,[3] was studied intensively by Coblentz[5] in the early years of the present century. Out of these studies came a recognition of the presence of "characteristic frequencies" for absorption by functional groups in organic molecules.

Increasing numbers of fundamental studies and analytical applications in the period before World War II led to a snowballing interest in all fields

[1] Newton, ref. 16.
[2] P. Bouguer, *Essai d'optique sur la gradation de la lumière*, 1729.
[3] Sawyer, ref. 10.
[4] A. Beer, *Ann. Physik. Chem.* (2) **86**, 78 (1852).
[5] Coblentz, ref. 5.

of spectroscopy that received great impetus from wartime investigations in electronics.   At the beginning of the war, emission spectroscopy, based on photographic detection, had already become a common method in analytical laboratories.   Absorption measurements, with few exceptions, were still limited to photographic detection, generally with a spectrograph

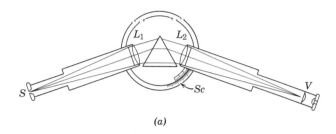

(a)

(b)

FIG. I-1.   (a) Bunsen spectroscope.   Radiation admitted by the slit S is collimated by lens L_1, dispersed by the prism, and focused by the lens L_2 and the eyepiece, V.   Angular position, which can be related to frequency or wavelength, is read from the scale, Sc. (Courtesy Brode, ref. 2.)   (b) An early commercial version of the Bunsen spectroscope, marketed by Hilger in 1875.   (Courtesy Hilger and Watts, Ltd.)

designed for emission studies, or were carried out on homemade spectrometers utilizing galvanometers that recorded vibrations originating inside and outside the laboratory in addition to the weak signals coming from the thermocouple detector.   A few commercial instruments were available before 1940, but they were very limited in capabilities.

Large scale application of spectroscopy to analytical, as well as theoretical, problems first became possible during and after the war with the introduction of commercial spectrometers based on electronic amplification and equipped with optical systems that could span the ultraviolet or infrared regions as well as the visible spectrum, and in this sense one might well describe the field of absorption spectroscopy as quite a new one. Indeed, certain branches are very new.   The Raman effect was discovered in 1928, and the field is just now overcoming its unique problems of instrumentation. Microwave spectroscopy, although achieved experimentally in very crude form in 1933, was really developed in the radar laboratories during the war and introduced to the world in 1946.   The so-called "resonance" techniques have been discovered entirely since the war.

Each portion of the electromagnetic spectrum yields information of one or more distinctive types, so that development of experimental methods for one region has supplemented and stimulated investigations in other regions. Before considering the characteristics of these regions, it is necessary to consider briefly the general properties of electromagnetic radiation and the connection between radiant energy and the atoms, ions, or molecules in which the chemist or physicist is interested.

I   Properties of Radiant Energy

Whether one prefers to think in terms of the classical wave picture for light or in terms of light quanta, or photons, it is only necessary to specify two properties of the radiation.   The quality is defined by giving the frequency, or the energy per photon, or the vacuum wavelength.   The quantity of radiant energy, which is termed the intensity of the beam, is related to the amplitude of the waves or to the number of photons present in the beam and may be specified in the common units of energy or power. These descriptions are related, often in a rather complex manner, to the concepts of color and brightness resulting from visual observation of light.[1]

The frequency is conveniently described as the number of waves, or wave maxima, passing a point of space in a given period of time.   If each wave maximum is separated by a distance λ from its neighbor,[2] and ν of these pass a point of space in unit time, the total distance traveled by one wave maximum in this time must be $\lambda\nu$.

$$\lambda\nu = v \qquad \text{(I-1)}$$

where v is the speed.

[1] Evans, ref. 58.

[2] The Greek alphabet will be found in Appendix IV.   Important symbols are indexed according to the approximate English equivalents.

The speed of all electromagnetic waves in vacuum is the same and is denoted by c. This is approximately 3×10^{10} cm/sec. In any other medium, however, waves of different frequency will travel at different speeds. The ratio of the speed in vacuum, c, to the speed in the material substance, v, is called the refractive index of the substance, n, and this will vary according to the frequency for which it is measured, even for the same substance.

$$n = c/v \qquad \text{(I-2)}$$

Often the change of refractive index with frequency is small, but it turns out that the cases in which refractive index does change rapidly with frequency are of more interest in spectroscopy.

It has been found that the frequency of the radiation is completely independent of the medium through which it is traveling. Combining equations I-1 and I-2, it is clear that the wavelength will depend upon the substance and will vary inversely with the refractive index. The refractive index is usually greater than 1 (see section II-2), and thus the speed, v, and the wavelength, λ, will be less in a material substance than in vacuum.

Einstein showed that it is necessary to assume all radiant energy to exist in discrete quanta, or photons. The frequency associated with each photon is proportional to the energy of the photon.

$$\text{E} = h\nu \qquad \text{(I-3)}$$

The constant, h, appearing in the equation is called Planck's constant and has a value of approximately 6.6×10^{-27} erg sec. (This is roughly 10^{-34} cal sec; the very small value of this constant is extremely important, as discussed in chapter V.) The energy of the photon, like the frequency, is independent of the medium in which measurements are made.

The significance of spectroscopic measurements lies in the association possible between the frequency of the radiant energy and the frequencies of molecular motions, or the energies of the photons and the energy separations associated with atomic or molecular states. As it has become possible to understand the absorption process, therefore, there has been a corresponding emphasis upon units of frequency and energy. The following statement indicates the change in practice which has occurred during the last half century.[1]

Until quite recently the frequency of light was seldom used or mentioned in connection with optical problems. Light was defined in terms of intensity and wavelength. With the modern development of the theory of spectra it has turned out that the frequency is the thing that matters, and very definite relations between the various lines of the spectrum of a given substance appear as soon

[1] Wood, ref. 18, p. 10.

as we substitute frequencies for wavelengths. Practically all researches in spectral theory are now reported with no mention at all of wavelengths, and it is accordingly now important for the student of modern optics to be able to think of light both in terms of frequency and wavelength.

Since there is no way of directly measuring a frequency as high as 10^{12} sec^{-1}, direct measurements must be in terms of wavelength (section II-3), and these are converted to frequencies by means of the experimentally determined speed of light in vacuum. For many purposes this is completely adequate, since the value of c is now known to about one part in a million. Wavelength measurements, however, can be made with an accuracy at least ten times better than this (one part in 10^7).[1] The experimental accuracy may be preserved if the experimental values are expressed in terms of the wavenumber, which is the number of waves, or wave maxima, per unit of length. The vacuum wavenumber, σ, is proportional to energy and to frequency but is not subject to the uncertainties associated with the values of c or h.

$$\sigma = \nu/c = E/hc = 1/\lambda_{vac} \qquad (I\text{-}4)$$

Alternatively, a frequency unit may be defined in terms of the speed of light in such a way that it is accurately related to the vacuum wavelength. This method is discussed below.

I.I Units for Energy, Frequency, Wavenumber, and Wavelength

Any unit of length is suitable, in principle, for designation of wavelengths, and the choice of unit thus depends primarily upon the magnitude of the wavelengths to be measured. In the ultraviolet and visible regions wavelengths are designated in ångstrom units, Å, or in millimicrons, mμ. Originally the ångstrom was defined as 10^{-8} cm, but it soon became apparent that the standard meter was too coarse a reference for wavelength measurements. (The scratches on the standard meter bar are not sufficiently sharp.) The ångstrom unit was therefore redefined in terms of the wavelength of the cadmium red line. More recently[2] the meter itself has been redefined to be 1,650,763.73 wavelengths (in vacuum) of the orange-red line of Kr^{86}, so the ångstrom may again be taken to be exactly 10^{-10} meter. Chemists often specify wavelengths in units of 10^{-9} meter, or 10 Å, a unit formerly called the millimicron but now more properly called the "nanon."[3] With modern spectroscopic instrumentation the millimicron, or nanon, offers no advantages over the ångstrom.

[1] Harrison, Davis, and Robertson, *J. Opt. Soc. Am.* **43**, 853 (1953).

[2] 11th General Conference on Weights and Measures, Paris, 1960.

[3] Commission on Symbols, Units, and Nomenclature (SUN) of the International Union of Pure and Applied Physics.

In the infrared region, wavelengths are expressed in microns, μ; one micron is 10^{-6} meter. Wavelengths of microwave radiation, which are short compared with radio waves but long compared to visible or infrared waves, are expressed in millimeters or centimeters. Values of wavelength or wavenumber should always be corrected to vacuum, although the correction from air to vacuum is often less than the experimental error or is incorporated into the calibration of the spectrometer.

In the cgs system, the unit of energy is the erg; in the mks system, it is the joule. Neither of these is directly related to the experimental methods of spectroscopy, and accordingly they are seldom employed for describing radiant energy. In the x-ray and ultraviolet regions the electron volt, ev, which is the energy acquired by an electron in falling through a potential drop of 1 volt, is sometimes directly related to the experimental measurements. Physicists often choose this unit for expressing ionization energies or for designating the position of an absorption or emission band in the ultraviolet region (or occasionally in the visible or near infrared regions as well).

The reciprocal second, sec^{-1}, is inconvenient for frequency measurements in spectroscopy. Microwave spectroscopists generally prefer megacycles per second, Mc/sec. The fresnel, f, defined as 10^{12} cycles/sec, has been proposed as a convenient unit for infrared, visible, and ultraviolet regions. It has not been widely accepted, probably owing as much to the lack of familiarity of workers with the numerical values that arise and the inconvenience of the conversion between the fresnel and wavelength units as to any objections about the uncertainty to be associated with values expressed in such a unit (due to uncertainty in the speed of light).

The wavenumber offers several advantages over wavelength, energy, or frequency. Conversion between wavelength and wavenumber requires only finding the reciprocal, with proper adjustment of the decimal point. Expressed in reciprocal centimeters, cm^{-1}, the wavenumber has convenient values in the infrared region. It retains the advantages of energy and frequency units in the interpretation of spectra.

The primary disadvantage of the wavenumber is the lack of significance of the term applied to molecular systems. It is quite proper to say that a molecule vibrates with a frequency of 3×10^{13} sec^{-1} (in the approximation of classical physics) and that it absorbs radiant energy with a wavenumber of 1000 cm^{-1}; it is not proper to say the molecule vibrates with a wavenumber of 1000 cm^{-1} or to call the quantity "1000 cm^{-1}" a frequency. This unfortunate dichotomy may be avoided if one defines a new unit of frequency that will give numerical values identical with those of the wavenumber expressed in reciprocal centimeters. This spectroscopic frequency

TABLE I-I

Conversion Factors for Frequencies, Energies, and Wavelengths[a]

Name of Unit	Symbol	Unit of	Equivalent to:					
			cycles/sec	cm⁻¹	ev	cal/mole	Å	meter
megacycle per sec	Mc/sec	ν	10^6	3.3356×10^{-5}	4.1355×10^{-9}	9.537×10^{-5}	2.9979×10^{12}*	2.9979×10^{2}*
reciprocal centimeter	cm⁻¹	ν/c	2.9979×10^{10}	1	1.2398×10^{-4}	2.859	10^8*	10^{-2}*
—[b]	—[b]	ν	2.9979×10^{10}	1	1.2398×10^{-4}	2.859	10^8*	10^{-2}*
electron volt	ev	E	2.4181×10^{14}	8.0658×10^3	1	2.306×10^4	1.2398×10^4*	1.2398×10^{-6}*
calorie per mole	cal/mole	E	1.0485×10^{10}	0.34975	4.3361×10^{-5}	1	2.859×10^8	2.859×10^{-3}*
joule per mole	joule/mole	E	2.506×10^9	8.3591×10^{-2}	1.036×10^{-5}	0.239006	1.1963×10^9*	0.11963*
erg (per molecule)	erg	E	1.5094×10^{26}	5.0348×10^{15}	6.2421×10^{11}	1.43956×10^{16}	1.9861×10^{-8}*	1.9861×10^{-18}*
ångstrom	Å	λ	2.9979×10^{18}*	10^8*	1.2398×10^4*	2.859×10^8*	1	10^{-10}
nanon (millimicron)	mμ	λ	2.9979×10^{17}*	10^7*	1.2398×10^3*	2.859×10^7*	10	10^{-9}
micron	μ	λ	2.9979×10^{14}*	10^4*	1.2398*	2.859×10^4*	10^4	10^{-6}

[a] See Table I-II.

[b] See p. 6 and Appendix II for a discussion of this spectroscopic frequency unit.

* Numbers marked with an asterisk are involved in a reciprocal relationship. For example,

$$10 \text{ ev} = 10 \times 2.306 \times 10^4 \text{ cal/mole} = \tfrac{1}{10} \times 1.2398 \times 10^4 \text{ Å}$$

TABLE I-II

Physical Constants [a]

Quantity	Symbol	Value
Speed of light in vacuum	c	2.997930×10^{10} cm/sec
Planck's constant	h	6.62391×10^{-27} erg sec
Boltzmann constant	k	1.38040×10^{-16} erg/deg
Gas constant	R	8.31429 joule/mole-deg
Rydberg constant	R_H	109677.576 cm^{-1}
	R_∞	109737.309 cm^{-1}
	cR_∞	3.289848×10^{15} sec^{-1}
	hcR_∞	2.17949×10^{-11} erg
Ionization energy of hydrogen	$R_H hc^2/e$	13.60 ev
Electronic charge	e	4.80273×10^{-10} esu
Bohr radius	a_0	0.529172 Å
Avogadro's number	N	6.02310×10^{23}
Mass of electron	m	9.1082×10^{-28} gm
Mass of proton	m_p	1.67237×10^{-24} gm

[a] Values are based on Cohen, Crowe, and Du Mond, *The Physical Constants of Physics*, Interscience, New York, 1957. See this reference for a discussion of the experimental and theoretical bases for these and the standard errors assigned to each. The mole is assigned on the scale $C^{12} = 12$. Values have been revised in accordance with Cohen and DuMond, *Phys. Rev. Letters* 1, 291 (1958).

unit should be defined as the frequency of electromagnetic radiation with a vacuum wavelength of 1 cm, so that the frequency, ν, in these units is numerically equal to the vacuum wavenumber, σ, in reciprocal centimeters (cm^{-1}), which in turn is identically equal to the reciprocal of the vacuum wavelength in centimeters.

Comparison of spectroscopic energies with thermodynamic energies involves a conversion from energy/molecule to energy/mole. The "mole" of radiation (a number of photons equal to Avogadro's number) is called the einstein, and the energy/einstein may be expressed in calorie/mole or joule/mole. Table I-I gives conversion factors between the frequency, energy, wavenumber, and wavelength units discussed. Table I-II gives values for some important physical constants.

1.2   Units for Radiant Energy, Power, Flux, or Intensity

Radiant power, or radiant flux, is the time rate of flow of radiant energy. The erg, joule, or other conventional energy unit is appropriate for measuring the total radiant energy absorbed from a beam; the radiant power is conventionally specified in watts or microwatts.   Any of several quantities proportional to energy may be called intensity, such as energy per unit volume or energy per unit time per unit area or solid angle.   Rather than select a restrictive definition, the term will be employed here in the generally understood loose sense and more specific terms will be introduced when numerical values or more precise description are required.   (When applied to an absorption band, the term "intensity" is roughly equivalent to the term "absorbance" defined in section 4.)   The intensity of an electromagnetic wave is proportional to the square of the amplitude of the wave.   In the quantum picture, the energy is the product of the energy per photon ($h\nu$) and the number of photons.

2   Energy Levels and Frequencies

The historical importance of optical measurements and theories in leading from the speculative philosophy of ancient times to modern experimental science can scarcely be overestimated.   The history of optics is to a large extent the history of modern physics.   Although the telescope was known to Galileo, in the early seventeenth century, it was Newton who provided a copious experimental basis for an understanding of optical phenomena and who provided a surprisingly complete picture of the nature of light and its origin.

Newton had concluded that[1] "Bodies are much more rare and porous than is commonly believed.... Gold has more Pores than solid parts," and had asked "Do not all fix'd Bodies, when heated beyond a certain degree, emit Light and shine; and is not this Emission perform'd by the vibrating motions of their parts?"

Newton's views concerning the corpuscular nature of light were abandoned during the nineteenth century, as they could not be reconciled with the observed wave properties.   The explanation of interference, diffraction, and refraction by Huygens, Young, and Fresnel, followed by the thorough exposition of the properties of all electromagnetic radiation by Maxwell (1860), seemed to have settled the corpuscle vs. wave question for all time, but only a few years later (1881–1889) Michelson and Morley conducted their experiments which showed an apparent absence of any

[1] Newton, ref. 16, pp. 267, 340.

medium capable of sustaining the electromagnetic oscillations. The investigation of this problem by Planck, Einstein, Bohr, and others led to our present concept of corpuscular radiation with wave-like properties.

For large systems, such as a radio antenna, the frequency of the radiation emitted is known to be equal to the frequency of oscillation of charge within the antenna. It is not possible to demonstrate such a correspondence when the emitting system is of molecular dimensions, but it has proved to be very helpful to assume that molecules do vibrate and rotate with frequencies very closely related to the frequencies emitted or absorbed. The details of this correlation, as well as the failure of attempts to draw similar simple correlations between electronic oscillations and ultraviolet-visible spectra, are discussed in the later chapters.

The most important result of the modern theory is the recognition that only certain energy values are possible for each atom or molecule. Transitions between states of different energy give rise to emission or absorption of radiation with a frequency related to the energy change of the atomic or molecular system by the Bohr equation $\nu = \Delta E/h$.[1] The aim of the spectroscopist is to measure the relative amounts of radiant energy absorbed or emitted at each frequency. From these measurements one can obtain information about the atoms or molecules involved, or, since different materials emit and absorb different frequencies and show different intensities of absorption, one can determine the amounts of various substances present in a mixture.

3 Types of Spectroscopy

Whether one is primarily interested in determining the structure of a single compound or in determining the amounts of various compounds present in a mixture, it is important to know the nature of the process giving rise to the absorption of radiation. In one case this information forms the basis for the theories which permit interpretation of the spectra; in the other case it allows one to predict how the spectra of various related compounds will differ, so that a frequency region can be selected that will distinguish between them.

Fortunately, although several processes leading to emission or absorption may occur in the atom or molecule, to a good approximation each of these processes is associated with radiation of very different frequency

[1] The total amount of energy, of a given frequency, absorbed by a sample is therefore proportional to the frequency and to the number of molecules absorbing. The number absorbing depends, in turn, on the energy of the incident beam and on the number of molecules present. This leads to Beer's law, equation I-5, relating the percentage of the incident energy transmitted to sample thickness and concentration.

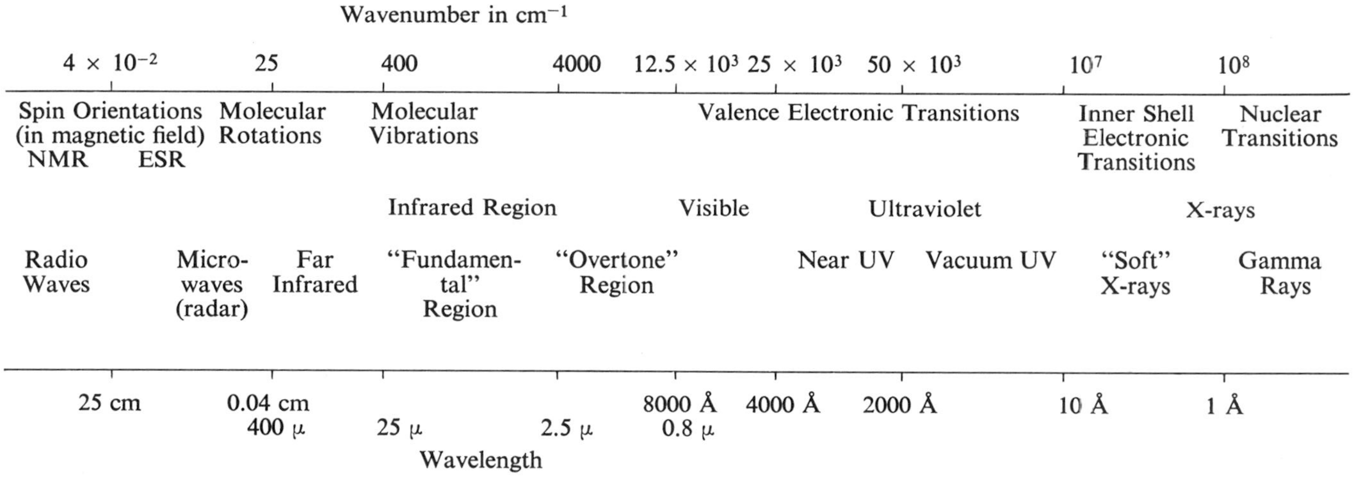

Wavenumber in cm⁻¹ — rendered below as cm^{-1}

$$\text{Wavenumber in cm}^{-1}$$

4×10^{-2}	25	400	4000	12.5×10^3	25×10^3	50×10^3	10^7	10^8

Spin Orientations (in magnetic field) NMR   ESR | Molecular Rotations | Molecular Vibrations | Valence Electronic Transitions | Inner Shell Electronic Transitions   Nuclear Transitions

Infrared Region | Visible   Ultraviolet   X-rays

"Fundamen-tal" Region | "Overtone" Region

Radio Waves | Micro-waves (radar)   Far Infrared | Near UV   Vacuum UV | "Soft" X-rays   Gamma Rays

| 25 cm | 0.04 cm 400 μ | 25 μ | 2.5 μ | 8000 Å 0.8 μ | 4000 Å | 2000 Å | 10 Å | 1 Å |

Wavelength

FIG. I-2. Schematic diagram of electromagnetic spectrum. Note that scale is non-linear. Boundaries between adjacent regions are generally quite arbitrary.

ranges, as indicated in Fig. I-2. Several types of spectroscopy may be distinguished on the basis of the frequency range in which measurements are made as well as the type of information sought. These branches of spectroscopy are indicated in Fig. I-3.

Very high energies, or high frequencies, will correspond to changes in the nucleus of an atom and will be independent of the environment of the nucleus. If a sample is irradiated with photons of less energy, electrons in the inner shells of the atoms will be knocked loose from the atoms. This will be accomplished by x-rays. As electrons return to their normal states in the atom, x-rays will be emitted. The frequencies of these rays will depend only on the atom, not on the state of chemical binding; this x-ray "fluorescence" is accordingly quite suitable for qualitative and quantitative identification of the elements present in a sample and is now commonly applied for these purposes.

Further reduction in energies leads to frequencies in the ultraviolet and visible regions of the spectrum. Electrons in the outer shells of atoms can be excited by strong heating or by bombarding the material with an electric arc, and the radiation emitted as the electrons return to their normal state can again serve for identification of the elements present. The emission spectrum in the ultraviolet and visible regions is nearly independent of chemical state, although exceptions to this are known. Emission spectra, including x-ray fluorescence spectra, are more easily measured for heavy metals than for the very light elements or non-metals.

Molecules cannot often be studied at the high temperatures required for thermal excitation of electrons, although observation of flames and of emission from the upper atmosphere are important exceptions. Molecules will absorb radiation, in some cases in the visible region but more often in the ultraviolet or far ultraviolet regions, as a result of the excitation of the outer, or valence, electrons. In most cases the energy absorbed is quickly converted to vibrational, rotational, and translational energy, but in some cases emission occurs, either immediately or after a short period of time. This is known as fluorescence or phosphorescence.

Frequencies falling in the infrared region are insufficient to disturb the electrons in a molecule, but they can cause the molecule to vibrate. The lower frequencies associated with the far infrared and microwave regions cause rotations of the molecules.

Microwave and radio-frequency radiation can be applied to studies of very low-energy transitions arising from reorientations of nuclear and electron spins in the presence of an applied magnetic field. This is called nuclear magnetic resonance or electron magnetic resonance, the latter being subdivided into paramagnetic and ferromagnetic effects.

Any process taking place in an atom or molecule associated with ab-

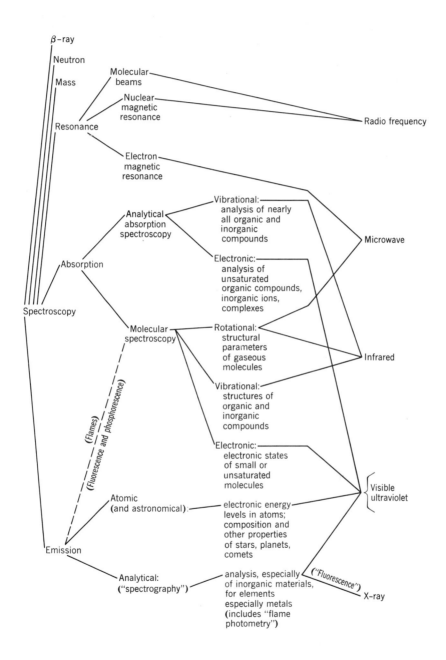

FIG. I-3.   Fields of spectroscopy.

sorption or emission of radiation is called a transition.   In general, one obtains absorption of energy only if the incident photons possess precisely the correct amount of energy for the transition to take place in the atom or molecule.   Energies too high are no more effective in bringing about transitions than are energies that are too low.   Raman spectroscopy is based upon an exception to this rule, for frequencies in the visible or ultraviolet regions may, under certain circumstances, be partially absorbed, causing the molecule to vibrate or rotate.   The photon is re-emitted with a new frequency, less than the original, as required for conservation of energy.   The frequency of the Raman line, ν_R, is given by the equation

$$\nu_R = \nu_E - \nu_v$$

where ν_E is the frequency of the incident radiation (the "exciting line") and ν_v is the vibrational frequency of the molecule.   The probability for this partial absorption is quite small.

The term "spectroscopy" has also been applied to several fields which do not involve electromagnetic radiation but which are based upon separation of a beam of particles according to their energy or other property.   Mass spectroscopy, for example, sorts out charged particles according to the ratio of charge to mass; β-ray spectroscopy measures the energies of electrons emitted from nuclei.

In Fig. I-3 a further distinction has been drawn depending upon whether the investigation is intended to determine structures of individual molecules or to analyze unknown materials, either qualitatively or quantitatively.   The former is often termed "molecular spectroscopy," the latter "analytical spectroscopy."   Absorption spectroscopy includes virtually all of molecular spectroscopy and much of analytical spectroscopy.

4   Laws of Absorption

Bouguer, and later Lambert, observed that the fractional part of the energy, or intensity, absorbed in a thin layer of material depended upon the substance and upon the frequency of the incident radiation and was proportional to the thickness.   Summation over a series of thin layers, or integration over a finite thickness, leads to an exponential relationship between transmitted intensity and thickness.   Beer demonstrated that the absorption coefficient introduced by Bouguer and Lambert was directly proportional to the concentration of the absorbing species in a solution. Combination of these results gives the relationship now commonly known as Beer's law.

$$I = I_0 10^{-abc}$$

or

$$A = abc = \log I_0/I \quad = -\log T \qquad (I-5)$$

In these equations I_0 is the intensity incident upon the first surface; I is the intensity transmitted through the thickness b; c is the concentration of the absorbing material; and a is the absorptivity, which depends upon the frequency of the radiation as well as upon the nature of the substance. The absorbance, A, is more simply related to the concentration and absorptivity than is I or the ratio of I to I_0 and is therefore commonly employed in quantitative measurements. The percentage transmitted, I/I_0, is known as the transmittance, T. Implications and limitations of equation I-5 are discussed in chapter IX.

5 Measurement of Absorption Spectra

Most measurements of the absorption of radiation must be made with a radiation source that emits a continuous range of frequencies. This is characteristic of nearly any body that emits as a result of high temperature. To obtain the information desired, therefore, it becomes necessary to separate the beam into parts according to frequency and to measure the absorption of each frequency interval separately. Spectrometers differ in the method chosen for separating the beam into frequency intervals and in the method chosen for determining I/I_0, the ratio of the intensity transmitted by the sample to the intensity that would be transmitted if the sample were not present.

5.1 Spectrometer Components

The spectroscope of Bunsen and Kirchhoff (Fig. I-1) contained the minimum essentials for separating light according to frequency. Light from the source passes through the narrow slit S_1 and is bent by the lens, L_1, into approximately parallel rays. These are bent by the prism, P, through an angle which depends on the refractive index of the prism material and hence depends on the frequency of the radiation. The lens L_2 may be moved in an arc to a position such that any desired ray coming from the prism will be intercepted and focused to the point S_2. The sensitive surfaces of the eye serve as a detector. Variations occur in the source and in the lens or mirror that collimates the beam coming from the first slit and sends it to the dispersing element. Various prism materials are available, depending upon the frequency range to be investigated, or a diffraction grating may replace the prism. The camera lens (L_2) may be a compound lens or a mirror, or it may coincide with L_1 or the grating. If the detector is a photographic plate or the human eye, no slit will be required at point S_2, but otherwise a slit is required in order that only the desired narrow portion of the spectrum will be passed to the detector. The sample which is to absorb part of the radiation can be placed at any point in the beam that is found to be convenient.

5.2 Types of Spectrometers

The term spectrum, the Latin word for image, was applied originally to the bands of color obtained with a prism and white light. The meaning has been broadened considerably to indicate any range of electromagnetic frequencies (or more loosely a wide variation in any quality) and especially the characteristic absorption or emission pattern of any substance in a given frequency range. Thus one may speak of the visible spectrum, meaning the colors of the rainbow; of the ultraviolet emission spectrum of iron; or of the infrared absorption spectrum of benzene. The term is also applied to the charts, recordings, or photographic impressions of these absorption or emission patterns. The plural form, spectra, is applied to the absorption or emission patterns of several substances or, in some cases, to a number of recordings of the spectrum of one material.

A spectroscope is an instrument, such as that of Bunsen and Kirchhoff, that permits visual observation of spectra. Instruments that record an image on a photographic plate are commonly called spectrographs, and those with electrical methods of detection and indication, even though they may produce a graphical record, are called spectrometers. A photometer is any device for measuring the intensity of radiation; thus any optical spectrometer may also be called a spectrophotometer. Often the same instrument may be adaptable to visual, photographic, or photoelectric detection, so that the distinction between these types is to a certain extent arbitrary and artificial. No attempt will be made here to distinguish between spectrographs and spectrometers, since most of the discussion will apply equally well for any type of detecting apparatus.

The simple spectroscope discussed above is a single-beam instrument; after measuring the intensity transmitted with the sample in place the sample must be removed and a reference material examined in the same way in order to find the transmittance. There will quite obviously be advantages in an instrument that will simultaneously determine the intensities transmitted by the sample and by a reference material and report the ratio, or the log of the ratio, directly.

Two basic types of double-beam spectrometers are available to provide a record of transmittance. These are distinguished by the manner in which the instrument is balanced. In an electronic-null spectrometer, the signal produced by the beam which has passed through the sample is electronically compared with the signal produced by the beam passing through the reference absorber.   In an optical-null spectrometer, the signals produced by the sample and reference beams are compared and the reference beam is attenuated by a comb or wedge that intercepts part of the radiation.   A phase-sensitive servomotor, driven by the amplified unbalance signal between the two beams, changes the position of the optical wedge until the unbalance signal disappears.

5.3   Recording and Presentation of Spectra

If one has available a signal coming from an amplifier indicating the intensity transmitted by a sample, it is a logical step to feed this signal into a recorder, put a motor on the frequency drive, and let the instrument record intensity and transmittance as a function of frequency.   Practically all spectrometers being sold today are so equipped, and many of those sold earlier without recording attachments are being converted.   In almost all cases except the very far infrared or the vacuum ultraviolet it is now appreciably more trouble to prepare a sample, even though this requires only an accurate dilution of a solution, than to scan the spectrum.   Records of transmittance or absorbance over the entire ultraviolet (from 50,000 to 25,000 cm^{-1} or 2000 to 4000 Å) or visible regions are routinely obtained in about 3 to 6 minutes.   The infrared region (5000 to 650 cm^{-1}) is commonly scanned in about 12 to 15 minutes.

Methods of presenting spectra have not yet been standardized, although certain customs are generally accepted.   The ordinate is a function of transmitted intensity, proportional either to total energy received by the detector, to the transmittance of the sample, or to the absorbance of the sample.   In some cases, log of absorbance or other functions of absorbance or reflectance may be plotted.   The abscissa is always a function of frequency, most often directly proportional to frequency or to wavelength, although for some instruments the scale is not linear in either.   In the ultraviolet and visible regions, absorption increases along the positive ordinate scale; in the infrared region, it is sometimes plotted in this direction but is often plotted in the reverse direction, for purely historical reasons.

5.4   Band Widths

Monochromatic radiation incident on the slit, S_1, of the spectroscope of Fig. I-1 will give rise to an image of the slit, and hence a line, at S_2.   If the lenses L_1 and L_2 have the same focal length, the width of the image will be the same as the width of the slit (except for very narrow slits), but the corners of the image will not be perfectly sharp because of imperfections of the optics and diffraction effects (see section II-3).   As the slit S_1 is made increasingly narrow, the image will become narrower until something approximating a limiting value, determined by the optical aberrations and diffraction effects, is reached.

The ability of the spectrometer to distinguish between two frequencies differing only slightly from each other will quite clearly depend on the widths of the images produced (relative to the separation of the images), since if these seriously overlap the observer will see one line rather than two.   The width of the image produced, for a given set of operating conditions, is thus an important measure of the quality of performance of an instrument.   The spread of the image along the frequency, wave-number, or wavelength scale is called the "spectral slit width."   It is very nearly proportional to the actual width of the slit S_1 (the "mechanical slit width") except for very narrow slits but depends on the dispersing element (the prism or grating) and on the optical design of the spectrometer.

Spectral slit width may be defined in several ways.   For example, one might illuminate the slit with monochromatic radiation and take the "half band width"[1] of the image to be the spectral slit width, as described above. In a recording spectrometer this would correspond to scanning past the frequency of the monochromatic line.   Alternatively one might illuminate the slit with a range of frequencies from a continuous source and then analyze the radiation passed by the exit slit, plotting intensity *vs.* frequency. In some cases the spectral slit width is taken to be synonymous with the resolution limit, that is, the distance in frequency, wavenumber, or wavelength units between two monochromatic lines which can just be distinguished by the spectrometer.   This is discussed in more detail in section III-5.5.

Molecules exhibit absorption over frequency regions varying from bands so narrow their widths can scarcely be measured to bands so broad they may cover tens, hundreds, or thousands of reciprocal centimeters. In some cases these apparent widths are the result of many closely spaced, narrow absorption bands which cannot be separated by the spectrometer employed; in other cases the bands actually correspond to continuous absorption over the broad frequency interval.   Knowledge of the true band width and contour is important in many theoretical investigations and is often helpful in qualitative analysis.

---

[1] The half band width is defined as the width of a band, in frequency, wavenumber, or wavelength units, half way up the band.   Since the shape of an absorption band is not constant on a transmittance scale, it is necessary to measure the half band width at an absorbance value equal to half the maximum absorbance.   For an emission line the width is measured at an intensity equal to one half the maximum intensity.

If the actual band width is comparable to the spectral slit width, the observed shape and intensity of the band will vary markedly as the spectral slit width is varied.   It is largely for this reason that a great deal of attention must be given to specification of the spectral slit width in reporting the results of spectroscopic measurements.

6   Applications of Absorption Measurements

From a record of transmittance *vs.* frequency, three types of information may be obtained.   The positions, or frequencies, of the absorption peaks depend upon what substances are present.   Except for minor changes due to change of state, each substance will always produce the same absorption pattern.   If a sufficient spectral region is covered, this absorption pattern can serve to characterize uniquely the compound involved.   In principle, and very often in practice, individual compounds may be identified unambiguously even when present in mixtures.

Positive identification of a compound should be made by comparing the observed spectrum with the spectrum, recorded under similar conditions, of an authentic sample.   In many cases identification can be made with a high degree of certainty, even in the absence of an authentic sample, from a knowledge of the relationship between chemical structure and spectra.   This method requires at least moderate understanding of the principles involved (these are summarized in chapters V, VI, and VII), as well as considerable familiarity with actual spectra of related compounds.

Quantitative analyses are based upon the validity (or approximate validity) of Beer's law (equation I-5) and the law of additivity of absorbance values due to different species present in a homogeneous mixture.   In general, it is first necessary to determine the absorption spectrum of each constituent of the mixture.   If a frequency can be found for each compound such that the compound in question absorbs strongly but the other constituents do not absorb, then each compound may be determined independently.   If this fortunate circumstance is not found, it is only necessary to measure as many frequencies as there are compounds to be determined.   This procedure gives a set of simultaneous linear equations which may be solved by conventional methods to find the concentrations. The choice of frequencies is often of great importance to the accuracy of the determination.   Measurements at more than the required number of frequencies make possible a partial elimination of random errors by finding the best set of concentrations according to the least-squares criterion (section IX-3.18).

The frequency of an absorption band, the band intensity, and the contour or structure of the band are valuable clues to the nature of the molecule responsible for the absorption.   It is possible, from an observation of the absorption pattern in the ultraviolet, the infrared, and the far infrared or microwave regions, to obtain such information as the size and shape of the molecule, including bond distances and angles; the strength, or stiffness, of the individual chemical bonds; the energy required to excite one or more valence electrons to excited states; and the properties of the molecule in these excited states.   In favorable cases additional information, such as the extent to which the molecular vibrations deviate from simple harmonic motion, the amount of interaction between various vibrational modes or between these and rotational motion, or the spins of the nuclei present in the compound, can be obtained.   An introduction to the methods of molecular spectroscopy is given in chapter X.

The broad classification of the applications given above cannot indicate the unusual power of spectroscopic methods in scientific research.   In chemical kinetics, bacteriology, astronomy, and many other fields, spectroscopy has been found to be an important tool that can quickly solve certain otherwise difficult if not impossible tasks.   Many compounds and free radicals have been observed and their properties determined by spectroscopic methods, even though it has not been possible to "capture" these for examination by conventional methods.   Temperatures and compositions of many astronomical bodies have been measured spectroscopically.   Classification of strains of bacteria, determinations of safety and potency of drugs, measurements of the attractive forces between molecules in solution, and accurate determinations of the thermodynamic properties of molecules are a few of the many examples of the application of spectroscopic techniques to the problems of other branches of science.

Problems

1.   Give the frequency, in cycles/sec, and the wavelength, in Å or in μ, for radiation of each of the following wavenumbers.

    (a) 50,000 cm^{-1} (b) 15,000 cm^{-1}
    (c) 1000 cm^{-1} (d) 300 cm^{-1}

2.   Give the wavenumber, in reciprocal centimeters, and the frequency, in cycles/sec, for radiation of each of the following wavelengths.

    (a) 4000 Å   (b) 8000 Å
    (c) 5 μ (d) 5 cm

3. For radiation of the frequency, wavenumber, or wavelength listed below, give the energy (in ergs) of one photon and the energy (in ergs and in calories) of one einstein.

    (a) 2500 Å   (b) 20,000 cm^{-1}
    (c) 3000 cm^{-1} (d) 3×10^{10} sec^{-1}

4.   Assume that a certain 50-watt low-pressure mercury arc has an efficiency (radiant-power output/power input) of 60% and assume that 40% of the radiant power appears

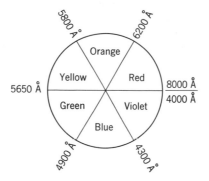

FIG. I-4.   Color wheel with approximate wavelengths.   For a more exact treatment see Evans, ref. 58, and references given therein.   See problem 7.

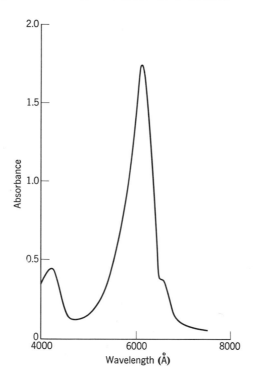

FIG. I-5.   Absorption spectrum of a commercial dye in water solution.   See problem 7.

as the 2537 Å line.   If the emission is uniform with respect to all directions, calculate the intensity of the 2537 Å radiation in the following units.

   (a) watt/cm² at a distance of 1 meter   (b) watt/steradian
   (c) erg/cm³ at a distance of 1 meter   (d) photon/cm³ at a distance of 1 meter

5. Calculate the half width, in appropriate wavelength units, corresponding to the following half widths.

(*a*) 1.5 cm⁻¹ at 30,000 cm⁻¹   (*b*) 15 cm⁻¹ at 1000 cm⁻¹
(*c*) 150 cm⁻¹ at 1000 cm⁻¹   (*d*) 15 cm⁻¹ at 30,000 cm⁻¹

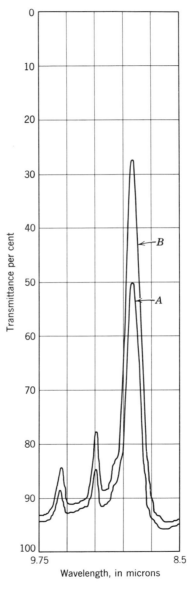

FIG. I-6.   Infrared spectrum of dioxane in CCl₄.   See problem 10.

6. The C—H stretching vibration has a frequency corresponding to a wavenumber of about 3000 cm^{-1}.

(a) Find the wavelength, in μ, at which this absorption band will occur in the infrared region.

(b) Find the wavelength at which this band will appear in the Raman spectrum when the exciting line has a wavelength of 4358 Å.

(c) Find the wavelength at which this band will appear in the Raman spectrum when the exciting line has a wavelength of 4047 Å.

7. The color exhibited by an absorbing material, either by reflection or transmission (except for the "surface colors" of certain pigments—see Wood, ref. 18, pp. 103–104,

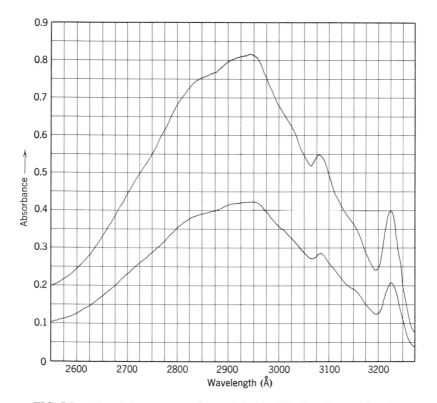

FIG. I-7.   Ultraviolet spectrum of 1-naphthol in CH_2Cl_2.   See problem 11.

509–510), will be the complement of the color absorbed.   Qualitatively this color may be predicted by means of the familiar color wheel shown in Fig. I-4.   What color would be observed for

(a) a compound with maximum absorptivity at 19,000 cm^{-1}?
(b) a compound with maximum absorptivity at 3720 Å?
(c) the compound with the spectrum shown in Fig. I-5?

8. The blue line of mercury is observed at 4358.35 Å in air (ref. 59).   Assume this to be "standard air" (dry air at 15°C, under a pressure of 760 mm Hg for 0°C and $g = 980.665$ cm/sec^2, with 0.03% CO_2).   Find

(a) the wavelength in vacuum
(b) the (vacuum) wavenumber in cm^{-1}
(c) the wavelength *inside* a cell containing water if $n = 1.3333$ for water (relative to air).

Assume Edlen's formula for the refractive index of air:

$$(n - 1)10^8 = 6432.8 + 2,949,810(146 - \sigma^2)^{-1} + 25,540(41 - \sigma^2)^{-1}$$

where σ is the wavenumber in reciprocal microns, μ^{-1} [*J. Opt. Soc. Am.* **43**, 339 (1953)].

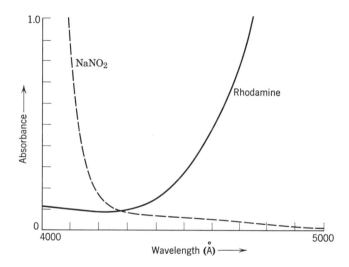

FIG. I-8.   Absorption spectrum of Rhodamine 5GDN Extra (0.02 gm/liter) in water and of NaNO$_2$, saturated solution in water, measured in cells of 1-cm path length. See problem 12.

9. Benzene has an absorption band in the vapor at about 40,455 cm^{-1} (2472 Å).   At what wavelength would this band be observed in isoöctane solution ($n = 1.3916$) if interaction between the benzene and isoöctane has a negligible effect on these energy levels?

10. In Fig. I-6 the transmittance of two samples is plotted against wavelength. Assuming Beer's law to be valid, find the concentration of the more dilute solution if the other solution has a concentration of 51.0 gm/liter.

11. In Fig. I-7 the absorbance of two samples is plotted against wavelength. Assuming Beer's law to be valid, find the concentration of the more dilute solution if the other solution has a concentration of 1.5 moles/liter.

12. The spectra of Rhodamine 5GDN Extra (du Pont) and of NaNO$_2$ in water solution are shown in Fig. I-8 as a plot of absorbance *vs.* wavelength.   (These are common

filter solutions to isolate the 4358 Å line of mercury for Raman spectroscopy.) What percentage of the incident 4358 Å radiation will be transmitted by

(a) 0.5 cm of the Rhodamine solution?

(b) 0.5 cm of the $NaNO_2$ solution?

(c) 0.5 cm of the Rhodamine plus 0.5 cm of $NaNO_2$?

II

Spectrometer components

The tremendous growth of spectroscopy in industry and the widespread adoption of the techniques by organic and analytical chemists have been made possible largely because instrumentation for the average worker has come to mean nothing more, in general, than turning dials or replacing vacuum tubes in a commercial instrument.   Nevertheless there are times when the operator must choose between two dial settings, two prisms, or perhaps two instruments.   The discussion that follows is intended to serve as a guide in making such choices.   Emphasis has been placed on the principles of operation rather than on the methods of instrument design.

The principles of optics and electronics that are employed are in large part common to all regions of the spectrum from the vacuum ultraviolet to the far infrared, and thus it is not possible to uniquely divide the discussion into separate units according to the frequency regions.   There are, on the other hand, important differences in details.   The major organization has therefore been on the basis of the functions of the components, while under each topic the visible and ultraviolet regions have been considered first (these being the most familiar and in many respects the simplest regions from the standpoint of instrumentation), and this is followed by a discussion of the infrared region.

The essential parts of any spectrometer are: a source of radiant energy, a monochromator to separate the radiation according to frequency, and a detector and indicating system (meter or recorder), with provision either before or after the monochromator for inserting a sample into the beam. In ultraviolet spectrometers the sample is nearly always placed after the monochromator, since there is occasionally danger of decomposing the sample or inducing fluorescence if high-energy (high-frequency) ultra-violet radiation strikes it.   In the infrared the sample is placed before the

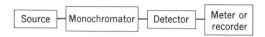

FIG. II-1.   Block diagram of spectrometer.   The sample is usually placed immediately before or after the monochromator.

monochromator (section 5).   Figure II-1 shows the components in a block diagram.

I   Sources

The ideal source of radiant energy would be one of uniform intensity throughout the entire region of its application, or perhaps with somewhat greater intensity in those regions where the transmittance of the optical system or the sensitivity of the detector are less.[1]   In particular, it should be free of dark regions or sharp, intense lines.   If the source is very much more intense in one region than in another, "stray" radiation becomes a problem.   This "stray light" consists of radiation of one frequency that emerges from the monochromator when it is set to deliver some other frequency.   If the source is of approximately uniform intensity (and transmittance and sensitivity are also approximately uniform), the require-ments on the monochromator are quite easily met in this regard, for it is not difficult to produce an optical system that will trap 99.9% or con-siderably more of the incident radiation of all frequencies other than the "one" sought (of course, a finite spread is always obtained).

Suppose, for example, that a monochromator is set to transmit all radiation of $40,000 \pm 100$ cm^{-1} (2500 Å).   If the source is of uniform intensity and less than 0.01% of the signal is to be "stray" of frequency between 12,500 and 25,000 cm^{-1} (visible light), then, since there are 6.25 intervals of 200 cm^{-1} in this region, less than $10^{-4}/6.25 = 1.6 \times 10^{-5}$ of the visible light of any particular 200 cm^{-1} interval may be allowed to pass out the exit slit.   But, if the source is 1000 times as intense in the visible

[1] An even better source would of course be a tunable monochromatic source, such as the klystrons and magnetrons of microwave spectroscopy.   The only mono-chromatic sources known for optical frequencies are atomic emission lines, of fixed frequency, and the laser and iraser, visible and infrared versions of the maser (for microwave amplification by stimulated emission of radiation).   There is no firm evidence yet that it will be possible to produce a laser or iraser tunable over any appreciable frequency range.

region as it is at 40,000 cm $^{-1}$, the monochromator must be 1000 times better to achieve the same net performance. To meet the specifications above a discrimination factor of $1/1.6 \times 10^{-8}$ would be required. Although such performance can be achieved, it is generally preferable to start with a more uniform source if one is available.

1.1 Black-Body Radiation

The basis of modern theories of radiation was laid by Planck in 1900 when he explained the observed frequency distribution of radiant energy emitted by a "black body," an object (such as a hollow sphere with only a small aperture) that is in thermal equilibrium with its own radiation. Classical mechanics had predicted that most of the radiation would be emitted at very high frequencies, since there are many more high frequencies than low frequencies and from the equipartition of energy principle all frequencies of oscillation should have the same average energy. (This has been called the "ultraviolet catastrophe.") Experimental measurements, on the other hand, showed that the distribution of energy with frequency had a definite maximum and the general form of a Maxwell-Boltzmann distribution curve.

Planck showed that, if the material oscillators of the black body could exchange energy with the radiation field only in units of energy equal to $h\nu$ and multiples of this, the energy could be given as a function of frequency by the equation

$$\frac{d\text{E}}{d\nu} = \frac{8\pi V \nu^2}{c^3} \cdot \frac{h\nu}{[\exp (h\nu/kT)] - 1} \qquad \text{(II-1)}$$

where V is the volume, k is Boltzmann's constant, T is the absolute temperature, h is 6.6×10^{-27} erg sec, and c is the speed of light. This equation accurately describes the observed distribution. For high frequencies it reduces to the formula of Wien, $d\text{E}/d\lambda = c_1\lambda^{-5} \exp (-c_2/\lambda T)$, where c_1 and c_2 are constants. For low frequencies (as the product $h\nu$ goes to zero) Planck's equation gives the Rayleigh-Jeans formula,

$$\frac{d\text{E}}{d\nu} = \frac{8\pi V \nu^2 kT}{c^3}$$

which had been derived on the basis of classical physics.[1]

[1] The number of modes of oscillation per unit volume, $8\pi\nu^2\,d\nu/c^3$, is multiplied by kT, the classical value for the average energy for each degree of freedom. The number of modes, or the number of wavenumber vectors in the interval $d\sigma$, is $4\pi\sigma^2\,d\sigma$ (the volume of a spherical shell in wavenumber space), multiplied by 2 because each wave can have either of two polarizations.

Two additional equations help to illustrate the dependence of the radiation on the temperature. Wien's Displacement Law states that the frequency corresponding to the maximum intensity is proportional to the absolute temperature, $\nu_{max} \sim T$. According to the Stefan-Boltzmann law, obtained empirically by Stefan and from a Carnot-cycle type of argument by Boltzmann, the total energy emitted in unit time is proportional to the fourth power of the temperature, $P \sim T^4$. A graph of the radiant energy emitted by a black body as a function of frequency, and a

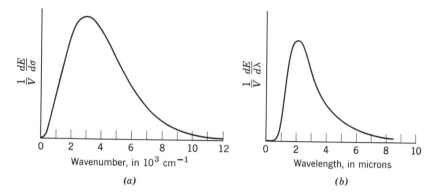

FIG. II-2. Black-body emission curve for a source at 1500°K: (a) erg/cm³ per cm⁻¹ *vs.* wavenumber in 10³ cm⁻¹; (b) erg/cm³ per micron *vs.* wavelength in microns.

similar plot in terms of wavelength, is given in Fig. II-2. Sources which emit radiant energy at all frequencies (continuous, or "thermal," sources) will at least approximately follow the black-body curve. Changing the temperature of these sources will produce a shift in the distribution of energy with frequency toward higher or lower frequencies. The emissivity of any substance depends on its absorption characteristics, as well as on the temperature, since a substance can only emit those frequencies which it can absorb (Kirchhoff's law).

1.2 Common Radiation Sources

In the visible and very near infrared regions a tungsten filament lamp is a very inexpensive but satisfactory source. Projector bulbs and automobile headlight bulbs are frequent choices for the visible region; a ribbon filament lamp, with lower filament temperature, is preferable for the near infrared. Other, more intense, sources are available, such as the carbon arc, but for most purposes there is no need for such great intensity.

Source intensity is more of a problem in the ultraviolet region. The common source is a hydrogen lamp, such as the Beckman or Nestor lamps.

The discharge in these tubes produces a reasonably constant level of intensity over the region commonly covered by commercial ultraviolet spectrometers (above 1850 Å, or below 54,000 cm^{-1}). The range of the former is limited in part by the thin glass window. The power output of the hydrogen lamp is largely limited by the localized heating produced by the discharge. Nearly a two-fold gain in intensity has accordingly been achieved on the Cary Model 14 spectrometer by operating the lamp at twice the rated power during the half cycle in which the shutter is open, and turning the lamp off, except for a trickle discharge, during the remaining half cycle.

The xenon discharge lamp[1] has shown considerable promise as a source for the ultraviolet region. The intensity is much greater than that of the hydrogen lamp. The primary difficulty has been with spatial stability of the extremely small, intense spot of light produced. The much greater intensity of the lamp in the visible region is a potential cause of serious stray radiation problems.

The mercury arc, a standard source for much ultraviolet work, is generally not suitable for absorption measurements because it is not sufficiently uniform with respect to frequency, even at high pressures. The low-pressure mercury arc is, however, very valuable for calibration purposes. In the near ultraviolet, above about 3300 Å (30,000 cm^{-1}), the tungsten lamp is most satisfactory.

In the infrared region the primary sources are the Globar and the Nernst glower. The Globar, a silicon carbide rod, is generally about 5 cm long and 5 mm in diameter, with silver-coated tips for good electrical contact. It is heated to approximately 1200°C by a current of about 4 amperes (200 watts). The distribution of energy with frequency is comparable to that of the Nernst glower, except that the operating temperature is somewhat lower; as the stability (lack of fluctuations of intensity) is very good, it can be employed in single-beam instruments without monitoring. Preheating is not necessary, but the Globar must be cooled by enclosing it in a water-cooled jacket.

The Nernst glower is a hollow cylinder of refractory oxides, about 3.5 cm long and 1.5 mm wide. Because of its negative thermal coefficient of resistance it requires a preheating mechanism and must be operated in series with a ballast, such as a light bulb. Although it is less constant in output than the Globar, the fluctuations are small changes over a period of minutes or hours which can be easily corrected by a monitoring system that includes a phototube to measure the output with feedback controls

[1] Baum and Dunkelman, *J. Opt. Soc. Am.* **40**, 782 (1950); W. T. Anderson, Jr., *ibid.*, **41**, 385 (1951). The former gives a comparison of the most common ultraviolet sources.

to adjust the voltage across the glower as necessary.   For double-beam instruments the monitoring system is not required.   The small size of the glower makes focusing somewhat critical, especially for double-beam spectrometers, but it has the decided advantage of not requiring water cooling.

In many plant-stream analyzers and in some of the newer, low-cost spectrometers the source is a coil of Nichrome wire.   This source has the advantages of large size and long lifetime.   An alumina tube, heated by a wire running through the center, has also been found to have good emission characteristics and a long life.   Below 400 cm^{-1} the Welsbach mantle is reportedly superior to any of the sources described above.   The carbon arc[1] will produce great intensity throughout the infrared, and it has been shown that it can be made quite stable by means of a constant-current power supply,[2] but it is relatively inconvenient and dirty.

2   Refraction and Dispersion

Light passing obliquely from one transparent medium into another is bent from its initial path.   Considering the light to consist of rays, which will tend to travel in straight lines, the angle of incidence may be defined

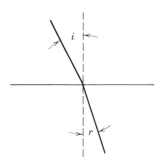

FIG. II-3.   The angle of incidence, i, and the angle of refraction, r, are related by Snell's law.

as the angle between the path of the light, as it approaches the interface, and the perpendicular to the interface at the point of incidence.   The angle of refraction is the angle between the ray, after it has passed the interface, and the perpendicular to the interface.   This is shown in Fig. II-3.

The angle of incidence, the angle of refraction, and the perpendicular to

[1] Rupert and Strong, *J. Opt. Soc. Am.* **40**, 455 (1950); **42**, 684 (1952).

[2] J. J. Jaffe, *J. Opt. Soc. Am.* **43**, 619 (1953).

the surface will be coplanar.   As the ray passes from a rare medium (such as vacuum or air) into a more dense medium (the meaning of this optical density will be specified more exactly below), it will be bent toward the perpendicular; hence, if it passes from the more dense into the less dense medium, it will be bent away from the perpendicular, for all optical paths are reversible.[1]   The ratio of the sine of the angle of incidence to the sine of the angle of refraction depends on the two media and on the nature of the light (the frequency), but, for a given frequency of radiation passing between two particular substances, the ratio of these sines will be a constant: sin i/sin r = constant.   The deviation of this constant from unity is clearly a measure of the relative densities, in the optical sense, of the two media.

If one chooses a single frequency of radiation for all measurements, and measures the value of sin i/sin r for a number of pairs of substances, the value of this constant for substances 2 and 3 will be the ratio of the value for substances 1 and 2 to the value for substances 1 and 3.   For example, consider the special case in which the yellow light from a sodium lamp passes from vacuum into water and from vacuum into a "dense flint" glass.   In the first case the ratio of sines will be 1.3333, and in the second the ratio will be 1.6499.   It is then possible to predict immediately that yellow light passing from water into a dense flint glass will be bent toward the perpendicular such that sin i/sin r = 1.6499/1.3333.

The ratio observed, as described above, in passing from vacuum into another substance is called the refractive index, or index of refraction, or sometimes the optical density, of the substance.   Then the ratio of the sine of incidence to the sine of refraction, in passing from a substance of refractive index n_1 into a substance of refractive index n_2, is equal to the ratio n_2/n_1.

$$(\sin i)_{n_1}/(\sin r)_{n_2} = n_2/n_1 \qquad \text{(II-2)}$$

This is Snell's law.   Table II-I lists refractive indices for several substances.

2.1   Classical Theory of Wave Propagation[2]

An alternative definition of the refractive index compares the speed of the radiation in vacuum to the speed in the substance.

$$n = c/v \qquad \text{(II-3)}$$

---

[1] All optical paths are reversible to the extent that they involve geometrical optics, or ray diagrams.   Processes such as scattering, absorption, and depolarization involve an increase of entropy and are inherently irreversible.   See R. Clark Jones, *J. Opt. Soc. Am.* **43**, 138 (1953).

[2] Some readers may wish to omit this section in a first reading.

TABLE II-I

Index of Refraction of Various Substances[a]

Substance	Index	Substance	Index
Air, 15°	1.0002765	NaCl	1.544
Water, 20°	1.33336	CaF_2	1.658
Zinc crown	1.517	Cyclohexane	1.429
Light flint	1.575	Benzene	1.501
Heavy flint	1.650	Methylene iodide	1.738
Silica	1.458	Quartz o	1.544
		e	1.553

[a] Values are given for substances in the vicinity of room temperature, relative to vacuum, for Na D light.   From *Handbook of Chemistry and Physics*, Chemical Rubber Company, Cleveland, Ohio.

A rigorous proof that these definitions are equivalent requires the application of Huygens' construction (see below).   A qualitative argument that is often applied envisions a company of soldiers marching in formation from smooth ground obliquely onto rough terrain.   Although the count may remain steady, the length of the step will be decreased by the more

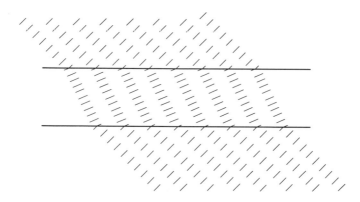

FIG. II-4.   When the waves striking a substance of high refractive index are slowed down, crowding occurs (the "tempo," or frequency, is constant) and the direction is changed toward the perpendicular.

difficult conditions, and hence the speed will decrease.   In the time required for the left-hand column to reach the boundary (Fig. II-4), the right-hand column will have traveled a smaller distance than normal and the line of march will be deflected toward the perpendicular.   As the right-hand column passes back onto smooth ground, the speed will increase and the line of march will be deflected an equal amount in the opposite direction, so that the final result (assuming the boundaries to be parallel) is a lateral displacement of the line of march but no change in direction.

The frequency of radiation is constant as the beam passes through various materials. As the speed decreases, the wavelength is simultaneously decreased, so that under all conditions

$$\lambda v = v \qquad (\text{II-4})$$

The cause of retardation for electromagnetic radiation passing through matter is not immediately apparent. Cauchy, in 1836, gave an argument based on the model of vibrations in an elastic solid and proposed that the refractive index should vary with the wavelength according to an equation of the form

$$n = A + B/\lambda^2 + C/\lambda^4 \qquad (\text{II-5})$$

Over limited regions such an equation agrees with experiment, but serious discrepancies appear as the wavelength approaches that of an absorption band, and contradictions occur even for passage through vacuum. Several others attempted to improve on Cauchy's treatment, but it was Maxwell and Sellmeier who correctly related the effect to the forced vibrations of the medium.

Charges[1] in any medium will have certain natural frequencies corresponding to rotations, vibrations, or electronic motions, and interactions between the field and these motions must be considered. If the damping, or retardation, forces on the material oscillators are very small, a radiation field of frequency less than the natural frequency of the oscillators will interact only negligibly with these. As the frequency of the radiation becomes nearly equal to the frequency of the oscillators, the oscillators will be set in motion, in phase with the applied field. The amplitude of the forced oscillations will be small at first but will become very large as the electromagnetic frequency becomes equal to the oscillator frequency. As the frequency begins to exceed[2] that of the material oscillators, the forced vibrations will again decrease in amplitude and will be 180° out of phase relative to the applied field (Fig. II-5).

The reason for a phase difference is readily seen by considering the nature of simple harmonic motion (section V-1.1). At the extremes of the motion the speed is zero; at the equilibrium point the speed is a maximum. An electric field applied to a pair of opposite charges which are

[1] The nature of the charges involved is discussed in later chapters. For present purposes one may consider a molecule such as HCl, which will have a small negative charge associated with the chlorine atom and a small positive charge associated with the hydrogen.

[2] The frequency range over which strong interaction can occur depends on the amount of damping, or the degree of anharmonicity, of the material oscillators.

bound together will tend to pull these apart or push them together, as shown in Fig. II-6.   The maximum acceleration due to the field will occur

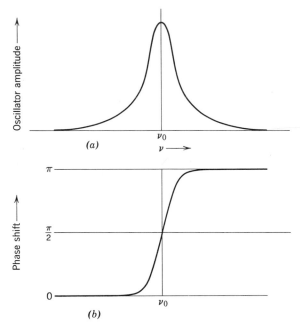

(a)

ν_0

$\nu \longrightarrow$

(b)

ν_0

FIG. II-5.   (a) Amplitude of oscillation of a slightly damped oscillator of natural frequency ν_0 plotted against the frequency of the driving impulses.   (b) Phase shift between the driven oscillator and the driving impulses on the same frequency scale.

when the field is a maximum; the minimum acceleration will occur when the field is zero.

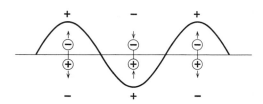

FIG. II-6.   Schematic representation of interaction of an oscillating electric field and a polar molecule.   The field alternately stretches and compresses the molecule, causing vibration of the molecule.

In Fig. II-7 the acceleration due to the electromagnetic field and the speed and acceleration of the harmonic oscillator are shown schematically for the case in which the imposed frequency is in phase with the motions of the oscillator, 90° ahead of the oscillator, and 180° ahead of the oscillator. When the imposed frequency is low the oscillator can follow the field, but the field works with the motion half of the time and against it half of the time, leading to no effective transfer of energy. The accelerations due to the field and to the natural restoring force of the oscillator are opposed. At resonance when the two frequencies agree and the phase difference is 90°, the applied field always accelerates the particle in the direction in which it is moving. In the absence of frictional or other damping forces, which would tend to change the frequency of the oscil-

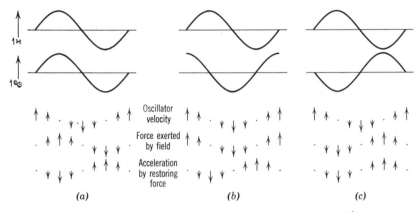

FIG. II-7. Relative phases and magnitudes of oscillator displacement, $\vec{x}$, applied field, $\vec{\mathscr{E}}$, and acceleration of the oscillator (by restoring force). These quantities are shown for the driving frequency (a) less than the resonant frequency, ν_0 ($\nu < \nu_0$, $\Delta\phi = 0$); (b) equal to the resonant frequency ($\nu = \nu_0$, $\Delta\phi = \pi/2$); (c) greater than the resonant frequency ($\nu > \nu_0$, $\Delta\phi = \pi$).

lator, the amplitude of the oscillation should tend to become infinite. When the frequency of the applied field is too high, the oscillator can no longer follow the field closely, and again the field accelerates the particle part of the time and decelerates it part of the time. (When the applied field is 180° ahead of the oscillator the accelerations of the field and oscillator are always in phase; this is roughly equivalent to doubling the strength of the spring—clearly this does not lead to a spontaneous motion of an oscillator.) These phase differences are shown by any system forced into oscillation. They are most simply observed by swinging a weight on the end of a string. If the hand moves slowly the pendulum will remain in phase with the motion of the hand, but if the hand is moved quickly the motion of the pendulum will be 180° out of phase with the hand.

Huygens' very important contribution to the theory of light consisted of his postulate that light waves, like waves of water, travel outward from any point in spherical arcs, and that at any point in space the wave surface acts as a secondary source, sending out new waves (Fig. II-8). He explained rectilinear propagation of light in a rather unsatisfactory manner by assuming that the secondary emission occurs along the "front" surface of the wave.   Young, Fresnel, Maxwell, and Sellmeier were among those who revised the Huygens postulates to achieve better agreement with experiment and with other principles of classical physics.

According to the classical theory of electromagnetic propagation, one may consider waves to be propagated, or transmitted, from point to point in the ether, the ether having the ability to follow the field in resonance

FIG. II-8.   Huygens' construction.   Each point on the wave front serves as a source of radiation, but because of interference the disturbance is propagated only perpendicular to the original wave front.

(that is, 90° behind the applied field) regardless of the frequency.[1]   Each point of the vibrating ether acts as a secondary source, the amplitude of the secondary emission being proportional to the acceleration (rather than the amplitude) of the fictitious ether oscillator.   The effect is shown in Fig. II-9, which shows the applied field, $\mathscr{E}$, the displacement of the oscillator, x, and the amplitude of the field arising from the secondary emission, $\mathscr{E}'$.   It may be noted that, surprisingly enough, the secondary emission, and hence the new wave which is to take the place of the "absorbed" wave,

---

[1] It is assumed that the ether can oscillate at any frequency, absorbing radiant energy from the field and re-emitting energy of the same frequency.   The ether is also assumed to exist throughout all space.   Although there is no good reason to believe the ether to exist, and good reason to believe it to be non-existent, the classical theory based on oscillations of the ether is helpful in describing the properties of the radiation itself.

is 90° out of phase with (and ahead of) the original.   This is a real effect, which can be experimentally observed under proper circumstances.

Imagine a series of points, in the y-z plane, which are simultaneously set into vibration in the plane such that they are all in phase.   This will give rise to a plane wave traveling along the x axis, or what may be called parallel rays.   Each point performing an oscillation along the z axis will emit radiation in a circular pattern in the x-z plane.   It can be shown by simple construction (due to Fresnel) that the waves coming from neighboring points destructively interfere[1] with each other in all directions except the line of motion perpendicular to the initial plane.   In the forward direction (along the x axis) it is necessary to consider the resultant

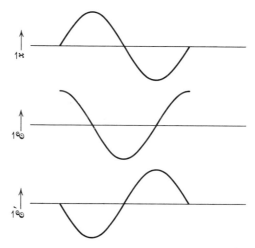

FIG. II-9.   Phase relationship between oscillator displacement, $\vec{x}$, the applied field, $\vec{\mathscr{E}}$, and the secondary emission, $\vec{\mathscr{E}'}$, for propagation in vacuum.

amplitude due to every point on the initial plane.   The amplitude arising from any emitting point will vary inversely with distance from the point. The infinite series obtained by summing over all emitting points has been shown to converge, and the resultant at any point P (Fig. II-10) due to a plane wave originating in the plane A is equal in maximum amplitude[2] to the wave at the plane A but 90° behind the wave coming from

[1] The intensity of the wave is proportional to the square of the amplitude.   If the two waves are superimposed, the amplitudes (not the intensities) are added, and the square of the sum gives the intensity at that point.   If two waves of equal amplitude are in phase, the intensity will be four times the intensity of either wave; if they are 180° out of phase, the resultant amplitude, and hence the intensity, will be zero.

[2] See Wood, ref. 18, for a discussion of this and other points discussed in this section. See especially pp. 8, 29–39, 157–162, and 469–476.

the center point, C. Thus one should expect a phase change in the wave as it travels from the plane to the point. It was noted above, however, that the waves emitted at C and the other points in the plane A, if they are excited by a plane wave coming from behind, are 90° ahead of the exciting wave, and these two effects thus cancel, causing propagation in vacuum without any change of phase whatever. (If the radiation comes through a pinhole at C, a phase shift of $+90°$ is observed.)

The fictitious ether oscillators which are assumed to be set in motion by the primary wave are 180° behind the secondary wave. The secondary waves that are emitted in the backward direction are therefore of precisely the proper magnitude and phase to bring the oscillators in the plane

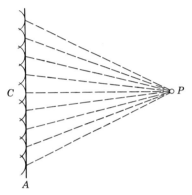

FIG. II-10. Phase shift on propagation. Resultant at P due to emission from all points in the plane A is 90° behind the emission at point C. This exactly compensates for the fact that the emission at point C is 90° ahead of the radiation incident at C. If an opaque screen is placed in the plane A, with a pinhole at C, the phase at P will be shifted 90° ahead. (See Fig. II-9.)

behind A to rest, thus accounting for the absence of an "afterglow" and the absence of a back wave.

If material oscillators are present, the secondary waves emitted by these will not in general be precisely 90° ahead of the primary wave but will be more or less than 90° out of phase depending on whether the frequency of the radiation is greater or smaller than the natural frequency of the oscillators. This causes a small phase shift as the wave is propagated through a material substance that has the net effect of giving the wave a velocity that is either greater than or less than the velocity to be expected in vacuum.

A plot of the square of refractive index as a function of frequency, in the idealized case of no damping, is shown in Fig. II-11. At the natural frequency of oscillation of the substance, ν_0, the wave would be absorbed, but calculated values would predict an infinite value for n as the frequency approaches ν_0 from below and an imaginary value as it approaches from above. Quite clearly, neither of these results is physically reasonable, the difficulty lying in the assumed absence of damping forces. When they are taken into account, the plot of refractive index against frequency resembles

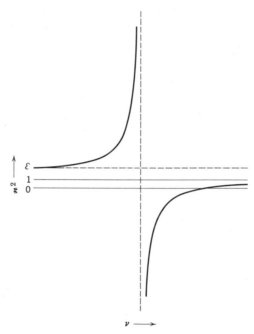

FIG. II-11.   Variation of n^2 with frequency for a single, strong absorption band, neglecting damping.

that shown in Fig. II-12a, and the absorption band is broadened as shown in Fig. II-12b.

For a substance which has only one important absorption band, the refractive index at low frequencies will just equal the square root of the d-c dielectric constant; it will increase smoothly and pass through a maximum, zero, and a minimum[1] and will then approach unity at very

[1] Soft x-rays have been dispersed with a prism, although the dispersion is slight.   As would be predicted, the rays are bent toward the apex, since the refractive index is less than 1.   Such refraction is of practical importance in aligning crystals for x-ray diffraction.

high frequencies.[1]   This is approximately the situation for the alkali metal vapors, although these actually have two bands (for example, the sodium D doublet), which give rise to two curves like that of Fig. II-12a.   Substances which have absorption bands due to rotations, vibrations, or additional electronic transitions will have similar fluctuations superimposed upon the effect of the most important electronic transitions.   Polar liquids show a very high refractive index at very low frequencies (the limiting value for water is $\sqrt{78.56}$) with a drop to normal values in the infrared and visible regions.   The frequency at which the refractive index drops co-

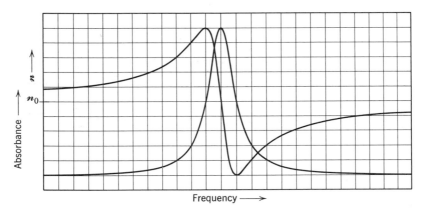

FIG. II-12.   Refractive index in the vicinity of an isolated absorption band.   The absorptivity is $a = \hat{a}(1/1 + x^2)(\sigma/n\sigma_0)$ where $x = 2(\sigma - \sigma_0)/(\Delta\sigma_{1/2})$ and $\sigma/n\sigma_0$ is essentially constant over the band.   The refractive index is given by $n^2 = n_0^2 + nF(x/1 + x^2) + F^2(1/1 + x^2)^2$, with $F = 1.15\hat{A}/b\sigma_0$, where $\hat{A}$ is the maximum absorbance and b is the cell length.   Since F is kept small in practice, this reduces to $n = n_0 + \frac{1}{2}F(x/1 + x^2)$. n_0 includes the effects of other absorption bands.

incides with the absorption frequency related to the rotation of the molecules in the liquid phase (Fig. II-13).

One of the best-known rules of the Special Theory of Relativity is that no object or signal can travel faster than the speed of light in vacuum (3×10^{10} cm/sec).   The existence of refractive indices less than 1 thus requires some explanation.   The apparent discrepancy lies in the failure,

[1] At very high frequencies the charges in the molecule can no longer follow the changes in the field, and therefore these charges have no effect on the field.   At low frequencies the dielectric constant is a measure of the total dipole moment of the substance in an electric field, including both the permanent dipole moment and the induced dipole moment.   The refractive index may be related to the dielectric constant by electromagnetic theory. $n = \sqrt{\kappa_e\kappa_m}$, where $\kappa_e = \varepsilon/\varepsilon_0$, $\kappa_m = \mu/\mu_0$. κ_e and κ_m are the electric and magnetic specific inductive capacities, the ratios of the dielectric constant and magnetic permeability to the values in free space.   Except in ferromagnetic substances κ_m may be taken as unity and $n^2 = \varepsilon/\varepsilon_0$.   Both n and ε vary with frequency.

thus far, to distinguish between group speed and phase speed. The relationship among frequency, wavelength, group speed, and phase speed may be described by imagining that it is possible actually to count

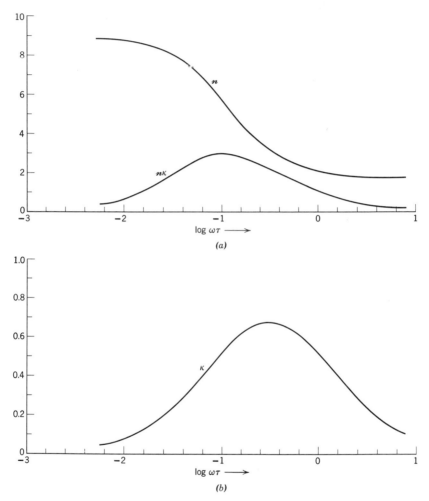

FIG. II-13. Variation of a polar liquid in the vicinity of the absorption band. (a) Refractive index and the product of refractive index and absorption coefficient. (b) Absorption coefficient, $\kappa = (\lambda/4\pi)\mu = (\lambda_0/4\pi n)\mu$, where $I = I_0 \exp(-\mu x)$. The frequency is expressed as $2\pi\nu$ times the constant τ which is related to the viscosity of the medium. (After P. Debye, *Polar Molecules*, Dover Publications, Inc., New York, 1929.)

the waves, or wave peaks, of a beam of light as the beam passes a fixed point in space.

In vacuum, it would be found that all waves travel at the same speed. The number of waves per second passing any given point in space will therefore be inversely proportional to the length of each wave (equation II-4). If a layer of water is placed in the path of the (visible) light it will be found, to a good approximation, that all the waves slow down by the same amount and that simultaneously each suffers the same percentage decrease in wavelength. The frequency (the number of wave maxima passing any point in space in unit time) remains unchanged for any particular type of wave.

A piece of glass inserted into the path will act differently upon the various frequencies of light present. It will not change the frequencies, but it will change the speeds of the wave maxima and the lengths of the waves to different extents. That is, the refractive index will vary with the frequency of the light; thus the speed, v, of the waves and the change in wavelength, $\lambda - \lambda_{vac}$, will also vary with λ or v.

A pulse of light, passing through glass, will be slowed down, and the various frequencies which constitute the pulse will move with different speeds. The refractive index is a measure of the speed of each wave maximum in a wave train of a particular frequency (equation II-3), but the pulse as a whole will move more slowly than this as a result of the constructive and destructive interference of the waves as they move with respect to each other (Fig. II-14).[1] The speed with which a signal may be sent from one point to another is determined by the speed of the pulse, or the group speed. The group speed, u, is related to the phase speed, v, by the equations

$$u = v \left[1 - \frac{\dfrac{v}{n}\cdot\dfrac{dn}{dv}}{1 + \dfrac{v}{n}\cdot\dfrac{dn}{dv}} \right] \tag{II-6a}$$

$$= v \left[1 + \frac{\dfrac{\lambda_{vac}}{n}\cdot\dfrac{dn}{d\lambda_{vac}}}{1 - \dfrac{\lambda_{vac}}{n}\cdot\dfrac{dn}{d\lambda_{vac}}} \right] \tag{II-6b}$$

$$= v \left[1 + \frac{\lambda}{n}\cdot\frac{dn}{d\lambda} \right] \tag{II-6c}$$

[1] This is merely the phenomenon of "beats" between wave trains of different frequencies. Since the individual wave trains contributing to the beat maxima and minima are moving with respect to each other, there is a continual shift of relative phase between them and a consequent shift of the positions of the beat maxima and minima with respect to the individual wave trains. A detector will record the arrival of the beats rather than of the individual waves.

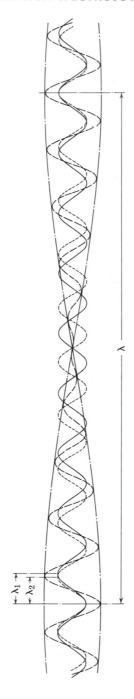

FIG. II-14.   The wavelength of the "packet" formed by the addition of two sinusoidal wave trains of wavelength λ_1 and λ_2 is given by the condition that $\lambda = n\lambda_1 = (n + 1)\lambda_2$, where n is the smallest non-zero integer that will satisfy the equation.   It follows that the frequency of the packet, or the "beat frequency," is $\nu = \nu_2 - \nu_1$.

If the dispersion, dn/dv, $dn/d\lambda_{vac}$, or $dn/d\lambda$, is zero, the group speed will be equal to the phase speed; otherwise the group speed will be less than v. The group speed will always be less than or equal to c.

It should be clear that a monochromatic beam will show no dispersion effects. All parts of the wave train will slow down (or speed up) by the same amount, so that there can be no interference due to one wave maximum catching up with another wave minimum. It might seem, therefore, that the group speed would become equal to the phase speed and thus could exceed the speed in vacuum. But in order to have a truly monochromatic beam the wave train must be of infinite length; otherwise a Fourier analysis will show the presence of many frequencies. Because no signal can be transmitted on an uninterrupted wave train, the group speed would not be experimentally defined for this limiting case.

2.2   Action of a Prism

A beam of light passing from a rare medium into a more dense medium will be bent toward the perpendicular, and on returning to the rare medium

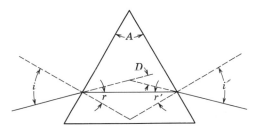

FIG. II-15.   Deviation of monochromatic radiation by a prism.

an exactly equal and opposite effect is observed. If the two perpendiculars are parallel, as in the case of passage through a plate with plane parallel faces, the beam will suffer a small displacement with no angular deviation. An angular deviation is obtained if the faces are not parallel. This is shown in Fig. II-15.

Let the angle of incidence of a ray of light on the first surface of a prism be denoted by i, the angle of refraction at this surface by r, the angle of incidence (within the prism) on the second surface by r', and the angle of emergence by i'. Then the angle of deviation of the beam is given by

$$D = i + i' - A$$

where A is the angle between the two surfaces of the prism (the apex angle). In practice the prism is so positioned that the angle of incidence,

i, is equal to the angle of emergence, i'. Under these conditions the ray within the prism is parallel to the base and the deviation, D, is a minimum. Setting $\sin i/\sin r = n = \sin i'/\sin r'$, the condition for minimum deviation is found to be

$$n = \frac{\sin \frac{1}{2}(A + D)}{\sin \frac{1}{2}A} \qquad \text{(II-7)}$$

If the prism material shows dispersion ($dn/dv \neq 0$), various frequencies will be bent through different angles, and a lens placed after the prism will focus these into a sharp image, or spectrum.   The condition of minimum deviation can be satisfied for only one of the frequencies present, but the angular deviation of other frequencies is generally not greatly different.

The behavior of refractive index in the vicinity of an absorption band was shown in Fig. II-12.   It will be observed that on either side of an absorption band the refractive index increases with frequency (dn/dv is positive).   Higher frequencies should therefore be bent more strongly than adjacent lower frequencies.   This has been called normal dispersion and is characteristic of prisms or lenses over any frequency range for which they are transparent.   If there should be an absorption band within the region of measurement, it will appear as if two spectra have been obtained, with the overlapping portions removed by absorption so that they are not visible.   In this case the higher frequency will be bent less than lower frequencies.   This has been called anomalous dispersion.

2.3   Prism Materials

Glass is an excellent prism material for the visible and very near ultraviolet regions.   The refractive index and the dispersion may be varied, to some extent independently, by proper choice of additive elements.   The flint glasses, containing lead, are generally preferred for prisms, a light flint for the higher-frequency region and a dense flint, which may even appear slightly yellow, for the lower-frequency portions of the visible (red, yellow, green) and the very near infrared.

Silica (SiO_2) is the most effective and economical material for prisms, as well as lenses, in the ultraviolet region.   Fused silica (or "fused quartz") may be handled quite similarly to glass, although the higher temperatures involved cause significant differences in details of the technique.   Quartz is the term properly applied to certain crystalline forms of silica.   These are anisotropic and are generally obtained from natural specimens.

Quartz prisms, of properly selected quality, will transmit somewhat farther into the ultraviolet (to about 1900 Å) than most fused silica (limited to about 2000 Å), apparently because of the importance of trace impurities in the amorphous material.   An absorption band at about 2450 Å

(35,500 cm^{-1}), due to traces of germanium,[1] increases in intensity upon heating the silica in a reducing flame. This band causes considerable difficulty in absorption cells which must be repaired. A very pure grade of silica, produced from $SiCl_4$, is considerably more transparent in the higher frequency region, permitting observation as far into the vacuum ultraviolet as the presence of air will permit (54,000 cm^{-1}, or 1850 Å).

Silica is not a good prism material in the visible region. It is completely transparent but has very low dispersion as compared to glass. It may, however, be employed in the visible region and into the near infrared to about 3000 cm^{-1} when the convenience of examining the extended region without change of prism material is sufficient to compensate for the relatively poorer performance. Below 7000 cm^{-1} the dispersion improves somewhat (Fig. II-16). An absorption band at 3650 cm^{-1}, arising from —OH groups in the silica, tends to be stronger in the synthetic material than in crystalline or fused natural quartz (Fig. II-17). Glass shows essentially the same absorption in this region as silica, except that the band due to —OH is stronger.

To work beyond the transmission limit of air in the ultraviolet requires special techniques which have set this region apart from the visible and near ultraviolet. Fluorite (CaF_2) is transparent to about 80,000 cm^{-1}, or 1250 Å, and is quite satisfactory as a prism material. Lithium fluoride is another potential prism material for the vacuum ultraviolet. Most recent investigations, however, have been carried out with grating monochromators rather than with prisms.

Absorption characteristics of ionic crystals in the infrared can be predicted reasonably accurately by consideration of the masses of the atoms. The absorption frequency varies inversely with mass, so that light atoms tend to absorb at high frequencies, heavy atoms at low frequencies, as shown in Fig. II-18. For example, LiF begins to absorb strongly at about 1750 or 1800 cm^{-1} and is therefore best as a prism just above this limit. Fluorite absorbs strongly about 1200 cm^{-1} and is thus the best prism material for the region between 1800 and 1250 cm^{-1}.

Sodium chloride, or "rock salt," is transparent throughout the visible and the infrared to about 625 cm^{-1}. The dispersion is very poor in the region from about 2000 to 10,000 cm^{-1}, but for convenience most commercial infrared spectrometers are designed to operate from 625 cm^{-1} to 4000 cm^{-1} (or higher, although the extended region is of little value). Sodium chloride is less expensive than many other optical crystals, only moderately susceptible to water vapor, and has quite satisfactory physical characteristics.

Potassium bromide will serve quite well for the region between 700 and

[1] See A. J. Cohen, *Phys. Rev.* **105**, 1151 (1957).

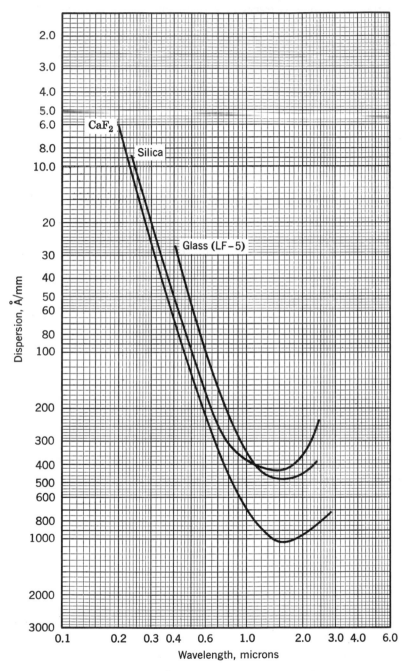

FIG. II-16.   Linear dispersion (Å/mm) *vs.* wavelength for various prism materials

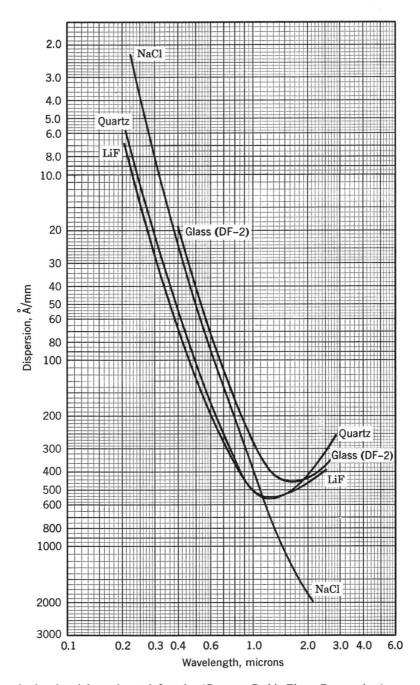

Dispersion, Å/mm

Wavelength, microns

in the ultraviolet and near infrared.   (Courtesy Perkin-Elmer Corporation.)

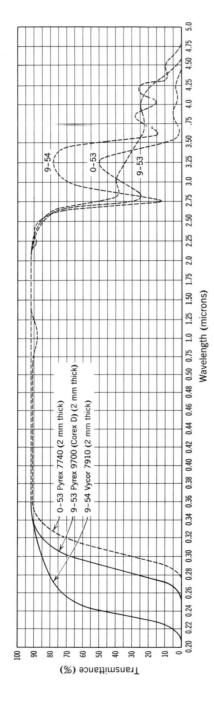

FIG. II-17a.   Transmission properties of glasses.   (Courtesy Corning Glass Works.)

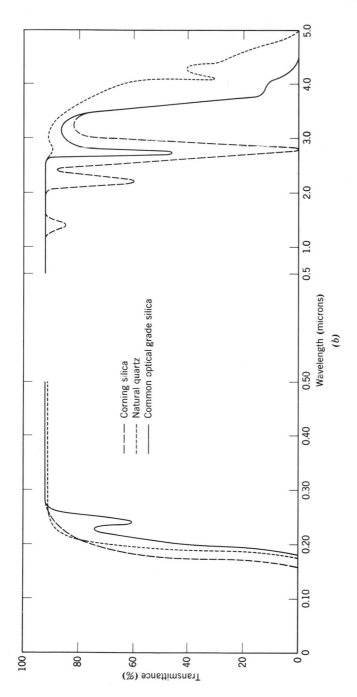

FIG. II-17*b*.   Transmission properties of typical samples of silica.   Properties can vary appreciably depending on selection and history of sample.

425 cm⁻¹, but it is of little value at higher frequencies. It is somewhat more susceptible to water vapor than rock salt, is softer, but is comparable in cost.

Thallium bromide-iodide, a mixed crystal[1] given the code designation KRS-5, is an orange-red material which is transparent from the low-frequency end of the visible to about 280 cm⁻¹ in the infrared. It covers the region just below that of KBr. The insolubility of KRS-5 in water makes it an important window material for certain applications, but it is highly toxic, subject to plastic flow, has high reflectivity, and is very expensive. It has been largely replaced as a prism material by cesium bromide.[2]

The dispersive power of cesium bromide in the low-frequency regions, 425 to 280 cm⁻¹, is quite good, comparable to KRS-5. The dispersion

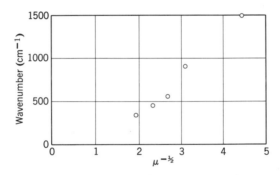

FIG. II-18. Absorption wavenumber plotted against the reciprocal of the square root of the reduced mass for KBr, KCl, NaCl, NaF, and LiF, showing that the mass is the major effect determining the absorption frequency. Note, however, that the force constant is also dropping with increasing ionic radius. (Cut-off wavenumber is taken such that $T = 10^{-\frac{1}{2}t}$ where t is the thickness in centimeters. Based on G. Joos, *FIAT Rev. Ger. Sci., 1939–1946*, Part II, The Physics of Solids, Optical Properties of Solids.)

drops off much less slowly with increasing frequency than for KRS-5 or KBr, so that a cesium bromide prism is almost as good as potassium bromide in the region from 425 to 700 cm⁻¹. The material is quite susceptible to water vapor and is expensive compared to KBr or NaCl. The mechanical properties of CsBr are quite satisfactory, but the large coefficient of thermal expansion can cause difficulties if not kept in mind.

Cesium iodide[3] has been shown to be a suitable material for extending

[1] Smakula, Kalnajs, and Sils, *J. Opt. Soc. Am.* **43**, 698 (1953).

[2] Ballard, Combes, and McCarthy, *J. Opt. Soc. Am.* **42**, 65 (1952).

[3] Plyler and Acquista, *J. Opt. Soc. Am.* **43**, 212 (1953); Ballard, Combes, and McCarthy, *ibid.* **43**, 975 (1953).

the range of a prism spectrometer to about 180 cm^{-1}.   Beyond this point
or perhaps beyond the cesium bromide limit, it is generally conceded to
be more profitable to change to grating dispersion than to struggle with
the unsatisfactory prism materials which are available.

In the visible or ultraviolet region one is working on the low-frequency
side of the absorption band of the prism.   The dispersion therefore increases as one goes to higher frequencies.   In the infrared the absorption
bands of the prisms lie at lower frequencies, so that the dispersion increases
with decreasing frequency of the radiation.   (In either case the higher

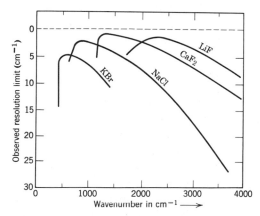

FIG. II-19.   Resolution limit *vs.* wavenumber for various prism materials in a single-
pass monochromator.   (After Gore, McDonald, Williams, and White, *J. Opt. Soc. Am.*
37, 23 (1947).).

frequencies are deviated more strongly.)   The dispersion becomes increasingly great as the absorption band is approached, but the transmission is necessarily decreasing as one approaches the absorption band.
The loss of energy due to absorption necessitates an increase of slit width
with a subsequent loss of resolution.   The optimum region of performance
of a prism thus falls near, but not too near, the absorption band.   This
effect is shown in Fig. II-19.   Those materials which are transparent over
a large region will necessarily have low dispersion throughout most of the
region.   A combination of prism materials is therefore necessary to obtain satisfactory performance over the large range of frequencies of
interest in spectroscopy.

3   Interference and Diffraction

A postulate of electromagnetic theory, which has been confirmed by careful experimentation, is the principle of superposition of wave amplitudes.   According to this principle, two or more waves which may happen to coincide in space and time will continue to act independently, so that intersecting beams show no interaction; but the intensity measured at any point will be proportional to the square of the sum of the amplitudes of all waves present, with due regard to the signs of the individual amplitudes. Since the square of the sum of amplitudes will not, in general, be equal to the sum of the squares of the amplitudes, the measured intensity will not be equal to the sum of the intensities and the waves are said to "interfere," either constructively or destructively.[1]

3.1   Principles of Interference and Diffraction[2]

The concept of interference was necessary to explain rectilinear propagation of waves and to explain the formation of wave packets, or beat frequencies, between coincident wave trains of different frequencies, leading to the appearance of a group speed less than the phase speed.   The concept of interference is equally necessary to explain why the approximation of rectilinear propagation sometimes breaks down.   Interference and diffraction effects are among the most obvious and most important phenomena which demonstrate the failure of a strictly corpuscular theory for light and for matter.

Interference may be observed quite directly by combining two waves of the same frequency and of known phase difference.   This is achieved by having the radiation come initially from the same point in space, such as a point on the surface of a lamp filament or a pin-hole in an opaque screen between the lamp and the point of measurement.   Such radiation, which has a fixed phase relationship between any two parts of the wave front, is called "coherent."   Radiation from independent sources, such as two lamps, two volume elements within the same lamp, or two pin-holes illuminated by a large lamp, is called "incoherent."

Two simple devices, due to Fresnel, for producing intersecting beams of coherent radiation are shown in Fig. II-20.   Light from a point source, S, reflected from two mirror surfaces which intersect at an angle slightly

---

[1] The intensity can only be measured by a process which involves absorption of the waves, thus destroying the wave front(s).   In this sense one may say that superimposed waves do not interfere (superposition principle) except as a consequence of the process of measurement.

[2] Some readers may wish to omit this section in the first reading.

less than 180°, will appear to come from the virtual source points S' and S''. Alternatively, the radiation may be refracted by two prisms of very small angle, again giving rise to two virtual sources.   In either case it is convenient to consider the virtual sources as if they were real sources of

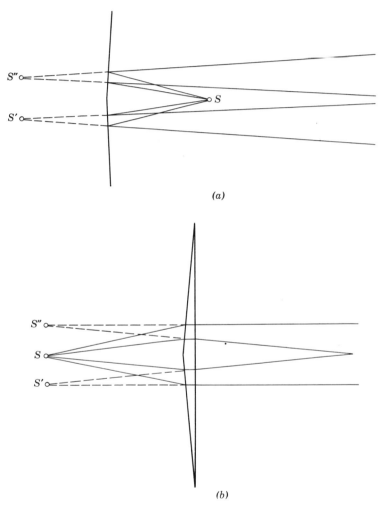

(a)

(b)

FIG. II-20.   (a) Fresnel mirrors.   (b) Fresnel biprism.   Actual source is at S; virtual sources (in phase) are at S' and S''.

identical phase and omit the mirrors or bi-prism from further consideration.

The interference pattern produced from two point sources of identical phase is shown in Fig. II-21.   The solid arcs represent the wave maxima, the dotted arcs the wave minima.   At an intersection of two maxima or two minima the intensity will be four times the intensity arising from either beam alone; at an intersection of a wave maximum with a wave minimum the intensity will be zero.   The positions of the maxima and minima will, of course, change with time, as the waves move forward, but the loci of constructive and destructive interference will remain fixed. These loci are indicated by heavy lines, a family of hyperbolas with foci

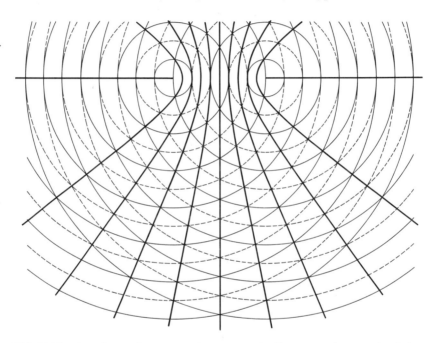

FIG. II-21.   Interference from two point sources. Radiant energy is transmitted along solid lines passing through intersections of wave maxima with maxima and intersections of wave minima with minima.

S' and S''.   A screen placed in the path of the rays will show bright bands separated by dark regions.

The results depicted in Fig. II-21 may equally well be obtained by illuminating two pinholes by coherent radiation, as shown in Fig. II-22. In this case, since the bright bands observed on the screen do not correspond to the images that would be anticipated from geometrical optics, the effect is given a special name, "diffraction."   Any number of pinholes, or slits, may be arranged as secondary sources (corresponding to S' and S'') and illuminated with coherent radiation, and the net intensity to be

expected at any point in space can be determined by a geometrical construction such as that of Fig. II-21.   The problem is simplified, and is
more pertinent to common experimental procedures, if a lens or concave
mirror is added to focus the rays coming from the slits onto a point or
(approximately) a plane.   Diffraction effects observed with the focusing

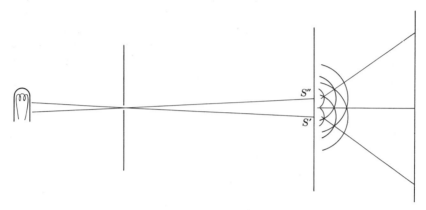

FIG. II-22.   Fresnel diffraction experiment.   Pinhole between source and slits acts as
a secondary source so that for small angles the radiation striking the two slits, S' and S'',
may be considered in phase.

lens present are called the Fraunhofer class of diffraction phenomena, to
distinguish them from the Fresnel class typified by Fig. II-22.
   An arrangement for observation of Fraunhofer diffraction from two
slits is shown in Fig. II-23.   Rays which are parallel to the optical axis

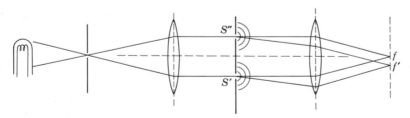

FIG. II-23.   Fraunhofer diffraction experiment.   Waves are in phase at f (on axis)
but may be out of phase at some other point, f'.

will be focused at the point f; other rays will be approximately brought
into focus at adjacent points in the plane of f, the position and the sharpness of focus depending on the angle between the rays and the optical axis.
Clearly, the rays emitted parallel to the axis from the very narrow slits, S'
and S'', will have the same phase if points along the plane perpendicular

to the optical axis are compared, and these rays will travel the same distance in reaching the point f. Constructive interference will therefore always be observed at the point f. Along any other direction the rays emitted from the two slits will not travel the same distance in reaching the focal plane, and it is necessary to find the difference in path length in order to determine the phase relationship between points on the wave front.

Consider two rays proceeding from S' and S'', making an angle θ with the optical axis (Fig. II-24). It is desired to know the phase relationship along the planes perpendicular to the motion of the rays, and since this difference will remain constant it is sufficient to find the phase difference along the line $S''T$. As the two beams travel an equal distance in reaching

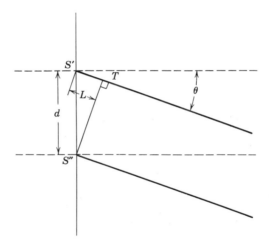

FIG. II-24.   Fraunhofer diffraction for perpendicular incidence on two slits.

S' and S'' and are in phase in the plane of these two slits, the beam at the point T will have traveled a distance L farther than the beam at the slit S''. The phase difference along the plane $S''T$ will be $2\pi L/\lambda$. In order for these rays to be in phase so that constructive interference may be observed, the path difference L must be an integral multiple of the wavelength. From the figure it is apparent that $L/d = \sin \theta$, and thus the condition for an intensity maximum at f' is that

$$L = n\lambda = d \sin \theta \qquad \text{(II-8)}$$

Equation II-8 will apply to any number of narrow slits, if these are evenly spaced with a separation of length d, provided the radiation incident on the plane of these slits is in phase. The case of a plane wave incident at an angle to the optical axis will be considered in section 3.2.

In the examples considered thus far it has been assumed that the slits were very narrow, or the pin-holes very small.   The intensity of each point of constructive interference might then be expected to be the same. In practice the central maxima are generally observed to be much stronger than those farther from the axis.   This is easily explained, if the effect of finite slit width is considered, as follows.

The addition of waves of the same frequency but different phase may be conveniently represented in geometrical form by vectors.   The length of the vector is made proportional to the maximum amplitude of the wave, and the angular position is determined by the phase angle.   Several simple examples are shown in Fig. II-25.   In the limiting case of con-

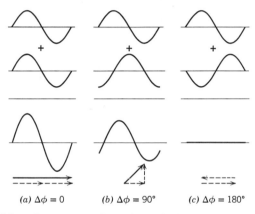

(a) $\Delta\phi = 0$ (b) $\Delta\phi = 90°$ (c) $\Delta\phi = 180°$

FIG. II-25.   Addition of two waves of equal amplitude.   (a) When phase shift is zero, resultant amplitude is twice original, resultant intensity is four times original.   (b) When phase shift is 90°, resultant amplitude is $\sqrt{2}$ times original.   (c) When phase shift is 180°, resultant amplitude is zero.

tinuously varying phase, the vectors will follow the circumference of a circle (Fig. II-26).

The intensity at any point in a Fresnel diffraction pattern will be the resultant of vectors of continuously varying phase corresponding to the adjacent points within the width of the slit.   The resultant of these vectors, and hence the intensity, will depend on the width of the slit, the distance of the plane of observation from the slit, and the wavelength of the light. The intensity at the center of the pattern may vary between zero and a value greater than the intensity incident on the slit as the slit width, distance, or wavelength is changed.   The total energy received in the plane of observation will, of course, be equal to the total energy incident on the slit; it is only the distribution of this energy among the various parts of the diffraction pattern that will vary.   The maximum resultant amplitude will occur when the extreme phase difference is 180°;[1] zero resultant amplitude will occur when the extreme phase difference is 360°. In the latter case, for each vector there will be a vector differing in phase by 180°, and the sum for each pair will be zero.

In the Fraunhofer class of diffraction phenomena the center of the pattern will always represent a maximum of intensity, since this point is optically equidistant from all parts of the slit. For any other angle between the optical axis and the rays emerging from the slit there will be at least partial destructive interference between rays coming from different elements of the slit, and the intensity will accordingly be smaller. The problem may be solved graphically by considering the vector sum for vectors of continuously varying phase. The length of the circular arc will represent the intensity incident on the slit, the length of the chord

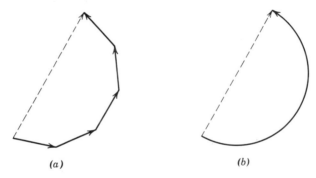

(a)   (b)

FIG. II-26. (a) Sum of five waves with phase shifts of 36°. (b) Equivalent resultant for waves of continuously varying phase.

connecting the ends of the arc will represent the resultant amplitude, and the angle swept out by the circular arc represents the phase difference, $\phi = 2\pi L/\lambda$, where L is the path difference for the extreme rays. For example, at the center of the pattern, where the path difference is zero, the arc is a straight line and is equal to the chord. As the angle between the rays and the optical axis increases until the path difference between opposite edges of the slit reaches $\lambda/2$, the arc becomes a semicircle and the chord is $2/\pi$ times as long as the arc. The intensity at this point is therefore only $(2/\pi)^2 = 0.406$ times that at the center. The intensity continues to fall, reaching zero when the circle closes on itself at a path difference of λ. The next maximum occurs when the path difference is $\frac{3}{2}\lambda$, corresponding to an arc of 540°, or one and a half times around the circle.

---

[1] A greater value would be obtained if all parts of the slit, of this same width, were in phase. This is possible only for Fraunhofer diffraction.

The ratio of chord to circumference in this case is only $2/(3\pi)$, and the intensity is less than 5% of that at the center.   The general shape of the

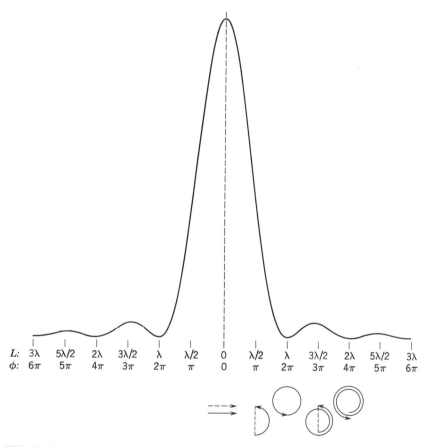

FIG. II-27.   Fraunhofer diffraction pattern produced by a single slit.   Intensity at any point is proportional to the square of the length of the chord connecting the two ends of a line of fixed length.   The path difference, L, is $d \sin \theta$, where d is the slit width and θ the angle between the emerging ray and the perpendicular; the phase difference is $2\pi/\lambda$ times the path difference.

fringe system and the geometrical models for calculating intensities at several points are shown in Fig. II-27.

3.2   Diffraction Gratings

The Fraunhofer diffraction pattern observed with two or more parallel slits may be considered to be the superposition of the patterns of each of the slits individually, as shown in Fig. II-27, crossed by dark bands in the positions of the minima calculated according to a modification of equation II-8. [The minima occur for $L = (n + \frac{1}{2})\lambda = d \sin \theta$.] Alternatively, equation II-8 may be considered as the equation determining the positions of the maxima, but the intensity distribution among these will be determined by the widths of the slits.

The patterns observed, with very narrow slits, for 1, 2, 3, 5, and 6 slits are shown in Fig. II-28. As the number of slits is increased, most of the

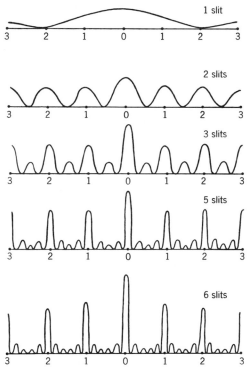

FIG. II-28. Intensity pattern formed by Fraunhofer diffraction from 1, 2, 3, 5, and 6 slits. From Wood, ref. 18.

secondary maxima decrease in intensity, while certain of them increase in intensity, approaching the intensity of the central image. The widths of the maxima decrease markedly, and the distance between the remaining maxima increases. Each of the maxima is called an "order," the number of the order corresponding to the value of n in equation II-8. If the slits are illuminated with radiation of two or more frequencies, each of these will produce its own diffraction pattern independently of the others. The central maxima will coincide, but in general the others will not, so that for each value of n there will be a complete spectrum (Fig. II-29).   This is the principle of the diffraction grating.

The discussion thus far has been in terms of slits in an opaque screen. Some diffraction gratings are essentially of this type, the radiation being transmitted through a transparent plate ruled with opaque lines. Most gratings, however, are based upon reflection from an aluminized surface. This has the advantage of eliminating absorption or dispersion effects due to the passage of radiation through the glass on which the grating is ruled. Typical gratings for the ultraviolet and visible regions may have 6000 to 18,000 grooves/cm; those for the infrared may have 3000 to 700 or fewer, depending on the exact region for which they are intended.   It will be noted that the number of grooves per centimeter is roughly equal to (or

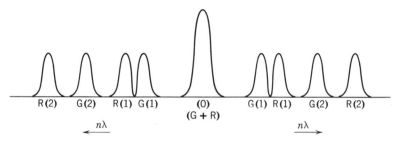

R(2)   G(2)   R(1) G(1)   (0)   G(1) R(1)   G(2)   R(2)
(G + R)

$n\lambda$ $n\lambda$

FIG. II-29.   Relative positions of images of monochromatic red and green lines formed by a diffraction grating.   (Relative intensities will be determined by blaze angle and groove width.)

less than) the wavenumber, in reciprocal centimeters, of the radiation to be dispersed.

A typical grating spectrograph, with photographic detection, is shown in Fig. II-30.   Radiation passing through the slit S is collimated by the mirror M and thrown onto the surface of the grating.   The grating throws (approximately) one order, or spectrum, in the direction of the camera; the other orders, which are sent off at various angles, are absorbed by the walls of the spectrograph.   The camera lens, L, focuses the light from the grating onto the photographic plate, P.   The angle at which the radiation leaves the grating determines the point of focus.

In general, the radiation coming from the collimating mirror or lens will not strike the grating along the perpendicular, but at an angle from the perpendicular which may be denoted by i.   For constructive interference at an angle θ (Fig. II-31) the path length difference between any two lines must be an integral multiple of the wavelength; hence, for N lines in a width W, the path difference must be $nN\lambda$, where n is the order of the spectrum (always an integer). The path difference for the incident light will be $W \sin i$; for the reflected light it will be $W \sin \theta$, with θ considered

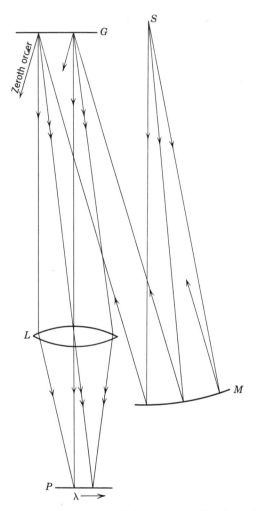

FIG. II-30. Grating spectrograph. Radiation enters at slit, S, is collimated by paraboloidal mirror, M, dispersed by the grating, G, and focused by a camera, L, onto the plate, P. (The camera will consist of a compound lens containing several elements.)

a negative angle if the incident and reflected beams are on opposite sides of the perpendicular. Combining these expressions gives $nN\lambda = W(\sin i + \sin \theta)$. If we let a be the width of the lines and b the distance between lines, then $W/N = a + b$.   The general equation[1] for the use of a reflection grating, at any angle of incidence, is then usually written

$$(a + b)(\sin i + \sin \theta) = n\lambda \qquad \text{(II-9)}$$

If we hold the angle of incidence constant, we may calculate the *angular dispersion*,[2] $d\theta/d\lambda$, by differentiating the preceding equation.

$$\frac{d\theta}{d\lambda} = \frac{n}{(a + b) \cos \theta} \qquad \text{(II-10)}$$

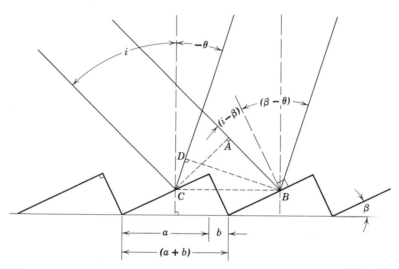

FIG. II-31.   Diffraction from a blazed grating.   The path difference is $\overline{AB} - \overline{CD} = (a + b) \sin i - (a + b) \sin(-\theta)$.   If this is an integral multiple of the wavelength, constructive interference will occur.   The maximum intensity will appear in that order for which $(i - \beta)$ is most nearly equal to $(\beta - \theta)$.

For small angles, θ, from the normal to the grating we may replace $\cos \theta$ by 1 and show that the change in angle is proportional to the change in wavelength.   At the photographic plate, therefore, the spectrum will be

[1] For a more detailed treatment, including the effects of interference due to the finite width of each line, see Wood, ref. 18, chap. VII.

[2] It will be observed that the angular dispersion of a grating is not a special form of dispersion as earlier defined, since no change in phase speed, or refractive index, is involved.   Angular dispersion of a prism is dependent on the dispersion of the prism material, however.   One must be very careful to distinguish, in each case, between the angular deviation of a beam and the angular dispersion.   We may note in passing that it is possible to have dispersion without deviation, deviation without dispersion, angular dispersion without dispersion, dispersion without angular dispersion, angular dispersion without deviation, and deviation without angular dispersion.

linear with wavelength.   The spectrum is said to be *normal* under these conditions.   This is an extremely important feature of gratings, since it permits linear interpolation between known wavelengths to determine the wavelength of another line.   Nearly all the early determinations of absolute wavelengths were performed with gratings, and much of the recent calibration work has been done this way, although the interferometer has proved more accurate for certain limited applications.

Rowland discovered that the lens and mirror shown in Fig. II-30 could be dispensed with if the grating itself were ruled on a concave surface. There are several distinct advantages to this method: (*a*) the range is not limited by absorption or dispersion characteristics of lens materials; (*b*) the spectrum becomes truly normal in this case, permitting more accurate wavelength determination; (*c*) the overlapping orders (for example, 2500 Å in the second order will occur at the same position as 5000 Å in the first order), which are typical of any grating, will be properly focused with a concave grating (but not with lenses since these are never sufficiently achromatic), thus permitting accurate comparison of wavelengths in different regions of the spectrum; and (*d*) the cost of the optics may be decreased by omitting the auxiliary focusing elements.   Concave gratings have been widely adopted in emission spectroscopy but are less suitable for absorption or Raman spectroscopy.

The total intensity striking a grating will be distributed among the various orders.   In general, only one order will be observed, so that it will represent a distinct advantage to concentrate as much of the intensity as possible into that single order.   This can be done by appropriately shaping the reflecting surfaces of the grating.   Modern gratings are made by aluminizing a flat disk of glass, which is then ruled with a diamond point on a special ruling engine.   The shape of the grooves can be varied by adjustment of the cutting edge.   The greatest intensity will occur in that order for which the ordinary law of reflection from the groove surface (angle of incidence equal to angle of reflection) is obeyed.   The intensity will also depend on the total reflecting area, hence upon the ratio of the area occupied by the reflecting surface to that occupied by the groove edge. Accordingly the grooves are cut as shown in Fig. II-31.   The angle β is called the *blaze angle*, since the grating, if viewed from this particular angle, will show a blaze of light.   It is possible to obtain efficiencies of 75% or more; that is, 75% of the reflected intensity will be concentrated in a single order.   Such a grating is called an *echelette*.

The ruling of a satisfactory grating is an amazingly difficult project, since the tolerances on the placement of each groove are so very small. Advances in the design and control of ruling engines over the last few years have made it possible, for the first time, to obtain relatively large quantities of good-quality gratings. Most gratings now sold are actually replicas of an "original": the ruled aluminum surface is covered with a plastic coating, which is removed, affixed to a glass plate, and aluminized. The plastic replica offers potentially better performance than the original, since the botttom of the cut is of better shape than the top. After the reversal, the original top has become the bottom of the groove, which is often in the shadow.

For wavelengths greater than twice the grating spacing, equation II-9 cannot be satisfied except in the zeroth order, which corresponds to undispersed radiation. No such limit exists for the high-frequency region; the grating equation can be satisfied for any high frequency in some suitably large order. The practical limit is set by the drop in reflectivity at very high frequencies and by the experimental difficulties associated with overlapping orders.

4   Lenses and Mirrors

The function of lenses is well known; they serve to concentrate or spread a beam of light. The action depends on the refractive index of the lens material or, more precisely, on the difference in refractive index between the lens and the adjacent medium. For a thin lens with a diameter small compared to the radii of curvature (Fig. II-32),

$$1/f = (n - n')(1/r_1 - 1/r_2) \qquad \text{(II-11)}$$

and

$$1/f = 1/q - 1/p \qquad \text{(II-12)}$$

where f = focal length
r_1 = radius of curvature of first surface
r_2 = radius of curvature of second surface
q = distance to the image
p = distance to the object
n = refractive index of the lens
n' = refractive index of the adjacent medium

All distances are taken as positive in the direction in which the light is traveling. The focal length and object and image distances are measured from the center of the thin lens.

The magnifying power, or simply "power," of a lens varies inversely with the focal length. For example, in the case of an eyepiece with an assumed eye-to-image distance of 25 cm, the magnifying power is given by $(1 + 25/f)$.[1]

[1] J. K. Robertson, ref. 17, pp. 119–123.

Equations II-11 and II-12 apply to diverging (or "negative") lenses as well as to converging (or "positive") lenses, but only in the limit of very thin lenses. In designing a real system it is necessary to base all calculations on Snell's law and to trace rays through the optical system by means of trigonometric calculations.[1]

The dispersive power of glass, silica, and the other substances discussed in section 2.3 introduces a serious difficulty when lenses are constructed of these materials. The refractive index varies with the frequency of the radiation and, as shown by equation II-11, this produces a change in focal

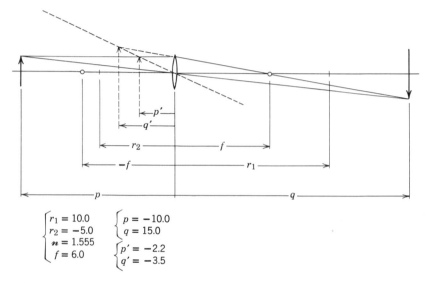

$$\begin{cases} r_1 = 10.0 \\ r_2 = -5.0 \\ n = 1.555 \\ f = 6.0 \end{cases} \quad \begin{cases} p = -10.0 \\ q = 15.0 \end{cases} \\ \begin{cases} p' = -2.2 \\ q' = -3.5 \end{cases}$$

FIG. II-32. Thin lens in air. Position of image may be found, for a thin lens, by drawing the ray that passes, essentially undisturbed, through the center of the lens and the ray that travels parallel to the optical axis on one side, passing through the focal point on the other side. Dotted lines show positions of object (p') and image (q') when a virtual image is formed by an object inside the focal length of the lens.

length with frequency. The effect produced is known as "chromatic aberration"; in the visible region the image produced by a cheap lens will be colored because at any given position of the lens and the viewing screen or eye only one color at a time can be in good focus. The effect is increasingly important as the power of the lens is increased. "Achromatic" lenses, which are largely free of chromatic aberration, may be constructed by combining simple lenses of different material to form a compound lens. It is possible to select the refractive indices, dispersions, and shapes of the lenses such that the dispersion produced by one component will just cancel

[1] See, for example, A. E. Conrady, ref. 13.

that produced by another, but the deviation of one will be larger than that of the other.   This chromatic compensation can be exact only at a number of frequencies equal to the number of component lenses, but the difference at intermediate frequencies will generally be small.

Achromatic lenses for the visible region are not very expensive because it is a simple matter to produce glasses of varying refractive index and dispersion by adjusting the elemental composition.   In the near ultraviolet, silica can be combined with fluorite to give an achromatic lens, but the high cost of fluorite restricts this procedure to lenses of moderate size. Lenses for the infrared region are most often made of KBr, with very weak focusing properties.   Silver chloride lenses have also been found suitable for special applications, such as beam-condensing units for illumination of small samples.   The difficulties of producing good lens systems for regions other than the visible are sufficient that lenses are seldom found except in parts of an optical system where focus is not critical.

Chromatic aberrations can be avoided completely by substitution of mirrors for lenses.   The focal properties of a front-surface mirror are not dependent on refractive index and are thus independent of frequency. The aluminized surface of a mirror is much softer than a glass or silica lens surface and is more susceptible to damage by abrasion or fumes. Mirrors must be protected from dust and must not be touched; even with normal precautions they will often show significant deterioration after several years and may require cleaning[1] or re-aluminizing.   The expense of having a mirror refinished is generally moderate.

The advantage gained by substitution of mirrors for lenses is significant in a spectrometer, for the range of the optics is limited only by absorption characteristics of lenses, windows, and prisms and by the dispersing power of a prism.   The same monochromator, by change of windows, dispersing element, source, and detector, as necessary, may serve, in principle, from the far ultraviolet to the far infrared, the entire region for which optical methods have been found advantageous.   For practical reasons, associated with low intensities, low reflectivities, and stray radiation, the range of monochromators is often limited to the region from the near ultraviolet (below 54,000 cm^{-1} or above 1850 Å) to the "moderately far" infrared (above about 100 to 300 cm^{-1}).

Either a lens or a mirror with surfaces that are spherical will provide a sharp focus for rays close to the optical axis but not for rays displaced

[1] Mirrors may be cleaned, when necessary, by very carefully swabbing them with dust-free cotton under the surface of a mild detergent solution.   This procedure helps to prevent entrainment of dust from the air in the swab during the cleaning.   The mirror should be rinsed with distilled water and then with ethanol before being placed in a dust-free place to dry.   This is a tricky process, however, and it is not recommended that those without prior experience attempt to clean expensive mirrors.

from the axis. The deviations are known as spherical aberrations. Figure II-33 shows the focal properties of a concave spherical surface both near the axis and at large apertures. Rays emerging from the center of curvature will, of course, be reflected back to the center of curvature no matter where they strike the sphere. Parallel rays passing close to the center of curvature will be brought to a focus at a distance midway between the center of curvature and the mirror surface. With increasing distance from the optical axis, however, the rays will converge to points closer to the mirror surface; rays striking near the edge of a hemisphere will be multiply reflected before crossing the optical axis. In practice this means that the focal length must be large compared to the diameter of the spherical mirrors.

Several methods of minimizing or avoiding the effects of spherical aberration are available. The Schmidt camera places a "corrector plate"

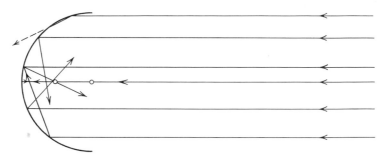

FIG. II-33. Focal properties of a spherical mirror. Rays near the optical axis are focused on the axis at a point midway between the mirror and its center of curvature, The aberration, or error of focus, increases with increasing distance from the axis.

in the path of the beam (Fig. II-34a). This is ground to a calculated aspheric shape which distorts the approaching wave front so that it will be brought to a good focus on the surface of a small sphere around the center of curvature. A small strip of photographic film, in a circular holder, is placed along the focal curve. It is much less expensive to produce a corrector plate, with small curvature, than to modify the curvature of the large spherical mirror, so that in applications such as astronomy, where high light-gathering power (see section III-2) is important, the Schmidt camera has become quite popular. The Maksutov camera is similar in principle, the corrector plate of the Maksutov camera consisting of a meniscus lens with spherical surfaces.

A paraboloidal mirror will collimate rays coming from a point source or will focus a beam of parallel rays to a point (Fig. II-34b). The aspheric paraboloidal surface is more difficult to produce, since grinding operations inevitably tend to favor plane or spherical surfaces, but mechanical methods have been developed for producing such mirrors in large quantity and with high quality.   The paraboloid does not require a corrector plate and is therefore truly independent of the frequency of the radiation. On the other hand, it will produce a good focus only at one point; it is therefore not suitable for photographing a large spectral region, and slit

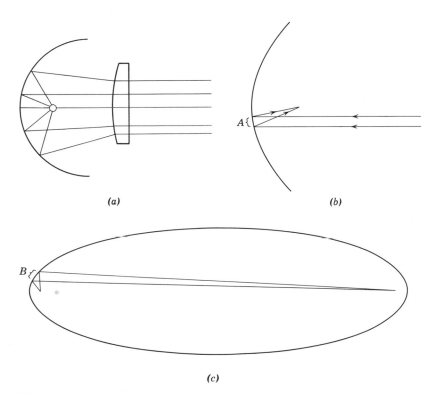

(a)   (b)

(c)

FIG. II-34.   (a) Schmidt camera.   (b) Paraboloid.   (c) Ellipsoid.   Sections A and B are cut "off axis."

heights must still be small compared to the effective aperture of the paraboloid.

In certain applications it is desired to focus rays coming from one point onto another point.   This is particularly true in focusing a beam coming from a monochromator onto a small detector.   An ellipsoidal mirror will perform this operation; the two source and image points are made the two focal points of the ellipsoid, as shown in Fig. II-34c.

A tore is constructed by rotating a circle about a line in its own plane. If the line is a diameter of the circle, a sphere is produced; more generally, a solid resembling an automobile inner tube is generated. A toroidal mirror will have a circular cross section along each of two mutually perpendicular planes, but the radii of curvature of these cross sections will differ. This is the shape of a patch on an automobile tube. Toroidal mirrors (Fig II-35) find occasional application where it is desired to condense a beam more strongly in one plane than in the other. The equivalent lens component would be a cylindrical lens plus a regular (spherical) lens, or a lens with a cylindrical correction.

An inherent disadvantage to mirrors is that the object and image necessarily lie on the same side of the mirror surface and in general must fall along the same line. It is possible to overcome this difficulty by passing the beam through the center of the mirror (Schwartzchild, Cassegrain, and Pfund systems), the fraction of mirror surface lost being very small in comparison to the total area. More often a spherical or paraboloidal

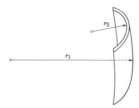

FIG. II-35.   A section of a tore with unequal radii of curvature.

mirror will be placed off the optical axis. For purposes of estimating the spherical aberration of such a system the effective aperture of the mirror must be taken as the distance between the optical axis and the outside edge of the mirror.

5   Detectors

Many different types of detectors are available for measuring the intensity of electromagnetic radiation. They operate, in many cases, on quite different fundamental principles and have maximum efficiencies in different regions of the spectrum or under different operating conditions. Detectors include the human eye, photographic emulsions, phototubes and photomultiplier tubes, barrier layer cells, photoconductive cells, thermocouples, bolometers, and the pneumatic cell. Other devices for storing and integrating or for multiplying light signals have been studied but have not yet been found to have significant application to spectroscopy.

Although the eye, when properly dark-adapted, is extremely sensitive,[1] it is not generally suitable for quantitative measurement of light intensity. Very small differences in intensity can be observed, but for many reasons the eye has been largely displaced in spectroscopic and colorimetric instruments by detectors which can produce quantitative deflections on a meter or recorder. It is, of course, nevertheless true that the eye is extremely valuable as a qualitative spectroscopic instrument and detector for the visible region.

The photographic plate has been almost completely replaced for absorption measurements but is still common in emission spectroscopy, for Raman measurements, and for very-high-resolution electronic spectroscopy. Its advantages for these purposes are significant: in a period of time which may vary from a small fraction of a second to weeks, the photographic plate will collect signals at thousands of distinct points in space, integrating each of them individually throughout the exposure period and simultaneously magnifying the effect of the light signal received by a very large factor. When the sample is destroyed or modified during the exposure period, as in emission spectroscopy, or the total illumination time is a limiting factor, as in Raman spectroscopy, the simultaneous measurement of intensities at all points of the spectrum is of extreme importance. The disadvantages of the photographic emulsion are no less significant, however. The multiplication factor depends on the catalytic effect of an excited chemical species formed by the illumination step. A small number[2] of photons, probably less than ten, is enough to cause the chemical reduction of an entire grain of the silver halide to metallic silver, producing a visible dark speck in the emulsion. As the size of the grains is increased the sensitivity of the emulsion is increased, a larger speck being produced for the original small number of incident photons; but the resulting "graininess" of the film causes some loss of detail in the image, so that images produced by adjacent frequencies can no longer be so clearly distinguished. Because the darkening of the plate is not a linear function of the exposure, a measurement of image darkness, or "density," requires a subsequent conversion by means of a calibration curve to obtain the intensity incident on the emulsion. This calibration curve varies from one batch of emulsion to another, so that accurate quantitative work requires calibration of each group of plates and preferably of each plate, especially since developing procedures can also influence the apparent intensity.

Over a wide range of exposure times, the blackening of the emulsion

[1] See, for example, Pirenne and Denton, *J. Opt. Soc. Am.* **41**, 426 (1951) and references given there; also A. Rose, *ibid.*, **43**, 715 (1953).

[2] J. H. Webb, *J. Opt. Soc. Am.* **40**, 3 (1950); L. M. Branscomb, *ibid.*, **41**, 255 (1951).

will be a function of the product of intensity of radiation and exposure time, so that a decrease in intensity may be exactly compensated by a proportionate increase in exposure time or vice versa. For very short or very long exposures this "reciprocity law" breaks down, the observed blackening being for either extreme less than would be expected.

Photographic emulsions have been produced with maximum sensitivities in various regions, as well as with a wide range of peak sensitivity, grain size, and contrast. Many of the emulsions required for spectroscopic measurements are available only on special order. Detailed information is available from the manufacturers. The low-frequency limit of photographic emulsions falls in the very near infrared, around 8000 cm^{-1}. The high-frequency limit is less definite. Standard emulsions are unsuitable for most of the vacuum ultraviolet region owing to absorption by the gelatin carrier, but with special plates it is possible to work throughout the vacuum ultraviolet region. In the x-ray region it is again possible to revert to commercially available film types.

The barrier layer cell, or photovoltaic cell, consists of an intimate junction of two dissimilar materials, such as a base metal and a semiconductor, which will develop a potential across the interface when illuminated. No external power supply is required, but because of the low internal impedance of the cell it is difficult to amplify the output. This cell is primarily of value when extreme simplicity of instrumentation is important, as in some relatively inexpensive colorimeters.

Practically all absorption spectroscopy in the visible and ultraviolet regions is now carried out with a photoelectric detector. A phototube consists of an evacuated glass envelope containing a surface coated with an active metal. Incident radiation causes emission of electrons from this surface by the photoelectric effect; these electrons are collected by a positively charged plate. The plate current is proportional to the intensity of the radiation.

If the electrons emitted from the cathode of a phototube are accelerated by a large potential and then allowed to strike another active surface, it is possible to get multiple emission of electrons from the second surface for each of the original electrons. These secondary electrons may, in turn, be accelerated and, upon striking the next surface, can give rise to a larger number of electrons. By combining ten or twelve such amplification stages, each with about a hundred volts potential difference, it is possible to get stable amplification of the original signal by a factor of a million or more.

The limiting signal-to-noise ratio obtainable from a photoelectric detector is determined by the "shot-noise," fluctuations in signal which result from the statistical nature of the processes involved.[1]   The fluctuation may be expected to be proportional to the square root of the number of events.[2]   The mean square shot-noise current, $\overline{i^2}$, is given by

$$\overline{i^2} = 2ei\,\Delta\nu \qquad\qquad (\text{II-13})$$

where e is the electronic charge, i is the photocurrent, and $\Delta\nu$ is the frequency band pass.   Thus the absolute noise output of a photomultiplier decreases as the total intensity of radiant energy striking the tube decreases, although the signal-to-noise ratio is best for large photocurrents. Even in the absence of an optical signal there will be some emission from the cathode surface.   This "dark current" increases with the area of the

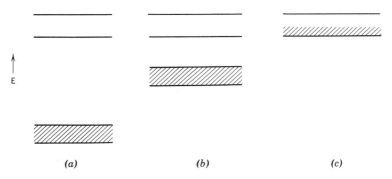

(a)   (b)   (c)

FIG. II-36.   Electronic energy levels in solids.   (a) Insulator; (b) intrinsic semiconductor; (c) metallic conductor.   If the number of electrons is just sufficient to fill completely the highest occupied energy "band," the solid will be an insulator or a semiconductor depending on the temperature and the energy gap to the lowest unoccupied level.   If an upper energy band is partially filled, the substance exhibits metallic conduction.   (The lower filled bands are not shown in the figure.)

active cathode surface and increases with temperature.   When necessary, it can be greatly reduced by cooling the tube to liquid nitrogen temperatures.

Photoconductive cells, such as lead sulfide, lead telluride, and gold-doped germanium, are semiconductors, with electronic energy levels within the crystal spaced as shown in Fig. II-36.   Electrons in the lower-energy state are bound to individual atoms, as in paraffin or glass.   As these electrons cannot conduct an electrical current, the "normal" resistivity of such materials is very high.   If an energy greater than the

[1] See "DuMont Multiplier Photo Tubes," published by Allen B. DuMont Laboratories, Inc., Clifton, N.J., for a detailed discussion of the design and performance of photomultiplier tubes.

[2] See, for example, Friedlander and Kennedy, *Nuclear and Radiochemistry*, chap. IX, John Wiley and Sons, Inc., New York, 1955.

threshold energy, $E_{Th} = h\nu_{Th}$, is supplied to an electron it can jump to the conduction band. In this state it behaves like an electron in a metallic conductor. The conductivity of the crystal depends, therefore, on the number of electrons in the conduction band at any given time. This number may be increased by supplying photons of frequency greater than or equal to the threshold frequency.

A small voltage impressed across a photoconductive cell produces an extremely small current when the cell is not under illumination. Radiant energy striking the cell causes a very large drop in resistance, with a correspondingly large rise in current through the cell. The current is amplified and the resultant signal fed to a meter or recorder.

The threshold frequency for photoconductors lies, in general, in the very near infrared. Below this frequency the photoconductor is transparent. Some materials, such as gold-doped germanium, have been developed with threshold frequencies falling in the infrared region in the general vicinity of 1000 cm^{-1}, but this energy is comparable to the thermal energies to be found in the crystal at room temperature. Even in the absence of radiant energy from an external source a significant fraction of the available electrons will be found in the conduction band. Good signal-to-noise characteristics can be obtained in this region only by cooling the detector, either to liquid nitrogen or to liquid helium temperatures. It is this characteristic of photoconductors which makes it appear unlikely that they will be developed for the lower-frequency regions of the infrared.

When measurements are to be made in a region for which no good detector is available, it becomes necessary to fall back on the thermal detectors. These detectors operate by absorption of radiation, followed by conversion of the energy of the photon to thermal energy. The temperature rise alters the properties of the detector material, and one of these properties can be measured to provide a quantitative indication of the temperature rise and hence the radiant intensity striking the detector. Devices of this type include the thermocouple, bolometer, and pneumatic cell.

Most modern thermocouples consist of a blackened gold leaf attached to the ends of two relatively massive pins. The gold leaf serves as receiver and as one of the thermoelectric materials of the junction; the pins, of a material such as doped tellurium, form the other junction. Electrical connections are made to the bottom of the pins and, by means of a thin gold wire, to the middle of the gold leaf, so that in effect there are two junctions in parallel. Typical area is about half a square millimeter, and the sensitivity varies from about 6 to 12 microvolts per microwatt of incident radiation. Evacuation of the housing decreases the heat dissipation, thus increasing the a-c sensitivity. Because the thermocouple element is so small, focusing of the beam onto the sensitive area is very critical. It is largely for this reason that the sample is placed before the entrance slit of the monochromator in an infrared spectrometer rather than between the exit slit and the detector.

In normal operation in the infrared region the radiant power striking the detector is in the range of a few hundredths to a few tenths of a microwatt, corresponding to a temperature rise of the thermocouple junction of about 0.001 to 0.01°C. This effect would be completely overshadowed by normal fluctuations in room temperature if no compensation were provided. Effects due to changes in ambient temperature may be largely eliminated by connecting two equivalent junctions in series in opposition to each other; one of the junctions is exposed to the beam while the other is affected only by the ambient temperature. Much better discrimination is provided by converting the d-c signal to an a-c signal by chopping the beam. If this signal is fed to an a-c amplifier, only the change in temperature caused by the beam is amplified and recorded. This also provides significant discrimination against noise.

The bolometer is fundamentally a small resistor with a high temperature coefficient of resistivity. The bolometer is placed in one arm of a bridge circuit so that a change in temperature of the element will cause an unbalance signal across the circuit, which can be amplified and recorded or sent into a servo circuit to reestablish a balance. The sensitivity of the bolometer depends on the temperature coefficient of resistivity as well as on the heat capacity and the absolute resistance of the element. Among the materials which have been found advantageous for bolometer construction are metals, such as nickel or platinum, thermistors, which are semiconductors, and superconducting materials, such as niobium nitride, operated at very low temperatures.

The pneumatic detector, or Golay cell, consists of a chamber filled with a non-absorbing gas and closed at one end by a flexible diaphragm. A blackened film in the center of the chamber absorbs the radiation and warms the gas, causing expansion of the gas and a distention of the diaphragm. The rear surface of the diaphragm is silvered and the motion of the diaphragm is detected by changes in a light beam reflected from this surface. Before and after reflection from the flexible diaphragm the beam from the incandescent lamp passes through a line grid. Small changes in the position of the diaphragm can thus cause significant changes in the intensity of the beam reaching the photocell. (See Fig. II-37.) Commercial models are available from the Eppley Laboratory, Inc., Newport, Rhode Island, and from Unicam Instruments Limited, Arbury Works, Cambridge, England.

There is very little difference in over-all quality of performance among the various types of thermal detectors. The performance cannot be measured by any single property but is influenced by size, sensitivity (in $\mu v/\mu w$), resistance, time constant, and noise characteristics, as well as linearity of response and convenience of operation. Cooled detectors offer real advantages for infrared measurements, but the cost has prevented their widespread adoption for commercial instruments. At

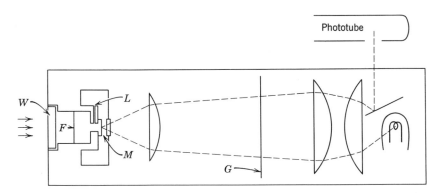

FIG. II-37.   Golay pneumatic cell.   Radiant energy passes from left to right through the window, W, into a small gas chamber, where it is absorbed by a blackened film, F. Pressure rise causes deformation of a flexible mirror, M, which causes a variation in the intensity of the light reflected from the lamp onto the phototube.   Because of the line grid, G, through which the light must pass before and after striking the flexible mirror, a small deflection causes a large change in signal at the phototube.   A small leak, L, stabilizes the detector against drift.

present nearly all commercial spectrometers for the infrared employ thermocouple detectors.

6   Amplification and Recording

Many different types of amplifier circuits have been incorporated into commercial spectrometers.   The design of these circuits depends on the optical system as well as the type of detector.   Only a few very general considerations will be treated here, and a few specific examples of design principles will be given in the following chapter.

The signal arising at the detector is generally quite small.   In an infrared spectrometer, for example, the signals may be roughly in the range of 0.05 to 1.0 μv.   This is the same order of magnitude as the stray signals that can be picked up by the shielded cables leading from the detector to the amplifier, and the desired signal could therefore become lost in the pick-up.   To avoid this, it is common practice to place a preamplifier as close to the detector as is physically plausible.   The signal is raised at this point to a level sufficiently high that stray signals added beyond this stage will not introduce significant error.

Single-beam instruments operate on the electronic-null principle.   In most designs the signal from the detector is amplified and fed into a potentiometer circuit.   The potentiometer may be balanced by hand, and the value of the transmittance or absorbance is then read directly from a dial attached to the potentiometer control knob.   Such an arrangement is commonly called a "densitometer."   Alternatively, the signal may be sent into a conventional recorder; the unbalance signal then operates a pen motor which drives the pen and slide-wire contact to the point of balance.

The first commercial infrared spectrometers were operated on un-chopped radiation and with a d-c amplifier.   If one chops the beam, a loss of energy results since only half as much radiant power is passed by the monochromator.   The advantages of this system are sufficient, how-ever, to more than compensate for the losses.   The "off" cycle provides a zero intensity level that makes it possible to eliminate the effects of drift in temperature, since only the alternating component of the signal is amplified.   Many instruments are designed to pass most of the stray radia-tion during the off cycle, so that this becomes a part of the d-c signal and is rejected by the amplifier.

An a-c amplifier is generally considered to be inherently superior to a d-c amplifier in terms of noise level and freedom from drift.   In addition, an amplifier which is accurately adjusted to accept only a narrow fre-quency band corresponding to the chopping frequency is capable of rejecting a large fraction of the noise that arises in the detector, the pre-amplifier, and the cables preceding the amplifier.

Noise may be defined as the random signal arising as the result of statistical fluctuations in any part of the circuit.   This may include ther-mal electronic motion (Johnson noise), statistical fluctuations of the tem-perature within a thermocouple or bolometer element, shot-noise in a vacuum tube or phototube, and "current noise" due to fluctuations in the resistance of some types of resistors.   Noise consists in most cases of approximately equal amounts of all frequencies (an exception would be 60-cycle pick-up), and therefore the amount of noise is proportional to the frequency band pass.   A filter decreases the band pass.

Amplification will increase the magnitude of the signal but will amplify the noise by the same amount.   Although much of the noise can be removed by filtering, there exists an optimum filter design for each system beyond which the desired signal is decreased as much as the noise.   It is because the ratio of signal to noise remains unimproved by amplification, and because this ratio at the recorder determines the accuracy with which one can read the signal, that the signal-to-noise ratio is considered more important than the absolute magnitude of the signal.

Production of alternating current is a simple process achieved in the present circumstances by the chopping of the beam. The more difficult process is reconversion of the alternating signal to direct current so that it may be measured in a standard potentiometric circuit of a single-beam instrument. The most efficient method, in terms of signal-to-noise ratio, is mechanical rectification in synchronism with the chopper. Breakers attached to the chopper shaft carry out this process. Since the electrical signal lags the radiation signal, the phasing of the breakers must be adjustable to provide the maximum efficiency. The problems in a double-beam instrument are slightly different; in a typical optical-null spectrometer the a-c signal is compared, for amplitude and phase, with a signal produced by a generator attached to the chopper shaft. Rectification is performed by electronic, rather than mechanical, means, but synchronization with the chopper is still an important feature of the design.

Chopping of the beam is optional in a single-beam instrument, but it is done in all current models for the reasons given above. A double-beam instrument must allow the radiation passing through the sample and reference compartments to follow exactly the same path through the monochromator to ensure that the beams will be equivalent, but the beams must be separable at a later stage so that they may be compared. The most efficient system for accomplishing this employs a rotating mirror segment that sends the beam from the sample and reference compartments alternately through the monochromator (or sends the beam from the monochromator alternately through the sample and reference compartments), since the output of the source is then allowed to strike the detector system at all times. This method does not, however, provide the zero-intensity reference level that is required for drift-free measurements of beam intensity, so the method is applicable only in an optical-null system which measures the difference in radiant power of the two beams and automatically adjusts this difference to zero by attenuating one of the beams.

If the beam is chopped and then divided at a later stage, a loss in energy is suffered, but it is possible to balance the signals electronically rather than optically, and at the same time to measure the absolute intensity striking the reference cell. This reference signal may be adjusted to a constant value by means of a servomotor which operates the monochromator slits. For measurements in which the accuracy is not primarily limited by the amount of energy available, the electronic-null principle has distinct advantages, especially in regions of strong absorption. The design is better suited for ultraviolet-visible spectrometers than for those operating in the infrared region, although the ratio-recording and memory systems, which are closely related, have been found satisfactory for infrared spectrometers.

7 Windows and Filters

Transmission properties of materials are of interest in many spectroscopic applications, including sample-cell windows, monochromator

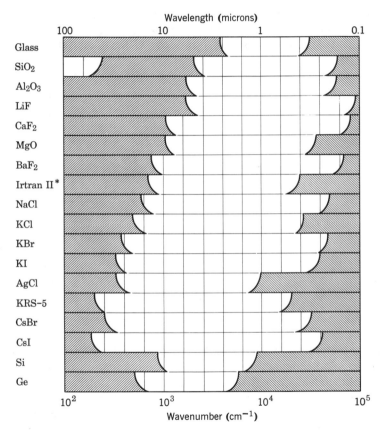

FIG. II-38. Approximate transmission ranges for window materials. Limits depend on thickness, purity, and performance requirements. (* Irtran products are made by Eastman Kodak Company.)

windows and lenses, filters for isolating narrow spectral regions or for eliminating stray light, and solvents or carriers for samples to be examined. Common solvents are given in chapter III. Figure II-38 shows the absorption characteristics of a number of materials which may be of value as windows or filters. Catalogs of commercial filters, of the gelatin or colored-glass type, may be obtained from the manufacturers (Eastman and Corning, respectively).

In addition to those filters which absorb the unwanted radiation there are some which scatter or reflect certain frequencies and transmit others. One of these is the Christiansen filter, discovered in 1884. Visibility of an object, or the ability of an observer to see the object, is dependent on reflection or absorption of light by the object or on refraction when the object is placed in non-uniform illumination. Many common materials are transparent but appear opaque because of strong reflection at the surface. This is especially true of powders. Other materials, such as cut

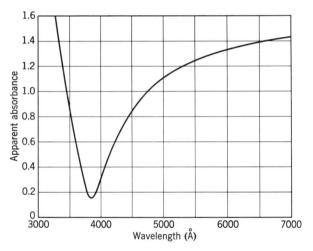

FIG. II-39. Christiansen filter. Uncompensated apparent absorbance for 1 cm thickness.

glass or diamonds, owe much of their characteristic appearance to refraction and can become nearly invisible if the illumination is made uniform. Since both reflection and refraction depend on a difference of refractive index at the surface, a transparent body suspended in a medium of matching refractive index will become invisible. This is the principle of the Christiansen filter.[1]

A powder surrounded by a liquid will scatter quite strongly all radiation for which there is a significant difference in index of refraction at the surface. The index will change with frequency for both substances, however, and it is possible to find combinations of solid and liquid substances such that the indices cross at a convenient frequency. At this frequency the

[1] See L. Auerbach, *Am. J. Phys.* **25,** 440 (1957); **28,** 743 (1960).

mixture will suddenly become transparent. Filters with quite narrow band pass can be constructed in this manner (Fig. II-39), and by adjusting temperature and composition of a binary liquid mixture it is possible to vary the position of the transmission band.

Filters may also be constructed to pass any desired frequency by adjusting the spacing between reflecting layers so that constructive interference

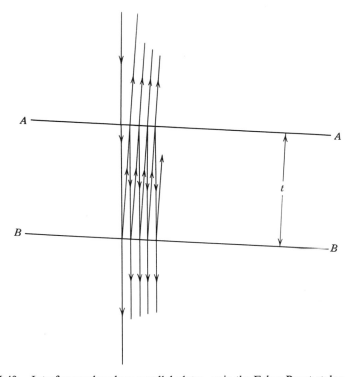

FIG. II-40.   Interference by plane parallel plates, as in the Fabry-Perot etalon.   If the beam is incident along the perpendicular, the reflected and refracted rays shown will interfere with each other; the intensity is found by adding amplitudes and squaring the sum of the resultant infinite series.   If the beam is not initially perpendicular to the surface A–A but is coherent (a plane wave, or parallel rays), the rays shown will interfere with other rays to give essentially the same result.

in the transmitted beam can occur only for the desired narrow region of the spectrum and overtones of this selected frequency.   The principle is most easily demonstrated by considering only two reflecting surfaces, such as those of the Fabry-Perot etalon, shown in Fig. II-40.   The etalon consists of two lightly silvered, exremely flat plates accurately positioned to be parallel to each other.

Consider the case of perpendicular incidence on the surface A–A from above.   A portion of the wave will be reflected and the remainder will pass to the surface B–B.   At the second surface, part of the wave will be reflected back toward A–A and the remainder will pass on through.   If the surfaces at A–A and B–B are equivalent, the fraction reflected upward at B–B can be shown to be equal to the fraction reflected upward at A–A, even though the direction of approach (and in general the angle of incidence) is different.[1]

To find the amplitude of the transmitted beam, we add the amplitudes (not the intensities) of the rays passed through the layer B–B, as smaller and smaller fractions of the initial beam suffer subsequent multiple reflections back and forth through the space between A–A and B–B.   Similarly, by adding the amplitude of the ray initially reflected upward at A–A to the amplitudes of the rays subsequently transmitted upward by this surface, the amplitude of the reflected beam is found.   The infinite series which are obtained by this means are convergent and yield the somewhat surprising result that the very weak rays transmitted upward at A–A may exactly compensate the initially reflected beam, resulting in no upward reflected beam at all.   The intensity of the transmitted beam will then just equal the initial intensity of the beam incident on the surface A–A.   We have assumed no absorption by the films; this is, of course, not realized in practice, but the result is otherwise independent of the fraction initially reflected.

If, for example, the upper surface reflects 80% of the incident beam, and transmits 20%, then it should be possible to add another equivalent reflecting layer, which will also reflect 80% and transmit 20% of the light incident on this surface, and obtain complete transmission of the beam for a wavelength such that

$$n\lambda = 2t \cos r \tag{II-14}$$

where n is an integer, λ is the wavelength in the space between A–A and B–B, t is the distance between the reflecting surfaces, and r is the angle of refraction in the medium between A–A and B–B.   The product $t \cos r$ is the distance traveled by the ray between planes; if this is just half of the wavelength, the rays which have traversed this distance and been reflected at B–B will be in phase with those initially reflected upward at A–A, except that the reflection within a less dense medium at the surface of a more dense medium (density meaning here, of course, the optical density, or refractive index) is accompanied by a change of phase of 180°, which is equivalent to half a wavelength path difference.

If the plates are unsilvered, monochromatic radiation will be alternately

[1] See Wood, ref. 18, pp. 192–196.

transmitted or reflected as the distance t or the angle r is varied, but the colored fringes observed with white light will be broad and poorly defined, owing to insufficient discrimination between adjacent wavelengths. The fringes will become increasingly narrow and sharply defined in white-light illumination as the number of reflections is increased by increasing the reflectivity at the surfaces, or as the number of subsequent layers of the same spacing is increased. The similarity in principle between a multiple-layer interference filter and a grating should be apparent. The only limits imposed on the effectiveness of such filters are the absorption by the reflecting layers and the uncertainty in positioning a large number of layers with truly uniform spacing. In practice the limiting effectiveness may easily be caused by the variation of angle of incidence within the beam rather than by the inherent band pass of the filter. Typical performance of modern multilayer interference filters is indicated by Fig. II-41.

In the infrared region, gratings provide an effective and convenient stray-light filter. The equation governing the operation of a grating may be written

$$n\lambda = d(\sin \theta + \sin i)$$

where θ, the angle of diffraction, and i, the angle of incidence, are measured in the same direction from the perpendicular. The grating spacing, or distance between grooves, is given by d, and n is the integer denoting the order. The angle of incidence will be equal, but of opposite sign, to the angle of diffraction for normal specular reflection, which represents the zeroth order of the grating. The zeroth-order beam is in the same direction for all wavelengths and thus represents undispersed light; the grating acts as a plane mirror.

The distribution of diffracted light among the various orders of the grating will be determined by the blaze angle of the grooves. The most intense order will be that for which the angle of incidence on the groove face is equal to the angle of reflection from that face. Assume, for example, that the grating available has 3000 lines/cm and has a blaze angle of 40°. If this grating is placed in the instrument, after the exit slit, instead of a plane mirror to deflect the beam through 90°, the greatest intensity of the diffracted beam for the higher frequencies, or shorter wavelengths, will be in that order which returns the light nearly back to the exit slit; the adjacent orders will have succeedingly smaller intensities. The zeroth-order intensity may be almost negligible.

As the wavelength increases, the angle for each order will increase. For a wavelength of $(1 + \sin i)$ times the grating spacing (in this case a wavelength of 5.7 μ or a wavenumber of $3000/1.707 = 1760$ cm^{-1}), the angle of diffraction of the first order will be 90°, that is, in the plane of the grating.

The full intensity of the incident beam must therefore fall into the zeroth order so that the grating acts as a plane mirror for this and all lower frequencies. The greatest portion of the stray light in the infrared region falls in the vicinity of the black-body peak, near 3000 to 5000 cm^{-1}. A

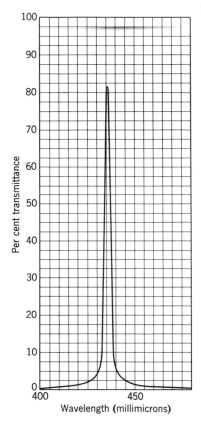

FIG. II-41. Transmission properties of a multilayer narrow-band-pass filter. (Courtesy Librascope Div.)

grating with 3000 grooves/cm will quite effectively eliminate this radiation from the beam without loss of energy at lower frequencies.

Problems

1. Calculate the relative intensities (dE/dv) emitted by a black-body source at 1500°K at

    (a) 6000 cm^{-1} (b) 3000 cm^{-1} (c) 600 cm^{-1}

Compare with the ratios for a black-body source at 2000°K.

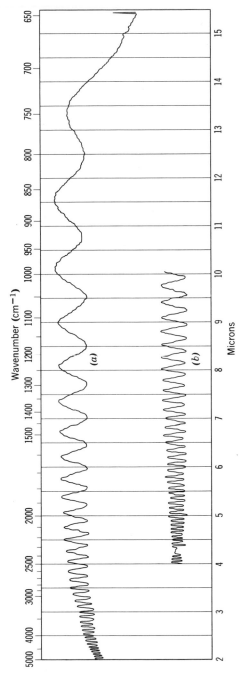

FIG. II-42.   Interference fringes from fixed-thickness infrared cells.   (*a*) See problem 7. (*b*) See problem 9.

2. Calculate the ratio of the energy/cm^{-1} emitted at 600 cm^{-1} to the total energy emitted by a black-body source

(a) at 1500°K   (b) at 2000°K

3. Given Planck's equation in the form dE/dv (equation II-1), show that an equivalent form is

$$\frac{dE}{d\lambda} = \frac{c_1}{\lambda^5[\exp(c_2/\lambda T) - 1]}$$

Find c_1 and c_2

4. Show, by differentiating equation II-1 and the equivalent equation for $dE/d\lambda$, that the "black-body peak" defined as the maximum of dE/dv vs. v occurs at a different place than if it is defined as the maximum of $dE/d\lambda$ vs. λ. Explain why this must be so.

5. The position of the maximum of the black-body curve observed with a CaF$_2$ prism is at a different place than when the same source is observed with a NaCl prism. Explain.

6. The windows of an empty sample cell can act as an interferometer when illuminated with monochromatic radiation provided the inner window surfaces are suitably close to plane parallel. Solve equation II-14 for the order and subtract adjacent orders to show that adjacent fringes have a constant wavenumber separation given by $\Delta\sigma = 1/2t$.

7. What is the thickness of the cell that gave the fringes shown in Fig. II-42a? (Assume the cell is filled with air and the convergence of the beam can be neglected.)

8. What is the maximum cell thickness that can be measured by the fringe method on a spectrometer that can just resolve a sine wave when it has a peak-to-peak spacing of 5 cm^{-1}?

9. What fringe spacing would be observed for the cell of Fig. II-42b if fringes could be seen when it is filled with a liquid of refractive index 1.40?

10. Distinguish between dispersion, angular dispersion, and deviation. Give examples of each with and without the others.

11. A certain grating has 750 grooves/cm and a blaze angle of 26° 45′. Calculate

(a) the wavelengths   (b) the wavenumbers

that will be observed at the blaze angle in the first five orders. (Assume that angle of incidence is equal to angle of diffraction.) In what order will the mercury green line (5461 Å) be observed closest to the blaze angle?

12. If the grating described in the previous problem is employed near the blaze angle (with angle of incidence equal to angle of diffraction), the spectrum will not be truly normal. Calculate the maximum wavelength error that would be made in an interpolation if the spectrum were assumed linear in wavelength over the interval between the CO$_2$ band at 2350 cm^{-1} and the HCl band at 2886 cm^{-1}; between the CO$_2$ band and the CO band at 2144 cm^{-1}. Calculate the wavenumber error that would be made if the spectrum were assumed linear in wavenumber over the interval between the CO$_2$ band and the CO band.

III
Spectrometer design and performance

The preceding chapter considers the individual components which are employed in spectrometers. This chapter considers how these components have been combined to create the various types of spectrographs and spectrometers to be found in modern laboratories. The functions of the instruments and the criteria for measuring their performance are also outlined.

1 Presentation of Spectra

The information obtained from a spectrometer is the amount of energy per unit time (the radiant power) transmitted by the sample and monochromator, or the ratio of radiant power transmitted by two optical paths, as a function of the frequency of the radiation. The intensity function is always plotted as the ordinate; the frequency function is plotted as abscissa. Various scales have been selected for each. The most advantageous scales are not the most common, since the choice is usually limited by instrumentation problems or by historical precedent.

1.1 Ordinate Scales

The signal from the amplifier may conveniently be fed directly to a recorder to produce a curve that will be linear in energy, and thus linear in transmittance. To obtain the transmittance of a sample, then, one simply measures the ratio of the deflections of the recorder pen with the sample in the beam and with the reference absorber in the beam. In the

89

absence of a recorder, the instrument is adjusted arbitrarily to read 100% transmittance for the reference absorber, and the transmittance of the sample is then read directly on the linear scale of a potentiometer with a linear slide wire.

A double-beam electronic-null spectrometer, with linear slide wire, records the ratio of energies of the two beams. This may be considered a special case of the single-beam method in which the deflection representing 100% transmittance is set equal to the width of the chart. If the chart is printed with a linear scale, varying between 0 and 100, the transmittance of the sample may be read directly from the chart. The double-beam electronic-null instrument is entirely equivalent to a single-beam instrument which automatically exchanges sample and reference cells in the optical path at a faster rate than can be accomplished by hand, simultaneously adjusting slit widths to maintain full-scale deflection for the reference signal.

An optical-null double-beam instrument operates on a somewhat different principle; the difference in radiant power in the sample and reference beams is automatically and continuously adjusted to be zero by means of an optical wedge driven into the reference beam to compensate for sample absorption. The position of the wedge which produces balance is recorded, and this position is linearly related to the ratio of transmitted intensities which is desired. Superficially, therefore, the optical-null instrument with linear wedge gives the same result as an electronic-null spectrometer with linear slide wire.

For most spectroscopic applications there is no reason to prefer a scale which is linear in transmittance. Such a presentation is, however, the simplest to obtain and it makes the least stringent requirements on the spectrometer. A much more convenient scale, especially for quantitative measurements, is one which is linear in absorbance, $A = \log(1/T)$. The instrumental difficulties that arise may be attributed to the expansion of the low-transmittance portion of the scale, where the signal to be measured is smallest in magnitude. For example, on a scale that varies linearly in absorbance from 0 to 2.0, half of this distance will be devoted to the region of less than 10% transmittance. Under these circumstances noise is a serious problem.

For thermal or uncooled photoconductive detectors, the noise arising at the detector is, at least to a good approximation, independent of the magnitude of the signal. At 10% transmittance, or an absorbance of 1.0, the signal has been reduced to 10%; at an absorbance of 2.0 the signal, and hence the signal-to-noise ratio, is only 1% of its maximum value. There is thus a tendency for the recorded linear absorbance curve to be quite noisy, or erratic, at high absorbance values (see problems 7 and 8).

In the ultraviolet and visible regions the problem is less serious, since the noise level decreases as the total illumination striking the photo-multiplier tube is decreased (equation II-13). The electronic-null design also avoids the dead region that is characteristic of optical-null instruments in regions of strong sample absorption.   Even so, it requires exceptionally careful design to permit the recording of spectra linear in absorbance at absorbance values greater than 2.5 or 3 (equivalent to 0.3% or 0.1% T). The linear absorbance scale is obtained by means of a logarithmic slide wire for the potentiometer.

Neither the linear transmittance nor the linear absorbance scales are convenient for recording the full absorption spectrum of a compound, for the stronger bands will flatten out or go off scale for a sample whose thickness is such that the weaker bands are not visible.   On the linear transmittance plot, the relative heights of absorption bands, as well as the shapes of the bands, will vary with sample thickness.   A linear absorbance plot will leave the band shapes and half widths unchanged, but strong bands will still go off scale and the absolute heights of all peaks will vary linearly with sample thickness.   These difficulties are overcome by plotting log A or log a, for on such a scale all bands intense enough to be measured may be shown on the same continuous curve as the strongest absorption bands.   Furthermore, the curve will be completely independent of cell length or sample concentration (assuming Beer's law). A change in these quantities will simply produce a translation of the entire curve, without changing the shape or size of the curve.

$$A = abc \qquad \text{(III-1)}$$

and therefore

$$\log A = \log a + \log b + \log c \qquad \text{(III-2)}$$

This provides optimum conditions for superimposing known and unknown curves for purposes of identification.   Chemical purity should be more easily determinable also, since the weaker bands are more prominent on such a scale than on the linear transmittance or absorbance plots.

For many purposes the choice of a most suitable scale for plotting of spectra is not determined by the considerations above but simply by the instrumentation available.   Copying of a curve by hand will cause a loss of information, and replotting onto a new scale is particularly objectionable in this respect.   If a choice is available, it would seem highly advisable to plot curves in absorbance for quantitative measurements, and to publish all curves, or record them for purposes of qualitative identification, on a scale of log A.   But it would be foolish to replot spectra for use in the same laboratory, for more would be lost through inaccuracies of plotting than would be gained by the change of scale.   The past experience of the operator who must recognize the curve shapes is a consideration that must also be kept in mind, although it seems likely that this factor will far more often be overweighted than slighted.

1.2   Abscissa Scales

Diffraction by a grating depends on interference effects and is thus dependent on the wavelength of the radiation.   Historically, the "normal spectrum" produced by gratings provided the first means for accurately determining the wavelengths or frequencies of light and, except in the very low-frequency regions, interference devices, either gratings or interferometers, still provide the only means for accurately measuring these quantities.   It is thus not surprising that early spectroscopic results were uniformly reported in terms of wavelengths, rather than energy, frequency, or wavenumber.   The spectrum produced by a prism is not linear in any simple function of wavelength or frequency, but it became customary to calibrate the dispersion of the prism in terms of known wavelengths measured by means of gratings.

Until fairly recently there has been little incentive to break away from the habit of plotting spectra on a linear wavelength scale.   By far the greatest number of spectra which are measured today are obtained by chemists who are concerned with analytical aspects of the curves.   For many chemists, positions of absorption bands are literally "magic numbers," to be remembered or found in the literature.   It is admittedly difficult to convince the novice that 1720 (cm^{-1}) is a better number to remember than 5.82 (μ), or that 39,400 (cm^{-1}) is more helpful in identifying the benzene maximum than is 254 $(m\mu)$.   As our understanding of spectra increases, however, it becomes necessary to think in terms of a quantity that is directly proportional to energy or frequency.   The advantages of a linear frequency, or wavenumber, scale are several.

1. The positions of the absorption bands are determined by the energy differences between molecular states or, in the classical picture, by the frequencies of the molecular vibrations, rotations, or electronic motions. The positions of the bands are thus readily correlated with the molecular phenomena, and knowledge of one is easily applied to the other.

2. The shape of an absorption band is an important property of that band.   Band shapes are nearly as significant as their positions for identification purposes, and in certain cases the band shapes provide assistance in understanding the nature of the transition giving rise to the band.   The width of an absorption band is very often an indication of the molecular environment.   A scale that is not linear with frequency will alter the

shapes of the individual bands, but, of even more importance, it will drastically change the relative widths of bands in different regions of the spectrum.

3. Displacements of the positions of absorption bands, due to change in molecular environment or to change in the molecule itself by chemical reaction, provide one of the most obvious sources of information about the nature of the change that has taken place. On a linear wavelength scale, the magnitude of the shift produced by a given change at the molecular level will depend strongly on the portion of the chart in which the shift is observed. Thus the typical question, "Is a shift of 0 05 μ to be considered significant?" really has no answer. But a shift of 50 cm^{-1} indicates a very real change in the forces or masses involved in a molecular vibration, wherever it may appear in the absorption spectrum. Similar considerations apply to shifts of ultraviolet absorption peaks, for example due to substitution on an aromatic ring.

4. In the infrared spectrum, only a few of the bands observed are "fundamental" frequencies, arising from the excitation of a single vibrational mode. Many of the bands, and especially the weaker bands, are due to combinations or overtones of these few fundamental frequencies. A combination band appears, to a good approximation, at the sum of the frequencies of the component vibrations, and it is thus quite easy to determine whether or not a particular band could be the sum of two other bands if one simply compares the frequencies (or wavenumbers) of the bands. On a wavelength scale it would be necessary to convert each of the band positions from wavelength to wavenumber before making such a comparison.

5. From the time that the Raman effect was first announced until the introduction of modern infrared instrumentation, the Raman spectrum was a more convenient characterization of molecular vibrations than was the infrared. It now appears that Raman spectroscopy will regain a considerable portion of its earlier importance as commercial Raman instrumentation gains momentum. Raman spectra are intelligible only when the shifts are measured in terms of a frequency scale. The frequency shifts observed in the Raman spectrum are then comparable with the frequencies observed directly in the infrared spectrum. Comparison of these values requires, of course, that they be expressed on comparable scales.

6. Electronic bands observed in the ultraviolet or visible regions frequently show fine structure, such as that exhibited by benzene. This structure is due to the superposition of vibrational transitions on the electronic transition responsible for the band. If these bands are plotted on a linear wavenumber scale, the separations of the bands from the band

origin are equal to the wavenumbers of the vibrations which are excited. Analysis of such a band, and correlation of the band structure with the molecular configuration, requires a uniform scale, proportional to frequency, for the ultraviolet, infrared, and Raman spectra. Correlations may also be made between fine-structure separations in the vibrational spectrum and the corresponding rotational or inversion transitions observed directly at lower frequencies. At present many of these correlations are important only to the physicist or physical chemist who attempts to fully interpret the spectra; it will almost certainly be only a matter of time until sufficient interpretation of this type is available to make it very helpful for identification and semiempirical extrapolation by analytical and organic chemists.

The dispersion of a prism is more nearly approximated by a function such as the square root of wavelength than by wavelength or wavenumber, and some instruments have been so designed that the abscissa is linear in this quantity. Since the size of the band on the chart is seldom a limiting factor in the observation of the band, the preference has been for wavelength or wavenumber scales. Because of the uneven distribution of vibrational bands, a linear wavenumber chart in the infrared requires a change of scale to accommodate the high-frequency region conveniently, and this instrumental difficulty has been a deterrent to the acceptance of this scale. Similar mechanical problems have prevented the appearance of linear wavenumber scales on commercial ultraviolet spectrometers. Most infrared spectrometers are now supplied with linear wavenumber cams when requested, and it seems likely that ultraviolet instruments will follow this trend in the near future.

Aside from the variations in the units for ordinate and abscissa, there is also an unfortunate lack of agreement on the direction in which these quantities should vary. Thus, if one is to plot absorption bands as a function of frequency, the absorption bands should logically point upward and the frequency should presumably increase toward the right. In the infrared it has been common practice to plot transmittance vs. wavelength or, for publication purposes, absorbance or log of absorbance vs. wavenumber. Fortunately these are simply reciprocals of each other, in terms of the direction of axes, so that if one inverts a T vs. λ curve it will correspond, in direction of axes, to an A vs. σ record. A similar system is commonly employed in Raman spectroscopy: the intensity of the bands is the ordinate, and the abscissa is the wavenumber shift. In the ultraviolet and visible regions the pattern has not been so consistent. Spectra are seldom plotted as transmittance curves, with absorption bands pointing downward, as was formerly customary, but the change to plotting absorbance was not accompanied by a change in the abscissa; thus wavelength nearly always increases to the right regardless of the ordinate function.

The disadvantages of replotting a curve by hand which were mentioned above apply equally well to the abscissa and to the ordinate. Since spectral data are not at present transferable quantitatively from one instrument to another, exact superimposability of curves is not yet of great importance, but there is reason to believe that it may become increasingly helpful in the near future as the variations between instruments become better understood and controlled.

Recent trends in the application of computer methods to spectroscopic data suggest important consequences for transferral of such data between laboratories. Methods which integrate under the absorption curves to determine the area lead to decreased sensitivity on the instrumental conditions. Efforts have also been made to adjust an experimental curve for the particular conditions under which the spectrum was recorded. This may help overcome present differences between instruments.

2   Monochromators

Spectrometer design would be quite trivial if it were possible to avoid aberrations, or deviations from ideal focus. Figure III-1 illustrates the simplest type of monochromator,[1] involving an entrance slit, a collimating lens, a dispersing element (in this case a prism), a focusing lens (often called the camera lens), and a photographic plate which serves as a detector. In a spectrograph of this type the entrance slit is usually manually adjusted for width and height, but there need be no other moving parts. The entire spectral region that can be investigated by the instrument is simultaneously focused onto the plate, forming a long, narrow image across the plate. Moving the photographic plate up or down will expose a new area to the beam, so that multiple exposures may be made on a single plate (the plates are most often 4 × 10 in. or 2 × 10 in.; the height of a single spectral image is on the order of 5 mm). This type of instrument is common for the ultraviolet and visible regions. The lenses are therefore of glass or silica, and the prism is of the same material. It is

[1] A monochromator is, as implied by the name, a device for splitting radiant energy according to frequency, or "color" in the broadest sense. It is sometimes advantageous to draw a distinction between a monochromator, which produces at an exit slit a single narrow frequency range, and a "polychromator," which will simultaneously focus all parts of a large frequency range in a given "focal plane." The latter system is that required for photographic detection or for the direct-reading emission spectrometers. We shall not usually make such a distinction here since there are many borderline systems which cannot be unambiguously described by only one of these names.

easy to see that the lenses will have a severe chromatic aberration under these circumstances, since the dispersive power of the lens material is far from negligible.   The higher frequencies, nearer the absorption band of the glass or silica, will be bent more strongly and hence focused nearer to the prism.   This can be compensated for by inclining the plate at a fairly sharp angle to the beam, at the same time curving the plate slightly as shown in Fig. III-1a   This also increases the total length of the spectrum on the plate.   (The linear, or plate, dispersion is increased without increasing the resolving power of the spectrograph.)

Only slight modification of the optical system described above is required when the prism is replaced by a grating.   For a transmission grating, it is

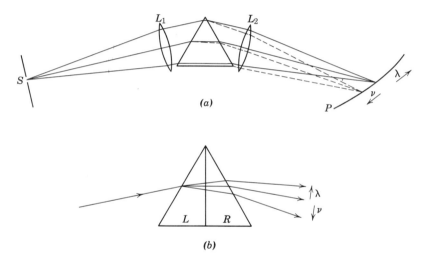

FIG. III-1.   (a) Prism spectrograph.   Light passing through the slit, S, is collimated by the lens L_1, dispersed by the prism, and focused onto the photographic plate P by the camera lens, L_2.   If the prism is of quartz, it should be of the Cornu design.   (b) Cornu prism.   A 60° prism is made of two 30° prisms cemented together.   One is of left-handed quartz, the other of right-handed quartz.

only necessary to replace the prism by the grating and to make the required changes in the positioning of the plate or film.   A reflection grating requires, of course, that the optical path be sharply folded.   In practice the simple optical system described is not considered suitable for a grating, since the grating offers advantages that are destroyed by the aberrations introduced by the simple lenses.

More typical of plane grating instruments is the spectrograph shown in Fig. II-30 (section II-3.2).   Light entering the slit is collimated by the large paraboloidal mirror, M, and strikes the grating, G, as approximately parallel rays.   The reflected and dispersed radiation is focused by the camera lens, *L*, onto the plate, *P*.   The camera in this case is more elaborate, consisting of a compound lens that eliminates serious aberrations over a large region of the spectrum.   The grating, at or near the perpendicular, gives a "normal" spectrum, that is, a spectrum which is linear with wavelength.   The more expensive camera design is intended to preserve this linearity; in practice this goal is approached closely enough that only a few calibration points are required for the entire spectrum. The emission spectrum of a noble gas, such as He, is convenient for this purpose.   By contrast, the emission spectrum of iron is nearly always photographed for calibration purposes on instruments of the type shown in Fig. III-1, since the spectrum is not even approximately linear in wavelength or frequency.   A prism or a plane grating will provide a stigmatic system, so that a point on the entrance slit is imaged as a point at the exit slit.

The light-gathering power of any optical instrument may be expressed

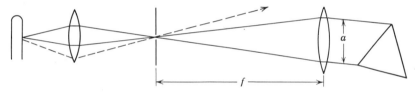

FIG. III-2.   A small ratio of focal length to linear aperture, *a*, permits the spectrometer to accept radiation from a larger cone.   Thus a low "*f* number" corresponds to a "fast" instrument.   For instruments with photographic detection the speed of the camera must also be considered.

in terms of the "*f* number," defined as the focal length divided by the diameter of the limiting aperture.   (More precisely, unless the limiting aperture is circular, it is necessary to find the circular aperture of equivalent area and take the diameter of this circle.)   The focal length of a monochromator is that of the collimating mirror or lens; the camera lens or mirror may have quite a different *f* number, but this is important only in the case of photographic detection.   The justification for calling the *f* number the "speed," or "light-gathering power," may be seen by consideration of Fig. III-2.   Neglecting diffraction effects at the slit, the angle formed by the rays emerging from the slit to strike the extreme portions of the mirror will also be the maximum angle from which rays of light may be accepted by the spectrometer.   If the "brightness" of the source is fixed, a larger angle of acceptance will, of course, mean more radiant power accepted by the monochromator.   A low *f* number corresponds to a "fast" monochromator, a large *f* number to a "slow" instrument.

For a spectrograph with photographic detection, similar considerations apply to the camera.   The aperture is determined by the size of the prism or grating, but a short focal length will produce a smaller, and hence more intense, image on the plate.   If the detector is a thermocouple, phototube, or other related type, the focal length of the mirror or lens is chosen to just fill the sensitive area of the detector, and hence the speed of this element is no longer of fundamental importance.

Spherical optics, whether lenses or mirrors, may cause serious aberrations quite apart from chromatic defects.   Their magnitude may be made arbitrarily small by increasing the radius of curvature, and hence the focal length, of the spherical components, or by decreasing the aperture while keeping the focal length constant.   The latter method severely restricts the resolving power of the monochromator and also decreases the speed. Increasing the focal length decreases the speed and increases the size of the spectrometer.   Where size or light-gathering power or both are considerations, it may be necessary to substitute aspheric surfaces, such as paraboloidal, ellipsoidal, or toroidal mirrors.

FIG. III-3.   Typical slit curvature for a commercial infrared spectrometer.   The sagitta is about 0.2 mm for a 1-cm slit height.

Even aspheric surfaces, however, are limited in performance by aberrations that are closely related to the problems of spherical aberration.   For example, if the entrance slit of a monochromator were as short as it is wide, a paraboloid would provide ideal collimation.   But, because of the relatively large slit height, the radiation coming through the ends of the slit will not be properly focused.   Much of this error can be eliminated by curving the entrance or exit slits to compensate for the effect of the mirror, but this remains a limiting factor on the speed and size of a monochromator.

The amount of slit curvature required in a typical commercial spectrometer is shown by Fig. III-3.   Only part of this arises from the effects of the collimating mirror, whether it is spherical or paraboloidal.   The prism or grating will also cause a curvature which may be equal to or greater than that produced by the mirror.   Rays coming from the ends of the slit travel through the prism at an angle from the horizontal, and since this is a longer path they will be bent more strongly.   The curvature of the image will thus be toward the high-frequency side.   Rays which strike a grating at an angle, on the other hand, are diffracted more toward the low-frequency portion of the spectrum.   In some cases the curvatures due to different elements may be made to cancel each other.

In a non-photographic spectrometer, the desired frequency interval will be isolated by the exit slit and focused onto the detector.   This closely approximates the situation of focusing radiation from one point onto another point, and thus an ellipsoid is the preferred aspheric surface. Photographic detection requires the focusing of a collimated beam onto the plate.   For this purpose a paraboloid does not offer any significant advantage over a spherical mirror, since the paraboloid will give the proper focus only at a single point.   It is possible to design lens systems, for the visible region, that will provide good focus over a relatively large area, but large lens systems are quite expensive, even for the visible region, and are quite impractical for the ultraviolet and infrared regions.   The Schmidt camera (section II-4) is a design which permits large apertures, short focal lengths, and good focal qualities for photographic detection to be combined at relatively low cost.

The principle of reversibility for light rays would indicate that under certain conditions spherical aberrations may be removed by returning the rays along the same or an equivalent path.   This is achieved by the Czerny-Turner mount, shown in Fig. III-4a.   The first spherical mirror introduces some aberrations, but the second mirror, similar to the first, compensates for these and provides a sharp focus.   The Ebert mount,[1] Fig. III-4b, is similar in principle.

A particularly popular prism mounting is the Littrow arrangement, shown in Fig. III-5.   In one form, the back surface of a 30° prism is silvered; the beam thus passes through the prism, strikes the mirror surface, and returns through the prism.   The small-angle prism does the work of a 60° prism in the system of Fig. III-1.   Alternatively, a mirror may be placed behind a conventional isosceles prism.   The latter method is preferred in the infrared region, since it avoids the difficulties that would be associated with the silvering of NaCl or other alkali halide crystals.

Some of the less common mountings for prisms or plane gratings are shown in Fig. III-6.   The Wadsworth-Littrow system gives a constant deviation as the prism and mirror are rotated as a unit.   The Féry prism[2] serves both as a dispersing agent and a focusing mirror.

The concave grating was mentioned above rather briefly.   Such a grating has the advantage that no additional lenses or mirrors are required and the overlapping higher-order spectra will be in proper focus.   The primary disadvantage is the astigmatism, which increases in the higher

[1] W. G. Fastie, *J. Opt. Soc. Am.* **43**, 641 (1952); **43**, 1174 (1953).

[2] C. Féry, *Compt. rend.*, **150**, 216 (1910); Baly, ref. 1, Vol. 1, p. 121.

orders of the grating.   An astigmatic system will image a point on the slit as a line at the photographic plate.   If the concave grating is properly aligned, the images from various parts of the slit will fall on top of each other, so that increasing the slit height will increase the intensity of the image but will only slightly increase the image height.   Difficulties arise when the grating is not positioned exactly right, for then the images from different points on the slit will be slightly displaced.   This results in a broadening of the image, with corresponding loss in resolution and very

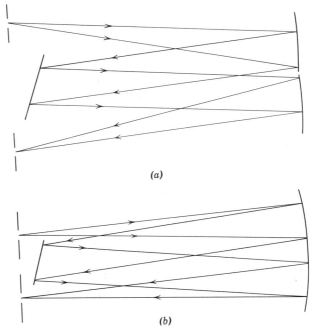

(a)

(b)

FIG. III-4.   (a) Czerny-Turner mount.   (b) Ebert mount.   In these mounts the colli-mators are spherical mirrors, but the spherical aberrations are largely cancelled by the symmetrical arrangement.

little gain in intensity of the image as the slit height is increased.   The amount of astigmatism will depend on the mounting arrangement of the grating.

A number of systems involving concave gratings may be mentioned briefly.   These are most often found in emission spectrographs but also in the occasional exceptionally high-dispersion spectrograph for electronic absorption spectroscopy.   The basis of these designs is the Rowland circle (Fig. III-7).   If a circle with diameter equal to the radius of curvature of a concave grating is drawn through the slit and the center of the grating, the grating will focus the spectrum onto the periphery of that circle.   Along the portion of the circle diametrically opposite the grating,

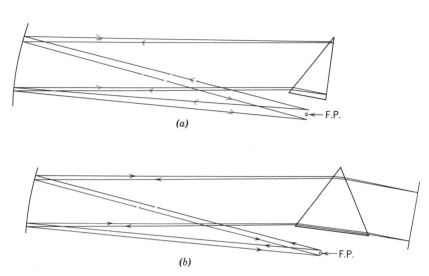

FIG. III-5.   Littrow mounts.   (*a*) Type common in ultraviolet and visible spectrometers.   Back surface of prism (usually 30°–60°–90°) is silvered.   (*b*) Type common in infrared spectrometers.   Prism (usually between 55° and 75° apex angle) is stationary; plane mirror behind prism rotates to scan spectrum.

the spectrum will be normal.   In the Rowland mount, the grating and camera are attached to opposite ends of a rigid bar of length equal to the

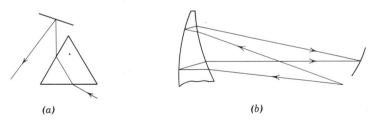

FIG. III-6.   (*a*) Wadsworth constant-deviation mounting.   As the prism-mirror combination turns, successive frequencies appear at the fixed exit slit, each having been dispersed by the prism at the appropriate angle for minimum deviation.   (*b*) Féry prism. The prism acts as focusing lens, mirror, and prism.

radius of curvature of the grating.   The grating and camera then slide in tracks fixed perpendicular to each other, with the slit above the juncture of the two tracks.

To avoid the problems associated with moving the grating and camera, the Abney mount leaves these fixed and moves the slit.   A more rigid mount, which is more satisfactory for precise work, is the Paschen, or

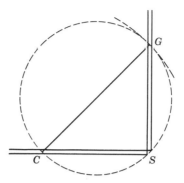

FIG. III-7.   Rowland mount.   The grating, G, and camera, C, are rigidly mounted on opposite ends of a bar such that they can slide along tracks.   The slit, S, is above the junction of the tracks.

Paschen-Runge, mount, shown in Fig. III-8.   The slit, grating, and photographic plates are positioned on portions of the Rowland circle.   Often the slit is placed in the wall of the grating room, the walls of the entire

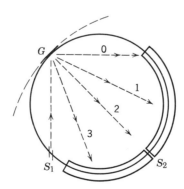

FIG. III-8.   Paschen mount.   One or more slits (S_1, S_2) and the grating, G, are rigidly fixed.   Plateholders are positioned at appropriate positions around the circle.   It is possible to photograph several orders simultaneously.

room are blackened to form the spectrograph housing, and the plates are placed in a circular frame, with no other plate holder.   By placing a second slit at the point S_2, with a tube connecting this point to the adjacent room, it is possible to alternate between two experimental source units without having to dismantle either to change sources.   This position also produces a brighter spectrum with less astigmatism.

The mounting systems described thus far require the full area, or a large fraction thereof, of the Rowland circle.   In a few instances, such as the direct-reading spectrometers where frequent access to the detectors is not required, the circle may be turned on edge, but usually the mounts require a large amount of floor space.   A particularly compact mounting is that due to Eagle and shown in Fig. III-9.   The grating may be moved toward or away from the plate and is turned simultaneously to lie always along the circle passing through the plate, the grating, and the virtual source

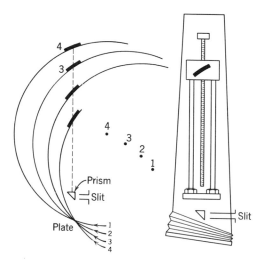

FIG. III-9. Eagle mount. Grating and photographic plate can be rotated about vertical axes. Grating also moves along the axis of the instrument. Circles 1–4 are Rowland circles, of the same diameter, with centers at points 1–4. (From Wood, ref. 18.)

position.   The mounting offers other advantages, including high brightness of the image due to decreased astigmatism.

Wadsworth designed a mount for the concave grating which requires supplementary optics but provides a stigmatic spectrum.   Light from the slit is collimated by a spherical or paraboloidal mirror and returned to the grating, which is alongside the slit, as in Fig. III-10.   In the radius mount,[1] the slit and plate holder are fixed.   The grating is attached to a movable arm, of length equal to the radius of the Rowland circle, which is pivoted at the center of the circle.

[1] See Sawyer, ref. 10, p. 161.

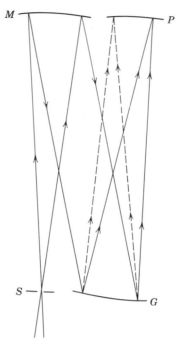

FIG. III-10.   Wadsworth mount for concave grating.   Distance from grating, G, to plate, P, is one-half radius of curvature of the grating. M is a collimating mirror.

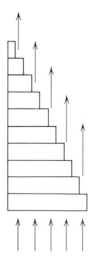

FIG. III-11.   Michelson's echelon.   A stack of m plates of glass or silica, cut from the same plane-parallel sheet, is equivalent to a grating of $(m + 1)$ lines with a spacing of $(n - 1)t$, where n is the refractive index and t the thickness of the plates.   The order is $(n - 1)\, t\sigma$ and the resolving power $(m + 1)(n - 1)t\sigma$.

The echelle[1] may be considered an intermediate case between the plane echelette grating and the echelon. An echelon (Fig. III-11) may be approximately described as a reflecting staircase, equivalent to a grating of very few lines (perhaps a few dozen) used in an extremely high order

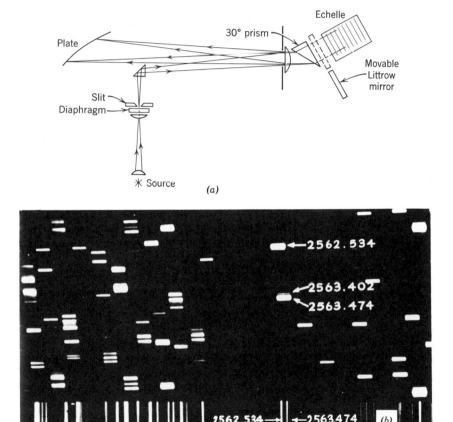

FIG. III-12. (a) Littrow-echelle system. Grating dispersion is in vertical plane, prism dispersion in horizontal plane. (b) Echellogram. Prism spectrum is shown below, prism spectrum dispersed vertically by echelle is above. (Note that horizontal slit is employed for prism-echelle spectrum to take advantage of echelle resolution.) (Courtesy Bausch and Lomb Incorporated, Rochester, N.Y.)

and yielding therefore extremely high resolving power, but with very low angular dispersion. The echelle is ruled with an intermediate number of

[1] Harrison, Archer, and Camus, *J. Opt. Soc. Am.* **42**, 706 (1952).

lines and is relatively easily made.   It is capable of producing extremely high resolving power, in the higher-order spectra, but it lacks the angular dispersion required to separate the overlapping spectra of adjacent orders. It is therefore crossed with a prism or another grating to separate the various orders into separate horizontal lines, the individual orders then exhibiting the great resolving power characteristic of the echelle.   In practice the vertical sorting is not quite so tidy, and it is not possible to label each horizontal line as one particular order of the echelle, but the principle is the same.   A single spectrum taken in a spectrograph containing an echelle crossed with a prism is shown in Fig. III-12b.

Additional insight into the functioning of the echelette, echelle, echelon, and prism may be gained by consideration of the gradual transformation of the echelette into a prism, as it passes through the other forms as intermediate cases.   The treatment is given in Wood.[1]

3   Commercial Instruments

Comparison of commercial spectrometers will show remarkable similarities between many of them in terms of the basic concepts of design, both optical and electronic, and in the accessories and operating variables which are available.   At the same time there are many striking differences, not all of which are obvious from a superficial examination of the instruments. The discussion which follows is not intended as a critical evaluation of any one instrument as compared to another, but rather as a review of certain features of instrument design with specific examples of instruments in which these features have been incorporated.   The arrangement is only in part chronological; in certain cases it is convenient to discuss modifications which have been added to an early instrument in connection with the earlier instrument, even though the modification itself may have first appeared in a competitive spectrometer.

An arbitrary division has been made into single-beam and double-beam instruments, despite the fact that for many purposes they must be considered contemporary and competitive designs.   Not all commercial instruments have been included; in particular, many of the comparatively inexpensive spectrometers, commonly known as colorimeters, have been omitted entirely even though they, also, can perform some of the same functions as a more expensive instrument.

[1] Wood, ref. 18, p. 287.

3.1   Single-Beam Spectrometers

3.11   Beckman DU

The first commercial spectrometer to be produced on a large scale in this country was the Beckman DU, a single-beam, non-recording instrument for the ultraviolet and visible regions.[1]   The optical system is shown in Fig. III-13.   For the ultraviolet region, a hydrogen discharge lamp with a very thin glass window serves as the source; this is replaced with a 6-volt tungsten lamp for operation in the visible region.   Radiation from the source, S, is reflected by a small mirror in the source housing onto the plane mirror next to the slit and is thus reflected into the monochromator. A spherical mirror collimates the beam and sends it into the 30° quartz Littrow prism.   The beam returns along virtually the same path, passing out the same slit, above the mirror, and then through the sample compartment and onto the detector, P.   The detector is either a red-sensitive or

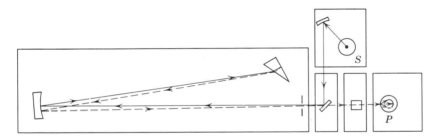

FIG. III-13.   Beckman DU spectrometer for ultraviolet and visible regions.   (Courtesy Beckman Instruments, Inc.)

an ultraviolet-sensitive phototube.   The phototubes may be rapidly interchanged by means of a rod which extends out of the case.   A photomultiplier tube, with associated power supply, is now available to replace the less sensitive phototubes.   Recent instruments also provide for rapid interchange of source units by means of a dual mount for them; motion of a mirror into or out of position will focus the appropriate source onto the monochromator.

The frequency range passing through the sample is controlled by rotating the prism by means of a rod passing through the top of the case, with an appropriate dial attached.   Slit widths are manually adjusted by means of a similar knob and dial.   The transmittance of a sample is determined by adjusting the instrument to read 100% T with a reference cell in place, then rebalancing the instrument with the sample in place by turning the knob attached to the potentiometer and the transmittance scale.

[1] Cary and Beckman, *J. Opt. Soc. Am.* **31**, 682 (1941).

Electrical circuitry of the DU is shown in Fig. III-14.   Power for the
filaments of the two amplifier tubes, and for the hydrogen or tungsten

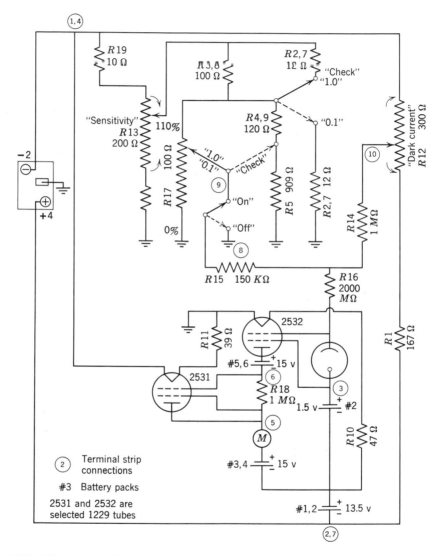

FIG. III-14. Simplified wiring diagram for Beckman DU spectrometer.   Based on
Beckman Drawing 2500F.

lamp, is provided by a 6-volt storage battery.   This also produces a
potential drop across the "dark current," "sensitivity," and "transmit-

tance" resistors.   Dry cells provide the additional voltage required for the phototube and amplifier.

The "dark current" potentiometer determines the bias voltage applied to the amplifier and phototube.   With the instrument turned on and the phototube switch "off" (shutter closed), the "dark current" control is adjusted to give a current reading on the galvanometer at the center of the scale ("zero" reading).   If now the shutter switch is turned "on," and the light is allowed to strike the phototube, the potential across the phototube will drop because of the photocurrent in the tube.   This makes the screen of the first amplifier tube less positive, thereby decreasing the current through the amplifier, and the needle will move to the left.   To restore the initial current value, the potential across the amplifier and phototube must be increased; this is accomplished by means of a transmittance potentiometer (R 17).   The greater the intensity of the light striking the phototube, the farther along the slide wire, toward $100\% \, T$, the contact must be moved.   The instrument thus operates essentially as a null indicating instrument, since the initial state of the amplifier, which is altered by the conduction of the phototube under irradiation, is restored by a change in the applied potential across the amplifier.   The accuracy of the spectrometer does not, therefore, depend on the characteristics of the amplifier (except for stability), but only on the assumption that the drop in potential across the phototube will be proportional to the radiant power striking the tube.   It is also necessary that the transmittance-potentiometer slide wire be linear so that the increase in potential produced by moving the contact on the slide wire will be proportional to the transmittance reading (that is, the change in potential will be proportional to linear displacement along the slide wire).

The range of intensities (and thus the range of transmittance or absorbance values) over which the instrument may be operated without changing the settings will be limited by the total change in voltage that may be produced by turning the transmittance knob.   To adjust this range to the particular sample and reference materials, as well as source output and detector sensitivity, the slits must be opened or closed.   Some additional correction is available, however, in the "sensitivity" control, which serves to vary the total potential applied across the transmittance-potentiometer slide wire.   Turning the "sensitivity" potentiometer to its clockwise limit will place the maximum voltage across the slide wire, and relatively "bright light" may be measured; that is, clear solutions may be observed with wide slits.   Turning the sensitivity control to the counterclockwise limit, or turning the main switch to the "0.1" position, will place a smaller voltage across the slide wire.   Full-scale motion of the transmittance knob will then correspond to a much smaller radiant power at the phototube.   This setting may be more appropriate when observing solutions which absorb strongly, or when it is desirable to keep the slits as narrow as possible.

Within the proper operating range of any detector and amplifier, the accuracy of an intensity measurement will always be improved if the total radiant power striking the detector is increased, since the signal increases more rapidly than the noise. (This does not mean that the absolute absorptivity of a sample is more accurately measured, but simply that the radiant power passed by the sample is more accurately determined. Thus spectral purity considerations are specifically neglected.) For the Beckman DU this means that the most accurate measurements will be possible when the sensitivity control is adjusted toward the clockwise limit. Since this implies wider slits, the resolution of the spectrometer under these conditions is a minimum, and thus the quantity that is measured may not be that which is sought. Such conflicts of interest are inherent in spectroscopic instrumentation. As the radiant power striking the phototube is increased, the noise produced at the phototube is increased so that the needle will appear much less steady, even though the accuracy is actually improved. The condition under which one measures the smallest signal ("sensitivity" control in counterclockwise position) is designated "low sensitivity." [1]

3.12 Beckman IR-2

An instrument which differs optically only in minor respects from the Beckman DU is the Beckman IR-2 infrared spectrometer, shown in Fig. III-15. To achieve better focusing on the detector, the sample precedes the monochromator and the optical path is traversed in the reverse direction. The 30° quartz Littrow prism is replaced by a 60° prism with a Littrow mirror behind it. The mirror, rather than the prism, is moved to change the frequency passed by the monochromator. A Nernst glower is mounted in the source housing at the right-hand end of the instrument, along with a glass chopper, a built-in gas cell, and a phototube which monitors the output of the glower, thus permitting accurate reproducibility of measurements. The signal from the thermocouple, after preamplification by a coupling transformer, passes to an a-c amplifier, a full-wave synchronous rectifier, a filter, and a d-c amplifier. The signal is then sent to a recorder or null potentiometer.

The IR-2A has a motor drive for the Littrow mirror to permit continuous recording of spectra over a range of frequencies, and an automatic slit drive to produce a constant I_0 line. This permits the entire region from 650 cm^{-1} to 4000 cm^{-1} to be scanned without manual adjustment of slit widths. The instrument is no longer in production.

[1] This might be called "high sensitivity" and a "low sensitivity limit." See p. 160.

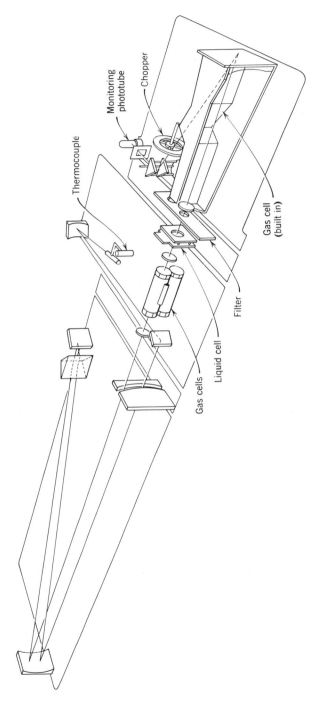

FIG. III-15.   Beckman IR-2 spectrometer for infrared region.   (Courtesy Beckman Instruments, Inc.)

3.13   Perkin-Elmer 12

An early commercial infrared instrument was the Perkin-Elmer Model 12A, which required point-by-point measurement of a spectrum. The later model, 12B, added a motor drive and recorder. The model 12C, in current production, added a chopper to the optical path and replaced the d-c breaker amplifier with an an a-c amplifier. The optical system of the 12C is shown in Fig. III-16.

Radiation from the Globar source is chopped and focused by the two mirrors, M_1 and M_2, onto the entrance slit of the monochromator. Sample cells are placed adjacent to the entrance slit. The paraboloidal mirror, M_3, collimates the beam and sends it to the prism and Littrow

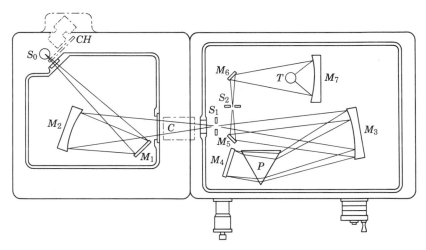

FIG. III-16.   Perkin-Elmer 12C spectrometer.   (Courtesy Perkin-Elmer Corp.)

mirror; upon reflection the beam is returned to the paraboloid and then to the small rectangular mirror, M_5, on the prism table, which deflects it onto the exit slit of the monochromator. A plane mirror, M_6, reflects the radiation to the ellipsoidal mirror, M_7, which focuses it onto the thermocouple element. The plane mirror, M_6, may be replaced by a grating or a scatterplate, which serves as a stray-light filter, or it may be removed from the optical path to allow the beam to pass out the port in the cover to another type of detector or another application. The position of the Littrow mirror is controlled by the motor-driven, calibrated drum at the front of the monochromator base. The slit width is manually controlled by a vernier drum at the left of the monochromator base. Alternatively, a string drive may be connected to the slit mechanism, which will be operated by the scanning motor to give a constant I_0 for the

NaCl prism.   Electrical slit cams are also available, for each of the prism materials, to achieve the same purpose with more versatility of program.

3.14 Perkin-Elmer 112

The basic model 12 spectrometer has been modified according to a design proposed by Walsh.[1]   The principle may be most readily visualized by considering the monochromator of Fig. III-16 as forming a full spectrum in the plane of the entrance slit.   Only a small portion of this spectrum is intercepted by the prism-table mirror and focused onto the exit slit.   A mirror inserted as shown in the position of M_5 in Fig. III-17 will intercept some other narrow frequency band and deflect it onto the

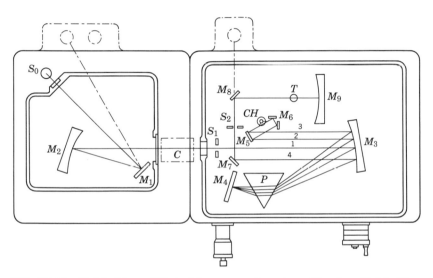

FIG. III-17.   Perkin-Elmer 112 double-pass spectrometer.   (Courtesy Perkin-Elmer Corp.)

right-angle mirrors, M_6.   Reflection from the right-angle mirrors will return the beam parallel to itself, but displaced very slightly, so that it will again strike M_5, then strike the paraboloid, the prism, the Littrow mirror, and return through the prism to the paraboloid.   The beam will have been further dispersed by the second pass through the prism (actually two more traversals, for a total of four), and will form a new spectrum in the plane of the entrance slit.   A small segment of the doubly dispersed spectrum will strike the prism-table mirror, M_7, and will pass through the exit slit. The detector will therefore receive two beams of radiation, of quite

[1] A. Walsh, *J. Opt. Soc. Am.* **42**, 94, 96, 496 (1952); **43**, 215, 989 (1953).

different frequencies.   The second-pass radiation will be more nearly monochromatic, and therefore of more interest.

To separate the signals due to the single-pass and double-pass radiation either of two methods, or both, have been found suitable.   A chopper, which consists of a rotating segment, is placed between the plane intercept mirror, M_5, and the right-angle mirrors, M_6.   Since this is the only chopper in the optical system, only that part of the beam which follows the specified path will be of alternating intensity and hence capable of being detected by the a-c circuits.   Stray radiation scattered from the surfaces of prisms, mirrors, and mounts will be discriminated against, as will the single-pass radiation.   Alternatively, the bottom half of entrance and exit slits may be blocked off; the single-pass radiation coming through the top half of the entrance slit will strike the bottom half of the exit slit and will be intercepted, while the second-pass radiation will pass through the top half of the exit slit.   This method provides less discrimination against stray radiation and limits the available slit height, but it is occasionally advantageous when it is desirable to chop the beam at an external point or when the relatively large single-pass signal would tend to saturate the detector or sharply increase the noise level.

Multiple-pass systems of higher order have been designed and found suitable for specialized problems.   The general characteristics of the multiple-pass spectrometer are high resolving power and low stray light, nearly equivalent to the performance of a double monochromator, at a cost only slightly greater than that of a standard single monochromator. The disadvantages are primarily the presence of a single-pass signal at the detector (not important with a thermal detector) and the "zero-level drift" caused by the emission of the chopper.   The zero drift is more a small annoyance than a serious disadvantage; since the chopper emits "heat waves" roughly according to the black-body curve, there is a very small chopped signal at the detector that will change from one region of the spectrum to another.   Thus the energy signal will vary slightly if one scans the spectrum with the shutter closed, but since this is reproducible it need not lead to any error of measurement.

3.15 Beckman IR-3

One of the most unique spectrometers that has been commercially produced is the Beckman IR-3, a single-beam, double monochromator instrument with unusual versatility.   The optical system is shown in Fig. III-18.   The Nernst glower, A, monitored by a phototube Z, throws a beam onto the mirror B, through the cell compartments G and I, and into the first monochromator, a conventional Littrow arrangement with a spherical collimating mirror at L.   The second monochromator is a mirror image of the first, except for prism orientation; thus most of the spherical aberrations are cancelled.   After passing through the two monochromators successively, the beam is sent through another pair of sample compartments, *R* and *T*, and then to a spherical mirror *V* which condenses the beam onto the thermocouple.   The window of the thermocouple housing is in the form of a hemispherical lens, and other lenses throughout the system provide supplementary weak focusing.   The beam is chopped at 10 cycles/sec at *C*.   Photomultiplier tubes at *Y* and *Y'* serve as alternative detectors for operation in the visible and ultraviolet regions.   The mirror *X* may be externally adjusted to throw the beam onto either of these.   An important feature of the mechanical design is the possibility of evacuating the entire spectrometer to eliminate atmospheric absorption.

Although the optical system of the IR-3 is of the single-beam type, the instrument will perform in many ways like a double-beam spectrometer.

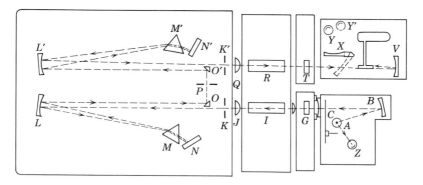

FIG. III-18.   Beckman IR-3 spectrometer.   (Courtesy Beckman Instruments, Inc.)

A comparison of two samples is made by running them consecutively, a wire or tape recorder serving as the link between the two scans.   The reference sample is scanned first, and the energy passed by this serves to operate an automatic slit control mechanism that adjusts the slits to keep the amplified signal from the detector constant.   Wider slits will therefore be required at lower frequencies (in the infrared) or in regions of absorption by the solvent.   Slit widths, as a function of the frequency, are recorded automatically during the standardization run.   When the sample is to be examined, the recorder takes over the control of the slit widths, reproducing the values that were found necessary to give constant energy with the reference cell in place.   Any decrease in intensity, therefore, must be due solely to the sample and not to the solvent, source, or other extraneous variables.   The resultant recording may be read directly as the transmittance of the sample.

The memory-standardization design maintains the signal-to-noise ratio constant by allowing the resolution to vary. Scanning speed is independently adjustable and is automatically controlled during the run to provide constant scanning time per spectral slit width. A strip of 35-mm film serves as the "cam" to determine the scanning rate; films can be made to produce records linear in wavenumber, wavelength, or a logarithmic function. Probably the chief advantage of the memory-standardization system is the possibility of comparing two samples, or a sample and solvent, in the same cell. If unusual cells are required, of long path length or for high or low temperature, this feature could be quite advantageous. The memory system was added to the IR-2 spectrometer to create the IR-2T. These instruments are no longer available.

3.2 Double-Beam Spectrometers

3.21 General Electric

In 1933 Hardy constructed a double-beam recording spectrometer for the visible region which has been marketed by the General Electric Company. A modification of the design was announced in 1956. Two simple

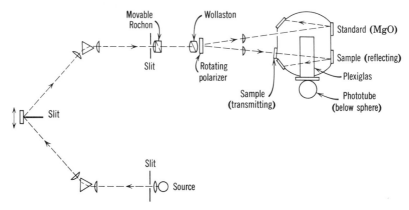

FIG. III-19.   General Electric spectrometer for the visible region.   (Courtesy General Electric Company.)

monochromators of the type illustrated in Fig. III-1 are combined, the common slit consisting of a single edge perpendicular to a plane mirror (Fig. III-19). The spectrum is scanned by moving this slit mechanism in the plane of the mirror.

The photometer, or intensity-measuring, section consists of a polarizer and a Wollaston prism, which serve as chopper and beam splitter, and a cesium oxide phototube that samples the radiation from an integrating sphere. The Wollaston prism is made by combining two quartz prisms, with proper choice of optical axes, so that a beam of light will be split into two beams, polarized in mutually perpendicular planes (Fig. III-20). A Rochon prism is also constructed of quartz prisms, but with optical axes arranged to pass the "ordinary" ray without deviation and to deflect the "extraordinary" ray out of the beam. The Wollaston prism, which remains fixed in position, will always send light of one polarization through the sample compartment and the ray polarized in the perpendicular plane will be sent to the standard, or reference sample. If now a polarizer is rotated in the path of the beams coming from the Wollaston prism, the two beams will be transmitted alternately as the plane of the polarizer coincides with the plane of polarization of one or the other of the beams.

If the intensities transmitted or reflected by the sample and standard are

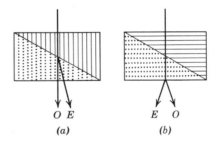

$O\ E$ $E\ \ O$

(a) (b)

FIG. III-20. (a) Rochon and (b) Wollaston prisms. Dots and lines indicate orientations of optical axes of the quartz. O and E represent "ordinary" and "extraordinary" rays, respectively.

the same, the phototube will receive only a d-c signal; if there is a difference in intensity, the phototube will receive a 60-cycle a-c signal (superimposed on a d-c background signal). The a-c signal is amplified and applied to a phase-sensitive servomotor that rotates a balancing Rochon prism located between the monochromator slit and the Wollaston prism. If the sample beam were blocked off, the intensity in the reference beam could be decreased an equivalent amount by placing in front of the Wollaston prism a polarizer that would pass only that portion of the incident light polarized in the plane corresponding to the sample beam; if the reference beam were blocked off, the sample beam intensity could be similarly decreased by passing only the plane of polarization corresponding to the reference beam. This is the function of the Rochon prism, the relative intensities of the light components polarized in the two planes depending on the angle of orientation of the prism, which is in turn governed by the servo-motor.

The pen is mechanically linked to the motion of the balancing prism by means of a cam that allows the trace to be linear in transmittance or reflectance, absorbance, log absorbance, or $\log [(1 - R)^2/2R]$, where R is the reflectance. A slit cam automatically adjusts the three slits to provide a constant band pass of 100 Å. Although this is extremely broad in terms of modern specifications, it is a very considerable improvement over the filter photometers previously employed, and the double monochromator very effectively eliminates stray radiation. For the determination of color, furthermore, this band pass is quite adequate, since sharp bands are not to be expected. The region from 3800 to 7000 Å may be scanned in 1 minute.

A distinctive feature of the Hardy design is the integrating sphere, coated internally with MgO for high reflectance (97% or 98%). If it is desired to measure the transmittance of a sample, the specimen is placed at the entrance to the sphere. The light transmitted by the sample is then reflected off a MgO block and the multiply reflected radiation sampled by the phototube, which is placed in an opening at the bottom of the sphere. The reference beam strikes a similar MgO block and furnishes the intensity standard. For measurement of reflectance, the sample is placed at the far side of the sphere, replacing the MgO block in the sample beam.

In the original design the reflecting surfaces were perpendicular to the incoming beams. The specularly reflected component would thus be returned through the entrance aperture, and only the diffuse reflectance measured. In current instruments the angle of incidence on the reflecting surface is 6°; the specularly reflected beam strikes an area adjacent to the entrance port and at the option of the operator may be trapped and removed from the sphere or may be reflected and diffused by a MgO block. To ensure that the phototube sampled the radiation density in the sphere, a diffusing glass was placed between the phototube and the sphere. This has now been replaced by a Lucite rod extending more than halfway into the sphere, which acts (because of its tendency for total internal reflection) as a conduit for transmitting the light more efficiently to the phototube. The integrating sphere depolarizes the beams before incidence on the phototube, a necessary condition for accurate comparison. It also provides a somewhat different type of transmission measurement from most instruments, since a large part of the scattered radiation will be included in the measured intensity. This can be helpful if one is concerned with the measurement of total light passed by a translucent sheet. Extensive discussions of the calibration and operation of the General Electric spectrometer are contained in the publications of the National Bureau of Standards.[1]

3.22 Cary Model 11

An instrument of exceptionally high performance in the ultraviolet and visible regions is the Cary ultraviolet spectrometer, produced by the Applied Physics Corporation.   Linear absorbance (model 11) or linear transmittance (model 10) scales are available; log (absorbance) may be plotted directly by means of an additional attachment.   Two monochromators, each containing a 30° quartz Littrow prism, provide high resolution, about 1 Å over most of the range, and extremely low stray light, less than one part in a million.   The reproducibility and accuracy of intensity measurements are sufficiently high (reportedly better than ± 0.004 in absorbance) that the limiting error is most often determined by other variables, such as residual films or dust on cell windows or chart-paper slippage or inaccuracies.

The optical system is shown in Fig. III-21.   A Nestor hydrogen lamp and a tungsten lamp may be rapidly interchanged.   A condensing lens focuses the source onto the entrance slit, D, of the monochromator.   The second monochromator compensates for aberrations introduced by the first.   After emergence from the exit slit, L, of the second monochromator, the radiation is divided by a "washboard" mirror, M, which deflects half of the beam upward at 45° and the other half downward at 45° from the horizontal.   The beams are collimated and sent through the sample and reference compartments, striking the respective photomultiplier tubes (1P28).   The chopper, C, modulates the beam at 60 cycles/sec.

The spectrometer operates on the electronic-null principle, a portion of the reference signal serving to balance the signal arising from the sample phototube.   The unbalance signal is amplified and operates the pen servomotor, which drives the pen and slide-wire contact to the point on the potentiometer slide-wire that will make the balance exact.   Variation in amplifier performance will change the driving signal to the pen but will not change the balance point.   It is difficult to produce or maintain two optical paths with identical characteristics; it is even more difficult to produce two detectors with precisely the same sensitivity.   These effects may be compensated for in the Cary by means of a "multipot" system, a set of 44 variable resistors which permit an exact balance of the "zero absorbance" signals at as many points in the spectrum.   This ensures a flat base-

---

[1] See, for example, K. S. Gibson, "Spectrophotometers," chap. 5 of ref. 35; *Natl. Bur. Standards (U.S.) Bull.* LC-547; Gibson and Keegan, *J. Opt. Soc. Am.* **28**, 372 (1938); Gibson, *Natl. Bur. Standards (U.S.) Circ.* 484; Judd, *Natl. Bur. Standards (U.S.) Circ.* 478.

line at all times in spite of aging of mirrors, lenses, or phototubes, or the substitution of a new set of photomultipliers with different characteristics. The signal from the reference phototube operates a slit servomechanism to maintain constant reference signal output. The photometric accuracy is therefore independent of the transmittance of the reference cell or the source output.   A choice of slit programs, over a wide range, may be made by adjusting the magnitude of the reference signal by means of a panel

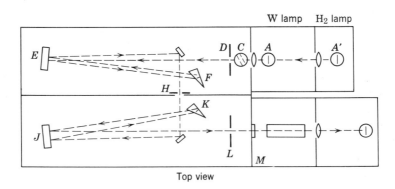

FIG. III-21.   Cary Model 11 spectrometer for visible and ultraviolet regions. (Courtesy Applied Physics Corporation.)

control.   The uncertainty in absorbance measurement is virtually constant over the full range of 0 to 3.5 in absorbance; higher percentage accuracy may thus be obtained at the higher absorbance values, the limiting factor being the increasing noise which makes it more difficult to determine the equilibrium value.

The full range of the Cary model 11 is from 2000 Å (50,000 cm^{-1}) to 8000 Å (12,500 cm^{-1}), although limitations imposed by source intensity, photomultiplier response, and the transmittance of quartz prisms and silica lenses effectively limit the range to about 2100 Å and 7000 or 7500 Å. This full range may be scanned at speeds from 1 Å/sec to 125 Å/sec. The collimated beams through the sample and reference compartments make it possible to choose cell lengths longer than 1 cm without loss of energy. Ten-centimeter cells may be accommodated in the standard compartment, or for special purposes the phototube compartment may be unbolted and placed at a greater distance. For measurements of gases at low pressure or concentrations, a 1-meter path-length cell is available which fits the standard cell compartment.

A new instrument, the Cary Model 15, combines the internal optics of the model 11 with certain features of the external optics of the model 14 (discussed below). The range has been extended into the far ultraviolet beyond the limit set by atmospheric absorption.

3.23 Baird Infrared Spectrometer

About the same time that the Cary model 11 was introduced, Baird Associates (now Baird-Atomic) began production of a double-beam

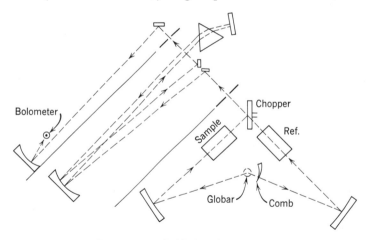

FIG. III-22. Baird infrared spectrometer.

instrument for the infrared region, following the design of Wright and Herscher. The optical diagram is given in Fig. III-22. The Globar is enclosed in a metal housing with two windows which permit illumination of two large spherical mirrors. They focus the two beams onto the entrance slit of the monochromator; in one case the beam passes through the reference compartment and through the open section of the chopper; in the other case the beam passes through the sample compartment and is reflected by the mirror portion of the chopper wheel. Adjustable shutters on the concave mirrors permit adjustment of the 100% line to correct for losses due to scattering or vignetting. The monochromator is a conventional Littrow design with a spherical collimating mirror and a very large (10-cm base and 8-cm height) 60° prism. A bolometer detector in a bridge circuit provides an alternating signal that is amplified and supplied to a servomotor. This drives the tapered comb into or out of the reference beam to produce a balance or optical null. The recorder pen is linked to the comb by a string drive. The record obtained is linear in transmittance and may be linear in wavenumber or wavelength. A lead storage battery provides the steady current required for operation of the bolometer. Changes in the controls and cabinet have been announced from time to time, as well as changes in individual components (models 4-55, KM-1, and NK-1).

3.24 Perkin-Elmer 21

The optical system of the model 12 has been combined with the necessary supplementary entrance optics to create a double-beam spectrometer (Fig. III-23) of high light-gathering power ($f/4.5$). A Nernst glower has been substituted for the Globar, thus eliminating the requirement of water cooling. Any drift in source intensity will affect both beams in the same manner and will not introduce any inaccuracy into the measurement. The mirrors M_1 and M_2 collect radiation from the source at nearly the same angle, and the two beams are then focused onto the image points I_1 and I_2 just inside the case of the spectrometer. Sample and reference cells are placed in the beams approximately at the point C, but very small samples may be inserted close to the image point, I_1, for maximum sensitivity. The optical wedge, a photoengraved diaphragm (Fig. III-24), is placed at the image point I_2. This arrangement causes a uniform loss of intensity from the area of the beam; otherwise the wedge might produce a shadow in its own image on the mirrors and non-uniformity of the reflecting surfaces would produce an effect equivalent to a non-uniform taper of the optical wedge. Mirrors M_6 and M_8 are so arranged that the reference beam will undergo the same number of reflections, at the same angles of incidence, as the sample beam. The sample beam is reflected from M_5 onto the chopper wheel and is reflected by the mirror half of this wheel onto M_9, which focuses the beam onto the entrance slit of the monochromator (S_1) by way of M_{10}. The reference beam, after reflection by M_6 and M_8, passes through the open portion of the chopper wheel onto M_9 and is focused, by way of M_{10}, onto the entrance slit. It will be observed that the monochromator is the mirror image of the model 12 monochromator but is otherwise identical with it. The recorder pen is mechanically linked

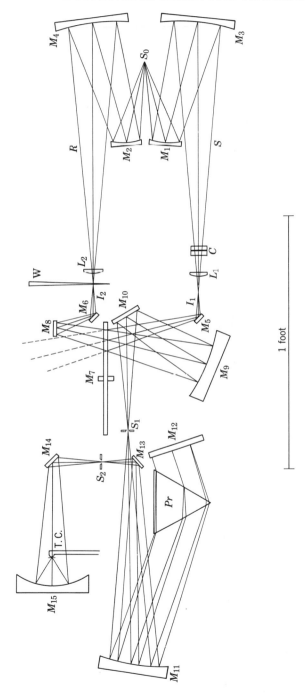

FIG. III-23.   Perkin-Elmer model 21 infrared spectrometer.   (Courtesy Perkin-Elmer Corp.)

to the optical wedge, which is driven by a servomotor actuated by the unbalance signal from the detector and amplifier.

A large number of additional features are now available for the model 21, such as expanded scales; linear absorbance rather than transmittance recording; double-passing of the monochromator (see discussion of model 112); automatic integration of area under an absorption band; and simultaneous recording on two charts or cards. Standard equipment permits such operations as cycling, to retrace automatically a given portion of the spectrum, and change of size of the recording to fit any convenient chart or filing card dimensions, as well as variation of scanning speed, pen response and damping, and slit-width program. Since the optics are all of the reflecting type, the spectrometer can be readily adapted

FIG. III-24.   Optical Wedge (mounted in carriage) for Perkin-Elmer 21 spectrometer. (Courtesy Perkin-Elmer Corp.)

to any part of the spectrum from the ultraviolet (about 2100 Å) to the far infrared (about 250 cm^{-1}) by substitution of the proper prism unit and changing the source and detector as required. Replacement of the Littrow mirror by a grating gives greatly improved performance in the high-frequency portion of the spectrum (model 221-G).

The Perkin-Elmer 421 employs the optical system of the 21 except that the prism is removed and the Littrow mirror replaced by two gratings, back to back. Each grating is used only in the first order to simplify the problems that result from overlapping orders. Interference filters act as order sorters and are automatically moved into position as the spectrum is scanned. To avoid the inaccuracies that are inevitably associated with the production of cams, the gratings are driven by a lead screw and cosecant arm. Because of the high dispersion provided by the gratings, the resolution limit of the 421 is on the order of tenths of a reciprocal centimeter throughout the spectrum.

3.25 Beckman IR-4

The first commercial infrared spectrometer to combine double-beam and double-monochromator design features was the Beckman IR-4. Figure III-25 shows the optical system, which consists of two $f/10$ Littrow monochromators, with spherical collimating mirrors, combined to cancel most of the aberrations.   Radiation from the Nernst glower is received by a single mirror and split into sample and reference beams by the rotating sector wheel, C_1.   The beams are recombined by a second chopper, C_2, synchronized with the first.   After passage through the double mono-chromator, the beam is condensed onto the thermocouple, which has a lens window.

Among the more unusual features of the IR-4 design are the prism inter-change unit, the design and placement of the control panels, and the pro-vision for single-beam operation.   The two prisms, with attendant mirrors and cams, are mounted on a single framework which may be lifted from the instrument and replaced, in a matter of minutes, by an equivalent unit for optimum performance in another region of the infrared.   Controls have been divided into two panels, which might be described as program-ing controls and operating controls.   The former are located in a recessed compartment below the recorder chart bed, with a sliding door for protection.   These include the controls for initial starting, selection of single-beam or double-beam operation, amplifier gain and response con-trols, and other adjustments which may be expected to be changed not more than once a day in routine operation.   The second set, which includes rate of scan, start and stop, and similar operating controls, is located in an exposed position at the left end of the chart bed.   The design is intended to combine simplicity of operation, to meet the requirements of the con-trol laboratory staffed primarily with semiskilled technicians, with built-in flexibility of operation for the research laboratory.   Single-beam opera-tion, available by turning a single knob, is intended for certain types of quantitative analyses.

The IR-7 is a modification of the IR-4 in which one of the prisms has been replaced by a grating.   A multilobe "star" cam sweeps the grating through successive orders to provide an automatic tracing of the spectrum through the full rock-salt region.   The resolution limit is on the order of tenths of a reciprocal centimeter.   The prism monochromator acts as an order sorter and contributes to some extent to the resolving power of the spectrometer.

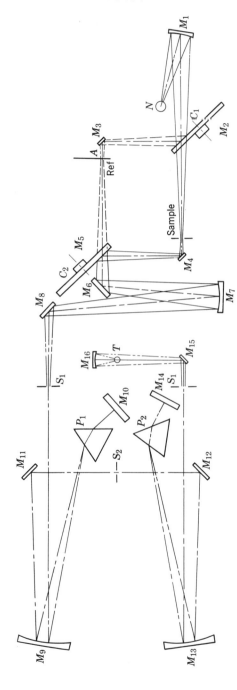

FIG. III-25.   Beckman IR-4 infrared spectrometer.   (Courtesy Beckman Instruments, Inc.)

3.26 Perkin-Elmer 13

An instrument of exceptional versatility is the Perkin-Elmer model 13 spectrometer, a ratio-recording instrument following the system developed by Savitzky and Halford.[1]   The model 13 combines many of the advantages of the single-beam instrument with provision for double-beam operation.   It is also particularly well suited to operation over the extended region covering the ultraviolet, visible, and near infrared, as well as the "fundamental" and far infrared portions of the spectrum.

Operation of the model 13 is shown in Figs. III-26 and III-27.   The source is a Nernst glower, monitored by a phototube.   After reflection at the large mirror M_1, a portion of the beam is intercepted by the mirror M_2 and is deflected through the chopper to the sample compartment.   The remainder of the beam passes over M_2, is deflected by M_3, and passes through the chopper into the reference cell space.   Mirror M_4 sends the beam from the sample area over the mirror M_5 to M_6; mirror M_5 reflects the reference beam against M_6.   The monochromator is identical with that of the model 12.   For single-beam operation the first beam splitter, M_2, is replaced by a full-size mirror.   Chopping before the sample compartment has the advantage of permitting observation of samples at elevated temperatures without interference due to the emission from sample or cell.   To observe emission spectra it is necessary to introduce the beam at a point before the chopper.

The principle of the ratio-recording system is indicated schematically by the resultant signal patterns shown in Fig. III-27.   The chopper is a 180° sector, which rotates at 13 cycles/sec, intercepting sample and reference beams at a phase difference of 90°.   The sample and reference signals each form approximately a square-wave pattern, therefore, with a phase shift of 90° between them.   Addition of the two signals, by the detector, gives a signal approximating that shown in Fig. III-27c, which specifically contains information on both I, the intensity transmitted by the sample, and I_0, the intensity transmitted by the reference.   The ratio of these, which is simply the transmittance, is plotted by the recorder.   The slits are automatically adjusted by a preset electrical cam to provide constant energy in the absence of sample or reference absorption or may be controlled by the reference signal to provide constant reference-beam energy.

Because the beam is split before chopping, the ratio-recording system involves a loss of energy in double-beam operation compared to the optical-null design.   This may be recovered by an increase in scanning time.   The design has found particular favor among those who are less concerned with rapidity of measurement than with the versatility of the

[1] Savitzky and Halford, *Rev. Sci. Instr.* **21**, 203 (1950).

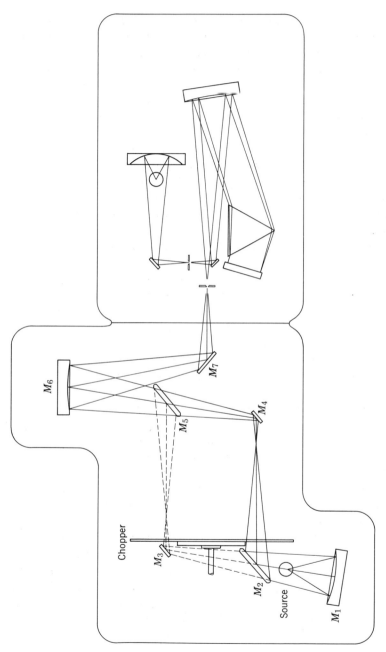

FIG. III-26.   Perkin-Elmer Model 13 spectrometer.   (Courtesy Perkin-Elmer Corp.)

single-beam instrument combined with the convenience of a linear transmittance record. A new spectrometer based on an improved but similar design is now available for the very far infrared (Perkin-Elmer 301).

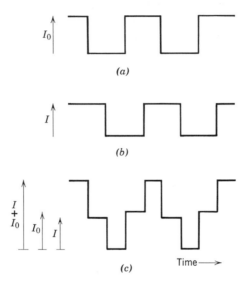

FIG. III-27. Signal pattern for Halford-Savitzky system (P-E 13). (a) Reference beam signal. (b) Sample beam signal. (c) Combination signal, with sample and reference choppers 90° out of phase.

An instrument based on similar principles has been designed by Hornig[1] and is available from the Farrand Optical Company.

3.27 Cary Model 14

Two significant trends in instrumentation over the last few years have been the tendency toward extension of the frequency range of spectrometers, especially from the ultraviolet and visible into the very near infrared, and the increasingly favorable attitude toward incorporation of the high-quality gratings now available into monochromators to replace or supplement the prisms which have been employed almost exclusively in the past. The Cary model 14, first introduced in 1952, was among the first to incorporate these features.

Figure III-28 shows the optical system of the model 14. For operation in the ultraviolet or visible regions, the radiation from the Nestor hydrogen lamp, A, or tungsten lamp, C, is focused onto the entrance slit, D, passes through the first monochromator, which contains a 30° Littrow prism of

[1] Hornig, Hyde, and Adcock, *J. Opt. Soc. Am.* **40**, 497 (1950).

high-purity silica, and passes through the intermediate slit, H, into the second monochromator. The grating is a 6000 grooves/cm echellete. The focal lengths of the prism and grating monochromators are 30 and 40 cm, respectively, and both have an aperture ratio of $f/8$. All three slits (D, H, and L) are curved and simultaneously adjustable. Since the fixed curvature of the slits cannot match the curvature of the image at the extremes of the spectral range, provision has been made for decreasing slit height, if desired, to improve the resolution at the limiting frequencies.

The beam emerging from the monochromator strikes the semicircular mirror, O, of the chopper assembly and is alternately reflected into the sample and reference compartments. The chopper disk, N, on the same shaft as the mirror segment, intercepts the beam between each half cycle

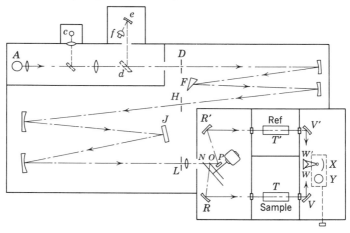

Fig. III-28.   Cary Model 14 spectrometer.   (Courtesy Applied Physics Corp.)

to provide a zero-energy level.   The sample and reference beams impinge alternately on the single photomultiplier detector, X.

For operation in the near infrared, the tungsten ribbon-filament lamp is slid into position to replace the photomultiplier tube and the mirror d is inserted to deflect the beam onto the lead sulfide photoconductive cell, f. The optical path is thus traversed in the reverse direction.   For special applications, such as measurement of the fluorescence spectrum, the positions of the photomultiplier tube and ultraviolet or visible source may be interchanged.

Although the electronic design of the model 14 is quite different from the model 11, the fundamental principles are similar.   The position of the slide-wire contact determines the attenuation applied to the reference signal before this is compared with the sample signal; the unbalance is amplified and applied to the pen servomotor.   Adjustment of the baseline is possible by means of a multipot system.

The recorder has an effective chart width of 20 in., achieved by a double-pen mechanism.   If the first pen goes off scale to the right at an absorbance of 1.0, the second pen continues the record, starting from the left-hand edge of the chart, extending the range from 1.0 to 2.0.   Scanning speed is adjustable between the limits of 0.5 Å/sec and 500 Å/sec.   Accuracy of the linear absorbance scale is reported to be ± 0.002 in the range from 0 to 1.0 and ± 0.005 near an absorbance of 2.0.

The advantage of combining a 30° Littrow silica prism with a grating is indicated by Fig. III-29.   Angular dispersion is plotted as a function of

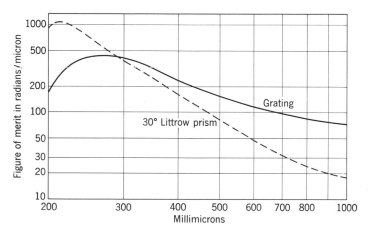

FIG. III-29.   Relative performance of 6000 grooves/cm grating and 30° silica Littrow prism as a function of wavelength.   (Courtesy Applied Physics Corp.)

wavelength, with corrections applied for the loss of efficiency of the grating at angles away from the blaze and the loss of efficiency of both grating and prism at very short wavelengths.   The silica prism also serves as an order sorter for the grating.   The high-purity silica permits an operating range from 1850 Å (54,000 cm^{-1}) to 2.6 μ (3850 cm^{-1}).

3.28 Unicam SP 100

An infrared spectrometer marketed by Unicam has a number of unusual features.   The instrument is housed in a vacuum-tight case to permit effective removal of atmospheric absorption.   A prism table, containing prisms suitable for various regions of the spectrum, may be rotated by remote control from outside the case to bring the best prism into position for the region to be examined.   A secondary monochromator, containing a grating, may be added to provide high resolution (Fig. III-30).

Those points in the electrical circuitry to be checked in the process of

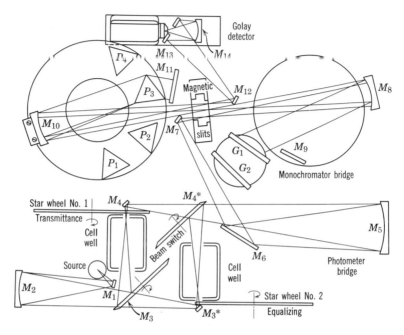

FIG. III-30.   Unicam SP 100 spectrometer.   Prisms and gratings can be interchanged by means of controls on the front panel.   (Courtesy Unicam Instruments, Ltd.)

trouble shooting have been brought to a panel at the front of the instrument.   By means of a set of knobs any of these may be read or certain signals may be displayed on a small oscilloscope.

3.29   Cary-White 90

The Applied Physics Corporation, in cooperation with John White, has produced the model 90 infrared spectrometer.   A conventional Littrow prism monochromator, with a large KBr prism, is combined with a Czerny-Turner grating monochromator (Fig. III-31).   The 750 grooves/cm grating covers the range of 4000 to 450 cm^{-1} in four orders.   High photometric accuracy is achieved with a ratio-recording system.   Resolution is comparable to the IR-7 and 421.

3.30   Perkin-Elmer 350

Recent developments in the technology of aluminizing and protecting mirrors have made it possible to produce stable mirror surfaces with

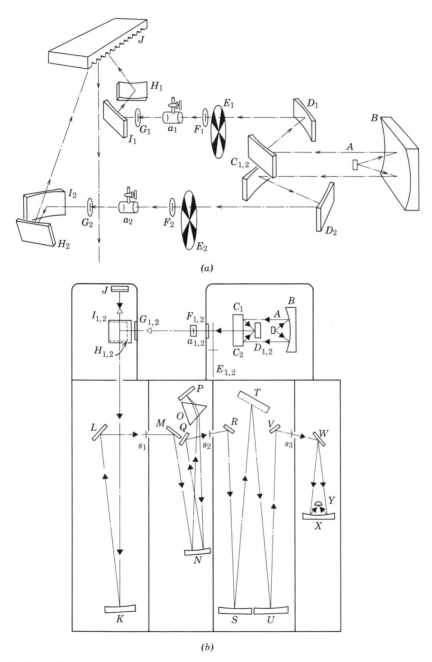

FIG. III-31. Cary-White 90 infrared spectrometer. (*a*) Entrance optics. (*b*) Mono-chromator optics. (Courtesy Applied Physics Corp.)

greatly improved performance in the far ultraviolet. Such mirrors have been incorporated into the design of the Perkin-Elmer model 350 spectrometer, which covers the range from 1750 Å (58,000 cm^{-1}) or beyond through the visible and the very near infrared to 2.7 μ (3700 cm^{-1}). A conventional double monochromator, with 30° silica prisms, is combined with an electronic-null system in which the reference signal is maintained constant by the slit servomechanism

3.3   Low-Cost Spectrometers

An important break-through in infrared instrumentation came in 1956 with the announcement of infrared spectrometers designed for sale at a small fraction of the cost of the more versatile instruments. By fixing such parameters as scanning period, resolution, and response and eliminating other adjustments, it was possible to make the new instruments, in spite of their lower cost and smaller size, capable of recording most routine spectra with negligible loss of quality. Many laboratories that could not previously afford an infrared spectrometer have found the new instruments a satisfactory and welcome addition to their equipment; other laboratories have found it advisable to acquire the less expensive instrument to free a higher-priced spectrometer for more exacting work requiring non-routine operating conditions. With increased availability of the instruments it is also more often possible to allow the individual chemist to scan his own routine samples without the delay and bookkeeping required by the procedure of having all spectra run by a central group of analytical spectroscopists. The new instruments are provided with a minimum of controls to make operation by the non-spectroscopist practical.

3.31   Perkin-Elmer 137 "Infracord"

The Perkin-Elmer Model 137 "Infracord" spectrometer (Fig. III-32) is a low-cost, double-beam, optical-null instrument. In the standard instrument the $f/5$ monochromator contains a 70° NaCl prism in a Littrow mount. The spectrometer is especially compact, a result achieved by employing paraboloidal, ellipsoidal, and toroidal mirrors. The source is an alumina rod. Spectra are recorded linearly in transmittance and wavelength on $8\frac{1}{2} \times 11$ in. preprinted chart paper.

Modified versions of the Infracord have been announced more recently. These substitute other prism materials or gratings for the NaCl prism. This makes it possible to extend the wavelength range available in the laboratory or permits medium-resolution (1–3 cm^{-1}) measurements in regions where this would not be possible with the rock salt prism.

A modification of the Infracord is the model 202, which employs a 60° silica prism in the optical scheme of Fig. III-32.   The instrument is the first to employ a photoengraved optical wedge for the ultraviolet and visible regions.   The usual disadvantage of the optical-null design at low transmittance values is overcome by means of an automatic gain control that varies the dynode voltage on the "end-on" photomultiplier tube to give constant photocurrent.   This permits accurate measurements, with-

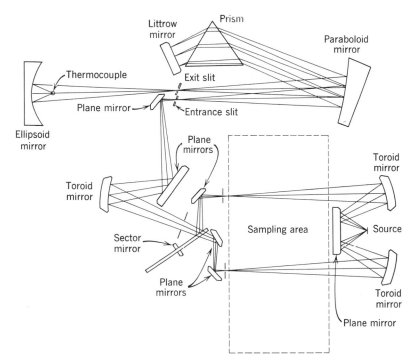

FIG. III-32.   Perkin-Elmer Model 137 "Infracord" spectrometer.   (Courtesy Perkin-Elmer Corp.)

out increased noise or loss of resolution, at very high absorbance values when making differential measurements.   The optical wedge is logarithmic, producing an ordinate scale that is linear in absorbance.   The range of the 202 is from 1900 Å to 7500 Å and from 0 to 1.5 in absorbance.

3.32   Beckman IR-5 and IR-6

One of the first low-cost spectrometers announced was the Beckman IR-6, a single-beam infrared spectrometer.   It was followed shortly by the IR-5, a double-beam spectrometer with essentially the same monochromator but additional entrance optics. In the IR-6 (no longer in production) stray radiation was minimized by an oversize entrance slit, alternately chopped in the center and at the ends. The radiation passing through the upper and lower extremes of the slit during the "off" phase of the main beam produced approximately the same quantity of stray as the radiation passing through the center section during the "on" cycle. To permit conventional sample cells, the optical path was reversed, with the sample placed behind the exit slit. The entire optical path was flushed with recirculated dried air to eliminate atmospheric absorption bands.

The Beckman IR-5 (Fig. III-33) differs from the IR-6 primarily in that the optical path has been turned around and equipped with the extra mirrors necessary for double-beam operation. The flat-bed recorder employs preprinted charts 7 × 24 in.

3.4   Other Instruments

The particular list of instruments discussed above is not intended to be exhaustive but is chosen to illustrate important variations in design, historical trends, and something of the scope of the instrumentation now commercially available. A number of other spectrometers should be mentioned as being of importance, although no list of reasonable length can hope to be truly complete. In the ultraviolet and visible regions, several instruments have appeared which combine the Beckman DU monochromator with external optics and electronics to produce a double-beam instrument with automatic recording. Among these are the Beckman DK-1 and DK-2, the Warren Spectracord 3000, and the Process and Instruments modification. The P and I spectrometer maintains the optical system of the DU but moves the sample and reference cells alternately into the beam.

The detector, amplifier, and recorder systems of the Spectracord Model 4000 (produced by the Perkin-Elmer Corporation) are essentially those of the model 3000, but a double monochromator provides higher resolution and lower stray light. The Spectracord instruments, as well as the Beckman DK spectrometers, are equipped for operation in the very near infrared region.

The Beckman DB ultraviolet spectrometer is a low-cost instrument similar to the DU except that oscillating mirrors alternately direct the beam through sample and reference cells. The detector is a 1P28 photomultiplier. The instrument is line-operated and attachments are available to make it an automatic recording spectrometer.

The Bausch and Lomb 505 spectrometer (Fig. III-34) is intermediate in price between the least expensive ultraviolet instruments and the standard

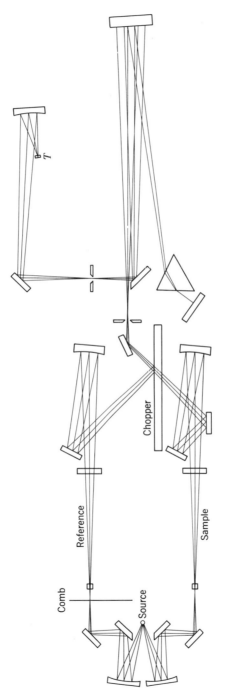

Fig. III-33.   Beckman IR-5 infrared spectrometer.   (Courtesy Beckman Instruments, Inc.)

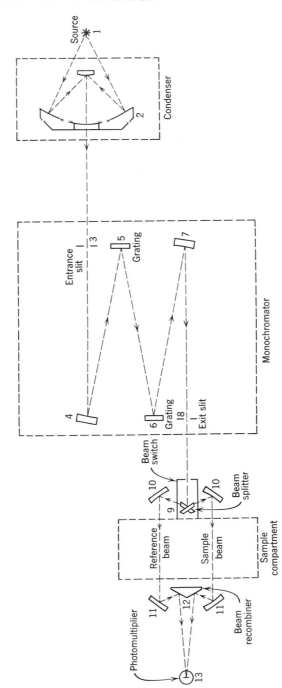

Fig. III-34.   Bausch and Lomb 505 spectrometer.   (Courtesy Bausch and Lomb Inc., Rochester, N.Y.)

recording instruments.   It has a single monochromator, though it employs two gratings in series between the collimator and "camera" mirrors. It is equipped for automatic recording.

Less versatile instruments include the Beckman model B, with a glass Féry prism; the Coleman Junior and Universal spectrometers; the Bausch and Lomb Spectronic 20; and a number of other instruments and monochromators, some of which are commonly made to the customer's specifications, produced by Farrand, Gaertner, and other companies.   A rather large number of filter photometers and visual color comparators have been put on the market, and new designs occasionally appear.

Certainly no discussion of spectroscopic apparatus could be complete without mention of the Hilger instruments.   During the last quarter of the nineteenth century and much of the first half of the present century, Hilger instruments were standard equipment in this country as well as abroad.   The infrared spectrometer produced by Adam Hilger, Ltd., about 1913 was almost certainly the first commercial instrument for this region.   Astronomical instruments, emission spectrographs and direct-reading spectrometers, ultraviolet and infrared absorption spectrometers, and Raman spectrographs and spectrometers are included in the Hilger line.   These instruments, as well as a number of other foreign spectrometers, merit careful consideration.

Very little information is available thus far concerning the details of the spectrometers now in production in the USSR.   The most commonly mentioned instruments are the IKS-11, a single-beam infrared spectrometer with some resemblance to the Perkin-Elmer 12, and the IKS-14, which is apparently a double-beam modification of the IKS-11.

None of the discussions of instruments should be considered an adequate presentation of the merits or possibilities of the apparatus.   Further information on these should be sought from the manufacturers before attempting to decide which is best adapted to the needs of a particular laboratory.   A very brief discussion of some of the important considerations in selecting an instrument is given in section 6.

4   Raman Spectroscopy

The problems of Raman spectroscopy are superficially identical with those of absorption spectroscopy in the visible region.   A basic form of the apparatus is shown in Fig. III-35.   The source is a low-pressure, high-intensity mercury arc, with proper filters to isolate an individual line, generally the blue 23,000 cm^{-1} line (4358 Å).   This essentially monochromatic radiation illuminates a glass tube with a flat window at one end and a suitable light trap at the other end.   The scattered light is observed at right angles to the incident radiation, to prevent the direct light from the arc reaching the spectrograph.   Most of the scattered radiation is of the same frequency as that coming from the arc (Rayleigh scattering), but a very small amount (roughly 0.1% of the 0.1% or less that is scattered) will have been shifted in frequency (Raman scattering) by amounts that correspond to the vibrational frequencies of the molecule   Thus the shifts in frequency are of the same order of magnitude as, and in many cases are identical with, the frequencies the molecule can absorb in the infrared region.

The particular problems associated with Raman spectroscopy arise from the extremely low intensities which must be detected.   The scattered radiation from the Raman tube is passed into the spectrograph and there dispersed according to frequency and focused onto the photographic plate.

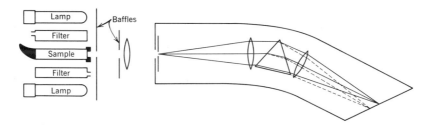

FIG. III-35.   Simple Raman apparatus.   The filter eliminates unwanted lines and keeps sample cool.   The scattered radiation is analysed by a fast spectrograph or spectrometer.

The fastest emulsions available (such as the Eastman 103a series) are preferred, since resolution is not so important as is speed, but exposures may still run from a few minutes, for very strongly scattering compounds, to several hours.   In the past it has even been necessary to run exposures as long as days or weeks in order to observe the scattering of some gases. Very great progress has been made in overcoming these difficulties, and it may be expected that more improvements will follow as the techniques become more widely applied.

By far the most common source for Raman work is the mercury arc and especially the blue line (22,937 cm^{-1} or 4358 Å).   The 2537 Å line, in the ultraviolet (39,400 cm^{-1}), has certain advantages when the sample is transparent in this region.   The higher frequency causes a higher intensity of Raman scattering for the same incident intensity, and the Rayleigh scattering can be removed by placing mercury vapor, at room temperature, in the optical path.   The disadvantages are the need for silica optics, including the arc and sample tube as well as the spectrograph, an increased probability of fluorescence, and the difficulty of obtaining high intensities without self-reversal in the arc (absorption of the radiation by cooler mercury vapor at the walls of the arc).   For samples that absorb in the blue, the mercury green line (18,300 cm^{-1} or 5461 Å) or the sodium doublet (17,000 cm^{-1} or 5890 Å) have been found satisfactory.   Among the other lines that have been employed are the helium line in the near ultraviolet (25,800 cm^{-1} or 3888 Å), and the mercury violet line at 24,700 cm^{-1} (4047 Å).   Often the spectrum will be observed under excitation with both the mercury blue and violet lines, since the former is a triplet (spacing about 60 and 100 cm^{-1}) and the latter is a doublet (spacing about 200 cm^{-1}). This provides a means of identifying lines which are caused by the weaker blue lines or by the weaker of the two violet lines, or by imperfections in the grating (grating "ghosts").

Arc intensities have been increased by introduction of the Toronto arc, a low-pressure, water-cooled arc with mercury pool electrodes.   Two styles are shown in Fig. III-36.   The water cooling serves to keep the pressure of the mercury vapor low, which is necessary for sharp-line emission.   In the water-jacketed arc the water circulating about the ends is cooler than that about the center; thus deposition of mercury on the walls of the center section is avoided.   The water-jacketed arc can be placed in a totally enclosing reflector, with the sample tube, thus greatly increasing the efficiency of illumination of the sample tube.   Such arcs are started by warming the mercury pools with hot water, then inducing ionization in the vapor with a Tesla coil (leak detector).   If the vacuum is sufficiently good (about 10^{-4} to 10^{-6} mm aside from mercury vapor), the arcs will fire on 110 or 220 volts direct current.   They commonly operate at about 15 amperes and 110 volts direct current.

Preliminary application of the ruby laser as a Raman source by Stoicheff and by Porto and Wood[1] has indicated that such a pulsed laser may be quite advantageous when combined with photographic detection. The gas-phase laser offers even greater promise, particularly if the sample can be placed inside the resonant cavity.

The sample tubes shown in Figs. III-37a and III-37b are more efficient than that of Fig. III-35.   In the liquid cell the intensity reaching the spectrograph is approximately doubled by the substitution of the mirror for the light trap at the back of the tube.   For gas samples, more efficient light-gathering power is required, since the scattering is proportional to sample density.   The multiple-reflection cell illustrated can increase the intensity reaching the slit by a factor of 10 or 20.

[1] Porto and Wood, Paper T 3, Columbus Symposium on Molecular Structure and Spectroscopy, June, 1961.

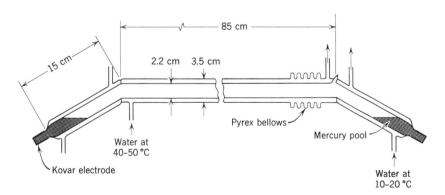

FIG. III-36.   Toronto-type mercury arcs for Raman excitation.   (Top) Commercial lamp (courtesy Applied Research Laboratories).   (Bottom) Arc for gas-phase Raman spectroscopy [B. P. Stoicheff, *Can. J. Phys.* **32**, 330 (1954).]

The circular Raman tube is inherently inefficient, since the slit can pass only a small strip from the center of the circular image produced by the condensing lens.   A cylindrical lens would put more of this radiation into the spectrograph, but the additional rays would enter at such an angle that they would miss the prism or grating and contribute only to the stray-light problem (see Fig. III-2, section 2).   An optical device that can increase the energy reaching the exit slit of the monochromator is the image slicer, which splits the circular image into a number of vertical strips, then moves them up or down and to the center.   The result is illumination of a slit that is several times as high.   In a photographic instrument this would simply produce an image of increased height but no greater density, but a photoelectric detector can accept the full amount of energy coming from the exit slit and hence a real gain in signal is achieved.   In the photographic instrument the intensity at the plate can be increased by means of a cylindrical lens placed directly in front of the plate.   This gives a shorter line which is more readily visible.

Most of the early Raman spectrographs contained prisms, sometimes two or three in series.   These have now given way to a large extent to grating instruments.   The gratings must be exceptionally free of imperfections for this application, since otherwise the ghosts[1] produced by the relatively intense Rayleigh radiation will obscure the Raman lines in the low-frequency region and may be mistaken for Raman lines in other parts of the spectrum.

A photographic emulsion is generally inconvenient and is considerably less sensitive than a photoelectric detector.   It is still a preferred detector for Raman spectroscopy in many laboratories, however, since it has the ability to integrate a weak signal over a long period of time.   Hence long exposures can give detectable spectra even for weak scatterers.   An electronic detector can also be made to integrate a signal over time, but it is impractical to spend a long period of time measuring intensity at each point in the spectrum as must be done with the photoelectric detector. On the other hand, very long exposures are not feasible in many cases, either for routine control applications or for unstable samples, and the reciprocity law (which states that the density of the image will be a function of the product of intensity and time) is not valid for very long exposures. For quantitative applications the non-linearity of photographic emulsions is another serious disadvantage.

The two horns of the dilemma of Raman instrumentation are the extremely small signal obtained and the relatively large amount of back-

---

[1] If there is an error in the spacings of certain lines, they may form an image in the wrong place.   The intensity of such a spurious line, or ghost, will be small but, if the primary line is extremely intense, the ghost may be of significant intensity.

ground or stray radiation. With photographic detection, the extraneous light causes fogging of the plate, obscuring weak lines and preventing long exposures. This is accentuated if the grating is not of extremely high quality. The noise generated in a photomultiplier tube is proportional to the square root of the total signal (equation II-13, section II-5) so that the presence of stray also causes a high noise level and prevents arbitrary increasing of the gain of the amplifier circuit.

The trend now is toward photoelectric detection combined with double-monochromator optics or some other means of eliminating the stray radiation. The problem which cannot be eliminated by improved optics or instrumentation is fluorescence by the sample, but this can often be quenched by the addition of small amounts of another compound or can sometimes be avoided by changing the excitation frequency (see chapter IV).

Photographic spectrographs such as those shown in Fig. II-30 and Fig. III-1 are quite suitable for Raman spectroscopy if they are "fast"

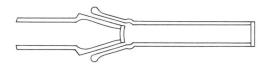

FIG. III-37a. Raman sample cell (liquid). The mirror at the left gives increased intensity of Raman radiation passing out through the window at the right compared to the cell of Fig. III-35 which has only a horn-shaped light trap.

instruments (section 2). The Hilger two-prism spectrograph has often been applied to Raman work and is now available with both photographic and photoelectric detection.

The Lane-Wells (Applied Research Laboratories) Raman spectrometer contains three prisms in series (Fig. III-38), with a Maksutov camera (section II-4) for photographic detection. To convert the instrument to photoelectric detection, a scanning exit slit is moved into the focal plane with a small mirror behind this slit to deflect the light down to a photo-multiplier tube. A Toronto mercury arc, with somewhat elaborate circuitry for starting and operation, is packaged as a separate unit.

The Perkin-Elmer model 12 spectrometer has been adapted to Raman spectroscopy by very minor changes, such as replacement of the prism and Littrow mirror with a plane grating and minor changes in optical components to match the grating characteristics. A photoelectric Raman spectrometer has also been produced by White.[1]

[1] White et al., *J. Op. Soc. Am.* **45**, 154–166 (1955); Bernstein and Allen, *loc. cit.*, pp. 237–249.

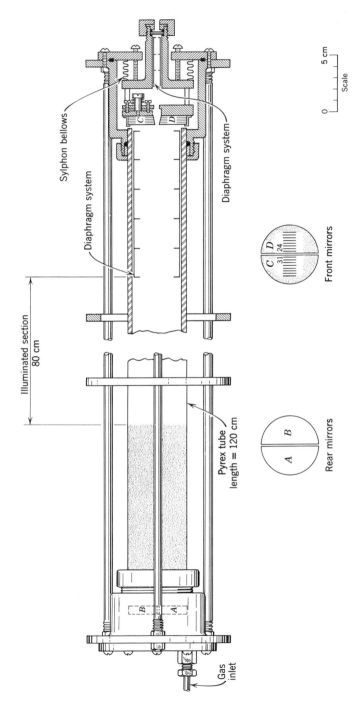

FIG. III-37b. Raman sample cell (gas). Multiple reflection between the two ends of the cell gives a large increase in intensity. [B. P. Stoicheff, *Can. J. Phys.* **32**, 330 (1954).]

It has been characteristic of Raman spectroscopy that relatively large volumes of liquid samples (10 ml or more) are required for satisfactory results.   The low intensity levels have made it difficult, also, to record the weaker lines by electronic methods.   An instrument designed to eliminate these difficulties has been produced by the Applied Physics Corporation. The Cary model 81 Raman spectrometer employs the optical system shown in Fig. III-39.   Radiation from a Toronto mercury arc passes through a filter cell, which serves also for temperature control of the sample, and strikes the sample cell.   A specially designed optical system, which includes an image slicer, focuses the scattered radiation on twin entrance slits, adjacent and parallel.   A double monochromator takes the radiation

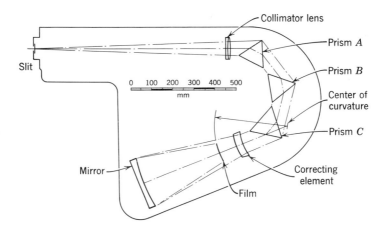

FIG. III-38a.   ARL Raman spectrometer.   For photographic recording the instrument acts as a three-prism spectrograph with Maksutov camera.   (Courtesy Applied Research Laboratories.)

from both slits and passes the dispersed radiation out through corresponding twin exit slits.   The monochromators employ 12,000 grooves/cm gratings, 10 × 10 cm, arranged in a Czerny-Littrow mount.   Corrector lenses improve the focus.   The beam is chopped and sent to two photomultiplier tubes; the signal from these tubes is compared, in an electronic-null system, with a reference signal of undispersed radiation from the arc sent to a reference phototube.   A number of unique design features have been incorporated which enable the entire spectrum from the exciting line (0 cm^{-1} displacement) to a shift of 4000 cm^{-1} to be recorded in as little as 5 minutes on samples as small as 0.25 ml.

At the sample cell, an image slicer takes the circular image that would normally be formed and converts it to a single long image which efficiently passes through the long entrance slit system at an angle consistent with the aperture of the monochromator.   Since slit widths are normally much less

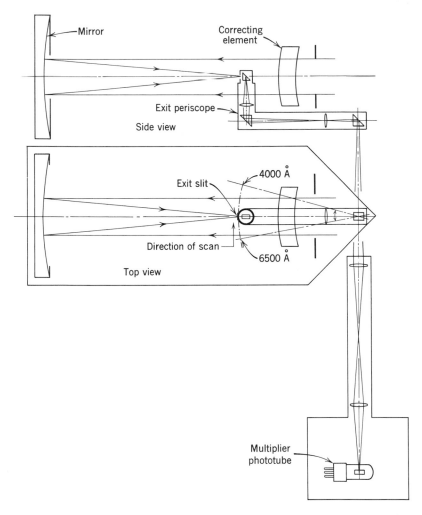

FIG. III-38*b*.   ARL Raman spectrometer.   For photoelectric recording a mirror system carries the radiation passing through an exit slit in the focal plane down to a photomultiplier tube.   (Courtesy Applied Research Laboratories.)

than 1 mm, which is small compared to the width of the image of the cell, it is possible to place two parallel slits in the image position.   These two slits more efficiently accept the light, and the image of each slit strikes a corresponding slit separating the two monochromators.   Stray radiation from the left-hand entrance slit will strike the right-hand exit slit, and vice versa, but the spacings of the slits are such that this stray light is very effectively eliminated by the second monochromator, producing mono-chromatic images at the twin exit slits of the second monochromator. Only in the vicinity of the exciting line is a significant amount of stray light transmitted by this twin-slit system, and provision is made for blocking

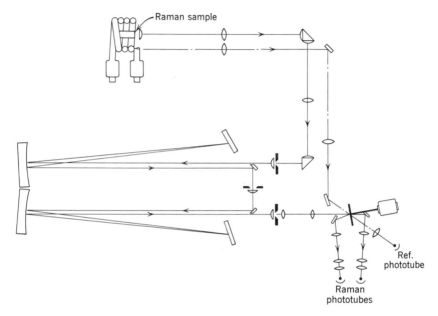

FIG. III-39.   Cary Model 81 Raman spectrometer.   (Courtesy Applied Physics Corporation.)

one of the slits (with a subsequent loss of 50% in energy) for scanning near the exciting line.

Chopping of the radiation and a-c amplification at the chopping frequency provides a drift-free system with high discrimination against noise, but it normally means that the beam is used only part-time, with a consequent loss of 50% in energy.   By reflecting the beam alternately to two phototubes, the advantages of chopping are maintained without the loss of energy.   The signals are combined before they reach the recorder. The tracing is linear in frequency and in intensity (intensity is proportional to concentration in ideal systems).

5   General Criteria of Instrument Performance

Given a particular spectrometer, one may ask how to measure its performance quantitatively. Certain aspects will be fairly obvious. For example, the calibration of the frequency scale in the ultraviolet and visible regions may be checked by observing the sharp emission lines of a low-pressure mercury vapor lamp or the emission lines of the rare gases. In the infrared it is generally necessary to rely upon sharp absorption bands. The stability of the I_0 line of a double-beam spectrometer or the zero-energy line of a single-beam instrument will be readily apparent. The signal-to-noise ratio, scale linearity, stray radiation, and resolution are examples of characteristics which are more difficult to determine or which may vary markedly with operating conditions.

5.1   Signal-to-Noise Ratio

The noise level, or size of the ripple in the recorded curve, will depend on the slit-width setting, the amplifier gain, the amount of damping or the setting of "response" or "period" controls, and the region of the spectrum in which the observations are carried out. It is therefore not possible to set an arbitrary standard for maximum noise level to be permitted. The instruction manual accompanying a spectrometer will generally suggest specific instrument settings under which the noise level should be measured, and acceptable performance under these conditions. These are generally average conditions to be expected of instruments coming from the factory or in service for some time under reasonable care. A careful operator who understands a little bit of electronics and is willing to give some attention to his instrument can often achieve somewhat better performance than these specifications. With some experience the operator will learn to recognize acceptable and unacceptable noise levels for the particular instrument.

5.2   Scale Linearity

Determination of the accuracy of the transmittance or absorbance scale of a spectrometer is a rather difficult operation, because the deviations from linearity which are sought are much smaller than the errors that would normally be introduced by reflection losses or deviations from Beer's law. The National Bureau of Standards has developed a method for absolute calibration of the ordinate at certain frequencies in the ultraviolet and visible regions in terms of an accepted value for the absorbance of a potassium chromate solution and a glass filter.[1]   In cooperative testing of these standards some rather large deviations have been observed, even among instruments of the same type, suggesting that the variations in operator performance may be considerably more important than individual instrument characteristics.   Similar difficulties have often been found in attempting to determine cell thickness by means of a "known" solution with the aid of Beer's law.

The most sensitive method for measuring ordinate accuracy seems to be the set of filters described by Cary.   Three filters, which are immersed in a liquid to control surface reflections, may be rotated into position in the beam individually or in combinations.   This provides, in addition to the three individual measurements, four checks on whether the observed sum of absorbances is identical with the calculated sum.   Under such carefully controlled conditions it is possible to measure deviations in absorbance of 0.001.   In routine operation, reproducibility is likely to be limited to ± 0.01 or 0.005 in absorbance, owing to such variables as dust or film on cell windows, variations in pen overshoot, or errors or changes in the chart paper.

Stable glass and silica filters are available for measuring absorbance in the visible and ultraviolet regions, but no equivalent standards have been found thus far for the infrared region.   A surprisingly stable, as well as simple and convenient, standard which is suitable for the entire region for the far ultraviolet to the far infrared is a piece of copper screen.   Diffraction effects, which would be anticipated, have not been observed, at least with heat-sensitive detectors or with photomultiplier tubes with frosted windows.   The probable limitation on these is dust and eventual corrosion.[2]   Screens are particularly convenient as "neutral-density" filters since almost any transmittance desired may be obtained by varying the mesh and the number of layers.   The variation of transmittance with frequency is smaller than for most commercial neutral-density filters.

Photographic emulsions are generally calibrated by means of a rotating sector wheel.   Application of this method to a spectrometer with internal chopping would require careful attention to relative speeds of the two chopping devices.

The limiting accuracy of the ordinate scale, from the instrumental standpoint, will vary considerably with the type of instrument.   The types may be conveniently broken down into those which depend on the optical wedge, on the amplifier, or on a potentiometer slide wire for accuracy.   It

[1] G. W. Haupt, Research Paper 2331, *J. Research Natl. Bur. Standards*, **48**, 414 (1952).

[2] Heidt and Bosley, *J. Opt. Soc. Am.* **43**, 760 (1953); Hausdorff, Sternglanz, and Williams, *Appl. Spectroscopy* **7**, 63 (1953).

will be assumed that the detector itself can be made to give a response which is proportional to the intensity of the radiation incident upon it.

An optical wedge can be made very accurate over most of its range, but it will necessarily deviate from linearity at the low transmittance end.

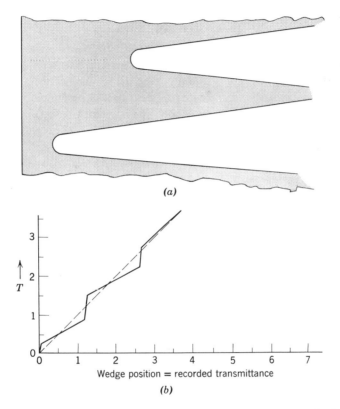

(a)

(b)

FIG. III-40.   Exaggerated optical wedge error.   (a) The narrow end of each triangular opening must show an abrupt drop in transmittance.   (b) The effects of the non-ideality of the wedge at low transmittance values can be minimized by intentionally overcorrecting just before the cut-off.   Thus the performance of a wedge might be somewhat like the solid line in the lower figure, in which actual transmittance of the wedge (ordinate) is plotted against the wedge position or nominal transmittance (abscissa). The deviation from the ideal (dash line) is small but cannot be eliminated completely.

This is a consequence of the end effects, shown on an exaggerated scale in Fig. III-40a.   Since it is impossible to approach zero width of a triangular cut in a truly continuous fashion, the practice has been deliberately to approximate the desired curve by means of a stepwise function such as those indicated in Fig. III-40b.   This approximation has a negligible

effect on the accuracy of quantitative analyses, especially since other uncertainties arise from the optical-null principle in this region of low transmittance which force the spectroscopist to avoid measurements in the
region.[1]

In most single-beam spectrometers the signal from the detector is amplified and supplied to a recorder or densitometer, either of which acts as
a potentiometer to measure the voltage output of the amplifier. Assuming
the potentiometer slide wire to be accurate, the principal burden of
accuracy is placed upon the amplifier, which must produce an output that
is proportional to the input signal over wide ranges of input signal.
Current design practices seem capable of keeping amplifier non-linearity
at a sufficiently low level that it does not adversely affect the over-all
accuracy of an analysis.

Double-beam electronic-null spectrometers offer an opportunity for
largely eliminating the dependence of the system for photometric accuracy
on the amplifiers. The reference beam intensity is maintained constant
by a servo mechanism, and a fractional part of the signal arising at the
reference phototube is bucked against the signal arising at the sample
phototube to produce a null balance. If the sample transmittance
changes, the signals become unbalanced. The unbalance signal is amplified and sent to the pen potentiometer to indicate sample transmittance
and to change the fractional part of the reference signal applied at the
sample phototube.

Linear potentiometer slide wires are readily available, with tolerances
well below the uncertainty appearing in other parts of a photometric
measurement. Logarithmic slide wires or other forms must be approximated by combining appropriate segments of linear resistors, but again
the approximation can be made sufficiently accurate that no error is
introduced into the final measurement.

5.3   Stray Radiation

No monochromatic sources, of continuously variable frequency, are
known for frequencies above 15 cm^{-1}. It is therefore necessary to work
with sources that emit a continuous range of frequencies, and the distribution of intensity with frequency is often quite unsatisfactory. A dispersing
agent, such as a prism or grating, acting on such continuous radiation, will
perform a gross separation of frequencies but cannot produce truly monochromatic radiation. Two distinct effects contribute to this failure: diffraction effects and optical aberrations cause a blurring of the image of the

---

[1] For one instrumental design which seeks to avoid all these difficulties see Herscher,
Ruhl, and Wright, *J. Opt. Soc. Am.* **48**, 36 (1958).

entrance slit on the exit slit, preventing separation of frequencies by the monochromator; and imperfections, inhomogeneities, and unwanted surface reflections permit a small fraction of the radiation to "escape" through the exit slit and strike the detector.   The first of these effects is predictable from the design characteristics and optical specifications of the spectrometer.   This will be considered in the following section.   The "stray" radiation is not really part of the optical design and the methods of removal of this or correction for it are much more empirical.   Approximate measurement of this unwanted signal is rather straightforward, but accurate determination can be extremely difficult.

In the ultraviolet region most of the stray radiation will be from the visible or near ultraviolet region, since the source intensity is generally greatest in this region.   An approximate check can therefore be made by means of a glass plate, which will absorb all frequencies above 30,000 or 35,000 cm^{-1} (about 3000 Å) but transmit most of the stray radiation when the instrument is set to pass a region near 40,000 cm^{-1} (2500 Å).   In the near ultraviolet or visible regions, filters are available which will absorb virtually all the radiation within a small interval and pass most other frequencies.   In the far ultraviolet a check is possible by means of a solvent, such as chloroform, which begins to absorb strongly at high frequencies.

Sources for the infrared are approximate black-body radiators and thus will show very much greater intensity at higher frequencies (up to about 5000 cm^{-1}, depending on source temperature and methods of measurement) than at lower frequencies.   At any given point in the spectrum practically all the stray radiation will thus be of a higher frequency than the nominal frequency setting of the monochromator.   LiF, CaF$_2$, NaCl, and KBr will pass all frequencies from the very near infrared, through the visible and ultraviolet, to the vacuum ultraviolet.   Each begins to absorb strongly at some point in the infrared region and continues to absorb over a very large range extending well into the far infrared.

Assume, for example, that one wishes to measure the amount of stray radiation at 900 cm^{-1}.   The energy level with a metal shutter blocking the beam is determined first; then a plate of CaF$_2$ is put into the beam and the metal shutter is withdrawn.   The difference in energy levels represents the amount of radiation which is passed by the CaF$_2$ (all above 1000 cm^{-1}) that is appearing as false energy when the monochromator is set at 900 cm^{-1}.   Any stray radiation of frequency less than the cut-off frequency will not be included in the determination.   This error is generally small enough that it need be considered only in the most accurate determinations, but it is a measurable error.   The equivalent determination in the ultraviolet region would be a comparison of a metal shutter with glass, chloroform, or a similar absorbing material, as suggested above.

An alternative to a cut-off filter is a substance with an extremely strong and sharp absorption band. In the infrared this is provided to a good approximation by the C—H out-of-plane bending motion of aromatic compounds or the C—Cl stretching frequency, each of which falls in the general vicinity of 700 to 800 cm^{-1}. For example, to determine the amount of stray radiation at the lower frequency limit for an infrared spectrometer with NaCl prism, one may conveniently run a curve of polystyrene film and measure the amount of energy passed at the strong absorption band at 700 cm^{-1},[1] or measure the energy passed by chloroform at 750 cm^{-1}. A measurement of this type also will give a slightly smaller value for stray radiation than the true value, in part because of the inherent width of the band but primarily because the sample, in the necessary thickness, will absorb an appreciable fraction of the radiation at higher frequencies. It would not be possible to estimate the magnitude of this effect without careful measurement of the near infrared absorption spectrum of the particular substance employed and a knowledge of the intensity curve for the source. At the same time, knowing the exact amount of stray radiation is not adequate for absolute compensation in a quantitative analysis, since the sample under analysis will also absorb some portion of the stray radiation.

Very few substances have sharp and strong electronic absorption bands except in the gas phase. A remarkable exception is the group of rare earth ions, which have a moderate number of bands throughout the visible and the ultraviolet. A particularly convenient form of these ions for the visible region, although probably not the best in terms of line width and separation, is a commercial mixture of rare earth salts consisting primarily of neodymium and praseodymium and known as "didymium." Glass plates containing this mixture in an appropriate concentration are commercially available.

A significant amount of stray radiation will always go undetected by methods such as those described. This is the "nearby stray," with frequency only slightly different from that which should be passed by the monochromator. The surface of any mirror, lens, or prism may be approximated by a perfectly flat plane with very small bumps distributed at random across the area. These irregularities have the effect of deviating portions of the beam through very small angles, leading to a very small amount of mixing of adjacent frequency regions in the focal plane of the

---

[1] This band transmits less than 0.01% in a film of 0.002-in. thickness. The adjacent band, at 755 cm^{-1}, transmits about $\frac{1}{4}$% in this thickness. The apparent intensities can change markedly if the sample is not homogeneous.

exit slit.   A novel and effective method for determining the amount of near-by stray has been described by Tunnicliff.[1]

Measurement of stray radiation is limited on an optical-null double-beam spectrometer by the uncertainty in the zero-energy level, but since such an instrument cannot measure such low intensity levels the presence of really small amounts of stray energy is not particularly important. Electronic-null spectrometers are capable of measuring much lower intensity levels, at least to absorbance values of 7 (corresponding to a transmittance of 10^{-7}, or $10^{-5}\%$).   Obviously, low stray light is important if any real meaning is to be assigned to these observed absorbance values. With a double monochromator it is possible to achieve stray radiation levels of less than 10^{-6} relative to the "true" signal.   Other methods of

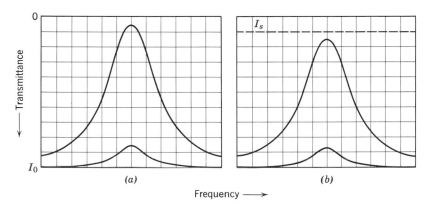

FIG. III-41.   Effect of stray radiation on strong and weak absorption bands. (a) Without stray radiation.   (b) With 10% stray radiation.   (Frequency scale is marked in units of the band half width for the Lorentzian bands.)

eliminating stray, such as double-passing of the monochromator or inserting absorbing filters, scattering plates, or gratings into the optical path, have been discussed in section II-7 and elsewhere.

The primary effect of stray radiation is a quantitative error which may be associated with an incorrect zero-energy line. Figure III-41 shows the effect of stray radiation on strong and weak absorption bands. If the line I_s is chosen as the zero-energy line, there will be very little error. There will be some residual error, however, since the actual intensity of stray radiation for a sample of low concentration will be higher than for the same substance at a high concentration. Proper calibration procedures can eliminate this error also, provided the composition of the

[1] J. Opt. Soc. Am. **45**, 963 (1955).

unknowns is a function only of the concentration of the compound to be determined.

A secondary, but important, effect appears when the amount of stray varies markedly with frequency over the region of the band. In such a case there will be an apparent frequency shift of the band maximum, as shown in Fig. III-42, which will vary slightly with the intensity of the absorption band. The intensity of the stray should change quite slowly with frequency in most regions, but, whenever the intensity of the desired signal drops off rapidly, as in the range below 750 cm^{-1} in a spectrometer

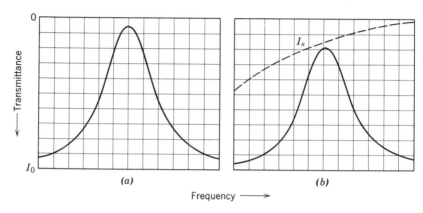

(a)   (b)

Frequency ⟶

FIG. III-42. Effect of non-uniform stray radiation. (a) Without stray radiation. (b) With stray radiation increasing to the left. Note the shift of the band maximum to higher frequency as well as the distortion of the band shape.

with NaCl prism or above 45,000 cm^{-1} (2200 Å) in a spectrometer with silica prism, it is necessary to open the slits and the relative intensity of stray and "true" signals will then vary rapidly.

5.4 Resolving Power

A theoretical limit to the ability of a monochromator to separate adjacent frequencies is set by the diffraction effect. Lord Rayleigh pointed out that in practice one can just distinguish two sharp lines of equal intensity as consisting of two, rather than one, if the central maximum of the diffraction pattern of one line falls on the first minimum of the diffraction pattern of the other.[1] It should be borne in mind that the calculation of the theoretical resolving power, which is defined by this criterion, assumes that aberrations due to mirrors, lenses, or other components are negligible; the line widths should also be negligibly small compared to the

[1] See Ditchburn, ref. 14, p. 237; also D. H. Rank, *J. Opt. Soc. Am.* **42**, 279 (1952).

separation of the lines.   Also, the intensities of the lines, in emission, or the intensity of the source for an absorption measurement, should be sufficiently great that the slits may be made very narrow in order to realize the full resolving power built into the monochromator.   In absorption spectroscopy one seldom satisfies any of these conditions, much less all three.   The theoretical resolving power of a monochromator is a convenient measure of its capabilities, however, and some understanding of the principles involved will aid in understanding the criteria for evaluation of dispersing elements, including gratings as well as prisms.

Fermat's principle states that the path followed by a ray of light will be such as to give the minimum (or in some cases a maximum) time of transit. Thus reflection from a plane mirror is such that the angle of incidence equals the angle of reflection; any other path can be shown to be longer. Snell's law and other formulas of optics may be derived by means of this

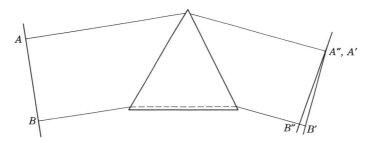

FIG. III-43.   Calculation of resolving power for a prism.

principle.   It will be applied here to find the resolving power of a prism, following the method of Lord Rayleigh.

Let AB (Fig. III-43) represent the wave front of a plane wave (that is, a coherent beam of parallel rays of light traveling in a direction perpendicular to the line AB will have the same phase at any instant along the line AB). $A'B'$ will represent a wave front for light of frequency ν_1 which has passed through the prism, and $A''B''$ will represent a similar wave front for light of a frequency ν_2, where $\nu_2 - \nu_1$ is very small.   A lens placed on the line $A'B'$ will focus the radiation of frequency ν_1 onto a screen or photographic plate, but a diffraction image will be formed since the beam is of finite width (determined by the height of the prism).   The light of frequency ν_2 will also pass through the lens at $A'B'$ and will give a diffraction pattern on a screen.   Assume that the distance $B' - B''$ is just equal to the wavelength corresponding to ν_2.   Then, at the position on the screen at which the central maximum appears for ν_1, the upper and lower halves of the beam of frequency ν_2 will destructively interfere, producing a minimum of intensity. This is then the condition for ν_1 and ν_2 to be just resolved by the prism acting at its theoretical maximum of efficiency.

The condition for the wave fronts to occur at $A'B'$ and $A''B''$ as assumed is that the optical distances along the paths $A-A'$ and $B-B'$, for ν_1, and $A-A''$ and $B-B''$, for ν_2, should be equal.[1] That is,

$$\int_A^{'A} n_1 \, ds = \int_B^{'B} n_1 \, ds \quad \text{and} \quad \int_A^A n_2 \, ds = \int_B^B n_2 \, ds \quad \text{(III-3)}$$

We wish the distance δL to be equal to λ, where

$$\delta L = \int_B^{B'} n_2 \, ds - \int_B^{B''} n_2 \, ds = \int_B^{B'} n_2 \, ds - \int_A^{A''} n_2 \, ds \quad \text{(III-4)}$$

Letting $n_2 = n_1 + \delta n$, and noting that A' and A'' are really the same point, this may be written in the form

$$\begin{aligned}
\delta L &= \int_B^{B'} (n_1 + \delta n) \, ds - \int_A^{A'} (n_1 + \delta n) \, ds \\
&= \int_B^{B'} n_1 \, ds - \int_A^{A'} n_1 \, ds + \int_B^{B'} \delta n \, ds - \int_A^{A'} \delta n \, ds \\
&= \int_B^{B'} \delta n \, ds - \int_A^{A'} \delta n \, ds \quad \text{(III-5)}
\end{aligned}$$

But δn disappears everywhere except inside the prism, and thus the integrals may be replaced by the product $\delta n(s_B - s_A)$, where s_B and s_A are the distances traveled in the prism by the extreme rays. s_A should be very small and may be taken to be zero; s_B is the base thickness, t, of the prism. Hence the path difference is simply $t \, \delta n$. In order for the two frequencies to be barely resolved this distance must be equal to the wavelength.

$$\lambda = \delta L = t \, \delta n = t \frac{dn}{d\lambda} \, d\lambda = t \frac{dn}{d\sigma} \, d\sigma = \frac{1}{\sigma} \quad \text{(III-6)}$$

The resolving power is defined to be

$$\text{R.P.} = \frac{\lambda}{\delta\lambda} = \frac{\sigma}{\delta\sigma} = \frac{\nu}{\delta\nu} = t \frac{dn}{d\lambda} = t\sigma^2 \frac{dn}{d\sigma} \quad \text{(III-7)}$$

For small angles, δL is $a \, d\theta$, where $a = \overline{A'B'}$ is the (linear) aperture and $d\theta$ is the difference in angular deviation for the two rays. It follows that

$$\text{R.P.} = a \frac{d\theta}{d\lambda} \quad \text{(III-8)}$$

It should be noted in particular that the resolving power is independent of the positioning of the prism or prisms, and for a given base

---

[1] The two rays will follow slightly different paths, but since the path is a minimum this small difference in path will produce only a second-order correction and may safely be neglected.

length is independent of the aperture, or the height of the prism.[1]   The
choice of prism vertex angle, and hence the prism height for a given base,
is dependent on considerations of reflection losses, which depend on angle
of incidence, and the desire for "speed," or light-gathering power, balanced
against the increasing cost of the prism as the volume is increased.   For a
set of prisms designed to go into a single monochromator it is customary to
leave the aperture constant and vary the base length and apex angle of the
prism for each prism material.

The angular dispersion of a prism may be very greatly increased by
inclining the prism sharply to the optical axis, as mentioned in chapter II.
It will be seen from equation III-8, however, that this does not require an
increase in the resolving power, since the effective aperture is decreased.[2]

One must also consider the effect of prism orientation on the speed of
the monochromator and on the focal properties of the monochromator
over a wide range of frequencies.   Nearly always it is found desirable to
set the prism for minimum deviation for some intermediate frequency.   It
has also been shown that the resolving power of a prism or a grating can
be improved by blocking off the central portion of the beam, but this is
not necessarily an economical way to improve the resolving power.   The
effective aperture, and hence the speed, will be decreased by this method,
and in most applications in absorption spectroscopy this is an important
limitation on performance.   Only if the slits can be kept very narrow will
this improve the observed resolution.

The resolving power of a grating may be expressed in terms of the
number of lines,

$$\text{R.P.} = nN \tag{III-9}$$

or in terms of the width of the ruled surface,

$$\text{R.P.} = W\left(\frac{\sin\theta + \sin i}{\lambda}\right) \tag{III-10}$$

[1] The definition of the prism base thickness as the longest distance traveled by the
beam through the prism must, of course, be kept in mind in consideration of prism
orientation.

[2] Concerning this demonstration of the dependence of resolving power on the base
length of the prism, Lord Rayleigh states: "That the resolving power of a prismatic
spectroscope of given dispersive material is proportional to the total thickness used,
without regard to the number of angles, or setting of the prisms, is a most important,
perhaps the most important, proposition in connection with this subject.   Hitherto in
descriptions of spectroscopes far too much stress has been laid upon the amount of dispersion produced by the prisms; but this element by itself tells nothing as to the power
of an instrument.   It is well known that by a sufficiently close approach to a grazing
emergence, the dispersion of a prism of given thickness may be increased without limit;
but there is no corresponding gain in resolving power."

It will vary with the angle of observation and the order of the spectrum observed. For a grating of N lines the resolving power in the nth order is Nn. As the line spacing is decreased, leaving the grating width unchanged, the number of the order appearing at a given angle will be inversely proportional to the number of lines ruled. For example, a grating of 7 cm ruled width containing 750 grooves/cm and blazed for 750 cm^{-1} in the first order (30°) will have exactly the same resolving power for the mercury green line in the 24th order (29° 26′) as will a 7 cm grating with 18,000 grooves/cm blazed for 18,000 cm^{-1} (30°), in the first order (29° 26′). In principle, therefore, one grating would cover the entire spectrum; there would seem to be no advantage to be gained in resolving power or in intensity by changing gratings so long as the ruled width is constant. In practice there is some variation in efficiency with order and there is a great difference in convenience. At the mercury green line (18,300 cm^{-1}, or 5461 Å) serious difficulties would be encountered with overlapping orders, in most applications, for a grating with as few as 750 grooves/cm, whereas the second-order spectrum for the 18,000 grooves/cm grating would consist of frequencies in the ultraviolet region and would be removed by any glass in the optical path.

5.5   Resolution

It has become customary to distinguish between resolving power, which is defined in terms of the Rayleigh diffraction limit, and resolution, or resolution limit,[1] which is the smallest frequency, wavenumber, or wavelength interval that can be separated. The former is determined solely by the optical design, and in particular by the prism or grating characteristics. The observed resolution depends on the resolving power, but also on the mechanical slit widths—and hence on source intensity, monochromator transmittance, and detector sensitivity—on the degree of perfection of the optical components, on the actual widths of the lines or bands which are to be separated, and on the properties of the electronics which contribute to the signal-to-noise ratio.

The speed, or f number, is a measure of the light-gathering power of a monochromator, which in turn sets a limit on the slit widths which can normally be employed. The f number is given by the ratio of the focal length to the aperture (defined here as the diameter of the circular aperture equivalent in area to the actual aperture of the monochromator). As all

[1] The term "resolution," like "sensitivity," can be confusing in that "high resolution" is indicative of a small numerical value for the quantity measured. To avoid such difficulties the term "resolution limit" is introduced here. "High resolution" corresponds to a low (numerical) "resolution limit."

camera fans know, a low value for this ratio, f/A corresponds to a faster system, capable of superior performance.   Radiation from the source is focused onto the entrance slit of the monochromator, which may be adjusted to the minimum width that will still give a detectable signal at the entrance slit.   Increasing the size of the source can increase the total amount of radiation striking the slit, but the emission from the edges of the source will not pass through the limiting aperture stop of the monochromator (Fig. III-2, section 2) and will contribute only to the stray radiation.   Increasing the aperture, which requires a larger prism or grating, or decreasing the focal length, will permit the emission from a larger source to be utilized.   The magnitude of the signal striking the detector is thus increased, or the same barely measurable signal may be achieved with narrower slits.

The spectroscopist is seldom concerned with calculations of resolution in order to find the ability to separate two adjacent lines.   Since the bands

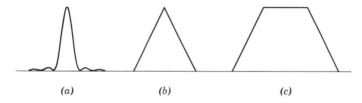

FIG. III-44.   Idealized exit slit functions.   (a) Diffraction pattern, for narrow slits. (b) Triangular function, for wide slits.   (c) Trapezoidal approximation to the pattern expected when slits are wide but unequal.   (See Coates and Hausdorff, *J. Opt. Soc. Am.* **45**, 425 (1955).)

normally encountered, except for gases, are quite broad, such a calculation will at best be an approximation; it is often more expedient simply to determine this experimentally if any real question exists.   The more important problem, which contains the question of separation of adjacent bands, is the effect of finite slit widths on the shapes and intensities of bands observed.   For such purposes it is convenient to speak of the "spectral slit width."

The radiation emerging from the exit slit of a monochromator to strike the detector is not homogeneous but contains a range of frequencies.   A plot of intensity *vs.* frequency for this radiation defines the "exit-slit function"; under certain idealized conditions this might have one of the forms indicated in Fig. III-44.   In general, there is reason to expect that the distribution will not be symmetrical about the central frequency, since the intensity incident on the entrance slit of the monochromator will generally vary with frequency, but this effect will be ignored here for simplicity.   In any of the cases shown, the spectral slit width may be defined [1] as the width in frequency, wavenumber, or wavelength units, at a point at which the intensity is just one half its maximum value (this is the "half band width" of any absorption or emission band).   Clearly the significance of the spectral slit width, so defined, will depend on the actual exit slit function, and since this is not known the spectral slit width must generally be considered to be an approximation.   It is, nevertheless, an important semiquantitative description of the operation of the monochromator, and considerable effort is being put forth to define this, both experimentally and theoretically, more precisely.   For most purposes it is adequate to assume the triangular form of Fig. III-44b.

The spectral slit width may be considered to arise from three sources. In the limit of very narrow slits the spectral slit width will be determined by the diffraction limit of the spectrometer, assuming aberrations of focusing to be negligible.   This term may be written as the frequency, wavenumber, or wavelength divided by the resolving power.   In the limit of wide slits, the spectral slit width will depend solely on the dispersion of the monochromator and the mechanical slit width.   The aberrations arising from imperfect optics may be considered to give rise to a "circle of confusion" of constant size at the exit slit.   For long wavelengths or for wide slits this may be negligible, but it can be quite important for short wavelengths and narrow slits.   Certain other effects, such as poor matching of the curvatures of the slit and image, can be conveniently combined with this aberration term.

To a first approximation the actual spectral slit width or resolution limit may be considered to be a sum of the contributions due to mechanical slit width, diffraction, and aberrations.   Since these effects are not strictly additive, this should give the correct value when any one of the terms predominates and should give an answer that is too large when two or more of the terms are comparable.[2]   To this first approximation,

$$\Delta\sigma = \Delta\sigma_s + \Delta\sigma_d + \Delta\sigma_a$$
$$= \frac{d\sigma}{ds}s + \Delta\sigma_d + \frac{d\sigma}{ds}s_a \qquad \text{(III-11)}$$

where $d\sigma/ds$ depends on the angular dispersion of the spectrometer, s is

---

[1] Another of the possible definitions of spectral slit width would make this identical with the resolution limit.

[2] No general treatment of the problem of addition of these terms has been carried out. If they can be considered to be strictly independent, the sum should be obtained by pythagorean addition, $\Delta\sigma = (\Delta\sigma_s{}^2 + \Delta\sigma_d{}^2 + \Delta\sigma_a{}^2)^{1/2}$.   Similar approximations have been applied by some workers in the field.   For moderately wide slit widths half of the diffraction term is often added to the $\Delta\sigma_s$ term.   There is experimental, as well as theoretical, justification for taking s as one-half the mechanical slit width.

the mechanical slit width, $\Delta\sigma_d$ is the diffraction limit of the spectrometer, and s_a is the mechanical slit width equivalent of the aberrations.

The quantities appearing in equation III-11 may be calculated from a knowledge of the size and dispersion of the prism or the properties of the

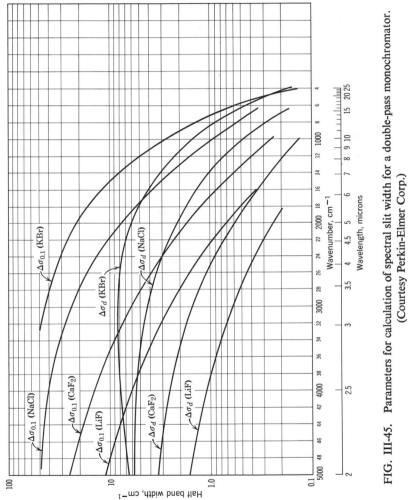

FIG. III-45. Parameters for calculation of spectral slit width for a double-pass monochromator. (Courtesy Perkin-Elmer Corp.)

grating, along with the mechanical slit widths and some estimate of the aberration limit. The results of such a calculation are generally made available by the manufacturer in the form of a dispersion curve, such as that shown in Fig. III-45. From this curve, for example, it follows that the diffraction limit for a sodium chloride prism at 1200 cm^{-1} is 0.73 cm^{-1}

and the geometrical limit will be 1.55 cm^{-1} times the mechanical slit width measured in tenths of millimeters.   The aberrations should be insignificant in this region.   For a mechanical slit width of 0.2 mm, therefore, the spectral slit width should be about 2 × 1.55 + 0.73 or about 3.8 cm^{-1}, for a double-pass monochromator such as the Perkin-Elmer 112.   For a single-pass instrument each term, and hence the spectral slit width, would be twice as great, except that narrower slits could probably be employed.

It is common practice to drive entrance and exit slits with the same mechanism, so that they are maintained equal or with a very small, constant difference.   The intensity at the entrance slit is fixed by source brightness, so that the energy passed by the entrance slit will be proportional to its area, or to its width.   The monochromator will form a spectrum in the plane of the exit slit; the brightness of this image will depend on the energy admitted by the entrance slit.   The fraction of this image passed by the exit slit, and hence the energy striking the detector, will be proportional to the exit slit width.   Thus the energy transmitted by the monochromator will be proportional to the product of entrance and exit slit widths, or to the square of the slit width when these are equal.

Changes in resolution, or spectral slit width, produce several effects on the spectrum.   As slit widths are increased, the bands become somewhat broader and some of the features may disappear.   At the same time, the peak intensity will drop, causing an apparent decrease in peak absorptivity.   Asymmetric bands will also show a small shift in position.   Each of these effects is readily predictable if one simply considers that the spectrometer is averaging the absorptivity over a certain range of frequencies (Fig. III-46).   As the width of the range is increased, the variations tend to be averaged out.   If the exit slit function were known, the shape of the band to be expected could be calculated from a knowledge of the true band shape.   The problem in practice, however, is often to determine the true band shape from the observed shape, without accurate knowledge of the exit slit function.

The area under an absorption band is somewhat less sensitive to spectral slit width than is the peak absorptivity.   For some quantitative analyses, especially where the band is widely separated from neighboring bands, it has been shown that superior quantitative analyses can be performed by plotting band area against concentration.   For certain theoretical studies an integrated absorption coefficient is required also.

5.6   Other Performance Characteristics

In most applications of absorption spectroscopy the resolution is among the least important characteristics of instrument performance.   The

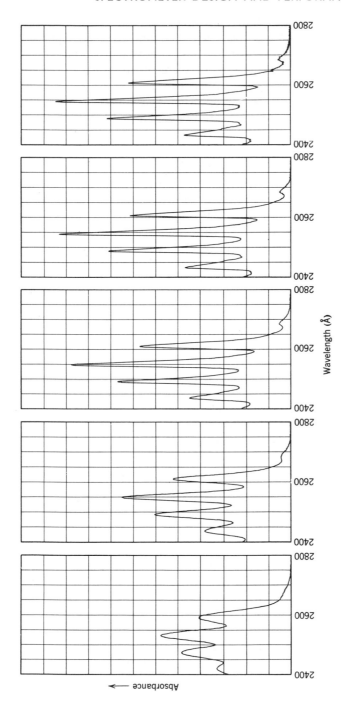

FIG. III-46. Effect of spectral slit width. The same sample of benzene in cyclohexane was scanned with different mechanical slit widths on the same spectrometer. Approximate spectral slit widths, at 2800 Å, are 44, 15, 5, 1.8, and 1 Å. Note shift in 2550 Å peak to right, due to band asymmetry (compare Fig. VIII-5a), for small increase in spectral slit width.

theoretical resolving power and the attainable resolution (which includes the effects of optical misalignment or defects) are, however, important since they can generally be "traded off" for improved performance in other directions.   The most important of these other properties are time of scanning, precision, and general convenience.

The time required to obtain a spectrum over a fixed frequency interval is determined by the intensity of the radiation striking the detector, and hence by a product of factors such as source intensity, slit width, and the reciprocal of the dispersive power of the monochromator.   In effect, the detector and amplifier integrate the radiation signal over a short period of time until a sufficiently large signal has been built up to activate the recorder.   In a given time, a prism of low dispersive power ($d\theta/d\nu$) will pass a larger signal, of lower spectral purity, through a given slit than a prism of high dispersive power with the same aperture.   Alternatively, with the prism of high dispersive power the slit widths may be increased, with a similar sacrifice in spectral purity.   In regions of negligible prism absorption, the latter is much more effective since the energy passed is proportional to the square of the slit widths.[1]

As the magnitude of the signal from the detector is increased, the accuracy of measuring this signal will increase.   Thus decreasing the rate of scan will improve the accuracy of measurement, for constant spectral purity.   Any combination of these factors of scanning time, spectral purity, and precision of measurement, within rather wide limits, may be obtained for a given instrument.

Convenience aspects include such characteristics as chart dimensions and avoidance of a change of grating order or prism in passing from one part of a spectrum to another, in addition to the rate of scan.   The limits set on the extent to which one can vary each of these independently is determined largely by the flexibility built into the spectrometer.   For many research applications great flexibility may be important, but for certain routine applications the flexibility would be a source of confusion and annoyance.   Thus the best choice for one laboratory is not necessarily best for another.

[1] For example, consider two prisms with dispersive powers in the ratio $D_1/D_2 = r$. Then, for the same mechanical slit width, the poorer prism, inserted in a given monochromator, will give r times the energy and will have a spectral slit width r times as large as the better prism in the same monochromator; that is, the better prism will give better resolution by a factor of r. For the same spectral slit width (same resolution), the better prism will have mechanical slit widths r times greater and will give r times the energy.   For the same energy, the better prism will have mechanical slits $\sqrt{r}$ times as large as the poorer prism but the spectral slit width of the poorer prism will be $\sqrt{r}$ times greater.

6 Selection of a Spectrometer

The wide variety of spectrometer designs now available commercially emphasizes the balance of qualities which must be achieved in any specific instrument.   The choice for a particular laboratory must take into account the immediate and projected need of the individual laboratory as well as the characteristics of the spectrometer.   The prospective purchaser should bear in mind that the introduction of spectroscopic equipment nearly always expands the need for such equipment, both by illustrating the presence of a need that already existed and by permitting an acceleration of work by freeing the laboratory workers of unnecessary labors more easily done spectroscopically.

Often one of the first choices to be made is between a single-beam and a double-beam spectrometer.   There is no simple answer to the question of which of them is "better" or "more economical."   Almost certainly, the total number of single-beam instruments sold is greater than the number of double-beam instruments that have been sold thus far, but the latter are far more popular now.   Many of the "characteristic" properties of each are actually due to accessory equipment or controls, so that it will be convenient to treat some of these independently.   Included also, in the brief outline below, are comparisons of electronic-null *vs.* optical-null systems.

Automatic slit servo mechanism
  1. Gives constant I_0, hence simpler interpretation of curves.
  2. More expensive unit, and units will be available only for certain prisms or gratings or for certain electronic systems.
  3. Operator has less control over slit widths, except at a single frequency; this leads to possible quantitative uncertainties.

Linear frequency or wavelength cam (see section 1.2)
  1. Simpler reading of frequencies or wavelengths; potentially more information presented (if linear frequency cam is chosen).
  2. More expensive unit, and units will be available only for certain prisms.
  3. Calibration dependent on a cam is less accurate than simpler drive calibrated by operator; deviations of cams are erratic, and thus it is not possible to achieve as fine a frequency calibration over the entire range.

Recording (*vs.* single-point measurements)
  1. Recording gives much more information and gives it more quickly.
  2. More expensive.
  3. Less advantageous for certain quantitative measurements (see section IX-3.13).

Double-beam (*vs.* single-beam) design
  1. Flatter I_0 line because of less atmospheric interference.
  2. Requires slit servo mechanism (which is optional on single-beam instruments).

3. Usually (but not always) comes equipped with linear frequency or wave-length cam.

4. More expensive because accessories (such as slit servo and linear ν or λ cams) are included as standard equipment, and because additional optical components are required; less expensive if certain reasonable requirements concerning flatness of I_0, time stability, speed, and simplicity of operation and interpretation are to be met.

5. Choice must be made between electronic-null, with loss of energy, or optical-null, with associated properties (especially loss of sensitivity and accuracy at low transmittance values).

6. Faster in most cases because reference need not be scanned separately each time a sample is run. (This is, of course, not always valid, since an I_0 is not always run with single-beam instrument but is sometimes run with double-beam instrument.)

7. Greater chance for misinterpreting results in regions of low energy in reference beam.

8. Less readily adapted to double-pass system. For comparable optical performance it is therefore necessary to have a double monochromator or a more elaborate and slower two-chopper system, both of which are more expensive.

9. Time stability is not so great a problem, since sample and reference are compared many times a second, rather than minutes or hours apart. This applies to amplifier drift and, to a much smaller extent, to frequency drift.

10. More accurate comparison of two samples can be made, since instrument subtracts automatically. Doing this operation by hand is considerably less satisfactory.

The combination of increased convenience and increased accuracy obtainable in double-beam systems has been so clearly demonstrated in recent years that single-beam instruments should be considered only for very special applications, such as for spectral regions for which double-beam spectrometers are not yet available.

Electronic-null, double-beam or single-beam (*vs.* double-beam optical-null)[1]

1. More accurate at low energy levels, including regions of low sample transmittance.

2. Operator has more warning of dead instrument, as when solvent or atmosphere absorbs, since slit widths will change or pen will approach zero-energy line.

3. If spectrometer is energy-limited, electronic-null double-beam instrument suffers from loss of energy by factor of 2; single-beam is as efficient per scan as optical-null but may require twice as many scans.

4. Machined optical wedges or combs are subject to erratic variations and are thus not as reliable for quantitative purposes.

Charts and recorders

1. Preprinted charts (for drum or strip-chart recorders) offer more convenience. They also tend to limit operator to a fixed scale size because operator does not want to abandon this convenience and because such

[1] This discussion does not apply to all instruments. Variations such as a logarithmic comb or automatic gain control producing constant photocurrent would require separate analysis.

instruments are not generally equipped with interval-marking pens.   They are generally somewhat more expensive per foot of chart but not necessarily so per spectrum.

2. Drum recorders permit paper to have smooth edges, a convenience in storing spectra.   Drum recorders encourage preprinted charts and subsequent loss of flexibility, due to operator inertia more than to limitations of chart size.   Standardizing size of spectra in this way is, however, a convenience for storing curves and for later comparison.   Neither preprinted charts for drum recorders nor strip-chart paper shows sufficient dimensional stability to meet requirements of most accurate work, so that it is necessary to take special precautions with either.

The performance qualities of any spectrometer will depend also on the frequency setting.   Thus it is easier to demonstrate good performance in the infrared at high frequencies, near the black-body peak, than in regions of lower source intensity; in the ultraviolet and visible there is a similar decrease in performance characteristics near the high- and low-frequency ends of the interval.   Better performance demonstrated in certain regions may be largely illusory, in the sense that it is based on instrument settings which would be totally unsuitable for scanning a full spectrum.

The most severe test of instrument performance generally arises when low signal levels are to be measured.   For an electronic-null spectrometer the noise level should be determined with an absorbing sample or filter in the beam; an optical-null instrument will be most severely tried when both sample and reference beams are strongly attenuated, as in differential analysis.

The relative merits of any two instruments for a particular individual and a particular type of operation will depend on such points as those listed above, but also on a number of hidden factors, such as the integration of a new instrument with spectrometers already in the laboratory, adaptability of special auxiliary equipment, the speed and quality of repair service available at the user's laboratory, and the potential new applications which might be opened up by the new instrument, even though they are not at present of importance, all combined with a certain amount of buyer and operator prejudice for companies, styles, or types of design.

If there is some question about the suitability of a particular instrument for a specific need, the manufacturer should be consulted.   In most cases he will be happy to demonstrate the instruments on representative samples supplied by the potential customer.

Problems

1. Show that for a source of fixed brightness the amount of energy, or the radiant power, passing through an optical system will vary inversely as the square of the f number.

2. (a) Show by means of an optical diagram and appropriate small-angle approximations that the focal point of a collimating mirror should lie midway between the entrance and exit slits (or the virtual positions of these if mirrors are interposed).

(b) Show that in a double-pass system the entrance and exit slits lie on the same side of the focal point, with the intermediate slits (the virtual exit slit for single-pass radiation and the virtual entrance slit for the second pass) at corresponding distances on the opposite side.

(c) Sketch a single-pass Littrow monochromator showing the optical axis of the paraboloidal collimator.

3. Total internal reflection occurs for rays approaching a less dense medium at angles greater than the critical angle, which is the angle of incidence for which the refracted ray would lie in the surface according to Snell's law.   Find the critical angle at an air interface for

(a) silica   (b) heavy flint glass
(c) water   (d) a substance of refractive index n

For which of the solids listed in Table II-I will an unsilvered 45-90-45 prism be a perfect reflector at the hypotenuse if the rays enter and leave perpendicular to the short sides? For which of the solids would total internal reflection be destroyed if the hypotenuse is covered with a thin layer of water?

4. How does the resolving power of a grating depend on

(a) wavenumber, for given angles?
(b) angles, for given wavenumber?

How does the angular dispersion $d\theta/d\lambda$ of a grating depend on

(c) wavelength or wavenumber, for given angles?
(d) angles, for given wavenumber?

How does the angular dispersion $d\theta/d\sigma$ of a grating depend on

(e) wavelength or wavenumber, for given angles?
(f) angles, for given wavenumber?

5. Derive equation III-9 by showing that radiation of frequency v_1 and radiation of frequency v_2 will just be resolved, by the Rayleigh criterion, if the path difference across N rulings is one wavelength greater for one frequency than for the other.

6. Calculate the spectral slit width in reciprocal centimeters according to the approximation of equation III-11 and Fig. III-45

(a) for an NaCl prism at 900 cm^{-1} with mechanical slit widths of 0.15 mm.
(b) for an NaCl prism at 3000 cm^{-1} with mechanical slit widths of 0.015 mm.

7. Calculate the ratio of

(a) absolute noise levels
(b) signal to noise ratios

for a phototube or photomultiplier tube for a sample transmittance of 100% and 1%, other conditions being equal and the stray radiation level and dark current noise considered negligible.   Compare with the same quantities if the detector is a thermal detector with noise independent of the radiation signal.

8. Calculate the absolute (peak-to-peak) noise level, or ripple, in absorbance units, for a thermal detector with a noise level of 0.5% at 100% T, at absorbance values of

(a) 0.0   (b) 1.0
(c) 2.0   (d) 4.0

9. Calculate the absolute noise level, in absorbance units, for a photoemissive detector with a noise level of 0.5% T at 100% T (assuming negligible stray radiation and dark current noise) at absorbance values of

  (a) 0.0   (b) 1.0

  (c) 2.0   (d) 4.0

10. Show that the diffraction limit of a prism or grating is equivalent to a mechanical slit width of $\Delta s = \lambda f/a$, where f is the focal length of the "camera" lens, or mirror, and a is the limiting aperture of the dispersing element.

11. (a) Show that the resolution limit of a prism, as a function of mechanical slit width, is given by $\Delta \sigma_s = (a/ft)(d\sigma/dn)s$, where a, f, and t are the limiting aperture of the prism, the focal length of the "camera" mirror or lens, and the thickness of the prism base, respectively.

(b) Show that the resolution limit of a grating, as a function of mechanical slit width, is given by $\Delta \sigma_s = (\sigma/2f \tan \theta)s$ for a single-pass Littrow monochromator.

12. Calculate the contributions to the spectral slit width to be expected for the diffraction limit, the aberration limit, and the mechanical slit width if a single-pass grating monochromator, employing a 750 grooves/cm grating of 6.4-cm ruled width and a paraboloid of 27-cm focal length, is operated with mechanical slit widths of 0.100 mm to observe the HCl fundamental at 2886 cm^{-1} in the fourth order.   Assume the aberrations of the monochromator are equivalent to a mechanical slit width of 0.030 mm.   The HCl rotational lines appear as doublets, because of the natural abundance of the two isotopes of chlorine, with a separation of about 2.0 cm^{-1}.   Should these be resolved under the stated conditions?

IV

Sample preparation

Infrared spectroscopy is complicated by its versatility. Many compounds do not absorb at all in the visible region or the near ultraviolet, and among them are many good solvents of varying chemical type. All liquids and nearly all solids absorb in the infrared region between 600 and 4000 cm^{-1}, and those liquids which are more nearly transparent are not good solvents for many of the substances which are to be examined. The need for a special chapter on sample preparation is occasioned largely by these problems of the infrared region.

1 Ultraviolet and Visible

Methods intended to develop color by chemical reaction, to permit a colorimetric determination, will be specifically excluded from this discussion. This is within the province of analytical chemistry and has been adequately treated in the literature of that field. It will be assumed here that the problem is to determine the absorption spectrum of a given compound, rather than the preparation or purification of the compound. Interpretation of the spectrum, which may strongly influence the manner in which the sample is to be examined, will be discussed in later chapters.

1.1 Solvents

Solvents that are transparent through most of the ultraviolet region are shown in Fig. IV-1. Others that are transparent in the visible region can be recognized by their appearance and have not been included. Water, ethanol, and cyclohexane or isoöctane (2,2,4-trimethylpentane) are transparent throughout the region accessible on most spectrometers and provide sufficient variation in solvent powers to be adequate for most samples.

Methylene chloride absorbs at a somewhat lower frequency than these solvents but is also a much superior solvent for many substances.   Chloroform and carbon tetrachloride are progressively poorer in transparency. Ethers, such as diethyl ether or dioxane, are very transparent and are good solvents for certain classes of compounds; they are less satisfactory in terms of chemical stability.

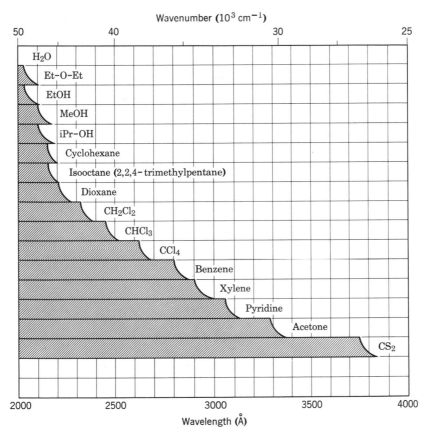

FIG. IV-1.   Useful range of solvents in the ultraviolet region, for 1 cm path length. Cut-off points are approximate, depending on purity of the solvent.

Distilled, or de-ionized, water is recommended to avoid deposition of trace residues, but the impurities found in water do not normally cause significant absorption in the accessible region of the ultraviolet.   Ninety-five per cent ethanol is suitable without further purification.   Absolute ethanol is often found to contain benzene, as a consequence of insufficient care in removing it after the azeotropic distillation to remove water. This can be easily checked by comparing the transmittance of the cell filled with ethanol to a cell filled with water in the 2500 Å region. Many other commercial-grade solvents, including carbon tetrachloride, chloroform, and methylene chloride, have been found entirely adequate provided some attention is given to the supplier. The standard grade of methylene chloride, for example, may differ markedly, and consistently, with the supplier.

Isoöctane and cyclohexane, in commercial grades, contain large quantities of aromatics and olefins. These compounds may be purchased in

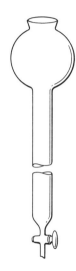

FIG. IV-2. Chromatographic column for solvent cleaning.

high purity (about 99 mole per cent)[1] and the remaining impurities removed by passage of the material through a silica gel column. For this purpose it is advisable to construct a column 1 to $1\frac{1}{2}$ in. in diameter, 3 to 6 feet long, sealed to the bottom of a 2-liter flask (Fig. IV-2). This permits cleaning large quantities of solvent at a time with only infrequent attention.

Packing of a column for purification of solvents may be accomplished by pouring the dry silica gel (Davisson No. 920, 8-200 mesh) into the column while agitating the column; for example, by "whipping" it with a short piece of heavy rubber tubing. After the liquid is added, the column should not be allowed to go dry, even in the upper regions. The effluent solvent should be compared with water for transmission in the ultraviolet.

[1] Phillips Petroleum Co., Bartlesville, Okla.

Some indication of the progress of column contamination is given by the variation in Christiansen filter effect (section II-7) associated with change of refractive index of liquid on the column.   For maximum purity of solvent and conservation of adsorbent it is sometimes advisable to carry out the purification in two steps, since the column will continue to take out most of the impurities (especially the aromatics) long after it begins to let small amounts of olefins through.   Stopcock grease should, of course, be avoided and is unnecessary while the stopcock is wet with solvent or for Teflon-plug stopcocks.   When flow is to be stopped overnight, the flask should be well filled and tightly stoppered before the stopcock at the bottom is turned.   This produces sufficient vacuum at the top to support the liquid column and prevent leakage around the stopcock.   Five gallons of hydrocarbon equal to or better than the most expensive grade commercially available may be prepared in this fashion with a few minutes' attention spread over several days and with the consumption of about a pound of silica gel, provided the total impurity content of the starting material is low.

Many solvents are now available in "spectroscopic grade."   Unless an actual analysis is provided it is not safe to assume that this represents the highest purity available, but only that those impurities which would interfere in the ultraviolet (or sometimes the infrared) have been removed. Since the cost of these solvents is much greater than standard grades, there is some justification for trying the standard grades first.

1.2 Concentrations and Dilutions

Finding the proper concentration, when previous experience with similar materials does not provide this information, can be a time-consuming operation.   To avoid needless quantitative dilutions or possible overlooking of relatively weak absorption bands the following procedure is recommended for liquids.   The pure material, if 2 to 3 ml is available, is placed in the cell and scanned from the visible region until total absorption occurs.   Nine-tenths of the liquid is poured out of the cell (since this is uncontaminated, it may be saved), the cell is filled with solvent, stoppered, and shaken, and the solution is scanned from a point overlapping the previous curve until total absorption again occurs.   Nine-tenths of the solution is poured out, the cell is again filled with solvent, and the steps repeated until the entire spectrum has been scanned.   At this point, by counting dilutions made, an approximate concentration is known for each segment of the curve and a solution can be made to the exact concentration required for any region.

The justification for the ten-to-one dilution method described lies in the fact that nearly all compounds show much stronger absorption as the vacuum ultraviolet is approached. The ratios of absorption coefficients in the 2500 Å (40,000 cm^{-1}) region to those in the 3500 Å (30,000 cm^{-1}) region are most often 100/1 or greater. Dilution by less than a factor of 10 is seldom justified for this reason and because most spectrometers have a usable range of at least a factor of 10 in absorbance. Although estimation of 10% of the cell volume is somewhat uncertain, the actual value of the dilution factor can be read from the chart in the region of overlap.

Nearly all spectra in the visible and ultraviolet regions are run in cells of 1 cm thickness. Necessary variations in effective thickness are more easily accomplished by changing concentration than by changing cell thickness. For certain samples other cell lengths or types are required; they are discussed in section 4.

1.3 Solid Samples

Solids of certain types may be easily examined in the visible or ultraviolet. Glasses, clear plastics, or thin films cast, painted, or evaporated onto transparent substrates, provided they have physical dimensions consistent with the sample compartment of the spectrometer, can be scanned to the point at which they become totally absorbing. Powders or irregular crystalline deposits will generally scatter too much in the ultraviolet to permit direct observation. These may sometimes be ground with NaCl or KBr and pressed into a pellet, as discussed in the following section. Single crystals do not show strong scattering but will often absorb too strongly for the absorption peaks to be measured. Amorphous glasses, with or without dissolved substances, and polycrystalline materials prepared by sublimation have been examined successfully. Gases represent no difficulty in the ultraviolet-visible region. Often the reflectance of a solid can be measured when the transmittance cannot.

2 Infrared

Absorptivities of many compounds are of the same order of magnitude in the infrared as in the ultraviolet. Cell thicknesses in the infrared region, however, vary from 0.03 mm or less to about 1 mm, seldom more, as compared to the "standard" 10-mm cell for the ultraviolet and visible region. The reason is that very few solvents are known which will transmit appreciably in any part of the infrared between 600 and 4000 cm^{-1} in a thickness of 1 cm. It is as if one were attempting to measure the ultraviolet absorption spectrum of chlorobenzene with benzene as the solvent.

Methods of overcoming the deficit of transparent solvents have included the following.   Compounds are run in two or more solvents; pure liquids or melts are scanned without solvent; very fine powders or large crystal plates are prepared and examined directly; films are cast from solution; powders are mulled with mineral oil or other heavy liquid; powders are ground with KBr and pressed into pellets; solid particles are suspended in dense liquids; amorphous solids are sliced with a microtome; reflectance measurements are substituted for absorption measurements; and samples are pyrolized and the pyrolysate is examined and empirically compared with similar materials.   Large single crystals and gases are handled by the usual procedures.   Each of these methods will be described briefly.

2.1   Solutions

Spectra of several solvents and mulling agents are given in Fig. IV-3. It will be seen that CCl_4 and CS_2 are quite unique in having very few interfering absorption bands.   Where it is necessary to examine the full spectrum between 4000 and 625 cm^{-1} the upper half may be run in CCl_4, the lower half in CS_2, provided the sample is sufficiently soluble in each of these.   Polar compounds, and particularly ionic compounds, are not very soluble in either of these solvents, nor in the relatively non-polar solvents which have broad "windows," or regions of transparency.   Polar solvents, such as water, alcohols, and ethers, show such strong infrared absorption that the bands tend to merge when thicknesses as great as 0.03 mm are scanned.   Dimethyl formamide is something of an exception; it has a broad window in the lower-frequency range.   Ten per cent solutions of dimethyl formamide in CS_2 work well for examining some polar compounds in this region.

Because of the unique position of water as a solvent for inorganic compounds and as a medium for biological systems, considerable attention has been given to the problem of obtaining spectra in water solution.[1] Solution thicknesses must be kept very small and special cell-window materials must be employed.   To examine the regions which are hidden by water absorption it is sometimes possible to substitute D_2O.

2.2   Liquids and Melts

Pure liquids must be placed in very thin cells, the exact thickness depending on the strength of the absorption, and therefore on how polar the molecule is, and on the particular region of primary interest.   Special cell designs may be required (section 4) if the stronger bands are to be kept to

[1] E. R. Blout, ref. 55, pp. 84–93; H. Sternglanz, *Appl. Spectroscopy* **10**, 77 (1956).

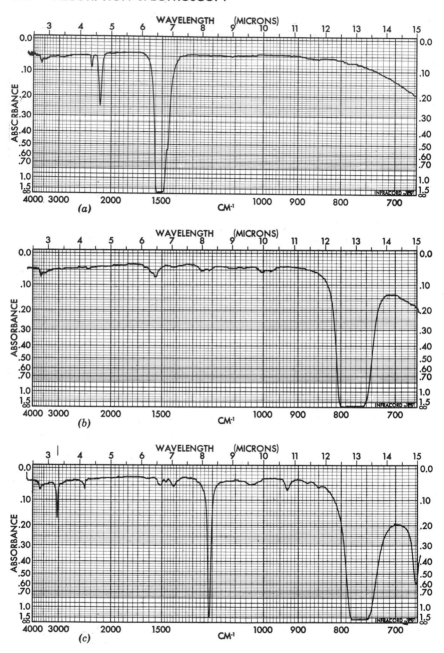

FIG. IV-3a. Infrared solvents. Top, CS$_2$; middle, CCl$_4$; bottom, CHCl$_3$.

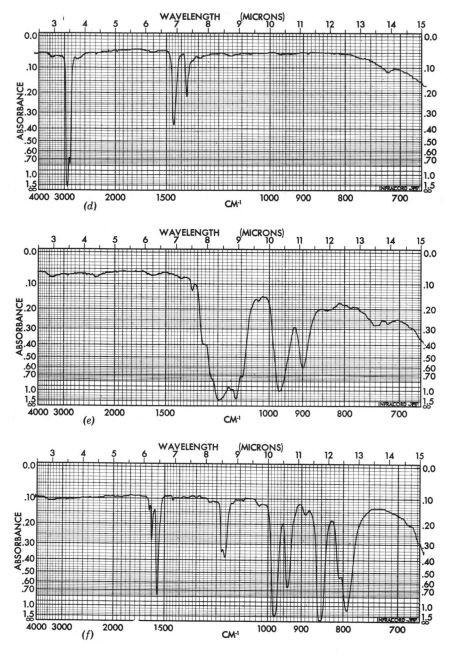

FIG. IV-3*b*. Infrared mulling liquids. Top, Nujol; middle, Fluorolube S; bottom, hexachlorobutadiene.

satisfactory intensity levels.   Compounds which are normally solid but which melt at temperatures not too much above 100°C may be placed between salt plates, heated while in the cell holder in the infrared beam with a heat lamp mounted above the cell, and scanned as a liquid at this higher temperature.   Spacers may or may not be desirable, depending on the viscosity of the sample and its absorptivity.   Quite often, good spectra are obtained by allowing a melt to cool and crystallize between the salt plates.   Bands are often sharper for solids than for liquids.   This method should be applied only with great caution, however, since the crystallization may take place with a preferred orientation such that the resulting spectrum will appear quite different from the spectrum of the same compound obtained under other conditions.   Considerable care is warranted in heating and cooling the salt plates slowly and uniformly to prevent strains which could crack the crystal.   The plates will separate more easily if they can be taken apart before the sample has solidified.

2.3   Solids

Powdered materials will, of course, tend to cause scattering as well as absorption, but this scattering is much less important in the infrared region than in the visible or ultraviolet (under certain circumstances the amount of scattering varies as the fourth power of the frequency).   Large crystal plates prepared from a melt or from solution, or very fine crystals prepared by precipitation from solution or by deposition from the vapor phase, will often show very limited scattering losses.

Amorphous solids, such as polymer films, have negligible scattering losses.   Such films are easily produced by dropping a saturated solution slowly onto a salt crystal, with or without supplementary heating to accelerate evaporation of solvent.   The diameter of the film should be considerably larger than the infrared beam, since edge effects from the deposition process cause a large variation in film thickness outside the central zone.   Some polymer films can be cast onto glass, mercury, or other resistant surfaces, then peeled off and mounted in a cardboard holder.   It is often impossible to remove all the solvent from cast films, even with several days of drying.   This is not of great importance in most cases provided one watches for the presence of solvent bands in the spectrum of the film.

Reflection occurs at a boundary between any two media of different indices of refraction, the percentage reflection for perpendicular incidence being given by the expression

$$R = \frac{(n_2 - n_1)^2}{(n_2 + n_1)^2}$$

for transparent substances of refractive indices n_1 and n_2. Surrounding the particles of a powder with a liquid of approximately the same index of refraction will accordingly greatly decrease the amount of scattering by the powder. The requirements on a liquid for this purpose are generally that it should have a moderate viscosity, few absorption bands or no absorption bands in the region of primary interest, and should mix well with the powder. For most samples a highly refined mineral oil, such as Nujol,[1] is excellent for this purpose. It consists of a mixture of hydrocarbons such that only the C—H stretching bands (2850–3000 cm^{-1}), the C—H bending modes at about 1468 and 1379 cm^{-1}, and the broad and relatively weak absorption band at 720 cm^{-1}, attributed to the methylene rocking vibration, are visible in thicknesses normally required. Other bands which would appear for the individual components of the hydrocarbon mixture are effectively diluted out. In the presence of mineral oil it is not possible to examine the C—H stretching or bending bands, but in most cases one knows beforehand whether or not C—H is present so that this is a very minor disadvantage. The hydrocarbon mixes well with most compounds, though not with compounds that tend to be ionic or slightly damp, and the refractive index in the infrared is close to that of most organic compounds.

When it is important to examine the C—H bands, hexachlorobutadiene or perfluorokerosene[2] can be substituted for the mineral oil. Even water, in very small amounts, is suitable as a mulling agent for certain materials. If this is to be done with rock salt plates, it is advisable to presaturate the water by dropping it onto a scrap piece of salt before adding it to the sample.

Two distinct schools of thought are to be found concerning the technique of mull preparation. Some workers grind the powder in an agate mortar, between glass plates, or in various ingenious devices of their own construction. A few drops of mineral oil are added and the grinding is continued until a smooth paste is obtained. The paste is then transferred to a salt plate, covered with a second plate, placed in a cell holder, and scanned. Depending on the care exercised, this method requires roughly 10 to 20 minutes per sample. The alternative method is to place a very small amount of the powder on the rock salt crystal, add a small drop of oil, and grind these together with another crystal. In 2 to 5 minutes a mull can be prepared in this manner which is equivalent, for most samples (but not all!), to that obtained by the more elaborate procedure. The faster method is not suitable for very hard, gritty substances and is

[1] Nujol is a tradename of Plough, Inc.

[2] Fluorocarbons are available from Hooker Electrochemical Co. (under the tradename of Fluorolube) and from duPont.

somewhat more likely to show orientation effects for those substances which crystallize as flat plates. Hygroscopic compounds are most easily mulled if they are worked very quickly after thorough drying.

The KBr pellet method was originated in 1951 by Stimson[1] and Scheidt.[2] Commercial dies of several varieties are now available and the technique has been widely accepted by certain groups, particularly those in the biological field. To prepare a pellet, the sample is ground with KBr or is precipitated with KBr from solution by freeze-drying. The mixture is added to the die, which is then evacuated to a pressure of a few millimeters of mercury, or less, to avoid entrapment of air, which would cause the pellet to become cloudy. The mixture is pressed at about 20 tons/square inch for a few minutes. The pellets thus produced are, under favorable conditions, completely clear.

The pellet method offers certain advantages over other sampling techniques, but it has also some serious shortcomings which must be taken into consideration. On the positive side, the absence of absorption by KBr in the entire infrared region down to roughly 400 cm^{-1} is the most obvious quality. About the same percentage of samples can be easily put into a good pellet as can be made into a good mull; the remaining few samples, in each case, will give good spectra only with difficulty. Because some of the "bad actors" for preparation of mulls are different from those for preparation of pellets, there is justification for employing each technique. In principle, quantitative analyses can be readily performed if one knows the concentration of sample in KBr and weighs carefully the total quantity of mixture pressed into the pellet of known diameter. In practice, the difficulties inherent in this procedure are sufficient (section IX-7) that it should not be undertaken lightly.

Two disadvantages of the pellet method merit special attention. As potassium bromide is hygroscopic, it is very difficult to prepare a pellet without some contamination by water. The amount of this contamination is generally greater for a pellet for which the salt has been ground with sample than in a pellet without sample prepared, otherwise, in similar fashion. In qualitative analysis the presence or absence of —OH or —NH is generally much more significant than the presence or absence of C—H; if C—H is important, mulls can be prepared with halogenated oils. Only with extreme care is it possible to obtain a spectrum of a pellet from which one can be certain that water has been excluded.

The second disadvantage, which was anticipated in the early days of the method but was only slowly recognized in practice, is a lack of reproducibility of spectra in pellets. In part this arises from variations in

[1] M. M. Stimson, *J. Am. Chem. Soc.* **74**, 1805 (1952).
[2] U. Schiedt, *Z. Naturforsch.* **76**, 270 (1952).

particle size, as in mulls; in a few instances actual chemical reactions with the alkali halide matrix have been shown to occur.   More often the effect seems to arise from changes in the sample due to the very high local temperatures and pressures developed during formation of the pellet.   In general, the sample is not dissolved in the KBr but exists as small particles; to the extent that solution can occur there can be very marked changes in intensity and position.   As a consequence of these uncertainties in sample spectra, many experienced spectroscopists are now extremely reluctant to interpret curves which have been obtained in this manner.   Certainly the novice should proceed with extreme caution.

The time required for preparation of a pellet is appreciably greater than for preparation of most mulls.   The investment required is also significantly greater, although this is not particularly important either in comparison with other expenses of setting up a laboratory or in view of the need for having the alternative procedure available.   The great popularity of the method in the medical and biological fields arises from the convenience of handling extremely small samples by diluting them with a transparent material.   When sample size is the overwhelming consideration, rather than preparation time, there seems little doubt that the pellet method, with freeze-drying, can give the most uniformly satisfactory results.

Uniform grinding represents a common problem to mull and pellet techniques when the highest quality of spectra are required.   Mortar and pestle grinding is often not adequate, nor is grinding in a ball mill.   Shakers, such as those designed as dental mixers, seem to be slightly better than either of the first two for certain materials.   Some samples that are particularly gummy, hygroscopic, or otherwise difficult to grind can be handled more readily under a solvent, such as ether, acetone, or carbon tetrachloride.   This often helps even though the sample is insoluble.   The possibility of picking up water from the atmosphere is increased somewhat by this procedure.

2.4   Other Methods

The techniques considered thus far represent the most generally successful procedures for obtaining spectra of solids and liquids.   There are certain other methods which are not so universally applicable but which may prove to be superior in any given instance.   One such method is the preparation of an emulsion of a sample that is insoluble in the relatively transparent solvents.   The emulsion may be treated in many respects as if it were a solution—for example, it may be put into a fixed-thickness liquid cell—but for quantitative measurements the particle or droplet size must be carefully controlled. A few substances, such as polyethylene, may be sliced into very thin sections with a microtome. The number of materials amenable to this treatment is, however, quite small.

When transmittance measurements are extremely difficult or impossible, either because the sample absorbs too strongly or because the sample of interest is a surface coating on a non-transparent backing, reflectance measurements may provide sufficient information. The reflectance depends on the absorption coefficient and shows a maximum near the position of maximum absorptivity. With considerable difficulty, it is possible to calculate from reflectance measurements alone the true positions of the absorption maxima.[1] For many purposes the reflectance spectrum itself may provide adequate identification or characterization.

The discrepancy between absorption and reflection maxima is primarily of importance for very strong absorption bands, such as that of silica. Ordinary reflection techniques are so insensitive, however, that these have been the only type of importance. A much more sensitive method, based on total internal reflection at the interface between a silver chloride dome and the sample, has been discussed by J. Fahrenfort.[2]

Many polymeric surface coatings are both insoluble and extremely difficult to grind into a fine powder. They represent some of the most intractable materials for the infrared spectroscopist. An ingenious method of characterization of such materials has been devised.[3] The material is heated in the bottom of a test tube. At the top of the tube a few drops of liquid pyrolysis products, which may be scanned in the usual manner, will accumulate. Identification is often possible by comparing the spectra of such pyrolysates with spectra of pyrolysates of known materials. The temperature should be reproduced as closely as possible.

Considerably more information may be obtained from spectra of gases or large single crystals than from liquids, powders, or solutions. Interpretation of rotational fine structure and band contours and of polarization measurements will be considered in later chapters. Studies of adsorbed monolayers represent an additional technique for application of infrared to problems of physical interest.

3   Very Near Infrared

Sample-handling techniques for the very near infrared are more like those of the ultraviolet and visible than the infrared. Most work in this region is performed on spectrometers designed for the ultraviolet and vis-

[1] I. Simon, *J. Opt. Soc. Am.* **41**, 336 (1951); P. O. Johnson, *ibid.*, **42**, 978 (1952).

[2] J. Fahrenfort, *Spectrochim. Acta* **17**, 698 (1961).

[3] D. L. Harms, *Anal. Chem.* **25**, 1140 (1953).

ible regions, and since glass and silica are transparent these cells are also applicable to this region. Absorption is due almost entirely to overtone and combination bands arising from changes in vibrational state; they are much weaker than the fundamental bands which occur at lower frequencies. Fortunately the absorption bands of solvents are correspondingly weaker, so that it is possible to obtain spectra in solutions of moderate concentration in cells of 1 cm or longer path length. The most prominent absorption bands are those due to the high vibrational frequencies, in particular those due to O-H, N-H, and C-H stretching modes. Since the intensities of the bands tend to decrease with increasing frequency, it is necessary to vary concentrations or cell lengths to obtain a good spectrum of the full region. As an example of this drop in intensity, it is possible to observe the fifth overtone of the C-H stretch of benzene as a weak band at the edge of the visible region with a 5-cm cell of pure benzene.

4 Sample Cells

For routine investigations in the ultraviolet and visible regions, cells of glass or silica are commercially available. Some of the common types are shown in Fig. IV-4.

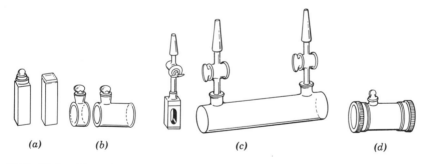

FIG. IV-4. Absorption cells for ultraviolet, visible, and very near infrared regions. (a) Rectangular cells, 1 cm; (b) cylindrical cells, 1 cm and 3 cm; (c) gas cells; (d) demountable liquid cell.

Infrared cells (Fig. IV-5) may also be purchased, but if any appreciable amount of work is to be done it is necessary to polish optical crystals routinely. In this case it will often be more economical and convenient to make and repair cells in the laboratory where they are to be used. The cell frames may be purchased from the instrument manufacturers or may be put together at small cost by any machinist.

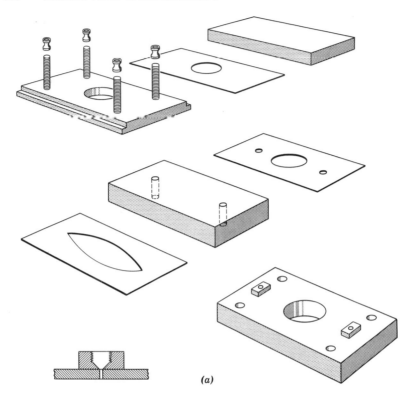

(a)

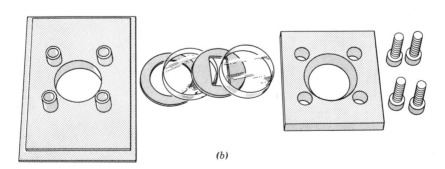

(b)

FIG. IV-5.   Infrared cells.   (a) Fixed liquid cell.   (b) Demountable cell.   (Courtesy Perkin-Elmer Corp.)

4.1   Construction of Fixed Liquid Cells

Many variations are to be found in frames for infrared liquid cells, but most of them are very similar in concept to that shown in Fig. IV-5a.   A brass plate, of suitable size to slide into the mounting bracket of the

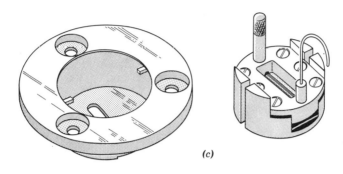

(c)

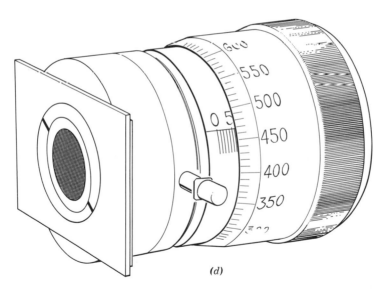

(d)

FIG. IV-5 (Continued). (c) Microcell and cell holder. (d) Variable-space cell. (Courtesy Perkin-Elmer Corp.)

spectrometer or to fit into the sample well, is provided with four threaded posts.   A gasket of paper or cardboard is placed on this, with a central hole at least as large as the hole in the brass plate, which in turn should preferably be as large as the beam which is to pass through the cell.   A polished crystal (see below) is placed on the gasket, followed by a spacer of lead, silver, or other unreactive metal.   Another crystal, drilled with two holes about $\frac{1}{32}$ in. in diameter, is placed on top of the spacer, a lead gasket is put on top, and another brass (or stainless steel) plate is slid over the posts and held in place with knurled nuts.   If the cell is to be temporary, the outside gaskets may be omitted and the sample placed on the lower crystal before the upper (undrilled) crystal is added.   Cells put together for a single scan, as in running mulls, thin liquid films, or "smears," can be held adequately with only two nuts rather than four.   This provides a convenient reminder—cells with four nuts are not so likely to be mistaken

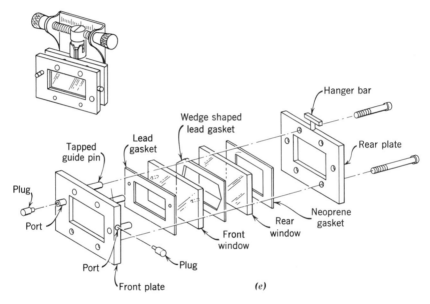

FIG. IV-5 (Continued).   (e) Variable-space cell, wedge design.   (Courtesy Beckman Instruments, Inc.)

for temporary cells and dismantled unintentionally—as well as representing a significant saving of time.

Cells of the type described above may be made liquid, and vapor, tight by amalgamating the spacer and the upper gasket with mercury before assembly.   The foil is cleaned of oxide by placing it in a petri dish containing dilute acetic acid (for lead) or ammonia (for silver or copper).   The spacer is then touched to a drop of mercury which is spread over the top and bottom surfaces of the foil by gentle rubbing with the finger.   After the excess mercury is squeezed off the surface, the foil is lifted from the dish (with a razor blade, if necessary, to prevent damage to thin foils), rinsed, dried by blotting, and placed on the crystal. Very thin foils can be amalgamated in place by adding a few small drops of mercury to the top; the mercury will penetrate through the metal to permit a good seal on both surfaces. The top gasket should also be amalgamated, at least in the vicinity of the filling holes, to prevent escape of liquid or vapor from around the filling channels.

Design of the upper plate of the frame is a matter of personal taste. It should preferably be long enough, at least at one end, that the completed cell will stand upright; alternatively a plate may be added perpendicular to the base plate at one end to serve as a stable foot. The filling holes may be straight, as shown, or one of them may form a right-angle bend and terminate at the end surface of the plate. This gives a longer path in the metal plate for the liquid, which in some cases could mean greater problems of corrosion or more waste volume for small samples; some workers consider the design preferable for ease of filling and cleaning. The filling holes in the top plate and in the crystal should meet the ends of the aperture in the spacer, as shown in Fig. IV-5a, in order that the cell may be effectively drained.

If the bottom surface of the filling hole in the upper brass plate is tapered, a particularly tight seal may be achieved by placing a clean lead shot in the hole and screwing a brass plug against it. The conical hole permits small samples to be placed at the very bottom of the brass plate and the seal, with lead shot, is made at a point that gives the cell a minimum waste volume and gives the liquid a minimum contact with the metal. Teflon plugs turned into the threaded terminals by hand will be self-threading and will form a tight seal, though at a higher point in the filling channel. If the cut-off cones of hypodermic needles are soldered into the brass plate, Teflon plugs will form a moderately tight closure without threading. This method has the advantage that hypodermic syringes may be fitted directly to the cell opening for filling or flushing.

After assembly of the cell parts the four nuts should be tightened firmly and uniformly by hand and the cell allowed to stand for a day before use to permit the amalgam to harden. The cell is filled from the bottom while held at an angle with the horizontal. If the cell is quite thin it will fill by capillary action. Care should be taken to prevent liquid from reaching the upper plug; if there is no air space in the cell, insertion of the plugs will build up a very large hydraulic pressure. The cell should be drained from the opening through which it was filled, then flushed with solvent and with dry air or nitrogen. A vacuum is the best method of removing the last traces of solvent. The purpose of first flushing with dry air is to prevent condensation of moisture on the cell windows as they are cooled by evaporation of the solvent. Unless the laboratory air is quite dry, a drying tube should be held over one cell opening when air is to be pulled through by a vacuum line.

4.2   Measurements of Cell Thickness

Commercial glass and silica cells have a fixed thickness which is generally marked on each cell.   Infrared cells may be made to any nominal thickness by proper choice of spacers, but the final cell thickness is left somewhat uncertain and may change slightly with time.

Infrared cells of thicknesses between about 0.03 mm and 1 mm can be constructed with lead spacers.   Cells of thicknesses between 0.03 mm and 0.01 mm are more easily made with silver spacers because of the greater strength of this metal.   Below 0.01 mm, one encounters difficulty in filling, emptying, and cleaning cells, and very small changes in cell depth will represent a large percentage change.   Special cell designs have been created for this thickness range.   Above 1 mm a lead spacer is no longer sufficiently pliable to form a good seal readily.   For such cells a brass spacer, machined to be quite flat, can be amalgamated between two lead spacers to form a gasket of the proper thickness.   The outer lead sheets are amalgamated, in turn, to the alkali halide crystal.

In principle, the thickness of a cell can be determined by comparing the absorbance of a solution in the cell to the absorbance of the same solution (or a solution related in a known way in terms of concentration) in a cell of known thickness.   In practice, the uncertainties seem to be somewhat larger than is desirable for a cell-thickness determination.

For thin cells, such as are common in the infrared, cell depths may be determined by measuring the interference fringes produced in the dry cell. (These fringes disappear when the cell is filled with a liquid, because the index of refraction of the liquid matches that of the crystal more closely than does air; this causes the intensity of the fringes to drop markedly.) The peak-to-peak spacing of the fringes, in reciprocal centimeters, is constant and equal to twice the reciprocal of the cell thickness, in centimeters (equation II-14).   For example, a 0.05-mm cell will show fringes 400 cm^{-1} apart; a 0.5-mm cell will show fringes 40 cm^{-1} apart.   The fringe intensity drops off with increasing order of the fringe, owing to imperfection of alignment of the plates.   The maximum thickness that can be measured by this method is thus limited by the frequency range of the spectrometer as well as by the resolution.   Random errors of measurement of spacing are largely eliminated if successive maxima and minima are numbered, starting at any point, and the wavenumbers of these (as abscissas) are plotted against the respective arbitrary index numbers. The slope of the straight line will be four times the cell thickness.

4.3   Polishing Crystals

Sodium chloride and potassium bromide crystals require frequent re-finishing if they are subjected to abrasion or moisture.   Since the polishing operation requires only a few seconds, or for the worst cases a few minutes, the procedure should be mastered and made a part of normal laboratory routine.   Three distinct methods are available, as well as variations for each of them.

The easiest method to master is polishing on a cloth lap.   This gives an excellent surface finish very quickly.   The cloth laps are prepared in pairs, one for polishing and the other for drying.   The polishing lap should be of nylon or other lintless material which is unaffected by laboratory solvents.   It is placed over a flat piece of brass or glass and held taught with rubber bands, an "O" ring, or other device.   The dry lap may be of nylon or of a cloth with heavy nap; the base need not be as flat for this lap.

The polishing lap is moistened with 95% ethanol or with water.   An abrasive such as Barnesite or Rareox (rare earth oxides) or alumina will increase the polishing speed.   After a few strokes on the moist (not wet) lap, the crystal is rapidly slid over to the dry lap and given a few strokes to remove the polishing agents.   The skill required increases with the polishing speed; with 95% ethanol a high gloss is acquired in a short time with little chance of getting into difficulty.   A significant advantage of the cloth lap is that it will give a clear finish even though the plate is not quite flat. This also represents a disadvantage, since continued polishing with this method may lead to plates which deviate significantly from flatness.   This can cause difficulties in preparing mulls or in examining very thin liquid films.

A very flat surface can be obtained in a short time if the rock salt is ground on a roughened glass plate.   With practice this method will give a surface almost as clear as will the cloth lap.   It is sufficiently versatile to be suitable for very rapid, rough grinding and for final polishing to optical flatness.

A small amount of 600-mesh Carborundum is placed on a piece of plate glass 8 × 12 in. or larger, and water is added to make a thin slurry.   Two or three minutes of grinding this under another piece of glass should give a uniform roughness.   After the abrasive has been rinsed from the surface the plate is ready to use.   The polishing action results from a combination of abrasion by the roughened glass surface and erosion of the surface by water.   The speed will therefore vary markedly as the amount of water present is changed.   With continued polishing over several months the surface will become less rough, also, and the speed will decrease; the clearest surface can be obtained with a plate which has been in use for some time, so that there is some advantage in having available two plates which can be reground alternately.

In normal operation sufficient moisture is obtained by breathing on the surface. The crystal is rubbed over this surface with very moderate pressure, then removed by sliding it over a dry edge. If left too long, the crystal may "freeze" to the plate, or, if worked too hard, small surface cracks may be produced. The polishing characteristics of the plate can be adjusted by controlling the amount of salt on the surface. Fastest polishing is obtained just after the salt has been washed off. If the surface is very wet a rough surface will be ground down quickly, but with an increased tendency for raised corners. Such preliminary rough grinding may be done on fine sandpaper, with similar tendencies for raised corners.

A pitch lap,[1] moistened with a slurry of alumina in water, offers the advantages of speed and flatness. It requires a greater expenditure of time to prepare and to maintain, but this time can be saved if any significant amount of polishing is to be done. For materials harder than sodium chloride the pitch lap represents the standard polishing procedure.

Whether the crystals to be polished are held with bare fingers or with rubber gloves or rubber finger cots is largely a matter of personal preference and skin characteristics. Finger cots are more comfortable than full gloves. The crystal should be held only at the edges. It should be noted in particular that facial tissue is not a good water barrier; a crystal protected by several layers of tissue can be rapidly fogged by picking it up with bare hands.

Sodium chloride and potassium bromide crystals cleave readily to give rectangular windows. A single-edge razor blade is placed as closely as possible along one of the cleavage planes and tapped lightly with a small hammer. Thick crystals should be split in two, then redivided, rather than attempting to split a thin slab away from the thicker piece. Subdivision may be continued until the piece to be removed is about 5 mm thick, depending somewhat on the cross-sectional area and the skill of the worker. Large pieces thinner than this tend to be quite fragile. A cleaved surface of rock salt is highly resistant to fogging, even in the presence of high relative humidity, if it is not touched with the hands or polished. Polished surfaces apparently regain this immunity if they are annealed at temperatures in the vicinity of 600°C.

Fluorite is quite hard and is insoluble in water. It should not require refinishing in normal use. Although it is a cubic crystal (face-centered

---

[1] For instructions concerning preparation of a pitch lap and polishing of rock salt by this and other methods, see Lord, McDonald, and Miller, *J. Opt. Soc. Am.* **42**, 149 (1952).

cubic) it has octahedral cleavage planes and will not cleave into rectangular windows.   It can be ground and polished with alumina, with alumina and EDTA (ethylenediamine tetraacetic acid), or with EDTA and sulfuric acid, on a pitch lap.   Final finishing is done with a very fine abrasive such as Linde "A" powder (alumina of about 0.3 μ particle size) on a pitch lap or a lap of 50% beeswax and 50% rosin, with or without EDTA.   Barium fluoride and lithium fluoride have physical properties similar to those of fluorite, except that lithium fluoride has cubic cleavage planes.

KRS-5 (thallium bromide-iodide) is subject to plastic flow and is highly toxic.   It should be protected from abrasion but is not water soluble. Silver chloride is available in the form of rolled sheets that may be cut to the size and shape desired.   It is reasonably stable in normal use but will deteriorate rapidly under ultraviolet irradiation unless protected by a coating such as silver sulfide, which is transparent in the infrared region but opaque in the ultraviolet.   Polishing is aided by sodium thiosulfate which serves as a solvent.

Holes can be drilled in the alkali halide crystals by means of a pin vise rotated by hand.   Faster drilling, with a hand drill or slow drill press, increases the likelihood of chipping.   Holes should be drilled from each side toward the middle, rather than all the way through.   Circular plates can be cut with a brass tube cutter and a slow drill press,[1] or they may be purchased in nearly any size desired from instrument manufacturers or suppliers of optical crystals.[2]

4.4   Gas Cells

The simplest type of gas cell consists of a piece of glass tubing with windows sealed onto the ends and an outlet tube with stopcock.   A spherical ground joint is preferable to a standard-taper joint for attaching such a cell to a gas-handling system, since it is often necessary to separate the joint while it is under vacuum.   If small quantities of gas are to be transferred completely into the cell it is helpful to have a small side arm, as in Fig. IV-6, which can be cooled to dry ice or liquid nitrogen temperatures.

For the ultraviolet region, silica windows are required; they may be sealed directly to a cell body made of silica, or may be attached to glass by means of graded seals.   For many purposes it will be adequate to attach silica windows to a glass cell body by means of Glyptal[3] or other adhesive.

[1] See Lord, McDonald, and Miller, *loc cit.*

[2] Harshaw Chemical Company, 1945 East 97th St., Cleveland 6, Ohio; Optovac Company, 59 Summer Street, No. Brookfield, Mass.; Isomet, Palisades, N.J.

[3] An insulating varnish available from General Electric Co.

For the infrared region, windows of NaCl, KBr, or CaF_2 are generally affixed to glass cells with Glyptal. A 50-50 mixture of beeswax and rosin, heated until it is smoking hot and applied with a medicine dropper, provides a supplementary seal that has good mechanical strength as well as good adhesive qualities.

Epoxy resins can form a tight seal with very good mechanical strength. They tend to be somewhat tricky to apply and difficult to remove.

Gas cells for long path lengths, based upon multiple traversal of the sample, are available commercially. An example of such a cell is shown in Fig. IV-7. Effective lengths of 40 meters have been obtained in laboratory-size cells.

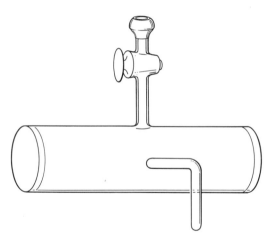

FIG. IV-6. Gas cell. Side arm is sometimes convenient for condensing vapors in filling cell. Ball joint is more easily removed from evacuated system than tapered joint.

4.5 Special Cells

Viscous liquids or strongly absorbing, non-volatile liquids can be placed between two flat plates without a spacer and mounted in a cell frame. Non-volatile liquids which require greater sample thickness may be scanned in the same manner with the addition of a metal spacer. Volatile compounds which must be run as very thin films are best put into a cell such as that shown in Fig. IV-8a. A convenient method for constructing such a cell from sodium chloride has been described by Friedel.[1] A dike of wax or stopcock grease is prepared around the circumference and a drop or two of water or ethanol added to etch a shallow cavity. A second

[1] Friedel and Pelipetz, *J. Opt. Soc. Am.* **43**, 1051 (1953).

dike is made inside the first and a moat is etched around the edge of the cavity. When a volatile sample is placed on the lower plate and an upper plate is added, the central region fills by capillary action from the reservoir in the moat. The outer rims, which are flat, form a tight seal to prevent rapid evaporation.

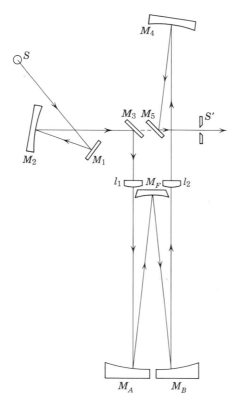

FIG. IV-7. Adjustable long-path gas cell (10 meters). Radiation from spectrometer source, S, strikes mirror M_3 and is multiply reflected between M_A, M_F, and M_B before being deflected by mirror M_5 onto entrance slit, S', of monochromator. (Pilston and White, *J. Opt. Soc. Am.* **44**, 572 (1954).)

Cavity cells (Fig. IV-8*b*),[1] made from a single crystal, are less expensive than conventional fixed-thickness cells. For some laboratories it is more economical to purchase expendable cavity cells than to maintain and repair conventional cells.

Variable path-length liquid cells are commercially available in two basic

[1] R. N. Jones, *Spectrochim. Acta* **12**, 183 (1958). Cavity cells are available from the Connecticut Instrument Corp., Wilton, Conn.

designs.   The simpler one consists of a wedge-shaped cell.   Since the liquid thickness is not uniform in such a cell there will be some distortion of band shapes and relative intensities.   This effect is minimized in practice by keeping the wedge angle small.   A preferable design, though more expensive to construct, consists of concentric tubes which are threaded as a micrometer screw.   As one of the cylinders is turned with respect to the other, the length of the cell will be increased or decreased.   The thickness is read directly from a scale on one of the tubes.   The windows, attached to the outer ends of the cylinders, are kept parallel.

For high-temperature measurements a small, electrically heated "furnace" is constructed into which the cell may be placed.   Glyptal varnish will withstand temperatures of 200 to 250°C.   Mercury amalgams and

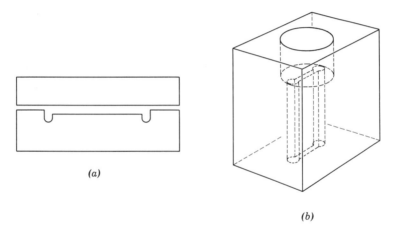

(a)

(b)

FIG. IV-8.   (a) Friedel cell for volatile pure liquids or slurries with volatile solvents. (b) Cavity cell.

stopcocks with low-melting greases should be avoided.   Some cells built for low temperatures are easily adapted to high temperatures by adding a heating coil around the sample cell or by substituting a hot liquid for the coolant.

Measurements to liquid helium temperatures may be carried out with a cell such as that shown in Fig. IV-9.   The space between the sample cell and the external windows is evacuated to provide insulation and avoid condensation of water vapor on the cool windows.   The sample is cooled by conduction through the metal frame which is in good thermal contact with the brass reservoir holding the coolant.   The liquid nitrogen jacket and copper shield greatly reduce the helium consumption.   A filling tube should run to the cell from the outside so that volatile samples can be

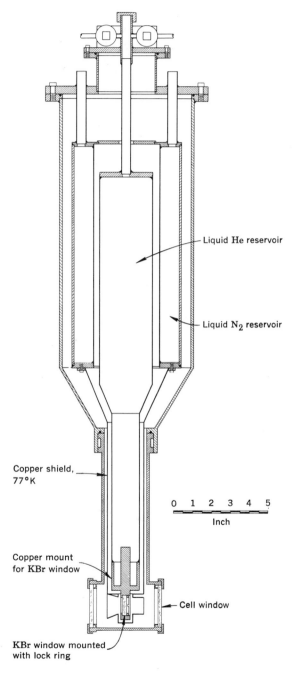

FIG. IV-9.   Cryostat for observation of infrared spectra at liquid He temperature.
(Courtesy H. W. Morgan.)

added after the cell has been evacuated and cooled. The external windows can be attached with Glyptal, since they are not subject to thermal shock, but the cell windows may require more attention, because Glyptal will sometimes crack at low temperatures. In the design shown the sample is deposited on a single KBr window. Directions for the construction of a cell of silver and silver chloride have been given by Lord.[1] Other designs have been described in the literature.[2]

For trace quantities, when the total amount of sample is restricted, it may be necessary to increase the path length of the sample without diluting the material.[3] A long cell of small cross-sectional area can be constructed from glass, metal, or Teflon tubing, with suitable windows attached at each end. The beam must be blocked from passing around the cell. The amount of energy transmitted by a capillary cell of this type will be small compared to the normal energy available but will sometimes be adequate for analytical purposes. The performance can be improved if auxiliary optics are added to condense the beam to a focus at the midpoint of the cell.

Sample cells for Raman spectroscopy are discussed in the following section and in section III-4.

5   Raman

The most desirable sample for Raman spectroscopy is a colorless, pure liquid, free of all dust particles. Solutions are almost as good, since there are many solvents, including water, that have weak Raman spectra or spectra consisting of only a few lines. It is desirable to have concentrations high to obtain adequate intensity from the solute. Excellent spectra have been obtained on gases and solids, but special equipment is desirable, as discussed below.

The intensity of Raman scattering is proportional to the number of molecules in the sample volume. In this respect solids present no particular difficulties. Some of the earliest Raman spectra were obtained on large single crystals. Powders produce Raman spectra that are intrinsically no less intense but are weakened by scattering within the powder. In addition, the scattering of the exciting line is so powerful that stray radiation in the spectrometer makes it difficult, if not impossible, to

[1] Lord, McDonald, and Miller, *J. Opt. Soc. Am.* **42**, 154 (1952).

[2] Wagner and Hornig, *J. Chem. Phys.* **18**, 296 (1950); Duerig and Mador, *Rev. Sci. Instr.* **23**, 421 (1952); Schoen, Kuentzel, and Broida, *ibid.*, **29**, 633 (1958).

[3] See D. S. Erley, *Appl. Spectros.* **15**, 80 (1961); G. R. Bird, *J. Opt. Soc. Am.* **51**, 579 (1961).

observe the Raman lines.   The only solution to this difficulty is to remove the exciting radiation.   This can be done for "resonance" lines, such as the mercury 2537 Å line or the sodium yellow doublet, by placing mercury or sodium vapors in the path of the radiation.   Most lines emitted by gaseous discharges are associated with transitions between two excited states, and the number of atoms or molecules in the lower excited state is so small that no appreciable absorption of the line occurs if the gas is at room temperature.

Narrow band selective filters, interposed between the sample and spectrometer, can decrease the stray radiation to satisfactory levels without serious attenuation of the Raman spectrum.   The best solution, in many respects, although it is also an expensive method, is to eliminate all stray radiation by means of a double monochromator.   By means such as these, good-quality spectra have been obtained from powders.   With such apparatus the effects of microscopic dust particles in liquid samples are also minimized.

Raman scattering from gases is weak because of the low concentration of molecules relative to condensed phases.   The intensity can be increased by as much as a factor of 10 or 20 by means of a multiple reflection cell such as that shown in Fig. III-37.   Two factors can work to the advantage of the experimenter in obtaining gas-phase Raman spectra.   Pure rotational Raman lines are usually much more intense than vibrational transitions.   Also, because the individual lines of a pure rotational or rotation-vibration spectrum are inherently sharp, little or no loss of speed is suffered as the resolution and plate dispersion are increased to the extent required to permit these lines to be seen.   Very few compounds have been adequately investigated with respect to the gas-phase Raman effect; many examples are known of the appearance of lines in the liquid which are believed to be forbidden, but only by examining the Raman spectrum of the vapor under favorable experimental conditions will it be possible to demonstrate the absence of the band for the isolated molecules.

Fluorescence of materials in the Raman tube can greatly increase the difficulty of obtaining good spectra.   The fluorescence radiation cannot be separated from the Raman bands by filters or monochromators, since the frequencies may be identical.   The presence of a strong background of fluorescent radiation may make it difficult to observe weak Raman lines. Improvement is sometimes obtained by the addition of small concentrations of a quenching agent, such as nitrobenzene, potassium iodide, or paraphenylenediamine.   If the fluorescence is due to an impurity, a physical or chemical separation may be possible.

Glass exhibits both weak fluorescence and a Raman spectrum, as well as strong scattering at each surface.   It is therefore advisable to keep the glass portions of the Raman tube shielded from the spectrometer whenever sample size permits.   Continuous background radiation from certain mercury lamps can also interfere strongly with the Raman spectrum. This situation can be improved by interposing filter solutions or gelatin filters between the arc and the sample.   This has the further advantage of removing other mercury lines that could produce weak Raman lines falling

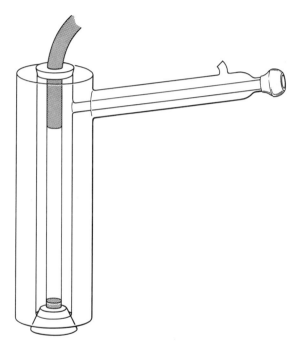

FIG. IV-10.   Simple low-temperature Raman cell.   Cold nitrogen gas flows through delivery tube and around Raman tube.   Gas escaping at bottom provides nitrogen atmosphere that avoids fogging of cell window.   Assembly shown fits inside filter jacket.

in the same region of the spectrum.   It has the disadvantage of reducing the intensity of the exciting line.   The Toronto-style mercury arc seems to be quite free of continuous background.   Certain other arcs, such as the sodium lamp, do not require filters.

Colored samples may tend to absorb, rather than scatter, the exciting line, but even more important is their tendency to absorb the Raman lines as they are produced.   There is a partially compensating effect, since the intensity of Raman scattering increases as an absorption band is approached (section X-3.4). Lippincott[1] has shown that for each colored sample and choice of exciting line there is an optimum concentration of sample for obtaining Raman spectra. Whenever possible, it is desirable to choose an exciting line at lower frequencies than the absorption band of the sample.

Although there are strong theoretical reasons for preferring to obtain Raman spectra on gases, there are strong practical reasons, as indicated above, for working with liquids. Substances that condense below room temperature can be examined as liquids by cooling the Raman tube with a stream of cold nitrogen gas inside an unsilvered Dewar flask. Figure IV-10 shows one type of apparatus that has been found suitable for moderately low temperatures (to about $-60°$ or $-80°C$ or perhaps somewhat lower). Nitrogen gas is precooled by bubbling through liquid nitrogen or passing through a copper coil immersed in liquid nitrogen. The cool gas passes over the Raman tube and leaks out at the bottom, providing a blanket of dry nitrogen that prevents deposition of water on the cold cell window.

[1] Lippincott, Sibilia, and Fisher, *J. Opt. Soc. Am.* **49,** 83 (1959); see also Vratny and Fischer, *Appl. Spectros.* **14,** 76 (1960).

V

Theoretical foundations

Spectroscopy is the observation of transitions between energy levels in molecules or atoms. From the energy of the transition (the energy of the photon absorbed or emitted) the difference in energy between states of the molecule is determined. Interpretation of a spectrum, either for the identification of the absorbing molecules or for determination of the properties of a known molecule, requires some understanding of these various states.

The energy of a molecule may be considered to arise from four sources: translational energy, rotational energy, vibrational energy, and electronic energy. Of these, the translational energy will be consistently ignored.[1] Rotational and vibrational energy may be treated in many respects by the methods of classical mechanics, although some results from quantum mechanics must be applied. The electronic energy must be treated almost exclusively by the methods of quantum mechanics except for certain very qualitative aspects. It will be assumed that the reader is unfamiliar with quantum mechanics and only moderately familiar with classical mechanics. The portions of these subjects that are required are summarized in this chapter.

1 Classical Mechanics

According to the classical picture, both the internal motions of molecules and the electromagnetic radiation that is absorbed or emitted are periodic in nature. The study of periodic motion is therefore of great importance. It will be seen in section 2 that the frequencies calculated in this section are related to the energies of the states when the rules of quantum mechanics are taken into consideration.

[1] See, for example, Wilson, Decius, and Cross, ref. 48, p. 40.

1.1   Simple Harmonic Motion

The periodic motion of interest is a particularly simple, and common, type known as simple harmonic motion. Imagine a wheel with a single handle revolving at uniform speed (Fig. V-1). The shadow cast by this handle when the sun is overhead will move back and forth, not at a uniform speed but rapidly through the midpoint and slowly near the ends of the motion. The movement of the shadow is called "simple harmonic" motion.

The ends of a tuning fork will undergo simple harmonic oscillations, as will a simple pendulum (for small oscillations), a mass on a spring, and

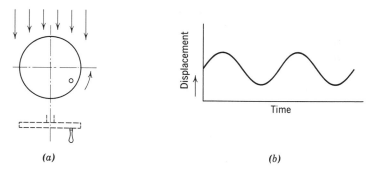

(a)   (b)

FIG. V-1.   Motion of a shadow cast by the handle of a wheel rotating at uniform speed is an example of simple harmonic, or sinusoidal, motion.

many other physical systems when they are only slightly displaced from equilibrium. If a pen is attached to the end of a tuning fork and a strip of paper drawn past at uniform speed, the resultant tracing, which gives the displacement as a function of time, will be a sine or cosine curve. Exactly the same type of curve, displaced slightly along the time axis, will be obtained if the velocity of the end of the fork is plotted against time, or if the acceleration of the end of the fork is plotted against time. This was discussed in section II-2.1 in connection with the interaction of vibrating charges with electromagnetic radiation. It follows from the fact that the derivative of a sine (or cosine) is a cosine (or sine) and the second derivative again gives a sine (or cosine).

The classical problems of a mass on a spring and a vibrating string will be treated below. In addition, the rigid rotor and certain properties of angular momentum will be treated, from classical as well as quantum mechanical viewpoints, in sections 2 and 3.

1.2 Mass on Spring

The linear extension of a spring is proportional to the force exerted, as shown by the fact that a spring balance has a linear scale. This means, in turn, that the restoring force exerted by the spring will be proportional to the distance it has been stretched. This is Hooke's law.

$$f = -kx \qquad\qquad (V\text{-}1)$$

where x is the distance the spring has been stretched, f is the restoring force, and k is the force constant of the spring.

Consider a mass, m, attached to one end of the spring, the other end of which is fastened to a fixed point (Fig. V-2). The force of gravity is constant and can be ignored, since it will only influence the equilibrium point

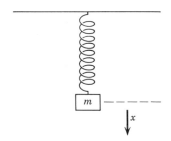

FIG. V-2. The displacement from equilibrium, x, of a mass m attached by a spring to a rigid support is sinusoidal with time.

and not the motions of the mass about this equilibrium position. (Alternatively the mass could be allowed to slide in a frictionless horizontal track.) The displacement of the mass from equilibrium is represented by x, the velocity by $\dot{x} \equiv dx/dt$, the acceleration by $\ddot{x} \equiv d^2x/dt^2$. Setting force equal to mass times acceleration gives

$$-kx = m\ddot{x} \qquad\qquad (V\text{-}2)$$

As the solution is known to be periodic, a reasonable trial solution will be

$$x = A \cos (bt + c) \qquad\qquad (V\text{-}3)$$

Substitution of this trial solution into equation (V-2) gives the equation

$$-kA \cos (bt + c) = -mb^2A \cos (bt + c) \qquad\qquad (V\text{-}4)$$

from which it is clear that V-3 is a suitable solution if, and only if,

$$b^2 = k/m \qquad\qquad (V\text{-}5)$$

After one period of the motion, x will return to its initial value; the cosine will repeat each time the argument $(bt + c)$ is increased by 2π. If τ is the period and ν the frequency of oscillation,

$$b(t_0 + \tau) + c = bt_0 + 2\pi + c$$

$$\tau \equiv \frac{1}{\nu} = \frac{1}{b} 2\pi \qquad \text{(V-6)}$$

$$\nu = \frac{1}{2\pi}\sqrt{\frac{k}{m}}$$

Taking b as the positive square root of k/m is equivalent to letting time move in only one direction. Equations V-5 and V-6 can be inserted into equation V-3 to make this

$$x = A \cos(2\pi\nu t + c) \qquad \text{(V-7)}$$

where A is the maximum amplitude of the motion and c is a constant that is determined by the choice of zero time. The constant c, called a phase factor, will frequently be omitted since it has no particular importance and does not influence the other equations that are commonly derived from equation V-7.

Equation V-7 is a satisfactory solution to equation V-2 but not a unique one—for example, a sine function or a sum of sine and cosine functions would work as well.[1] Equation V-6 is, however, a unique consequence of equation V-2 and is a result that will be applied many times in the chapters that follow.

The energy of the classical mass and spring is constantly undergoing conversion between potential energy and kinetic energy. At the midpoint, as the mass passes through its equilibrium position, the potential energy is zero and the total energy is equal to the kinetic energy; at the turning points of the motion the kinetic energy is zero and the total energy is equal to the potential energy. From the latter condition the total energy may easily be shown to be $\frac{1}{2}kA^2$.

Two masses, m_1 and m_2, attached by a spring of force constant k, will undergo simple harmonic motion. The restoring force is proportional to the total distention of the spring, hence to the sum of the displacements of the masses. This restoring force is equal to the inertial force, mass times acceleration, for *each* mass. Solving the equations of motion in much the same way as before, this leads to the equation

$$\nu = \frac{1}{2\pi}\sqrt{k\left(\frac{1}{m_1} + \frac{1}{m_2}\right)} \qquad \text{(V-8)}$$

[1] The general solutions to V-2 are $x = A \cos(\omega t + c)$ or $x = A \cos \omega t + B \sin \omega t$, where $\omega \equiv 2\pi\nu$. Setting $c = 0$ and setting $B = 0$ are thus equivalent.

which may be abbreviated to the form

$$\nu = \frac{1}{2\pi} \sqrt{\frac{k}{\mu}} \qquad \text{(V-9)}$$

by defining the "reduced mass," μ, such that

$$\frac{1}{\mu} = \frac{1}{m_1} + \frac{1}{m_2} \qquad \text{(V-10)}$$

Systems containing more than two masses will follow similar, though more complex, equations. In particular, the frequency of any motion will be increased (or left unchanged, as a limiting case) if any of the force constants in the system is increased, and the frequency of any motion will be decreased (or left unchanged) if any of the masses is increased.[1]

The derivation of equations V-6, V-7, and V-8 assumed that there were no forces acting on the mass other than the Hooke's law restoring force (and constant forces, such as gravity). In particular it was assumed that there was no friction or other damping force, so that Hooke's law applied exactly. In practice, damping forces play an important role, as mentioned in section II-2.1. Any deviations from Hooke's law cause some "anharmonicity." The presence of these forces does not, however, invalidate equation V-6 for small oscillations, since the frequency of the motion is relatively insensitive to such forces.[2] Only for large amplitudes of vibration will correction terms become important.

If forces giving rise to anharmonicity are considered, it is found that the motion can no longer be described by the single "fundamental" frequency given by equation V-6. It is necessary to include also multiples of this frequency, or "overtones." Equation V-7 then becomes

$$\begin{aligned}
x &= A_1 \cos{(2\pi\nu t + c_1)} + A_2 \cos{(4\pi\nu t + c_2)} \\
&\quad + A_3 \cos{(6\pi\nu t + c_3)} + \cdots \\
&= \sum_{n=1}^{\infty} A_n \cos{(2\pi n\nu t + c_n)} \qquad \text{(V-7a)}
\end{aligned}$$

If the anharmonicity is small, as it must be for small oscillations, $A_1 \gg A_2 \gg A_3 \gg \cdots$. For larger systems with more than one fundamental frequency, combination frequencies must also be included as a consequence of anharmonicity. It should be kept in mind, however, that, so long as the vibrations are harmonic, each independent oscillator can vibrate with only one frequency, its fundamental frequency. The number of independent oscillators, and hence the maximum number of

---

[1] Rayleigh, ref. 28, pp. 110–111.
[2] See Rayleigh, ref. 28, p. 46.

fundamental frequencies, will be $3N - 6$ for a non-linear molecule of N atoms (section VII-1).

1.3 Vibrating String

An important problem of classical mechanics is the transverse vibration of a stretched string. It will be adequate for present purposes to make the usual simplifying assumptions: that the string is uniform, the tension on the string is great enough that it will not be appreciably increased by the vibrational motion, and the displacement of small amplitude and a smooth function of position.

Consider a small segment of the string. The only forces acting on this segment are exerted by the adjacent segments and thus may be represented by vectors of equal length directed outward from the

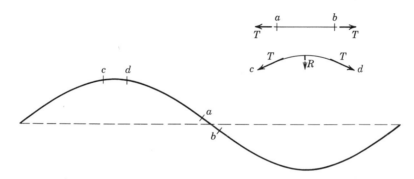

FIG. V-3.   Net force on string segments is proportional to the curvature, or the second derivative of the displacement with respect to position.   It vanishes for the straight segment a–b but is non-zero for the segment c–d and perpendicular to the segment.

ends of the segment (Fig. V-3). If the segment is linear, the vector sum of the forces will be zero; only if the segment is curved will there be a net force, and it will be in such a direction as to tend to straighten the segment. The resultant force on any segment will be proportional to the curvature and proportional to the tension.

Let the displacement of any point of the string be given by y, the position of the point along the string by x, the tension by T, and the mass of the string, per unit length, by δ. The curvature at any point is d^2y/dx^2, and the acceleration of the point, necessarily perpendicular to the equilibrium axis, is d^2y/dt^2. Setting force equal to mass times acceleration gives the equation

$$T\frac{d^2y}{dx^2} = \delta\frac{d^2y}{dt^2}$$

or

$$v^2 \frac{d^2y}{dx^2} = \frac{d^2y}{dt^2} \tag{V-11}$$

where

$$v^2 = \frac{T}{\delta} \tag{V-12}$$

The displacement, y, will be expected to vary with position, x, and time, t, in a periodic manner.   A trial solution of the form

$$y = A \sin (ax + bt + c) \tag{V-13}$$

is suggested, where A, a, b, and c are to be determined.   Substitution of this trial solution into equation V-11 produces the equation

$$v^2a^2y = b^2y$$

and thus

$$y = A \sin a(x \pm vt + c') \tag{V-14}$$

The displacement will be constant if $x = \mp vt - c'$, or for a particular value of the displacement $dx/dt = \mp v$.   The constant v is therefore the velocity of a wave moving along the string.   The constant $c'(ac' \equiv c)$ is a phase factor, of no immediate importance, A is the maximum amplitude of a wave, and the constant a is yet to be determined.

In order to exert tension on the string it must be fixed at both ends.[1] At these points, $x = 0$ and $x = L$, the displacement will always be zero. This provides two "boundary conditions" which serve to fix two of the constants in the solution.

Setting $x = 0$ gives the condition

$$y = A \sin a(\pm vt + c') = 0$$

and therefore

$$\pm vt + c' = \frac{n\pi}{a}$$

where n is an integer.   Insertion of this result into equation V-14 puts this into the form

$$y = A \sin (ax + n\pi)$$

Setting $x = L$,

$$y = A \sin (aL + n\pi) = 0$$

and therefore

$$aL + n\pi = n'\pi$$

or

$$a = \frac{n\pi}{L}$$

[1] This restriction does not, of course, apply to all wave motions.

(Since n and n' are arbitrary integers, the difference between them may be represented by the same symbol n.)   The solution has now been put into the form

$$y = A \sin \frac{n\pi x}{L} \tag{V-15}$$

It will be observed that equation V-15 no longer explicitly contains the time.   It cannot, therefore, be a satisfactory solution of the original wave equation, V-11, unless $v = 0$ (no tension) or unless A depends on the time. Assuming the latter, insertion of equation V-15 into equation V-11 gives the condition

$$\ddot{A}(t) = -\left(\frac{n\pi v}{L}\right)^2 A(t)$$

This will be satisfied if the function $A(t)$ is of the form

$$A(t) = A \cos\left(\frac{v n\pi t}{L} + \phi\right)$$

The complete solution to the problem of the vibrating string may therefore be written

$$y = A \sin \frac{n\pi x}{L} \cos\left(\frac{v n\pi t}{L} + \phi\right) \tag{V-16}$$

or as a sum of such terms with various values of the integer n.   The constant A is the maximum amplitude and ϕ is a phase angle.

Equation V-16 represents a "standing wave," confined by the boundaries of the string, as contrasted with the "traveling wave" of equation V-14. Each point along the string will oscillate with a maximum amplitude given by $A \sin(n\pi x/L)$.   For certain points, for which nx/L is integral, the maximum amplitude will be zero; these are the "nodes."   The factor $\cos[(v n\pi t/L) + \phi]$ determines what fraction of its maximum amplitude any point on the string will have at a given time.   That is, a point at a distance x along the string will undergo simple harmonic oscillations with a maximum amplitude of $A \sin(n\pi x/L)$ and with a frequency $nv/2L$ or $(n/2L)\sqrt{T/\delta}$.   The value of the integer n depends, in practice, on the manner in which the string is set into oscillation.   The form of the vibration for several small values of n is shown in Fig. V-4.

An alternative method of finding the solution of equation V-11 provides some insight into the significance of some of the terms in the solution as well as certain applications of the solution.   Equation V-14, $y = A \sin a(x \pm vt + c')$, describes a wave train traveling along the string with a velocity of $\mp v$ in the positive x direction.   If such a wave train strikes a perfect reflector, it will be reflected backward to produce a wave train obeying the equation $y = A \sin a(x \mp vt + c'')$, the value of c'' depending on the position of the reflector as well as the value of c'. It is convenient to choose initial conditions such that $c' = c'' = 0$. The resultant motion is the sum of the two motions.

$$y = y_1 + y_2 = A \sin a(x + vt) + A \sin a(x - vt)$$

$$= 2A \sin (ax) \cos (avt) \qquad\qquad (V\text{-}17)$$

This is of the same form as equation V-16; the condition that $a = n\pi/L$ must be applied to equation V-17 if the string is fastened at $x = 0$ and $x = L$ (or if the wavelength was originally $L/n\pi$) and the replacement of A by $2A$ is trivial since the amplitude has been treated as arbitrary. A

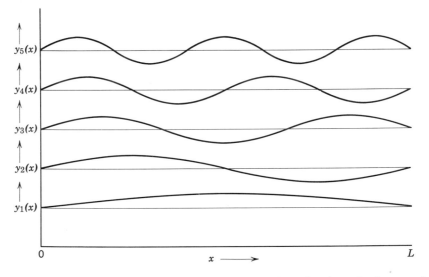

FIG. V-4. Amplitude of motion, $y_n(x)$, against position for a vibrating string for several values of the integer n.

standing wave may thus be considered as arising from the reflection of a traveling wave train.

The physical significance of the treatment of the last paragraph is shown by the fact that standing waves are produced when light waves are reflected. If a photographic film is placed in intimate contact with a reflecting surface and illuminated with collimated monochromatic radiation, nodes will occur at the reflecting surface and at integral multiples of the wavelength away from this surface. Since the intensity at these nodes is zero at all times, there can be no possibility of photochemical action along these planes and the film shows alternate layers of clear film and deposited silver.[1]

For present purposes one of the most important characteristics of the solutions to the wave equation is the appearance of the integers, n. They occur naturally as a consequence of the boundary conditions. This is typical of problems involving differential equations and many examples of integral parameters are met in spectroscopy. These integers are called "characteristic values" or "eigenvalues" (German *eigenwert*).

The distinction between the appearance of overtone frequencies (values of n greater than 1) in this problem and in the problem of the mass on a spring is important. As shown by equation V-7a, frequencies that are multiples of the fundamental vibrational frequency enter into the motion of the mass on a spring only as a consequence of anharmonicity. They represent minor mathematical corrections to the motion, never appearing by themselves as the dominant term. The vibrating string, by contrast, exhibits terms containing the higher frequencies within the approximation of simple harmonic motion. The actual motion may be accurately described, in principle, by any one of the infinite number of frequencies $n(v/2L)$, or by any linear combination of these, depending on how the string is struck, plucked, or bowed.

The cause of this difference is a basic property of mechanical systems. The number of "degrees of freedom" is the number of coordinates required to describe the system.[2] The number of frequencies of oscillation possible for any system of N degrees of freedom (momentum coordinates) is just N. The mass on a spring has only one degree of freedom and one fundamental frequency. The vibrating string consists of an infinite number of masses, thus permitting oscillation with any of an infinite number of frequencies.[3]

Equation V-11 can be extended to problems involving wave motion in three-dimensional space by the addition of terms involving the other coordinates. Designating the amplitude of the three-dimensional wave by Ψ, the equation becomes

$$\frac{\partial^2 \Psi}{\partial x^2} + \frac{\partial^2 \Psi}{\partial^2 y} + \frac{\partial^2 \Psi}{\partial z^2} = \frac{1}{v^2} \cdot \frac{\partial^2 \Psi}{\partial t^2} \qquad \text{(V-18)}$$

[1] For a more detailed description see Wood, ref. 18, p. 211.

[2] Sometimes the term refers to the sum of position and momentum coordinates (for example, in calculating classical specific heats the contribution of $\frac{1}{2}R$ is summed over all degrees of freedom that enter the expression for total energy in a quadratic form); more often the term is taken to mean only the number of position coordinates, or the equivalent number of momentum coordinates.

[3] See Rayleigh, ref. 28, pp. 53–55, 172–176.

This can be abbreviated by replacing the differential operators $\partial^2/\partial x^2 + \partial^2/\partial y^2 + \partial^2/\partial z^2$ by the symbol ∇^2 to give the form

$$\nabla^2 \Psi = \frac{1}{v^2} \cdot \frac{\partial^2}{\partial t^2} \Psi \qquad \text{(V-18}a\text{)}$$

This equation is applicable to vibrations of material bodies and also to electromagnetic radiation.

1.4 Virial Theorem and Equipartition Principle

Certain principles of mechanics are completely independent of the nature of the forces acting within a system. This is true, for example, of such laws as the conservation of energy. Other generalizations can be drawn that are less broad but may nevertheless be useful because they apply to all systems for which the form of interaction is known, even though the problems may be much too complex for an exact solution. The virial theorem and the equipartition principle fall into the second category.

Assume that all interactions between the particles of a system can be written in terms of a potential function, v, that is a homogeneous function of degree n in the coordinates. Then a relationship exists between the time-average values of the kinetic and potential energies of the system. Specifically, the virial theorem states that

$$\bar{T} = (n/2)\bar{v} \qquad \text{(V-19)}$$

Two examples are of particular interest. For the harmonic oscillator the potential function is of the form $\sum_{i,j} \tfrac{1}{2}k_{ij}x_i x_j$, which is homogeneous and of degree 2. For such a system, therefore, the average values of the kinetic and potential energies are equal: $\bar{T} = \bar{v}$. For coulombic forces the potential function is of the form $\sum_{i>j} \frac{q_i q_j}{r_{ij}}$ so that $n = -1$ and the virial theorem requires that $\bar{T} = -\tfrac{1}{2}\bar{v}$.

In every case the total energy is $E = T + v = \bar{T} + \bar{v}$. For the harmonic oscillator the total energy is one half the average value of the kinetic or potential energies; for coulombic fields the total energy is equal and opposite to the average kinetic energy, or equal to one half the average potential energy. The virial theorem is as applicable in quantum mechanics as in classical mechanics.[1]

---

[1] For more general statements of the virial theorem of Clausius and variations on it see Corben and Stehle, ref. 25, p. 202, or Goldstein, ref. 26, p. 69. Application of the virial theorem to quantum mechanics is discussed, for example, by Kauzmann, ref. 31, p. 229.

Quadratic dependence of energy on coordinates is common to many types of motions.   It applies to translational energy in an ideal gas ($\frac{1}{2}mv_x{}^2$), to rotational energy ($\frac{1}{2}I_a\omega_a{}^2$), and to the kinetic and potential energies of a harmonic oscillator.   Assume that the energy can be written in the form $E = E_0 + \sum_i a_i s_i{}^2$, where the coordinates s_i are continuous in the interval $-\infty$ to $+\infty$ with equal *a priori* probability for all values, so that the probability of s_i falling in the interval s_i to $s_i + ds_i$ is proportional to the size of the interval, ds_i.   Then it follows that the average value of the energy in the degree of freedom described by s_i will be $\frac{1}{2}a_i\overline{s_i^2} = \frac{1}{2}kT$. This is the law of equipartition of energy in its usual form.   It says, for example, that the average translational energy of a gas along any axis will be $\frac{1}{2}kT$, or the total kinetic energy will be $\frac{3}{2}kT$ per molecule or $\frac{3}{2}RT$ per mole. The average rotational energy about any axis, the average kinetic energy of any mode of vibration, or the average potential energy of any mode of vibration will similarly be $\frac{1}{2}kT$ according to classical theory.

The law of equipartition as stated is a special case of a more general result that can be expressed in the form

$$\overline{\left(q_i \frac{\partial E}{\partial q_i}\right)} = kT$$

Unlike the virial theorem, the law of equipartition breaks down when the quantization of energy levels becomes important.   The dependence of specific heats on temperature arises from this quantum effect and is one of the very few consequences of quantum mechanics that can be directly observed on a macroscopic scale.

2   Quantum Mechanics

Classical mechanics provides an extremely accurate and self-consistent description of the behavior of nearly all physical systems of "ordinary" size.   In certain extreme cases, particularly for very high speeds, it is necessary to modify the rules of Newtonian mechanics according to the principle of relativity, but the resultant system is still described as classical mechanics.   There are, however, certain phenomena involving radiation or very small particles that cannot be described by the laws of classical mechanics.   Quantum mechanics provides a self-consistent set of rules for describing these systems.   The modification of quantum mechanics to include relativistic effects has not yet been entirely successful, but this will not cause any difficulties in the problems of interest.

Quantum mechanics is often considered to be a more general formulation than classical mechanics; in this view classical mechanics becomes only a special case of quantum mechanics. A more convenient, and more easily defensible, approach considers classical mechanics as a complete description of all systems, except that it must be modified from its historical form (in order to achieve consistency with itself) in certain respects that are of importance almost exclusively for very small systems. In particular, it should be emphasized that most of the laws and methods applied to small systems, as well as large, are laws of classical mechanics. In quantum mechanics there is involved a certain amount of mathematical reformulation but much more there is involved a new appreciation of the importance of careful interpretation of calculated values for small systems.

2.1   Uncertainty Principle[1]

Any measurement on a system represents an interaction between the system and the measuring instrument. Applying Newton's third law, the action of the measuring device on the system will always be equal to the action of the system on the device. This does not present any real problem if one attempts to measure the position of a book; the momentum transfer from a photon to the book upon reflection will not cause a detectable displacement of the book. The same photon, if it could be reflected off an electron, would transfer the same amount of momentum to the electron, and this would cause a noticeable change in the momentum of the electron. The change in the momentum produced $(\overrightarrow{\Delta p})$ will be indeterminate since the exact angle of collision is unknown, but it will have a maximum value that will increase as the size of the photon (the wavelength) is decreased. This does not limit the accuracy with which the position of the electron can be determined, since arbitrarily small photons can be selected to act as the probe; nor does it limit the accuracy with which the momentum, or velocity, can be determined—in principle electrons can be sorted according to momenta to any desired degree of accuracy by constructing a sufficiently large and homogeneous magnetic field. The real limitation appears when position and momentum are to be measured simultaneously. Any measurement of position must make the momentum somewhat uncertain, and any measurement of momentum necessarily makes the position somewhat uncertain.

Consider, for example, the process of defining the position of an electron by means of a narrow slit. Clearly, if the electron gets through the slit the position has been defined, at some time, to a tolerance equal to the dimensions of the slit. For large slit widths the electrons will appear to pass through the slit undisturbed and strike a detector placed along the

[1] See especially Heisenberg, ref. 30, and Bohm, ref. 29.

line of flight. As the slit becomes more and more narrow, a high percentage of those electrons which pass through the slit will miss the detector placed along the straight-line path, but will show up in adjacent regions of space. This effect is known as diffraction; the relative number of electrons striking any point behind the slit may be quantitatively calculated by assuming the electrons to follow the diffraction pattern of waves.

No general agreement has been reached concerning the fundamental interpretation of this uncertainty.[1] For present purposes it will be quite sufficient to observe that theories which are to be checked by experiment must predict the same results that the measurements will give. If the measurements are necessarily subject to an inherent uncertainty, the theories must incorporate this uncertainty at some point, whether it has "fundamental" significance or not (that is, whether or not there may some day be a way of circumventing the experimental limitation).

Stated more quantitatively, the theory must predict that any experiment will give an uncertainty in measurement of position, Δx, and an uncertainty in measurement of momentum, Δp, which are related by the condition[2]

$$\Delta p \cdot \Delta x \geqslant \tfrac{1}{2}\hbar \qquad\qquad \text{(V-20)}$$

where $\hbar$ is Planck's constant, 6.6×10^{-27} erg sec, divided by 2π. This is the uncertainty principle due to Heisenberg.

2.2 Schroedinger Equation

It can be readily shown[3] that a sufficient condition for an uncertainty relation of the type $\Delta A \cdot \Delta B \geqslant \gamma/2$ is that A and B shall not commute. That is, $AB \neq BA$ or, more specifically,

$$AB - BA = i\gamma \qquad\qquad \text{(V-21)}$$

This seems like a strange type of quantity, for we are accustomed to commutative algebra. There are, however, at least two reasonably common examples of non-commutative quantities which may serve to make theory correspond with experiment. One example is matrices (see Appendix I); the other, which is more familiar to most chemists and physicists, is an operator such as d/dx, for quite clearly $(d/dx)\mathbf{x} f(x) \neq \mathbf{x} (d/dx) f(x)$.

---

[1] Compare, for example, D. Bohm, *Causality and Chance in Modern Physics*, D. Van Nostrand Co., Inc., Princeton, N.J., 1957; *Phys. Rev.* **85**, 166, 180 (1952); with H. Margenau, *The Nature of Physical Reality*, McGraw-Hill Book Co., Inc., New York, 1950. Also A. Landé, *American Scientist* **47**, 341 (1959), and N. R. Hanson, *Am. J. Phys.* **27**, 1 (1959).

[2] The quantities Δx and Δp are to be taken as the root-mean-square deviations from the mean value, or expectation value.

[3] See, for example, Schiff, ref. 33, pp. 54–55.

Heisenberg developed a satisfactory theory by letting position and momentum variables be represented by matrix operators; Schroedinger developed an equally satisfactory theory by means of differential operators. Very shortly thereafter Schroedinger was able to show that Heisenberg's matrix mechanics and his own wave mechanics were simply different ways of representing the same equations.

Schroedinger represented the momentum, p, by the operator $i\hbar\, \partial/\partial x$ and let the position be represented by the operator $\mathbf{x}$. (The discussion of the significance of this choice will be left to textbooks on quantum mechanics.) From the condition kinetic energy + potential energy = total energy, and letting kinetic energy = $\frac{1}{2}m\dot{x}^2 = p^2/2m$, the classical equation $p^2/2m + \mathrm{v} = \mathrm{E}$ goes over to the quantum mechanical equation

$$\frac{-\hbar^2}{2m}\frac{\partial^2}{\partial x^2}\Psi + \mathrm{v}\Psi = \mathrm{E}\Psi \tag{V-22}$$

The total energy, E, is represented by the operator $-i\hbar\, \partial/\partial t$. With this substitution, and extending the equation to three dimensions, the Schroedinger equation becomes

$$\frac{-\hbar^2}{2m}\nabla^2\Psi + \mathrm{v}\Psi = -i\hbar\frac{\partial}{\partial t}\Psi \tag{V-22a}$$

The similarity of this equation to the wave equation, equation V-18, should be apparent. The solutions of this equation, also, may be periodic in nature, the exact form depending on the potential energy term, which describes the particular physical problem. There are, however, some distinct differences that should be kept in mind to prevent too close an association between these two equations.

In the first place, whereas equation V-18 is of second degree in time, the Schroedinger wave equation, V-22a, is of the first degree in time. This is important, for it means that, if we know the state (position and momentum coordinates) at any time, we may find the state at any later time. If the equation were of second degree in the time, it would be necessary to know the state and the time rate of change of state in order to predict the state at a later time; there would be too many arbitrary constants.[1] Equation V-22a with real coefficients is not a wave equation at all, but describes a diffusion process such as the diffusion of heat through a body. The imaginary coefficients cause the solutions to be complex (that is, the solutions may involve $\sqrt{-1}$) and take on a periodic nature for certain boundary conditions.

The second important distinction arises in the assignment of meanings to the separate terms. It will be recalled that the wave equation for the

[1] Although this could be avoided for some choices of functions and their interpretation, it can be shown that these are no more satisfactory. See Bohm, ref. 29, pp. 84–88.

vibrating string arose from the condition that $f = m\ddot{x}$, with the force given by $T\, \partial^2/\partial x^2\, y$ and the acceleration given by $\partial^2/\partial t^2\, y$.   In the Schroedinger equation the term of the form $c_1\, \partial^2/\partial x^2\, \Psi$ represents the kinetic energy, $\frac{1}{2}m\dot{x}^2$, and the potential energy term, which is related to the force, is specified by the quantity v.   There is quite obviously not a close correspondence between the individual terms of these two equations and the solutions will not necessarily be similar.   In both cases, however, arbitrary integers, or eigenvalues, will arise from the introduction of boundary conditions. These eigenvalues will specify the form of the motion, or the state of the system.   The state of the system is completely described by the function y or Ψ, including the appropriate eigenvalues.

The equations of quantum mechanics, as well as many of the interpretations of physical phenomena on the submicroscopic level, seem to be very different from classical mechanics, with which we are much more familiar. In terms of the numerical answers that may be calculated, however, one find that only in extreme cases (primarily for very small systems) are the differences appreciable.   Actually, this could be readily anticipated, since science is by nature a correlation of experimental observations.   If classical mechanics had not correctly described the results of nearly all the events that we can observe, it could not have been maintained as such a very important part of our fundamental description of the universe.   The most significant deviation from classical mechanics that will be encountered is associated with the very heart of quantum mechanics, specifically the "quantization" of states, or the introduction of integers, or eigenvalues, into physical problems in which they would not be expected to appear by classical mechanics.

Three problems of particular interest are the translation, vibration, and rotation of physical bodies.   These are examined from the viewpoint of quantum mechanics in the following three sections.

2.3   Particle in a Box

A particle placed in a box from which it cannot escape, with no forces acting on it except upon collision with the walls, would be expected, classically, to spend as much time in any one small region as in any other. That is, every volume element would be equally probable or equally accessible.   Nor is there any reason to restrict the possible energy, or momentum, values of the particle to any particular value or set of values.

It is known, however, that particles act in some ways like waves, with a wavelength given by the de Broglie relationship

$$\lambda = h/p \qquad\qquad \text{(V-23)}$$

One of the interpretations associated with the de Broglie equation is that the probability of finding the particle in any given region of space is determined by the amplitude of the wave in that region. Since the particle cannot enter, or pass through, the walls of the box, the amplitude of the wave must be zero at each wall (Fig. V-5). The length of the box must accordingly be an integral multiple of the half wavelength of the particle.

$$2L = n\lambda = nh/p = nh/\sqrt{2m\mathrm{E}}$$

or

$$\mathrm{E} = \frac{h^2}{8m}\frac{n^2}{L^2} \tag{V-24}$$

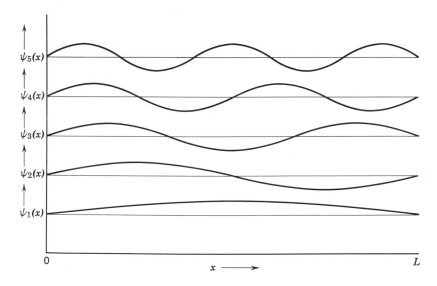

FIG. V-5. Amplitude of the wave function, $\Psi_n(x)$, plotted against position, x, for several of the lowest-energy states of a particle in a box. (Cf. Fig. V-4.) The particle density, or probability of finding the particle, is proportional to the square of the function shown.

For a three-dimensional box, with sides of lengths a, b, and c, the energy is similarly restricted to the values

$$\mathrm{E} = (h^2/8m)(n_a^2/a^2 + n_b^2/b^2 + n_c^2/c^2) \tag{V-25}$$

where n_a, n_b, and n_c are integers.

Because of the term h^2/m, as well as the factors $1/a^2$, $1/b^2$, and $1/c^2$, the energy levels will nearly always be extremely close together, so that they may be regarded as forming a continuum. This will always be true, for example, for molecules of a gas in a closed vessel. As the mass becomes very small, as it does for an electron, and the dimensions become small—comparable to molecular dimensions—the energy levels can become quite widely spaced.   Equations V-24 and V-25 have been applied with remarkable success to some problems involving electrons traveling in relatively uniform electrical fields within large molecules.

2.4   Harmonic Oscillator

The potential energy for a harmonic oscillator is a quadratic function of displacement from equilibrium.

$$V = \int_0^x f \, dx = \int_0^x \hbar x \, dx = \tfrac{1}{2}\hbar x^2 \tag{V-26}$$

The solution of the Schroedinger equation for the harmonic oscillator (equation V-22 plus equation V-26),

$$-\frac{\hbar^2}{2m} \nabla^2 \Psi + \tfrac{1}{2} \hbar x^2 \Psi = E\Psi \tag{V-27}$$

bears no resemblance to the classical solutions, equations V-6 and V-7. For example, in the lowest of the discrete energy states, the amplitude, or wave function, is given by

$$\Psi_0 = \left(\frac{\alpha}{\pi}\right)^{\frac{1}{4}} \exp\left(-\alpha x^2/2\right) \exp\left(iE_0 t/\hbar\right)$$

and for the next state

$$\Psi_1 = \left(\frac{4\alpha^3}{\pi}\right)^{\frac{1}{4}} x \exp\left(-\alpha x^2/2\right) \exp\left(iE_1 t/\hbar\right)$$

where $\alpha = m\hbar/\hbar_2$.   The energy of the oscillator can take on only the values

$$E = (v + \tfrac{1}{2})\hbar\sqrt{\hbar/m} \tag{V-28}$$

with integral values of v.

An apparent agreement between the classical and quantum results[1] is to be found if the wave function, or the square of the wave function, is plotted against the displacement, x, as shown in Fig. V-6.   The lowest energy state of the quantized oscillator resembles the lowest energy state of the classical oscillator except that, as might be expected from the requirements of the uncertainty principle, the position is uncertain by a small amount.   The energy of this state is accordingly not zero but $\tfrac{1}{2}\hbar\sqrt{\hbar/m}$.   The first excited state of the quantized oscillator bears a

[1] See also S. T. Epstein, *Am. J. Phys.* **27**, 291 (1959).

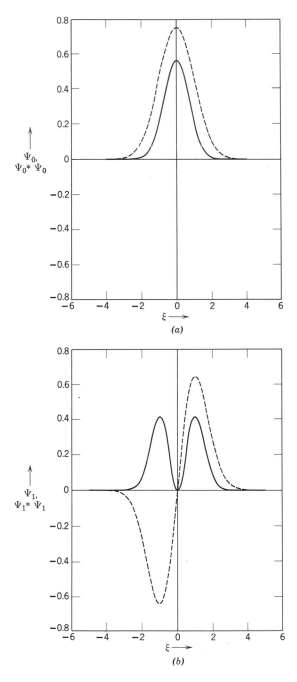

FIG. V-6. Harmonic oscillator wave functions. (a) $v = 0$. (b) $v = 1$. Dotted line represents ψ, solid line represents $\psi^*\psi$. Ordinate is in units of $\alpha^{1/4}$ (for ψ) or $\alpha^{1/2}$ (for $\psi^*\psi$); abscissa is in units of $\alpha^{1/2}x$.

220

significant resemblance to the excited classical oscillator. The wave function of the quantized oscillator changes sign at the midpoint and each part changes sign with a frequency given by E/h, which would seem to correlate with the classical picture of oscillation back and forth from one side to the other. It is the value of $\int_{x_1}^{x_2} \Psi^* \Psi\, dx$ that gives the probability of finding the oscillator with a displacement between x_1 and x_2. This value is always symmetrical with respect to the midpoint, as would be expected from the symmetry of the physical problem.

The analogies drawn in the preceding paragraph between the quantized oscillator and the classical oscillator are at best somewhat questionable. Since it is impossible to make successive measurements of position without disturbing the motion, it is inherently impossible to show that the oscillator goes back and forth from one side to the other, or to determine a frequency for such motion if it does exist. Furthermore, the simple analogy appears to break down rather badly for somewhat larger quantum numbers, as shown in Fig. V-7. Only in the limit of very large quantum numbers does the wave function approach the classical distribution function. It is nevertheless possible to correlate the quantum mechanical results with the classical results by considering the transition from macroscopic (classical) to microscopic (quantized) oscillators.

Consider an oscillator, such as a mass on a spring, which can be shrunk or expanded at will without any change in its fundamental characteristics. If the system is large, it will vibrate at a fixed frequency but with any amplitude we may desire. Continuous addition of energy will continuously increase the amplitude but will not change the frequency. Now suppose that we attempt to add energy to the oscillator by means of a periodic impulse, loosely coupled to the oscillator. If the frequency of the impulses happens to agree with the frequency of the oscillator, the conditions for resonance are established and energy will be very effectively transferred to the oscillator. But, if the frequencies differ very greatly, the periodic impulses will give up energy to the oscillator on one oscillation and take it back on another occasion. The net result over any large number of oscillations will average out to no transfer of energy in either direction. Thus we find a definite frequency for the oscillator, $\nu_0 = (1/2\pi)\sqrt{k/m}$, no definite energy, and a definite frequency for absorption, agreeing with the frequency of the oscillation.

Now the oscillator is allowed to shrink, retaining always the same period of motion as long as it can be seen. Eventually it will become impossible to tell whether it is still moving, but it will still absorb energy if this energy is supplied in the form of periodic impulses. From a purely quantum mechanical treatment it is possible to show that the oscillator can

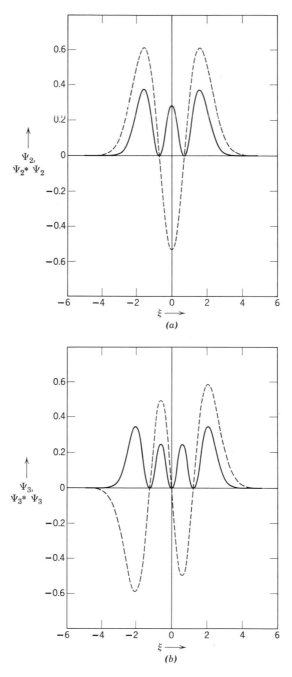

FIG. V-7.   Harmonic oscillator wave functions.   (a) $\mathbf{v} = 2$.   (b) $\mathbf{v} = 3$.

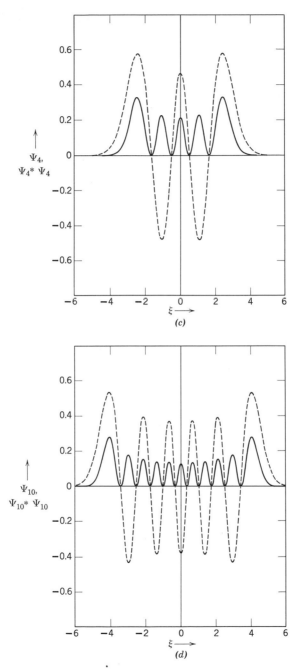

FIG V-7 (Continued).   (c) $v = 4$.   (d) $v = 10$.   See Fig. V-6.

only change from one fixed energy level to an adjacent level; the "selection rule" is that $\Delta v = \pm 1$, and therefore

$$\Delta E = (v' + \tfrac{1}{2})\hbar\sqrt{k/m} - (v'' + \tfrac{1}{2})\hbar\sqrt{k/m} = h\nu = h\nu_0,$$

where ν is the frequency of the electromagnetic radiation with energy equal to the change in energy of the oscillator and ν_0 is the frequency of the classical oscillator. Thus, although it is not possible to show that the oscillator has a periodic motion when it is reduced to the molecular size, it does absorb radiation with the frequency that it would be expected to have. It seems quite reasonable, therefore, to talk of quantized oscillators as if they surely had a frequency $\nu_0 = (1/2\pi)\sqrt{k/m}$. Accordingly equation V-28 is written

$$E = (v + \tfrac{1}{2})h\nu_0 \qquad\qquad (V\text{-}28a)$$

The transition from a quantized oscillator to a classical oscillator can be accomplished by increasing the quantum number; for example, by leaving force constant and energy fixed and increasing the mass. In the limit of large quantum numbers the probability distribution (Fig. V-7c) becomes equal to that expected for a classical oscillator, but the quantum mechanical equations do not tell us that the oscillator will now move in any particular manner. It is typical of quantum mechanics that it provides less information than the corresponding classical equations.[1]

2.5 Rigid Rotor

The energy of rotation of a rigid body is given by

$$E = \tfrac{1}{2}I\omega^2 \qquad\qquad (V\text{-}29)$$

where ω is the angular frequency or angular velocity, the rate of change of angle with time, $\omega \equiv d\theta/dt$. The moment of inertia, I, depends on the mass of each particle in the body times the square of its distance from the axis of rotation. For example, the moment of inertia of any rigid body about the z axis is

$$I_z = \sum_i m_i(x_i^2 + y_i^2)$$

The angular momentum, P, is the product $I\omega$.

For a rigid body without symmetry there will be three unique, mutually perpendicular axes about which the moment of inertia will be either a maximum or a minimum. These are called the "principal" axes of the body. An arbitrary rotational motion can be described as a sum of rota-

---

[1] Quantum mechanics can, however, be put into a form more nearly resembling classical mechanics by means of the wave-packet formulation.

tional motions about the three principal axes.   The energy may then be written

$$E = \tfrac{1}{2}I_A\omega_A{}^2 + \tfrac{1}{2}I_B\omega_B{}^2 + \tfrac{1}{2}I_C\omega_C{}^2$$
$$= P_A{}^2/2I_A + P_B{}^2/2I_B + P_C{}^2/2I_C \qquad \text{(V-30)}$$

It is convenient to classify rigid bodies into four categories, as follows. If all three principal moments of inertia are different, the body is called an "asymmetric rotor" or an "asymmetric top."   If two of the moments are equal, it is a "symmetric rotor," or "symmetric top."   A "spherical rotor," or "spherical top," has all three moments of inertia equal.   A linear molecule, although it fits the definition of a symmetric rotor, is considered separately since the third moment of inertia is essentially zero. It will be convenient to treat the symmetric rotor, then generalize to spherical rotors and linear molecules.   The asymmetric rotor is discussed in chapter X.

The energy of a symmetric rotor takes the form

$$E = P_A{}^2/2I_A + (P_B{}^2 + P_C{}^2)/2I_B \qquad \text{(V-31)}$$

since $I_B = I_C$.   The total angular momentum is the resultant of the three components $\vec{P_A}$, $\vec{P_B}$, and $\vec{P_C}$ and, since these are vector quantities,

$$P^2 = P_A{}^2 + P_B{}^2 + P_C{}^2 \qquad \text{(V-32)}$$

Substitution of this into equation V-31 gives the classical equation for the energy of a symmetric rotor.

$$E = P^2/2I_B + P_A{}^2(1/2I_A - 1/2I_B) \qquad \text{(V-33)}$$

The first term of equation V-33 refers to the total angular momentum, the second to the angular momentum about the unique axis.   This result is the basis of the quantum mechanical treatment of the rigid symmetric rotor.

For a freely rotating rigid body the total angular momentum, according to quantum mechanics, must be (section 3.2)

$$P = J(J + 1)\hbar^2 \qquad \text{(V-34)}$$

where J is an integer.   The component of P along any unique axis must be

$$P_A = K\hbar \qquad \text{(V-35)}$$

Combining the quantum mechanical restrictions on the angular momentum with the classical expression for the energy gives the quantized energy levels of the symmetric rotor,

$$E = J(J + 1)\hbar^2/2I_B + K^2\hbar^2(1/2I_A - 1/2I_B)$$

or

$$F(J, K) = E/h = J(J + 1)B + K^2(A - B) \qquad \text{(V-36)}$$

where the energy levels (or term values), in frequency units, are given in terms of the quantum numbers, **J** and **K**, and the constants

$$A \equiv h/8\pi^2 I_A$$
$$B \equiv h/8\pi^2 I_B \qquad \text{(V-37)}$$

The constants A and B are equal for a spherical rotor. The second term of equation V-36 drops out, leaving

$$F(\mathbf{J}, \mathbf{K}) = \mathbf{J}(\mathbf{J} + 1)B \qquad \text{(V-38)}$$

as the appropriate form for a spherical rotor. The same equation applies for a linear molecule, for reasons which are somewhat less obvious.

Linear molecules will have a vanishingly small value of the moment of inertia I_A. The rotational constant A will accordingly be very large. For any non-zero value of **K** the rotational energy will also be extremely large, as shown by equation V-36. At normal temperatures the energy available to the molecules is far less than hA so that, for all linear molecules (assuming no electronic angular momentum), **K** must be zero. Equation V-36 thus reduces to equation V-38 for linear molecules. One must conclude that spherical rotors and linear molecules obey the same equation, V-38, for quite different reasons; the former because of symmetry, the latter for purely quantum mechanical reasons.

It is of interest to notice that there is no "zero-point" rotational energy, since **J** and **K** can be zero. Also, since the levels vary according to a quadratic equation in quantum numbers, the spacing between adjacent levels becomes larger, rather than smaller, for large quantum numbers. Classical systems appear to have continuous rotational energy levels only because the rotational constants, A, B, and C, are extremely small, not because the quantum numbers **J** and **K** are large.

2.6 Born-Oppenheimer Approximation

The discussion of the previous sections has been concerned with idealized systems—simple harmonic oscillators which do not rotate, rigid rotors with no vibration or "internal" structure, and the properties of a particle in a box when the box is not allowed to expand and contract or to rotate. Molecules do not belong to any one of these idealized models for they do rotate and vibrate simultaneously, and this does, in effect, change the size of the box in which the electrons move. It would seem, therefore, that an accurate and complete treatment of a molecule would be exceedingly complicated if not impossible.

Born and Oppenheimer[1] showed that the influence of vibrational or

[1] Born and Oppenheimer, *Ann. Physik* **75**, 457 (1927).

rotational motions on electronic states should be almost negligible. Similarly, the vibrations will be nearly unaffected by motions of the electrons (provided the electronic state remains unchanged) or by rotations of the molecule, and the rotational motion, for any given vibrational and electronic state, should be nearly that of the rigid rotor. It should then be possible to write the total energy as a sum of the energies associated with each type of motion.

$$E = E_{trans} + E_{el} + E_{vib} + E_{rot} + \cdots \qquad (V\text{-}39)$$

Additional terms, including the translational energy, must be added, as indicated in the equation. They include the energy levels associated with spins or with quadrupole moments (section I-3).

The basis of the Born-Oppenheimer approximation may be considered to lie in the very different magnitudes of the frequencies associated with each of the forms of energy. Because of the very small mass of the electron, electronic motions are very much faster than motions of the nuclei. The vibrations take place so slowly, relatively, that they may be considered to take place in an average electronic field.

As rotational motions are generally very much slower than vibrational motions, the moment of inertia, although it oscillates with the vibrational motion, may be considered to take on an average value in treating the rotations. The actual value of this average moment of inertia will depend on the electronic state and, slightly, on the vibrational state. The rotational motion causes some distortion of the molecule (centrifugal distortion); this may be considered an influence of the rotation on the vibrational state, since it changes internuclear distances, but the effect is generally small compared to rotational energies and hence vanishingly small compared to vibrational energies.

In quantum mechanics the Born-Oppenheimer approximation is stated in the form

$$\Psi = \Psi_{trans}\Psi_{el}\Psi_{vib}\Psi_{rot} \qquad (V\text{-}40)$$

Equation V-39 follows from this factorization of the wave function.

3   Angular Momentum

Mechanics is based in large part upon certain quantities which have been defined in such a way that they remain unchanged when changes occur within the isolated system under investigation. The best-known example is the law of conservation of energy; it has been found possible to define the energy of a system in such a way that no matter what changes occur the total energy of the system and its surroundings will remain constant.

Only a few other quantities exhibiting this quality have been found, the most important of these for mechanics being linear momentum, mv, and angular momentum $I\omega$.[1]

The conservation laws of classical mechanics—conservation of energy, linear momentum, and angular momentum—are carried over as basic postulates of quantum mechanics. They are related by the same equations as in classical mechanics: the energy of translation of a rigid body is equal to $p^2/2m$ and the energy of rotation of a rigid body is equal to $P^2/2I$, where p and P are the linear and angular momenta, respectively, m is the mass, and I is the moment of inertia. For isolated systems the total energy, the linear momentum, and the angular momentum will be "quantized"; that is, they will be specified by eigenvalues of a differential equation and are therefore not only constant but also often restricted to discrete values. The linear momentum is treated in section 2.3, as the problem of a particle in a box; the angular momentum is considered in section 2.5, in treating the problem of the rigid rotor. In this section the method and significance of representing angular momenta by vectors and the modification of the classical picture by quantum mechanics will be considered briefly.

3.1 Vector Representation

The general definition of a vector is a set of numbers arranged in a fixed order. For example, the vector $\vec{x}$, in n-dimensional space, is defined by the numbers $(x_1, x_2, x_3, \ldots, x_n)$. The sum of two vectors, $\vec{x}$ and $\vec{y}$, is defined as the sums of the corresponding sets of numbers, $\vec{x} + \vec{y} = (x_1 + y_1, x_2 + y_2, \ldots, x_n + y_n)$. The inner, scalar, or dot product of two vectors is the sum of the products of corresponding numbers; $\vec{x} \cdot \vec{y} = x_1 y_1 + x_2 y_2 + \cdots + x_n y_n$. There will be just n vectors, of those consisting of n numbers, which are linearly independent. The choice of these vectors will be to a large extent arbitrary, but if one writes down $n + 1$ such vectors it will be possible to write one of them as a linear sum of the others. $\vec{v}_j = a_1\vec{v}_1 + a_2\vec{v}_2 + \cdots + a_n\vec{v}_n + a_{n+1}\vec{v}_{n+1}$ (the sum is over all indices from 1 to $n + 1$ except j), where the $\vec{v}_i$ are the vectors consisting of n numbers apiece and the a_i are constants, or ordinary numbers.

The vectors defined in this way have certain properties in common with "physical" quantities and may therefore represent these physical quantities in some mathematical equations. For example, a point on a line

---

[1] Volume is also conserved, and this plays an important, if generally unnoticed, role in thermodynamics, but in mechanics one is seldom concerned with this property. Until recently it was believed that parity, as defined in quantum mechanics, was also conserved, but violations of this rule are now known.

may be represented by a number, which could be called a one-dimensional vector.   There is only one independent one-dimensional vector, since any number may be expressed as a constant times another (non-zero) number. The points on a plane may be designated by assigning two numbers to each point, the two numbers associated with any point defining a two-dimensional vector.   Similarly the points in three-dimensional space may be associated with sets of three numbers, or with three-dimensional vectors. To each point in space there will then correspond one, and only one, three-dimensional vector (for a specified coordinate system).   The concept of vectors is much more general than their application to analytical geometry, and it is often convenient to speak of vectors of dimension much larger

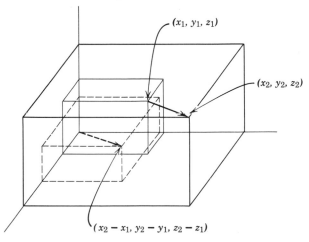

FIG. V-8.   The displacement from the point represented by (x_1, y_1, z_1) to the point (x_2, y_2, z_2) may be represented by the vector from the origin to the point $(x_2 - x_1, y_2 - y_1, z_2 - z_1)$.

than three.   In Appendix I, vectors of dimension greater than three will be considered.   In the present section only three-dimensional vectors are required.

A displacement is defined by the final and initial points in space and therefore by the two vectors that can be associated with those points. Subtraction of the initial vector from the final vector gives another vector which characterizes the direction and magnitude of the displacement.   The line drawn from the origin (the point associated with the vector $(0, 0, 0)$) to the point associated with the difference vector will be parallel to the original displacement and of a length equal to the magnitude of the displacement (Fig. V-8).   A displacement occurring in unit time is a velocity, and so a velocity, or a momentum, may be described by a vector.   Similarly accelerations, or forces (defined in terms of the accelerations they will produce), are "vector quantities."

The definition of a vector is not the same as the definition of a velocity, or a force, or a displacement. It is not surprising, therefore, that if one examines carefully the correspondence between them some differences can be found. As a specific example, since the association between a force and vector is made in terms of magnitude and direction, but not position, the sum of two equal and opposite forces will always be identically zero if calculated from the simple vector representation. Yet it is well known that "couples," consisting of two equal and opposite forces applied to different points on a body, exist. Such a couple leads to a rotation of the body, rather than to a displacement along a straight line. To describe

FIG. V-9. A clockwise rotation is represented by a vector pointing away from the observer (the direction in which a normal, or right-hand, screw would move). The angular velocity, $\vec{\omega}$, and the angular momentum, $\vec{P}$, lie in this same direction.

the action of such a force couple it is necessary to assign additional properties to the "vectors" that will probably not be appropriate for description of some other physical quantity that might otherwise be represented by a vector.

A rotation may also be represented by a vector, although the limitations are somewhat greater in this case than in the representation of linear motion. A rigid body rotating freely in space will rotate with a constant angular speed, ω, about an axis fixed in space. The angular momentum, $I\omega$, will be constant in magnitude, and if it is arbitrarily associated with the direction of the axis it will be constant in direction as well. It is possible, therefore, to associate vectors, $\vec{\omega}$ and $\vec{P}$, with the angular velocity and angular momentum, as shown in Fig. V-9. The "sense" of these vectors is the direction of motion associated with the rotation of a right-handed screw.

The vector representation of angular momentum is quite satisfactory when considering the conservation of angular momentum. The effect of an impulse applied to a rotating system is nicely described by adding the angular momentum produced by the impulse to the angular momentum of the original system. For example, Fig. V-10 shows a spinning gyroscope with an angular momentum $\vec{P}$ along its axis. The force of gravity acts to pull the top of the gyroscope downward, imparting an angular momentum

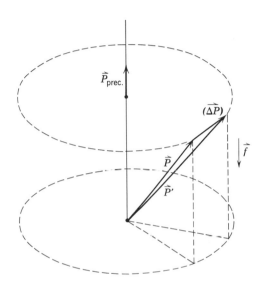

FIG. V-10. Precession of a gyroscope. A body rotating with angular momentum, P, acted on by a vertical force f will acquire an increment of angular momentum ΔP perpendicular to the plane in which the rotating axis would tend to fall under the vertical force. The vector sum is $\vec{P} + \vec{\Delta P} = \vec{P'}$, a new vector of the same length as $\vec{P}$ but displaced from it about the circle. This leads to a small angular momentum, $\vec{P}_{\text{prec}}$, called a "precessional" motion.

$\vec{\Delta P}$ (about the point of contact of the axis with its support) directed perpendicular to the vertical plane that includes the axis of the gyroscope. The vector sum of these two angular momenta, $\vec{P}$ and $\vec{\Delta P}$, is the new vector $\vec{P'}$. The effect of the gravitational pull is thus to make the gyroscope now rotate with its axis along the direction of $\vec{P'}$. Continued gravitational pull causes the gyroscope axis to "precess," the upper end traveling in a circle above the point of support.

Limitations to the vector representation of rotational phenomena are found in the properties of rotations themselves. The resultant of two rotations will in general depend on the order in which they are carried out

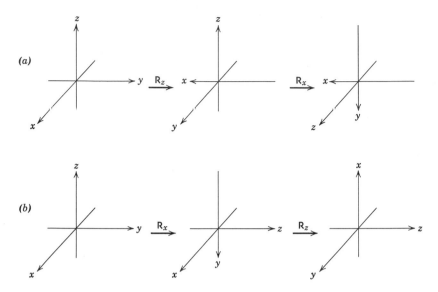

FIG. V-11. The resultant of two finite rotations depends on the order in which these are carried out. The product $R_x R_z$ (a) leads to a different result than the product $R_z R_x$ (b).

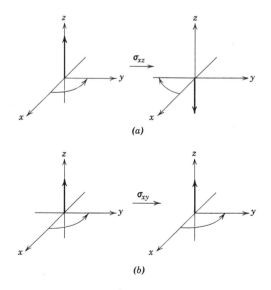

FIG. V-12. The symmetry properties of rotations are opposite to those suggested by the vector representation of the rotations. (a) Reflection in a plane including the axis of rotation reverses the direction of the rotation; (b) reflection in a plane perpendicular to the axis of rotation has no effect on the rotation.

(Fig. V-11), but the sum of two numbers, and therefore the sum of two vectors, is independent of order. This introduces a fundamental difficulty into the representation of a rotation by a vector. The difficulty may be avoided if only infinitesimal rotations are considered; for many purposes, as for the definitions of angular velocity and angular momentum, this is quite adequate.[1] Another important limitation concerns the symmetry properties of rotations. Reflection in a vertical plane of a rotation about the positive z axis (Fig. V-12) gives a rotation about the negative z axis, but an examination of the vector representation alone would suggest that the rotation should be unchanged. Reflection of the same rotation in a horizontal plane, on the other hand, does not change the direction of rotation, even though the vector representation would suggest that the direction should be reversed. Because of this difference, a vector representing an angular momentum is sometimes called an "axial" vector, in contrast to "polar" vectors which change sign on inversion.

3.2 Quantum Mechanical Model of Angular Momentum Vectors

A rigid body rotating freely in space will have a constant angular momentum, both in magnitude and in direction. For a very small system this condition will not be observable, since any method that may be chosen to determine the angular momentum will interact with the system, causing a significant change in magnitude or direction, or both, of the angular momentum. A typical experiment that may be performed is to place a collection of atoms or molecules in a uniform magnetic field and observe the emission or absorption of radiation from them. The magnetic field will exert a force on the rotating body, provided the rotation has associated with it a magnetic moment as well as an angular momentum, and the energy of the system will depend on the orientation of the axis of rotation with respect to the applied magnetic field. It is possible to determine, from the frequencies emitted or absorbed, the energy and hence the orientation of the axis of rotation (or at least the changes in these quantities).

The applied magnetic field will act on the rotating body much as a gravitational field acts on the gyroscope of Fig. V-10. The axis of rotation will precess about the direction of the applied field, so that the magnitude of the angular momentum is constant but the direction is not. The "constants of the motion" are then the projection of the angular momentum vector on the axis of the field and the magnitude of the total angular

---

[1] Just as velocity is defined as dx/dt, angular velocity is $d\theta/dt$ and angular momentum, $I\omega$, is $d(I\theta)/dt = I\,d\theta/dt$. Only $d\theta$, an infinitesimal rotation, appears in these definitions. Hence ω and $P = I\omega$ can be represented by vectors.

momentum.   It can be shown by solution of the equations of motion that the projection on the axis must be equal to $\mathbf{K}\hbar$, where $\mathbf{K}$ is an integer (or in some cases a half integer); the magnitude of the angular momentum must, however, be equal to $\sqrt{\mathbf{J(J + 1)}}\,\hbar$, where $\mathbf{J}$ is an integer (or half integer).   It is clear, therefore, that the angular momentum vector can never be exactly aligned with the axis of the field (Fig. V-13).   This is a consequence of the Uncertainty Principle. $\mathbf{K}$ is limited to values ranging from $\mathbf{J}$ to $-\mathbf{J}$ in integral (only) steps, or a total of $2\mathbf{J} + 1$ values.   It is often convenient to speak of the angular momentum of a system with

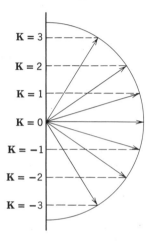

FIG. V-13.   Possible orientation of the angular momentum, with respect to an applied field, for a rigid rotor with quantum number of angular momentum $\mathbf{J} = 3$. The magnitude of the angular momentum is actually $\sqrt{3 \times 4}\,\hbar$, but the maximum projection is exactly $3\,\hbar$.

quantum number $\mathbf{J}$ as if the angular momentum were exactly $\mathbf{J}\hbar$, but it must be kept in mind that the value is actually $\sqrt{\mathbf{J(J + 1)}}\,\hbar$.

4   Transitions between States

Volume and pressure are absolute quantities, as measured in the laboratory, in the sense that each has a natural, unique reference to which the value zero is assigned.   Temperature, with the assistance of well-established theory, has a similar "absolute zero" and can be given a meaningful value on an absolute scale.   Energy has no such unique reference level. Measurements of energy must always determine a difference between energy levels; any values assigned to these levels must be consistent with the measured difference but are otherwise quite arbitrary. It is just such energy differences that are found from spectroscopic measurements, with the implicit assumption that the energy gained or lost by the molecule is equal to the energy of the photon absorbed or emitted, and thus equal to Planck's constant times the frequency associated with the photon.

Much of spectroscopy is concerned solely with the determination of energy differences between various states of atoms or molecules and with the conclusions which can be drawn from these energy values. Such measurements cannot, however, be completely separated from the question of how likely it is that a particular transition will occur, and hence how intense the corresponding absorption or emission band will be. The theory of intensities is not nearly so well developed as the theory for prediction of relative energy values of the states. Only a brief introduction to the problems of intensities will be given here, the remainder being left for more advanced treatises and the current literature. In the following sections certain of the principles underlying spectroscopic intensities will be considered. The method of application of these to various types of transitions will be indicated in the chapters to follow.

4.1 Maxwell-Boltzmann Distribution

An infinite number of states is available to any molecule, but since only a finite amount of energy will be available to a collection of molecules it can be shown that only a relatively few states are likely to be populated by an appreciable number of molecules. The calculation of the numbers to be found in various states can be carried out by the methods known as statistical mechanics.

A particularly simple problem of statistical mechanics is to find the relative populations of two states of energy, E_1 and E_2. This ratio, the number in state E_1 divided by the number in state E_2, is just

$$n_1/n_2 = \exp\left[-(E_1 - E_2)/kT\right]$$

where k is the Boltzmann constant (or the gas constant, R, if E is energy per mole) and T is the absolute temperature. Often there will be more than one state of the same energy; such states are said to be "degenerate." It is then most convenient to sum the numbers over all the degenerate states, but since these have the same energies they will have the same populations and it is enough to multiply the number in any one state by the degeneracy —the number of states of that energy. Designating the degeneracy of the "level" of energy E_i by the symbol g_i, the equation for relative populations becomes

$$\frac{n_1}{n_2} = \frac{g_1 \exp\left(-E_1/kT\right)}{g_2 \exp\left(-E_2/kT\right)} \tag{V-41}$$

The term "energy level" will be employed in this sense of including all states of the same, or almost the same, energy. The distinction is not always clear cut, but it is usually interpreted in the spirit of the Born-Oppenheimer approximation. That is, an electronic state may include many vibrational or rotational levels, a vibrational state may include many rotational levels, and so forth.

The relative populations of energy levels enter into all calculations of intensities, since the number leaving any level by absorption or emission of radiation will be proportional to the number of molecules in that level. For optical frequencies (infrared and above) the populations of the ground states may be considered to be independent of the radiation field. At room temperature only those states which are less than 600 cm^{-1} above the lowest energy state are likely to be appreciably populated.

4.2   Charge Distributions

Any arrangement of electrical charges can be described mathematically, to any desired degree of accuracy, as a summation of simple arrangements

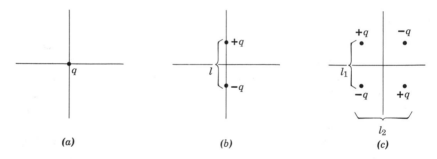

(a)   (b)   (c)

FIG. V-14.   Idealized charge distributions.   (a) Monopole; (b) dipole; (c) quadrupole. The magnitude of each moment is independent of the origin of the coordinate system if, and only if, all lower-order multipole distributions vanish.   In an idealized multipole the distance between charges is decreased to zero and the magnitude of the charges is increased such that the appropriate products (equations V-42) remain constant.   Then all higher-order multipoles also vanish and are independent of the choice of origin.

such as those shown in Fig. V-14.   The first term in the expansion is the net charge of the total assemblage.   Since this term is the same as would be produced by a point charge of this magnitude at the electrical center of the array, it is called the "monopole" term.   From a distance large compared with the dimensions of the charge distribution the monopole term will accurately represent the effect of the entire collection of charges.

At a smaller distance it may be necessary to include a second term in the expansion, equivalent to the arrangement shown in Fig. V-14b. This consists of two equal and opposite charges, of magnitude q_2, separated by the distance l_2, giving rise to a "dipole" moment of $q_2 \cdot l_2$. The dipole moment has a direction as well as a magnitude and is therefore represented by a vector. For even greater accuracy a third term, equivalent to the configuration of Fig. V-14c, is included. This arrangement has no monopole or dipole moment but has a "quadrupole" moment, which must be represented by a tensor of second rank rather than by a vector.[1] Higher-order terms could also be included, but in nearly all practical applications it is found to be sufficient to include only the first non-vanishing term.

If the charge distribution consists of discrete charges, e_i, located at the points given by coordinates x_i, y_i, z_i, the magnitudes of the monopole, dipole, and quadrupole components are given by the following sums.

$$\text{Monopole:} \qquad q = \sum_i e_i$$

$$\text{Dipole:} \qquad M_x = \sum_i e_i x_i$$

$$M_y = \sum_i e_i y_i$$

$$M_z = \sum_i e_i z_i$$

$$\text{Quadrupole:} \qquad Q_{xx} = \sum_i e_i x_i^2 \qquad\qquad \text{(V-42)}$$

$$Q_{xy} = \sum_i e_i x_i y_i$$

$$Q_{xz} = \sum_i e_i x_i z_i$$

$$Q_{yy} = \sum_i e_i y_i^2$$

$$Q_{yz} = \sum_i e_i y_i z_i$$

$$Q_{zz} = \sum_i e_i z_i^2$$

For continuous charge distributions the summations are replaced by integrals.

The description of an array of charges as an equivalent assembly of multipoles is somewhat arbitrary, but it often has the advantage of corresponding closely to idealized physical models. For example, an ion in solution is, in general, neither a point charge in terms of molecular and intermolecular dimensions nor is it spherical, since it is surrounded by a

[1] See, for example, J. A. Stratton, *Electromagnetic Theory*, pp. 64–69, 172–183, McGraw-Hill Book Company, New York, 1941.

small number of solvent molecules. It is nevertheless convenient to consider it as a point charge for most purposes. A molecule such as HCl, on the other hand, has no net charge but has a large dipole moment; it is convenient to imagine it to consist of a positively charged hydrogen and a negatively charged chlorine, the magnitudes of the charges being such that the product of the charge and HCl bond length will give the observed dipole moment.

In addition to the natural dipole moment of any system, an induced dipole moment can be produced by the application of an electric field. The electrical field distorts, or polarizes, the charge distribution, displacing the positive and negative charges with respect to each other until the restoring forces match the polarizing force of the applied field. The magnitude of the induced dipole is proportional to the strength of the applied electrical field, but the relationship is, in general, complicated by the fact that the distortion occurs preferentially in certain directions which may not correspond to the direction of the field.

The induced dipole, $\vec{\mu}$, is given in terms of the applied field, $\vec{\mathscr{E}}$, by the equation

$$\vec{\mu} = \alpha\vec{\mathscr{E}} \tag{V-43}$$

where α, like the quadrupole moment, is a symmetrical tensor of the second rank. This simply means that α, the polarizability tensor, contains six independent components, as indicated by rewriting equation V-43 in the expanded form

$$\mu_x = \alpha_{xx}\mathscr{E}_x + \alpha_{xy}\mathscr{E}_y + \alpha_{xz}\mathscr{E}_z$$
$$\mu_y = \alpha_{yx}\mathscr{E}_x + \alpha_{yy}\mathscr{E}_y + \alpha_{yz}\mathscr{E}_z$$
$$\mu_z = \alpha_{zx}\mathscr{E}_x + \alpha_{zy}\mathscr{E}_y + \alpha_{zz}\mathscr{E}_z \tag{V-43a}$$

with $\alpha_{xy} = \alpha_{yx}$, $\alpha_{xz} = \alpha_{zx}$, and $\alpha_{yz} = \alpha_{zy}$. It is apparent, from these equations, that a dipole moment can be produced in the x direction by an electrical field along the y axis or the z axis, as shown in Fig. V-15. The components of the polarizability tensor will vary as a bond is stretched or compressed. It is this variation that gives rise to Raman scattering.

4.3 Intensities

According to classical electromagnetic theory, radiant energy is emitted whenever a charge is accelerated. In most cases of interest the charge acceleration occurs within a system that is electrically neutral—for example, in a radio antenna or a vibrating molecule. The charge distributions for these systems are adequately represented by oscillating dipole moments. For harmonic oscillations the dipole moment may be written in the form

$$\vec{M} = \vec{M_0} \cos (2\pi\nu t) \qquad \text{(V-44)}$$

The total energy emitted per unit time by such an oscillating dipole is[1]

$$\frac{d\mathrm{E}}{dt} = \frac{16\pi^4\nu^4}{3c^3} M_0{}^2 \qquad \text{(V-45)}$$

The classical expression for the dipole moment (see preceding section) is

$$\vec{M} = \sum_i e_i\vec{r_i} = \vec{M_0} \cos (2\pi\nu t) = \sum_i e_i\vec{r_{i0}} \cos (2\pi\nu t) \qquad \text{(V-46)}$$

where the vector r_i gives the instantaneous position and r_{i0} is the maximum displacement from equilibrium of the ith charge. A transition is to be

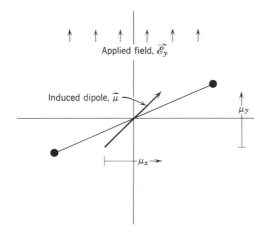

FIG. V-15. Induced dipole moment. Charges in an anisotropic region, such as a chemical bond, will tend to move in preferred directions. An electric field, $\vec{\mathscr{E}_y}$, might therefore produce an induced dipole, $\vec{\mu}$, with components μ_x and μ_y perpendicular and parallel to the field, respectively.

expected, according to these classical equations, if and only if the frequency of oscillation of the dipole moment agrees with the frequency of oscillation of the electric field. Note in particular that the requirement is not that the molecule have a permanent dipole moment in its equilibrium position but rather that, during the vibration, there should be a *change* in the dipole moment. M_0 is the amplitude of the fluctuating moment; if there is also a permanent dipole moment it should be added to equations V-44

[1] N. E. Gilbert, *Electricity and Magnetism*, Revised Edition, p. 463, Macmillan, New York, 1941; Ditchburn, ref. 14, p. 415.

and V-46, but it will not directly affect equation V-45, which gives the intensity of absorption or emission of radiation.[1]

The exact positions of electrons in molecules cannot be known, according to quantum mechanics.   It is necessary, therefore, to treat the assembly of discrete charges as a continuous distribution, averaged over a time much smaller than a vibrational period (section 2.6).   The sum over individual electrons at fixed points is replaced by an integral over the equivalent continuous distribution, or the vector $\vec{r_i}$ is replaced by its average, or "expectation," value, $\int \Psi^* \mathbf{r} \Psi \, d\tau$.   The dipole moment becomes $M = \int \Psi^* e\mathbf{r} \Psi \, d\tau$.

In the classical picture it was the change in dipole moment due to the vibration which produced absorption or emission.   Expressing this in the language of quantum mechanics, we would say that the time-average charge distributions in the initial and final states must be different and, in particular, there must be a non-vanishing dipole moment associated with the transition from the initial state to the final state in order to cause such a transition to occur.   The dipole moment associated with the change of state is[2]

$$M_{nm} = e \int (\Psi_m^* \mathbf{r} \Psi_n + \Psi_n^* \mathbf{r} \Psi_m) \, d\tau$$
$$= 2e \cos (2\pi\nu_{nm}t) \int \psi_m^* \mathbf{r} \psi_n \, d\tau$$
$$= 2e \cos (2\pi\nu_{nm}t) r_{nm} \qquad \text{(V-47)}$$

The frequency ν_{nm} is defined to be

$$\nu_{nm} = (E_n - E_m)/h \qquad (E_n > E_m) \qquad \text{(V-48)}$$

and arises from the time dependence of the wave functions, $\Psi_n = \psi_n e^{iE_n t/\hbar}$. The symbol r_{nm} represents the integral $\int \psi_m^* \mathbf{r} \psi_n \, d\tau$.

Substitution of the dipole moment as defined in V-47 (rather than V-46) into the classical expression, V-45, gives the energy emitted per unit time per molecule.

$$\frac{dE}{dt} = \frac{64\pi^4 \nu_{nm}^4 e^2}{3c^3} (r_{nm}^* r_{nm})$$
$$= h\nu_{nm} A_{nm} \qquad \text{(V-49)}$$

The quantity A_{nm} defined by this equation is called the Einstein coefficient

[1] It is perhaps worth emphasizing that it is not the amplitude of the vibration that is primarily responsible for the intensity of an absorption band.   The amplitude is fixed by the force constants, masses, and geometry; in fact, those transitions in which the change of amplitude is greatest (overtones) are generally quite weak.   It is primarily the difference in electrical character of the atoms and the amount of asymmetry of the form of the vibration that determine the intensity, as shown by the fact that the expression for the intensity of a vibration involves derivatives evaluated at the equilibrium position.

[2] W. Heitler, *Quantum Theory of Radiation*, second edition, p. 106, Oxford, 1944.

for spontaneous emission.   It has the physical significance of a transition probability (number of transitions per unit time) from an excited state to a state of lower energy.

Equation V-49 does not provide for the absorption of radiation, nor for the "induced emission" which occurs in the presence of a radiation field.   The number of induced absorption transitions must be equal, at equilibrium, to the sum of the spontaneous and induced emission transitions.   Denoting the induced transition probabilities by B_{nm}, where $B_{nm} = B_{mn}$, the condition for equilibrium is

$$\rho(\nu)B_{mn}N_m = A_{nm}N_n + \rho(\nu)B_{nm}N_n \qquad (V\text{-}50)$$

Substitution of the radiation density (equation II-1) for $\rho(\nu)$ and expressing the number of molecules in the upper state, N_n, in terms of the number in the lower state and the Boltzmann factor[1] (equation V-41), provides a relationship between the two Einstein coefficients, A_{nm} and B_{nm}.

$$B_{nm} = \frac{c^3}{8\pi h \nu_{nm}{}^3} A_{nm}$$

$$= \frac{8\pi^3 e^2}{3h^2} (r_{nm}{}^* r_{nm}) \qquad (V\text{-}51)$$

For a sample containing N_m molecules in a volume V, the energy absorbed per unit time from a field of energy E_0 in the volume V and frequency interval $\Delta\nu$ will be

$$\left(\frac{dE}{dt}\right)_{mn} = \frac{E_0 N_m h \nu_{nm} B_{nm}}{V \Delta\nu} \qquad (V\text{-}52)$$

and the emitted intensity will be

$$\left(\frac{dE}{dt}\right)_{nm} = N_n h \nu_{nm}\left(\frac{E_0}{V \Delta\nu} B_{nm} + A_{nm}\right) \qquad (V\text{-}53)$$

It is assumed in these equations that the frequency interval is sufficiently small that E_0, ν_{nm}, A_{nm}, and B_{nm} may be considered constant.

Although the observed intensity should depend on a difference between absorbed and emitted energy, in practice equation V-53 may be ignored except for very low frequencies (microwave region and below).   For the optical regions the number of molecules in excited states is small, the incident intensity is very small, and only a small part of the emitted

[1] The radiation density is

$$\frac{1}{V}\frac{dE}{d\nu} = \frac{8\pi h\nu^3}{c^3}\frac{1}{e^{h\nu/kT} - 1}$$

and

$$N_n = e^{-h\nu/kT}N_m$$

intensity will find its way to the detector.   Under these circumstances the fraction of the incident energy absorbed in any thin layer, dx, is

$$\frac{d\mathrm{E}}{\mathrm{E}_0} = -\frac{N_m h\nu_{nm} B_{nm}\, dt}{V\, \varDelta\nu}$$

$$= -\frac{N_m h\nu_{nm} B_{nm}\, dx}{V\, \varDelta\nu c}$$

$$\frac{d\mathrm{E}}{\mathrm{E}_0} = -\frac{h\nu_{nm} B_{nm}}{\varDelta\nu c} C\, dx \tag{V-54}$$

This will be recognized as Beer's law with the absorptivity given by

$$a = h\nu_{nm} B_{nm}/c\, \varDelta\nu \tag{V-55}$$

and the concentration, C, equal to N_m/V.

According to the classical theory[1] of radiation, an oscillator with the charge e and an associated mass m should give rise to a total absorption, found by integrating the absorptivity over the entire band (or over all frequencies), given by $\int a\, d\nu = \pi e^2/2.3mc$. This is essentially the value found for absorption, such as the D lines of sodium, in which one would expect one and only one electron to contribute to one band or band system.   Most absorption bands observed have much smaller values of the absorptivity; classically one might say that less than one electron is participating in the transition, but it is more realistic to say that the transition involves compensating changes in the distributions of other electrons, or that it involves a change in electron distribution that is less than would be expected if the electrons acted independently, or simply that the probability of an incident photon causing a transition is small.   It is nevertheless convenient to consider the problem as if it involved a fractional part of an oscillator, or an oscillator of less than the expected absorption power.

The "oscillator strength" of a transition is defined in terms of the measured strength of the absorption.   For weak absorption bands the oscillator strength, f, is given in terms of the maximum absorptivity, $\hat{a}$, and the half band width, $\varDelta\nu_{1/2}$, by the equation

$$f = 2.3(mc/2e^2)\hat{a}\, \varDelta\nu_{1/2}$$

where e, m, and c are the electronic charge and mass and the speed of light, respectively.   Under the same assumptions f is related to the integrated absorption coefficient by the expression

$$f = 2.3(mc/\pi e^2) \int_0^\infty a\, d\nu$$

The absorptivity in these expressions is in units of area/molecule.

[1] See, for example, Ditchburn, ref. 14, p. 460.

This discussion has been limited to emission and absorption associated with a change in dipole moment.   Actually, other mechanisms can also cause emission or absorption, and even though these processes are much less likely they are observed under appropriate experimental conditions. For example, a change in quadrupole moment will give rise to transitions which are roughly 10^{-8} as intense as the electric dipole transitions; a change in magnetic dipole can give rise to transitions (by coupling with the magnetic, rather than the electrical, component of the electromagnetic field) which are roughly 10^{-5} as intense as electric dipole transitions.   If the electromagnetic field can induce a dipole moment in the molecule, the possibility of Rayleigh or Raman scattering exists.   The probability for such scattering depends on the integral $\int \Psi_m{}^*\alpha\Psi_n \, d\tau$, where α is the polarizability tensor.

Emission processes, including the virtual absorption and re-emission associated with Rayleigh and Raman scattering, depend on the fourth power of the frequency, as shown in equation V-49.   This has important consequences which have been mentioned in connection with sample preparation (section IV-2.3) and the techniques of Raman spectroscopy (section III-4).

4.4   Selection Rules

Since the number of energy levels for any molecule is infinite, it would seem that the spectrum might be exceedingly complex.   The observed simplicity of molecular spectra may be attributed to the existence of certain "selection rules" which govern the intensities of the lines or bands associated with the many transitions that might occur.   A discussion of these selection rules can profitably be separated from a discussion of intensities, however, because the arguments involved are essentially qualitative and simple as compared to the treatment of the preceding section.

Formal selection rules give no information concerning how strong a band will be if it satisfies certain requirements, that is, if it is "allowed." The selection rules do say that under certain circumstances a band is "forbidden" and must have zero intensity.   Often a band will be forbidden for an idealized system, such as a harmonic oscillator or a molecule without spin-orbit coupling, but will be allowed for a system which is not of this type, for example, an anharmonic oscillator or a molecule in which spin-orbit coupling does occur.   For convenience, such bands are generally referred to as "forbidden" bands, and the relatively small intensities for these bands which are actually observed provide information about the true nature of the molecule.

It is possible to derive the selection rules by examination of the transition moment, $\int \Psi_m{}^* \mathbf{O} \Psi_n \, d\tau$, for the particular operator, $\mathbf{O}$, and the wave functions of the system under consideration. For example, if $\mathbf{O}$ is the dipole moment operator and Ψ_m and Ψ_n are harmonic oscillator wave functions, it can be shown that Ψ_m and Ψ_n must differ in vibrational quantum number by one unit. Proofs of these relationships are given in books on quantum mechanics. Classical or "old quantum theory" arguments are often simpler and provide more insight into the physical processes involved.

For a harmonic oscillator, classical theory predicts that the field must have the same frequency as the oscillator. Absorption of a photon of frequency $\nu = \nu_0$ causes a change in energy of the oscillator by an amount $\Delta E = h\nu_0$. Equating this energy change with the expression (equation V-28a) $\Delta E = \mathrm{E}(\mathbf{v}') - \mathrm{E}(\mathbf{v}'') = (\mathbf{v}' + \frac{1}{2})h\nu_0 - (\mathbf{v}'' + \frac{1}{2})h\nu_0$ shows that the selection rule must be

$$\Delta \mathbf{v} = \pm 1 \tag{V-56}$$

for a harmonic oscillator. If the oscillator is somewhat anharmonic, the motion must be described in terms of the frequencies $\nu_0, 2\nu_0, 3\nu_0, \ldots$, and the oscillator can then absorb a photon with frequency ν_0 or $2\nu_0$, and so on. The intensities of the overtone bands give an indication of the amount of anharmonicity of the vibration (section X-3.2).

An electromagnetic field with a frequency greater than all the vibrational motions can induce a dipole moment in a molecule. The frequency of oscillation of the induced dipole will correspond to the frequency of the imposed field. The magnitude of the induced dipole will depend on the polarizability of the molecule, and this polarizability may fluctuate as a result of the vibrational motion of the molecule. This has the effect of superimposing the vibrational frequency on the imposed frequency, leading to beat frequencies which are the sum and difference of these two. One should expect from this classical argument that a high-frequency line would be scattered with weak components at frequency shifts of ν_0 above and below the incident frequency. These weak components are observed (Raman scattering), although the relative intensities are influenced by the Boltzmann factor according to the more accurate quantum mechanical treatment. If the vibration is anharmonic, then weak scattering at the overtone frequencies will also be observed.

Many of the "fundamental" particles, such as protons, electrons, and photons, possess an intrinsic angular momentum which has become generally known as "spin." Since angular momentum is conserved, the absorption or emission of a photon must produce a change in angular momentum of the molecule. The spin of the photon is one unit (h) and the total angular momentum of the molecule must change by this amount;

$\vec{\Delta J} = 1$. Only the magnitude of **J** is important for a free molecule, and the change in magnitude of **J** must be integral since only those states differing by integral values are possible according to the laws of quantum mechanics. The maximum increase in the magnitude of **J** is just one unit, the maximum decrease is one unit, and the only possible intermediate value for the change is zero. $|\mathbf{J}_i + 1| \geqslant |\mathbf{J}_f| \geqslant |\mathbf{J}_i - 1|$. The selection rules for change of angular momentum on absorption or emission of a photon are thus

$$\Delta J = 0, \pm 1$$

but

$$\mathbf{J} = 0 \leftrightarrow \mathbf{J} = 0 \tag{V-57}$$

since one unit added vectorially to zero cannot give zero.

Raman scattering may be considered to consist of two steps, the absorption of a photon followed by the emission of a new photon of different frequency. The total change in angular momentum is thus two units, $|\vec{\Delta J}| = 2$. Then $|\mathbf{J}_i + 2| \geqslant |\mathbf{J}_f| \geqslant |\mathbf{J}_i - 2|$ and the selection rules for Raman scattering are

$$\Delta J = 0, \pm 1, \pm 2$$

but

$$\mathbf{J} = 0 \leftrightarrow \mathbf{J} = 0 \tag{V-58}$$

$$\mathbf{J} = 0 \leftrightarrow \mathbf{J} = 1$$

The selection rules for angular momentum may also be derived in approximate form on the basis of the frequencies of the motion. Since for a linear molecule or spherical rotor

$$\mathrm{E} = P^2/2I = \tfrac{1}{2}I\omega^2_{\mathrm{rot}} = J(J + 1)\hbar^2/2I$$

the frequency of rotation is, from this combination of classical and quantum equations, $\omega_{\mathrm{rot}} = \sqrt{J(J + 1)}\,\hbar/I$. The energy absorbed if J increases by one unit is

$$\Delta \mathrm{E} = J'(J' + 1)\hbar^2/2I - J''(J'' + 1)\hbar^2/2I$$

$$= J'\hbar^2/I$$

$$= \hbar\omega_{\mathrm{abs}}$$

and therefore $\omega_{\mathrm{abs}} = J'\hbar/I = J'\omega_{\mathrm{rot}}/\sqrt{J(J + 1)} \approx \omega_{\mathrm{rot}}$. The frequency absorbed is approximately equal to the classical frequency of rotation of the molecule in its final state.

The polarizability is independent of direction along any given axis (or, better, the polarizability depends on direction but not on sense). So far as the polarizability is concerned, therefore, a rotation of a molecule by 180° represents a full cycle of polarizability. The polarizability "rotates" with twice the frequency of the molecule, and the frequency absorbed can be twice as great, by this mechanism, as the frequency of classical rotation.

Equations V-56, V-57, and V-58 are not the only selection rules but they are, in some respects, the most universally applicable.   In addition, there are restrictions on change in the projection of angular momentum along an axis, a limitation on change in spin of the electrons, and restrictions that arise because of the particular symmetry of the molecule.   The effects of symmetry are contained in the statements made previously that there must be a change in dipole moment, or other pertinent quantity, for the transition to be possible by the absorption or emission of radiation.

Some of these additional selection rules will be considered in chapters VI and VII.   The powerful methods that have been developed for treating molecular symmetry are given in section X-1.

Problems

1. Derive the equations for the vibrations of a mass hanging on a spring, including the effects of gravity.

2. Derive equation V-8 for the vibration of a diatomic molecule.

3. Show that the product of the root-mean-square momentum and the root-mean-square amplitude, calculated by the classical equations for the ground vibrational state of a quantized harmonic oscillator (energy $\frac{1}{2}h\nu$), is in agreement with the Uncertainty Principle.

4. In the Bohr model the kinetic energy in the ground state is $T = p^2/2m = Ze^2/2r$. Taking $\bar{\bar{x}} = r/\sqrt{2}$ as a measure of the uncertainty of position along an axis and $\bar{\bar{p}}_x = p/\sqrt{2}$ as the measure of uncertainty of momentum along the same axis, show that a minimum value for the radius can be calculated by means of the Uncertainty Principle, $(\Delta x)(\Delta p) \geq \hbar/2$. Compare with the Bohr radius (see equation VI-1), $a_0 = \hbar^2/Ze^2m$.

5. Calculate the first three energy levels for a particle in a one-dimensional box

   (a) when the particle is an electron and the box is 5 Å in length
   (b) when the particle is a red blood cell (about 2×10^{-10} gm) in a box of length 0.1 mm.

Calculate also the quantities $\Delta E/hc$, in cm^{-1}, and $hc/\Delta E$, in Å, for each of these particles.

6. Find the rotational constant and quantum number for a baton 24 in. long, with the mass of 24 oz localized equally in the two ends, spinning at 60 rpm.   Find the difference in rotational energy and in angular frequency corresponding to $\Delta J = 1$ under these conditions.

7. Find the classical rotation frequency for a hydrogen molecule (bond length 0.71 Å) with rotational energy of kT at 300°K and at 90°K.   Find the quantum number, J, necessary to give these rotational energies.

8. The tension on an A string (440 sec^{-1}) of a violin is 10^9 dyne, the linear density is 6.8 mg/cm, and the length between nodes is 30.8 cm.   Assume the string is plucked at its midpoint, the configuration at $t = 0$ being triangular with an altitude of 0.5 cm.

   (a) Find the first five coefficients A_n in the expression for the displacement as a function of time and position,

$$v(x, t) = \sum_{n=1}^{\infty} A_n \sin(n\pi x/L) \cos(v n\pi t/L + \phi)$$

(b) Plot each of the five terms and the sum of the first two, three, four, and five terms for $t = 0$. Compare with the known value of $y(x, 0)$. (The coefficients A_n are found by multiplying both sides by sin $(n\pi x/L)$ and integrating over $x = 0$ to $x = L$; that is,

$$A_n = (2/\pi \cos (vn\pi t/L + \phi)) \int_0^L y(x, t) \sin (n\pi x/L) \, dx$$

9. The general solution of the Schroedinger equation for a particle in a box defined by the potential function $v = \infty$ for $x \leqslant 0$, $v = 0$ for $0 < x < a$, $v = \infty$ for $x \geqslant a$, is

$$\psi = A \exp i\kappa x + B \exp -i\kappa x$$

(a) Show that this is an eigenfunction of the Schroedinger equation for any constant potential.

(b) Find the energy of a particle in the box ($0 < x < a$). Show that your result is equivalent to equation V-24 if κ is the de Broglie angular wavenumber of the particle,

$$\kappa = 2\pi/\lambda = p/\hbar = \sqrt{2m(E - v)}/\hbar$$

10. Find the expectation value for the momentum,

$$\bar{p} \equiv \langle p \rangle \equiv \int \psi^* \mathbf{p} \psi \, dx = \int \psi^* \left(-i\hbar \frac{\partial}{\partial x} \right) \psi \, dx$$

and the expectation value for p^2,

$$\overline{p^2} \equiv \langle p^2 \rangle \equiv \int \psi^* \mathbf{p}^2 \psi \, dx = \int \psi^* \left(\hbar^2 \frac{\partial^2}{\partial x^2} \right) \psi \, dx$$

for each of the following wave functions which describe a particle in a box.

(a) $\psi = A \exp i\kappa x$
(b) $\psi = A \exp -i\kappa x$
(c) $\psi = A (\exp i\kappa x + \exp -i\kappa x)$

Which of these is an eigenfunction of $\mathbf{p}$? of $\mathbf{p}^2$? Discuss the physical significance of the answers found. (Note that ψ is an eigenfunction of an operator $\mathbf{Q}$ if $\mathbf{Q}\psi = q\psi$, where q is a constant, to be interpreted as the value that the physical quantity corresponding to the operator $\mathbf{Q}$ will necessarily have when the system is in the state ψ. If ψ is not an eigenfunction, then a measurement of q may give more than one possible value, the average value to be expected for a series of measurements of q being given by $\langle q \rangle = \int \psi^* \mathbf{Q}\psi \, d\tau$.)

11. Find the commutator, $[\mathbf{x}, d/dx]$, of the operators $\mathbf{x}$ and d/dx from the explicit equation

$$(x \, d/dx - d/dx \, x) f(x) = [\mathbf{x}, d/dx] f(x)$$

where $f(x)$ is an arbitrary function. Show that the choice of operators, $\mathbf{x} = x$ and $\mathbf{p}_x = -i\hbar \, d/dx$, is consistent with equations V-20 and V-21.

12. Show that $\mathbf{E}$ and $\mathbf{t}$ satisfy the equation $[\mathbf{t}, \mathbf{E}] = i\hbar$ if $\mathbf{E} = -i\hbar\partial/\partial t$ and $\mathbf{t} = t$.

13. The molecule NO has a state of energy above its most stable state corresponding to a wavenumber value of 121.1 cm^{-1}. Find the population in the upper level at 300°K, assuming the same degeneracy, or statistical weight, for the two levels.

14. Calculate the dipole moment in debyes (1 D $= 10^{-18}$ esu/cm) to be expected for HCl (bond length 1.27 Å) if the molecule were purely ionic, with one electronic charge at each nucleus. The observed dipole moment is 1.03 D; what formal charge on the two nuclei would produce this value?

15. Find the oscillator strength in terms of the integrated absorptivity when the absorptivity is in the usual units of L/mole-cm and the integration is over all wavenumbers in units of cm^{-1}.

16. In the classical treatment of the Raman effect the emitted frequency is the frequency of oscillation of the dipole moment of the molecule, $\mu = \alpha \mathscr{E}$, where $\mathscr{E} = \mathscr{E}_0 \cos 2\pi \nu t$ and, if the molecule is vibrating with a frequency ν_0, $\alpha = \alpha_0 \cos 2\pi \nu_0 t$. Show that μ oscillates with the frequencies $\nu \pm \nu_0$.

17. Under certain conditions it is to be expected that an absorption band will have a contour described by the Lorentz equation, with absorptivity proportional to $[(\nu_0 - \nu)^2 + (\frac{1}{2}\Delta\nu_{1/2})^2]^{-1}$, where ν_0 is the frequency at the band center and $\Delta\nu_{1/2}$ is the half band width. In evaluating $\int a \, d\nu$ over an entire band it can be assumed that $\nu_0 \gg \Delta\nu_{1/2}$ and the integration can be carried out for the frequency interval 0 to ∞.

(a) Find the percentage error in evaluating the area under such an absorption curve if the integration is extended over an interval equal to twice the half width, $\nu_0 - \Delta\nu_{1/2}$ to $\nu_0 + \Delta\nu_{1/2}$.

(b) Find the percentage error if the integration extends over a range of $4\Delta\nu_{1/2}$.

VI

Electronic states
and electronic spectra

In the late nineteenth century the discovery of the electron, as a particle that obeyed Newton's laws[1] and constituted part of all matter, promised to provide one of the last pieces of the puzzle of the nature of matter and radiation. Newton's corpuscular theory of light had been replaced by the Huygens-Fresnel wave picture, which had in turn been justified and extended by the electromagnetic theory of Maxwell. The relationship between matter and radiation became more evident when a small charge was known to exist within the atom.

1   Atomic Structure and Spectra

From Maxwell's equations it was known that a charge undergoing an acceleration would radiate an electromagnetic wave; if the charge were oscillating, the frequency of the waves would be the frequency of oscillation of the charge. An obvious method of accelerating the electron would be to put it into a "planetary" orbit about a positively charged nucleus. The attractive force of the nucleus for the electron would constantly change the velocity (in direction, not in magnitude) of the electron, and the electron should accordingly radiate with a frequency equal to the frequency of the rotation. The simple picture had a seemingly insurmountable flaw, for if the electron lost energy by radiation it would move toward the nucleus. This would be evidenced by a rapidly increasing frequency of rotation as the electron spiraled into the nucleus. Such an atom would

[1] Relativistic effects, though often important for electrons, were not recognized in the early experiments.

thus be unstable and would give rise to a continuous range of frequencies, rather than a set of discrete frequencies.

To avoid the self-annihilation of the atom, it was considered necessary to postulate additional forces which would maintain the electrons in their natural positions. J. J. Thomson undertook the task of synthesizing these ideas into an atomic model, in which the electrons were assumed fixed in a uniform sphere of positive charge. The vibrations of the electrons were assumed to give rise to the observed frequencies. By regarding the electron as a strain center in the ether, Thomson and others also attempted to explain the inertia of matter as a consequence of the inertia, or inductance, of the electromagnetic field. This ambitious theory was seriously challenged by the experimental results of Rutherford and his co-workers, who demonstrated the existence of a very small, very heavy nucleus in a virtually "empty" atom.

By this time the spectra of many atoms had been observed and catalogued. Rydberg and Ritz showed that the frequencies belonging to the "principal" or "trunk" series, and to the "second subordinate," "main branch," or "sharp" series, could be represented by an equation of the form [1]

$$\frac{\nu}{N} = \frac{1}{(s + a)^2} + \frac{1}{(r + b)^2}$$

where s and r represent running indices which vary in integral steps, a and b are constants characteristic of the element, and N is a universal constant. If the terms occurring on the right side of the equation are catalogued, it is found that the number of terms is significantly less than the number of lines, since the same term may occur in more than one series. Also, as pointed out by Ritz, the difference between any two of these terms will give the position of a line in the spectrum.[2] The Ritz combination principle predicted the presence of many lines which were subsequently observed experimentally.

No explanation for the particular form of regularity could be found for some time; indeed there was considerable doubt about the nature of the process which gave rise to emission. It was generally believed that the emitted wave originated in a disturbance of electrons within the molecule or atom, although it was suggested [3] that "the electrons responsible for the

[1] See, for example, A. Schuster, "Spectroscopy," in *Encyclopedia Britannica*, eleventh edition, Cambridge, England, 1911.

[2] Exceptions to this, particularly in heavy atoms, are to be found as a consequence of selection rules. In the hydrogen atom the selection rules are always satisfied by one or more of the components of the degenerate energy levels defined by the principal quantum number n. See also White, ref. 46, p. 15.

[3] A. Schuster, *loc. cit.*

radiation are probably few and not directly involved in the structure of the atom." Severe difficulties arose in attempting to explain the observed temperature dependence of radiation intensity, as well as the very large number of frequencies observed for each element. It was suggested that free electrons (postulated by Thomson to be present in all matter, but more mobile in conductors than in non-conductors) might attach themselves to a molecule or detach themselves from it. Moderately convincing arguments in favor of this hypothesis were put forward, but no detailed description of the process was provided that could fit all the known facts.

1.1 Bohr Model

Niels Bohr[1] provided the first real breakthrough in 1913 when he suggested that certain of the laws of classical electromagnetic theory might not be valid at the atomic level. Specifically Bohr proposed (1) that the electron of the hydrogen atom moved in a classical planetary orbit, in the coulombic field of the nucleus; (2) that such motion was *not* accompanied by emission of radiation; (3) that only certain orbits were possible—those which gave the electron an angular momentum of an integral number times $h/2\pi$—and the electron could be found only in one of these special orbits; and (4) that jumps between permitted orbits were possible, the energy difference being gained or lost by means of absorption or emission of radiation. The frequency emitted or absorbed could be related to the energy difference of the two levels by means of Planck's equation, $v = \Delta E/h$.

An electron traveling in a circular orbit at a distance r from a stationary nucleus of charge Ze will experience a centripetal force, according to Coulomb's law, of Ze^2/r^2 and thus a radial acceleration of mv^2/r. Equating these and requiring that $mvr = nh$ leads to the equations

$$T = \tfrac{1}{2}mv^2 = Ze^2/2r$$

$$r = \frac{Ze^2}{mv^2} = \frac{mZe^2r^2}{n^2\hbar^2}$$

$$V = \int_\infty^r Ze^2 \, dr/r^2 = -Ze^2/r$$

$$E = T + V = -Ze^2/2r$$

$$= -\frac{Z^2e^4m}{2n^2\hbar^2}$$

$$= -\frac{Z^2}{n^2}\,hcR \tag{VI-1}$$

[1] N. Bohr, *Phil. Mag.* **26**, 1–25, 476–502, 857–875 (1913); **27**, 506–524 (1913); **29**, 332–335 (1915).

R is the Rydberg constant, which has a value for the hydrogen atom of $109,677.576 \pm 0.012 \, \text{cm}^{-1}$. This varies slightly from one atom to another, increasing with increasing atomic mass toward a limiting value of $109,737.309 \pm 0.012 \, \text{cm}^{-1}$, since the nucleus is not truly stationary and the mass m above must be replaced by the reduced mass for electron and nucleus.

Equation VI-1 applies to all hydrogen-like atoms and ions, H, He+, Li2+, ..., and for these it is extremely accurate. The treatment originally given by Bohr was later modified to include elliptical, as well as circular,

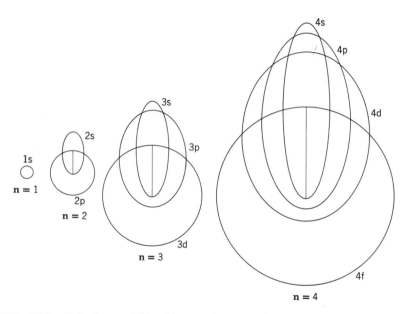

FIG. VI-1. Bohr-Sommerfeld orbits. Major axis of ellipse is proportional to n^2, minor axis to **kn**.

orbits and to account for relativistic effects. These variations do not significantly change the expression for the energy of the orbits.

According to the Bohr-Sommerfeld model the principal quantum number, **n**, is a measure of the average distance of the electron from the nucleus. The major axis of the elliptical orbits is proportional to n^2, the minor axis to **kn** where k is a positive, non-zero integer less than or equal to **n**. The "azimuthal" quantum number, k, is not only a measure of the eccentricity of the orbit but also of the angular momentum, which is just **k$\hbar$**. The forms of the Bohr-Sommerfeld orbits are shown in Fig. VI-1.

The Bohr model explains the spectrum of hydrogen and the hydrogen-like ions very adequately.   The frequencies of the lines are obtained by combining Planck's equation with equation VI-1 to obtain

$$\nu = Rc(1/n_2{}^2 - 1/n_1{}^2) \qquad\qquad \text{(VI-2)}$$

The similarity of this equation to that proposed by Ritz is quite apparent. The individual "terms," or "term values," are to be interpreted as the energies of the various states expressed in frequency or wavenumber units. The Lyman series, which is observed in emission or absorption in the far ultraviolet (above 82,000 cm^{-1}, or below 1216 Å), is obtained from equation VI-2 by setting n_1 equal to 1.   This series corresponds to transitions to or from the ground state of the hydrogen atom.   The Balmer series, in the visible region, is obtained by setting $n_1 = 2$; the Paschen series by setting $n_1 = 3$; the Brackett series by setting $n_1 = 4$; and the Pfund series by setting $n_1 = 5$.   In each case the integer n_2 is allowed to take on all values greater than n_1.   These series correspond to transitions in which the lower state is an excited state of the hydrogen atom.   Except at very high temperatures (for example, in certain stars) these series are observed only in the emission spectrum.

For the hydrogen atom the energy depends only on the principal quantum number n, except for an extremely small dependence on k that arises from relativistic effects.   The alkali metals behave in many respects like hydrogen, since the outermost electron moves in a field of nearly spherical symmetry produced by the nucleus and the inner electrons.   The spectra are more complex, however, since the degeneracies of the hydrogen atom are split in the alkali metals.   A brief examination of one of these spectra will not only assist in understanding the states of the hydrogen atom but will also introduce the system of nomenclature that has become universal in spectroscopy, valence theory, and many other branches of physics.   To avoid a later change in notation the newer results of quantum mechanics concerning the angular momentum values will be incorporated into the treatment.

The spectrum of lithium is represented in Fig. VI-2.   On this figure the three series, known as the "principal," "sharp," and "diffuse" series, have been indicated.   The first is so named because it is the only series observed in absorption under laboratory conditions (this is the Lyman series for hydrogen).   The sharp and diffuse series are named because the individual lines tend to have the corresponding appearance.   In Fig. VI-3 the energy levels for the lithium atom are shown, along with the transitions between these levels that give rise to the spectrum.   It will be observed that the members of the sharp series correspond to transitions from the lowest of the levels for each value of n.   These levels are therefore designated s levels; they represent the minimum amount of angular momentum (one

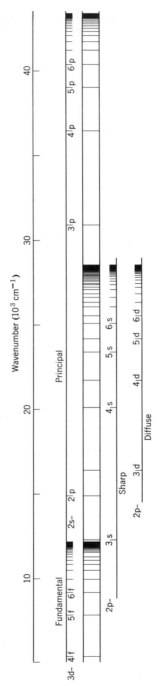

FIG. VI-2.   Representation of the emission spectrum of lithium, showing the assignment of lines to the overlapping series.

unit according to the Bohr picture, but zero according to current theory). The principal series consists of transitions from (or to) the next lowest levels in each set, which are designated p states.   In the same way the

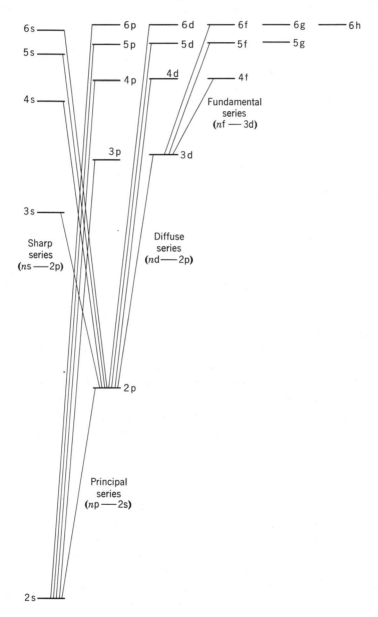

FIG. VI-3.   Energy levels of the Li atom.

initial states of the diffuse and fundamental series transitions are known as d and f states.   States of higher angular momentum are given the subsequent letters of the alphabet, g, h, i, . . . (but j is omitted because of the identity of I and J in German).   Table VI-I summarizes this notation.

TABLE VI-I

Old Quantum Theory, k	New Quantum Number, $l = k - 1$	Magnitude of Angular Momentum	Designation of State
1	0	0	s
2	1	$\sqrt{2}\,\hbar$	p
3	2	$\sqrt{6}\,\hbar$	d
4	3	$\sqrt{12}\,\hbar$	f
5	4	$\sqrt{20}\,\hbar$	g

According to quantum mechanics the total angular momentum is actually $\sqrt{l(l + 1)}\,\hbar$ (section V-3.2), as indicated in the third column of the Table.

The levels shown in Fig. VI-3 are necessarily degenerate, with the exception of the s series, since an angular momentum of magnitude $\sqrt{l(l + 1)}\,\hbar$ can have $2l + 1$ possible orientations in space (Fig. V-13).   The p states have a degeneracy of three for this reason, the d states a degeneracy of five, f states a degeneracy of seven.   The intrinsic angular momentum of the electron produces an additional two-fold degeneracy.

Attempts to extrapolate the Bohr model to more complex atoms were generally unsuccessful, but the Bohr model did give a qualitative picture of atomic structure that proved of great value in the interpretation of many of the previous observations of physicists and chemists.   It was, for example, on the basis of the Bohr model that G. N. Lewis was able to construct his picture of chemical valence that has been the foundation of modern chemistry.

1.2   Quantum Mechanical Model

The failure of the Bohr-Sommerfeld model to predict accurately the energy levels of complex atoms may be considered to arise from two fundamental difficulties.   One is the question of interpretation, for the theory assumed predictable orbits for the electrons and thus did not account for the uncertainties in position that must be found in any experiment.   The second is associated with the very specific, but arbitrary, method by which the proper orbits are chosen.   The restriction of the angular momentum of the single electron of hydrogen-like atoms to integral multiples of $\hbar$ is not only essentially correct (to the extent indicated by Table VI-I) but is also adequate for fixing the energy of an electron in a Bohr circular orbit.   In a two-electron atom, or a more complex system, this simple device is not adequate.   In particular, the simple Bohr picture does not provide any means for fixing the relative positions, and hence the interaction energy, for the electrons.[1]   The total energy of the helium atom is not even approximately the sum of the energies that would be

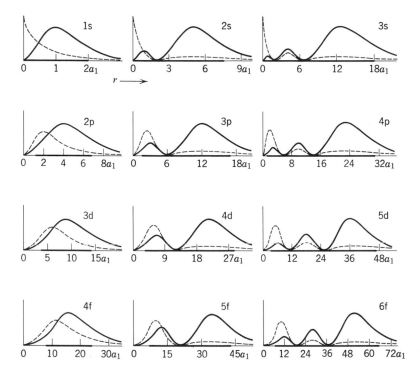

FIG. VI-4.   Probability density, $\psi^*\psi$ (dashed line), and radial distribution function, $4\pi r^2 \psi^* \psi$ (solid line), for orbitals of the hydrogen atom.   Heavy lines along the horizontal axis show the excursion of the electron in the Bohr-Sommerfeld orbits with angular momentum $\sqrt{l(l + 1)}\hbar$.   Distance is in units of the Bohr radius, $a_1 = 0.529$ Å.

calculated for a helium nucleus and each of the electrons present by itself, since the interaction energy between the electrons is comparable in magnitude with the ionization energy of the helium atom.

The new quantum mechanics, largely formulated by de Broglie, Heisenberg, Schroedinger, and Dirac but shaped by the contributions of many others, overcomes the difficulties of the old quantum theory by constructing

[1] Bauman and Considine, *J. Chem. Phys.* **34**, 1388 (1961).

formal rules on the foundation of the uncertainty principle, employing the methods of operator mathematics (section V-2). Details of the solution of the Schroedinger equation for the hydrogen atom will be postponed to chapter X, but an examination of certain of the results will illustrate both the differences and the similarities between the Bohr model and the exact quantum mechanical solution.

The shapes of the Bohr-Sommerfeld orbits were shown in Fig. VI-1; Fig. VI-4 gives the range of variation of r for them, along with the probable position of the electron as determined by the wave-function solution. Two

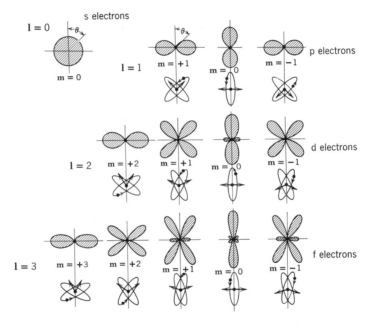

FIG. VI-5. Angular dependence of hydrogen-atom orbitals. Functions plotted in Fig. VI-4 should be multiplied by the corresponding function shown above. The related classical orbits are also shown. (From White, ref. 46.)

curves, representing the answers to two distinct questions, are given. If one asks, "Where is the electron most likely to be found?" this can be answered by evaluating $\int \Psi^* \Psi \, dx \, dy \, dz$ for various volume elements in space. The dotted curve, $\Psi^* \Psi$, may be considered the probability per unit volume.

It will be observed that the maximum probability for each of the s states occurs at the nucleus. This is consistent with the known tendency of the proton to attract the electron according to Coulomb's law, but it seems to disagree very strongly with the Bohr picture of an electron moving around the nucleus at a distance of about half an ångstrom.   This discrepancy disappears if one asks the question about the location of the electron in a somewhat different manner: "At what distance from the proton is the electron most likely to be found?"   To answer this it is necessary to compare the probability of finding the electron within a shell of radius r_1 and thickness dr with the probability of finding the electron in another shell of the same thickness but of radius r_2.   For this purpose one chooses a volume element of $4\pi r^2\,dr$, corresponding to the volume of a thin shell of radius r.   The product $\Psi^*\Psi 4\pi r^2\,dr$, known as the radial distribution function, is plotted in Fig. VI-4 as a solid curve.[1]   The agreement between the maximum of the radial distribution curve for the 1s state and the value predicted by the Bohr model for this state is certainly noteworthy.

Only the radial dependence of the wave functions in indicated by curves such as those of Fig. VI-4.   In Fig. VI-5 an attempt is made to depict the variation in magnitude of $\Psi^*\Psi$ with angle for certain planes through the nucleus.

I.3   Quantum Numbers and Term Symbols

Three coordinates are necessary to specify the position of any point particle in non-relativistic classical mechanics.   The same number of coordinates, or quantum numbers, will be required in non-relativistic quantum mechanics.   To distinguish between the states described by a probability function, Ψ, and the orbits of the Bohr model, the states described by electronic wave functions (exclusive of spin) are called "orbitals."   For an electron in a hydrogen atom the orbital is specified by the quantum numbers **n, l,** and **m.**

The principal quantum number, **n,** is a measure of the average distance of the electron from the nucleus but, whereas n^2 represented the major axis of the ellipse of the Bohr orbit, **n** gives the number of nodal surfaces of the orbital wave function according to quantum mechanics.   The interpretation of **l** as the (orbital) angular momentum has already been discussed (Table VI-I).   The third quantum number, **m,** specifies the projection of the orbital angular momentum along any axis.   Associated with the orbital angular momentum (given classically by $I\omega$, or mvr) is a magnetic moment, analogous to the magnetic field produced by a current flowing in a loop of wire.   In a magnetic field the energy of the electron will depend on how the magnetic moment is aligned with respect to the

[1] The ordinate in the graphs of Fig. VI-4 may be considered to be $\Psi^*\Psi$ measured along a particular line passing through the nucleus.   More specifically, the wave function may be written as the product of three functions; $\Psi = R(r)\Theta(\theta)\Phi(\phi)$.   The first, $R^2(r)$, is plotted in Fig. VI-4; the angular terms are represented in Fig. VI-5.

field, but since the magnetic moment is fixed (antiparallel) with respect to the angular momentum, which can take on only certain positions with respect to any axis, it follows that the magnetic moment can be oriented in only a few ways and hence the energy can take on only certain discrete values. In the absence of complications, therefore, a state in which the electron has an angular momentum l will be split by a magnetic field into $2l + 1$ states, corresponding to the $2l + 1$ possible values of the quantum number m. Each of these states will have an angular momentum along the axis of the imposed magnetic field equal to mh, and a magnetic moment along the same axis of $-(e/2mc)mh$, or $-m$ Bohr magnetons. To obtain full agreement with experiment it is necessary to include the effects of the magnetic moment associated with the electron spin angular momentum (section X-2).

In relativistic mechanics four coordinates are required to fix the position of any point particle in space-time. This makes it necessary to add a fourth quantum number in order to completely describe the electron. The additional quantum number is associated with the direction of the intrinsic angular momentum of the electron, commonly known as the spin. To explain this intrinsic angular momentum it is sometimes imagined that the electron spins on its own axis; such a picture accounts for some of the properties of the electron. As there are serious difficulties to such an interpretation, however, it should not be taken very seriously. The intrinsic angular momentum of the electron has a magnitude of $\sqrt{\frac{3}{4}}\,\hbar$; hence it can have a projection of only $\pm\frac{1}{2}\hbar$ along any axis.

In light atoms there is virtually no interaction between the spin and the orbital angular momentum. The difference in energy between the two possible orientations of the spin is vanishingly small. The spin is, therefore, the least important of the quantum numbers. On the other hand, the very fact that the spin is left unchanged by nearly all forces acting on the atom makes it a convenient label and for this reason it plays a prominent role in many theoretical treatments.

The vector sum of orbital and spin angular momenta is restricted to discrete values and is given the designation $\vec{j}$. The total angular momentum of the electron is then $\sqrt{j(j + 1)}\,\hbar$. In an atom with more than one electron the vector sum of the orbital angular momenta, $\vec{l}_i$, is indicated by the symbol $\vec{L}$; the vector sums of the spins, $\vec{s}_i$, by the symbol $\vec{S}$; and the total angular momentum by the symbol $\vec{J}$, where $\vec{J} = \vec{L} + \vec{S}$. The projections of any of these along an axis are then designated M_L, M_S, or M_J. Just as the electronic states with $l = 0, 1, 2, \ldots$ were called s, p, d, $\ldots$ states, the states of the atom with $L = 0, 1, 2, \ldots$ are called S, P, D, $\ldots$ states. This indication of electronic properties with small letters and atomic properties with capital letters is quite general.

The states of an atom are represented by "term symbols" based on the value of the total orbital angular momentum, $\mathbf{L}$. To the basic symbol (S, P, D, F, . . .) indicating the value of $\mathbf{L}$ is added a left superscript which gives the value of the "multiplicity," $2S + 1$, where S is the quantum number of total electron spin. A right subscript may be added to indicate the value of $\mathbf{J}$. For example, the ground state of the hydrogen atom ($\mathbf{L} = \mathbf{l} = 0$; $\mathbf{S} = \mathbf{s} = \frac{1}{2}$; $\mathbf{J} = \mathbf{L} + \mathbf{S} = \frac{1}{2}$) has the term symbol $^2S_{1/2}$ (read "doublet S one half"). The alkali metals will have the same term symbol, since closed shells are spherically symmetrical and do not contribute angular momentum of any kind. The nitrogen atom in its lowest energy state has two electrons in states with $\mathbf{n} = 1, \mathbf{l} = 0$; two with $\mathbf{n} = 2, \mathbf{l} = 0$, and three with $\mathbf{n} = 2, \mathbf{l} = 1$. This is called an electronic "configuration" and is written

$$(1s)^2(2s)^2(2p)^3$$

For this particular configuration three states are possible (sec. X-2.13), depending upon the relative directions of the angular momenta of the three 2p electrons. The lowest state is a $^4S_{3/2}$ (read "quartet S three halves"), the next a ^2D, the highest a ^2P. The last two will each consist of two states, $^2D_{3/2}$, $^2D_{5/2}$ and $^2P_{1/2}$, $^2P_{3/2}$. The difference in energy between components of these doublets will be very small. All terms for which $\mathbf{L} \geqslant \mathbf{S}$ will split into $2S + 1$ states, as suggested by the name "multiplicity" given to this quantity. If $\mathbf{L} \leqslant \mathbf{S}$ only $2L + 1$ states will arise, since $\mathbf{J}$ varies between $|\mathbf{L} + \mathbf{S}|$ and $|\mathbf{L} - \mathbf{S}|$, but such terms are given the same multiplicity designation as if the full amount of splitting occurred.

An additional symbol is sometimes added to the term symbol to show "parity," the behavior of the total electronic wave function on reflection through the origin (inversion). If the wave function remains unchanged, as it will for one electron in an s or d state, the state is called "even"; if the wave function changes sign, as it will for one electron in a p or f state, the state is called "odd." Odd states are indicated by a right superscript o, with no mark for even states, or the even and odd states are distinguished by a right subscript g (even, for German *gerade*) or u (odd, for German *ungerade*). The latter is the more explicit, since the parity is often not specified and the absence of a symbol cannot be taken as an indication that the state is even.

Determination of the possible states of an atom requires an application of the Pauli Exclusion Principle. According to this rule the total electronic wave function must change sign if any two electrons are exchanged. One consequence of this is that no two electrons can be in identical states; that is, no two electrons can have the same set of four quantum numbers in any atom or molecule.   It is, of course, this restriction that gives rise to the Periodic Table of the elements.

A quantum number indicates the value of a physical quantity that remains constant with time.   In classical mechanics such quantities are called "constants of the motion."   They are direct consequences of the conservation laws: conservation of energy, linear momentum, angular momentum, or projection of angular momentum along an axis parallel to an applied force.   It is important that the quantum numbers chosen correspond to physical quantities which are truly constant.   Consider, for example, the classical problem of a ball swinging on the end of a string. So long as the ball is moving in a circular orbit, the velocity will be constantly changing and would not be a good choice for describing the motion. The angular velocity, or angular momentum, would be constant and would provide much of the information that could be specified about the motion. If now the string should break, the motion of the same ball could be conveniently described in terms of a constant linear velocity but not in terms of angular velocity.

In the preceding discussion little attention was paid to the validity of the quantum numbers which were derived for the hydrogen atom when these numbers are applied to larger atoms.   The number of states, and the number of parameters required to describe these states, will be constant as the forces are changed (Ehrenfest's Adiabatic Theorem).   Thus, because it is known that four quantum numbers are necessary for an electron in a hydrogen atom, it follows that an atom with N electrons will require $4N$ quantum numbers.   The best choice of these is not immediately obvious.   For many purposes it does no harm to assume that the four quantum numbers, **n**, **l**, **m**, and **s**, for each electron are valid as well as certain vector sums of these, such as **L**, **S**, and **J**.   However, certain predictions based on such assumptions are not in agreement with experiment for heavy atoms.   The observed behaviors are described in terms of "coupling" rules which attempt to specify which vector sums will be constant and which will be constant in magnitude but not in direction. Variations in coupling give rise to changes in intensities of spectral lines as well as to changes in energies of individual states.

Transitions are possible for any value of Δn.   There must be a change in angular momentum of the atom upon absorption or emission of a photon.   The selection rules expressing this are $\Delta l = \pm 1$ for the electron involved and $\Delta L = \pm 1$ for the atom.   Transitions with $\Delta l = 0$ or $\Delta L = 0$ are forbidden by the spherical symmetry of light atoms but may appear for heavier atoms in which the coupling conditions are different.   For light atoms also the spin is unaffected by the transition; $\Delta S = 0$.   It is this restriction that makes the "multiplicity" such a convenient label for the individual states, for transitions will occur only between states of the same multiplicity.   In addition, there is a rigorous condition that radiative transitions will take place in the free atom only between even and odd states; $g \leftrightarrow u$, $g \not\leftrightarrow g$, $u \not\leftrightarrow u$.

1.4 Periodic Table and Ionization Energies

The Schroedinger equation cannot be solved exactly for atoms containing more than one electron.   Calculations by approximation procedures work quite well for two-electron problems but become exceedingly complex as the number of electrons increases.   It is therefore necessary to extrapolate from simple cases, making adjustments as required to conform to experimental results.

It is particularly illuminating, for purposes of understanding molecule formation, to examine the relationship between ionization energies and the Periodic Table.   The ionization energy of an atom is the amount of work that must be done to remove the outermost electron from its normal state to a distance sufficiently great that it is effectively free of the field of the ion.   It is essentially the difference in energy between an atom and its free, singly charged ion.

The total energy of an atom can be shown (by the Virial Theorem) to be proportional to its average potential energy.   This is determined by coulombic forces and depends only on distances and the number of charges acting on the electron.   For hydrogen-like ions the force acting on the electron, at a given distance, is proportional to the nuclear charge, but the equilibrium distance varies inversely with nuclear charge.   The ionization energy is accordingly proportional to the square of nuclear charge.   For atoms such as the alkali metals, on the other hand, the valence electron is effectively attracted by a sphere of unit charge of increasing radius as atomic number is increased.   The ionization energy in such a series drops as the size of the atom is increased.

If each electron in helium were independent of the field due to the other electron, the ionization energy of helium would be expected to be four times as great as that of hydrogen.   If the second electron were effectively shielded from the nucleus by the first electron, the ionization energy of helium should be approximately the same as that of hydrogen.   The observed result must fall between these two limits; it is found that the ionization energy is just about twice that of hydrogen.   This result can be generalized as follows.   The ionization energy varies linearly with effective nuclear charge (charge on nucleus minus number of inner electrons screening the nucleus), except that whenever two electrons must be put into the same orbital there is a decrease in stability of roughly 1 to 3 ev.

Ionization energies are shown in Fig. VI-6, plotted against atomic number. Lithium has a triply charged nucleus and two 1s electrons screening the 2s electron from the nucleus. Beryllium has one more charge on the nucleus, the same number of screening electrons, but the second 2s electron goes into the same orbital as the first. The ionization energy of beryllium is thus twice that of lithium minus about $1\frac{1}{2}$ ev. In boron, carbon, and nitrogen the electrons go into 2p orbitals There are three 2p orbitals, and the electrons go into separate orbitals to keep as far from each other as possible. They are only partially screened by the two 2s electrons; drawing a straight line through the three

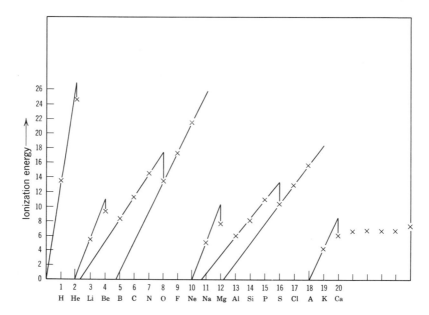

FIG. VI-6.   Ionization energy plotted against atomic number.

points suggests an effective nuclear charge of about 2.7 for boron. An additional 2p electron added to form oxygen must go into one of the three orbitals already occupied; there is a corresponding drop in ionization energy below the extrapolated value, and for the same reason the ionization energies of fluorine and neon are similarly depressed. Sodium begins a new cycle in essentially the same pattern.

At the transition elements a difference appears. Additional charges are being added to the nucleus, but the compensating electrons are going into the 3d orbitals, which are moderately effective at screening the outermost 4s electrons. The ionization energy stays roughly constant through this process, then repeats the pattern through the remainder of the table. Second and third ionization energies follow the same rules.

It is not clear just why the ionization energy should be so nearly linear with effective nuclear charge, or why the extra repulsion energy associated with putting two electrons into the same orbital should be so nearly constant. However, each of these empirical rules has an analog in problems of molecular structure.

2   Molecular Electronic States and Spectra

Calculation of the properties of molecules is more difficult than for atoms because of the lower symmetry as well as the generally larger number of particles. These difficulties are partially circumvented in most discussions of molecules by approximations of two types. It is assumed that the atoms constituting the molecule can be described in terms of hydrogen atom wave functions with only minor modification of these functions by the bonding process. It is also assumed that the electrons in the inner shells (electrons inside the outermost, or valence, shell) are unaffected by the bonding process.

It should be remembered that these approximations are not justified by theory or by experiment except in a very qualitative sense. Many molecules can be conveniently described in this way, but many others exhibit properties which are incompatible with this simple picture. Emphasis in this chapter will be placed on the qualitative properties of molecules. Application of this picture to the identification of substances by means of their electronic spectra will be considered in chapter VIII, and more exact methods of describing the electronic states will be discussed in chapter X.

2.1   Principles of Chemical Valence

Molecules are held together by the same forces that hold atoms together, the coulombic interaction between charges. Magnetic forces must sometimes be considered, but only as a small perturbation, since the magnitude of these effects is very much smaller than the energy associated with chemical binding. Nuclear forces are very powerful but of extremely short range. They may be neglected at distances as great as 10^{-2} Å. Gravitational forces are completely negligible at all distances for charged particles.

An understanding of the nature of chemical binding can best be obtained by means of a model related to the Bohr model of atomic structure. The potential field that will be seen by an electron moving in the vicinity of two protons is plotted by means of contour lines in Fig. VI-7.   An electron at a distance r from one nucleus of charge Ze has a potential energy of $-Ze^2/r$; for an electron midway between two such nuclei at a distance r from each the potential energy is $-Ze^2(4 - Z)/2r$.   The difference is $Ze^2(2 - Z)/2r$, which represents the energy[1] of stabilization of the electron between the two nuclei as compared to the dissociated system of an electron at a distance r from one nucleus with the other nucleus removed to a great distance.

A static system of charges cannot be stable (Earnshaw's theorem); in either the atom or the molecule, the potential energy can be lowered by allowing the electron to fall into a nucleus.   The large amount of kinetic energy produced as the electron is accelerated toward the nucleus would be expected, classically, to be dissipated by radiation.   This is not possible if the radiation process is restricted to transitions between certain allowed levels.   Thus, if the electron can be put into a lowest allowed level near the nuclei, it must remain in that same energy state until disturbed by outside forces.   The change in potential energy associated with a displacement toward a nucleus will give rise to an equal and opposite change in kinetic energy, as in the motion of a pendulum or a mass on a spring.   The total energy will be constant and equal to half the average potential energy.

In discussions of chemical bonding emphasis is sometimes placed on the kinetic energy.   For example, it is argued that as the available space is increased the energy is lowered; this has been given at times as a cause for formation of a bond when two atoms, such as two hydrogen atoms, come together.   The conclusion that a bond is formed is experimentally confirmed, but the argument employed is open to serious question.   According to equation V-25 it is clear that for a particle in a box the energy does indeed vary inversely with the square of the dimensions of the box.   But it must be remembered that this is solely kinetic energy; the potential energy has been assumed zero throughout the box.   If the "box" arises from coulombic forces, the virial theorem must be obeyed in the form $\bar{T} = -E = -\frac{1}{2}\bar{V}$.   Thus an increase in the average kinetic energy represents a lower value of E (E more negative) or a *more stable* system. Increasing the width of the potential well, if one still can apply equation V-25 qualitatively at least, should therefore represent a higher-energy, or less stable, state.

The physical reasoning behind the last conclusion is not hard to find. Any particle with kinetic energy greater than zero will tend to wander.   It can only be confined by means of a fence or by putting it into a well.   The greater the kinetic energy, the deeper is the well required to contain the

[1] This is only potential energy, but the total energy is proportional to average potential energy (section V-1.4).

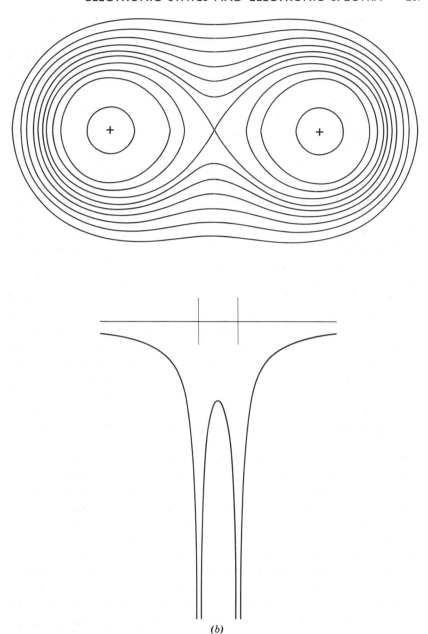

(b)

FIG. VI-7. (a) Equipotential lines about two equal positive charges. (b) Potential field due to two protons, along internuclear axis; positions of protons are indicated by vertical lines.

particle.   The total energy drops because the potential energy falls twice as fast as the kinetic energy climbs.   There is ample evidence that equation V-25 can be applied to certain problems involving potential wells produced by charged particles, but the information obtained is the spacing of energy levels for certain electrons moving in the field produced by other charges.[1] One must not conclude that a closer spacing of levels in butadiene than in butane indicates that butadiene is more stable than butane, nor that the π electrons in butadiene are more firmly bound than the σ electrons.

The equipotential lines for a single nucleus are concentric circles about the nucleus.   An electron in a circular Bohr orbit follows these lines.   An electron following the equipotential lines in the vicinity of two nuclei will move about both nuclei, if it has an energy great enough to move from one to the other.   On the basis of these purely classical considerations and with the benefit of knowledge of the success of the Bohr model, it seems quite reasonable to expect that the system consisting of two protons and one electron, the hydrogen molecule ion, H_2^+, should be stable.   This species has actually been observed and the dissociation energy ($H_2^+ \rightarrow H + p$) has been found to be 2.648 ev.   The electron distribution, found by solving the Schroedinger equation (exactly), is indicated in Fig. VI-8.

By analogy with the energies found for electrons in atoms it might be expected that, as a first approximation, the dissociation energy would vary linearly with the number of electrons between the nuclei, except for the discrepancy of about 1 to 3 ev when two electrons must go into the same orbital.   The observed value is indeed in surprisingly good agreement with this semiempirical prediction.   The observed dissociation energy of H_2 is 4.476 ev, which is about 0.8 ev less than twice the value for the hydrogen molecule ion.   (See also section VII-2.)

It might be expected that addition of a third electron would further increase the dissociation energy, by a somewhat smaller increment.   In the case of the hydrogen molecule this is not true, for reasons which are best expressed in terms of the hydrogen atom quantum numbers.   It seems reasonable to believe, and calculations support the assumption, that the hydrogen atom states with $n = 2$, which lie 82,000 cm^{-1} above the ground state, will carry over into high-energy states of the hydrogen molecule, since the magnitude of the interaction energy is only about one third as great.   About each of the two protons, therefore, an electron will find only two low-energy states corresponding to the 1s orbitals of the hydrogen atom.   Of these four states two will be symmetrical with respect to the

---

[1] This may be compared with the motions of the nuclei in a molecule.   The nuclear motions follow a quadratic potential function to a good approximation even though the total kinetic and potential energies depend on an inverse-square potential.   See problem VI-8.

two protons and two will be antisymmetrical; in the symmetrical states the electron will be in an orbital such as that of the hydrogen molecule ion, largely between the protons, whereas in the antisymmetrical states the electron spends more time in the region outside the nuclei.   One is tempted to apply the classical picture of an electron moving back and forth from one proton to the other, spending most of its time at the extremes of the

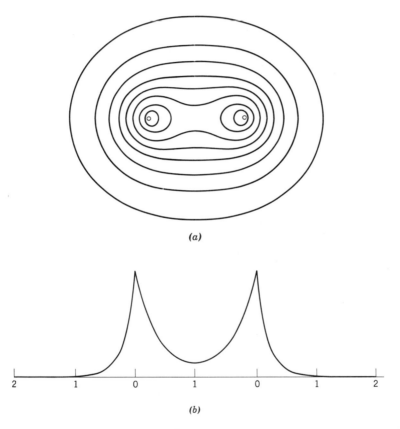

(a)

(b)

FIG. VI-8.   Electron density in H_2^+.   (a) Contour lines for electron wave function. (See Bates, Ledsham, and Stewart, *Phil. Trans. Roy. Soc.* **A246**, 215 (1953).)   (b) Electron density plotted against distance along the internuclear axis.

motion, and in some respects this picture seems to be helpful in characterizing such states.   Certainly it is observed that an electron in such an antisymmetrical state does not contribute to the chemical binding but rather tends to make the molecule unstable.

In general, it seems reasonable to expect that the number of low-energy orbitals available in a molecule will be determined by the number of low-energy orbitals in the respective free atoms, since the energy of bond formation is usually comparable to or less than the energy gap between the low-energy orbitals in the atom and the orbitals of the next shell or subshell. Elements of the first row of the Periodic Table will accordingly have a maximum of eight low-energy states; if each pair of occupied states is called a chemical bond, the reason for the observed tendency of these elements to form four bonds becomes apparent (BF_4^-, CH_4, NH_4^+).   Li and Be have fewer low-energy states; O and F (and N) have some of these orbitals filled completely by their own electrons.   The well-known rules of chemical valence are thus a consequence of (a) the binding effect due to the electrons between nuclei, (b) the number of low-energy states available in the vicinity of each atom, and (c) the restriction imposed by the Pauli Exclusion Principle on the number of electrons that can go into an orbital.

There is no reason to assume, from the arguments given above, that an electron must spend its time between two, and only two, nuclei.   Thus it is possible to have several nuclei bound simultaneously, with all the electrons moving freely between them.   Benzene and other aromatic molecules are known to be bound by such "communal" electrons; certain elements of group three form compounds (B_2H_6, Al_2Cl_6) in which it is necessary to assume that more than two nuclei are bound by each electron; and the binding of Na, Cu, Fe, and other metals is quite clearly an example of positively charged kernels bound by electrons which are, to a good approximation, free to move throughout the entire volume of the metal crystal.   Even in saturated molecules, such as CH_4, it can be shown (section X-2.3) that the electrons are not strictly localized between pairs of nuclei.

2.2   Description of States

States of electrons in molecules are classified in much the same way as in atoms.   The principal quantum number, **n**, is carried over from the ground state of the atom and is considered to be the most important in fixing the energy of the state.   The angular momentum of the electron further influences the energy, as it does in multi-electron atoms.   The magnitude of the angular momentum is not quite so important, however, as is the value of its projection on the internuclear axis.   The spin has no appreciable direct influence on the energy.

Detailed descriptions of electronic states will be postponed to section X-2, but a few characteristics are particularly helpful in understanding the elementary aspects of chemical bonding and electronic spectra.   The lowest-energy state for an electron in a diatomic molecule will be one in which the electron is most likely to be found between the nuclei, as in Fig. VI-8. Such a state is represented schematically in Fig. VI-9a. It can be shown that such a state, like the s state of an atom, has no angular momentum along the axis. A higher-energy level will be one in which the electron has unit angular momentum along the axis. Orbitals of this type (Fig. VI-9b) have a nodal plane passing through the two nuclei. They are necessarily doubly degenerate since the angular momentum can be pointed in either direction along the axis.

To distinguish between the projected angular momentum of an electron in a molecule (particularly a diatomic molecule) and the angular momentum of an electron in an atom, the molecular states are given Greek letter symbols. For example, the projection of l is given the symbol λ and states with $\lambda = 0, 1,$ or 2 are designated σ, π, or δ orbitals (only σ and π occur, with possible rare exceptions). The projection of the orbital angular momentum of the molecule along the internuclear axis is indicated by the symbol Λ and states with $\Lambda = 0, 1, 2 \ldots$ are given the term symbols Σ, Π, Δ, ... The total orbital angular momentum, when this is important, retains the symbol $\mathbf{L}$ and the total spin angular momentum retains the symbol $\mathbf{S}$. The projection of $\mathbf{S}$ on the axis is designated Σ, and the value of this quantity is specified by the multiplicity, defined as $2\Sigma + 1$. The total angular momentum of a molecule (diatomic or polyatomic), including electronic orbital and spin momenta and rotation of the entire molecule, but excluding nuclear spins, is given the symbol $\mathbf{J}$, as for atoms. The more important of these conventions are summarized in Table VI-II.

TABLE VI-II

Notation for Molecular States, Based on Angular Momentum

Physical Quantity	Quantum Number	Designation of States when Quantum Number has the Value		
		0	1	2
Projection of a.m. of one electron on axis	λ	σ	π	δ
Projection of molecular electronic orbital a.m. on axis	Λ	Σ	Π	Δ
Projection of molecular electronic spin a.m. on axis	Σ	Singlet	Triplet	Quintuplet
		(Doublet, quartet, etc., are also possible)		
Total molecular a.m. (excluding nuclear spins)	$\mathbf{J}$			

On the basis of these notation conventions, the orbitals depicted in Fig. VI-9 are called σ and π orbitals.   As in atomic orbitals, two electrons

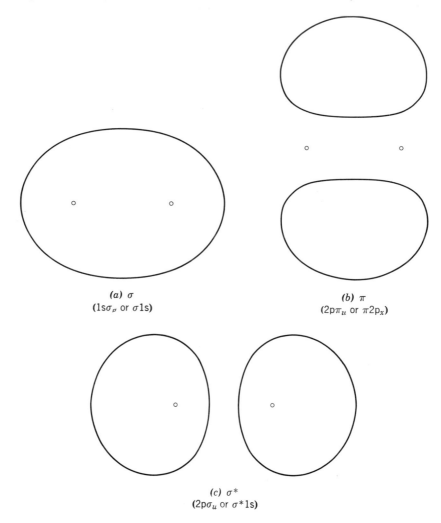

(a) σ
($1s\sigma_g$ or $\sigma 1s$)

(b) π
($2p\pi_u$ or $\pi 2p_x$)

(c) σ^*
($2p\sigma_u$ or $\sigma^* 1s$)

FIG. VI-9. Bonding and antibonding orbitals. (a) Contour line (constant electron density) for a bonding sigma orbital. (b) Bonding pi orbital. (c) Antibonding sigma orbital. These are drawn to the same scale and represent the same magnitude of the wave function. (Based on Bates, Ledsham, and Stewart, *loc. cit.*)

can be put into each orbital with four going into the two degenerate π orbitals. This notation should not be confused with statements concerning the atomic orbitals from which the molecular orbitals are formed.

A molecular σ orbital can be formed from atomic s, p, d, or f orbitals; a molecular π orbital, from atomic p, d or f orbitals, and so forth.   It should also be borne in mind that these designations are accurately defined only for diatomic molecules.   They may be carried over with some changes to linear polyatomic molecules but are only rough approximations when

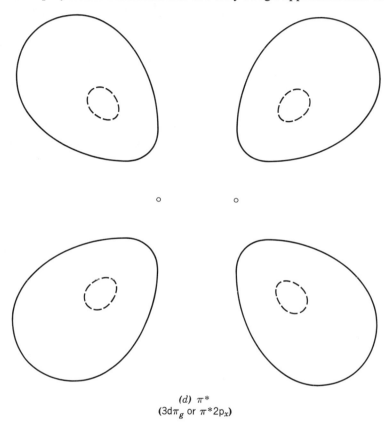

(d) π^*
$(3d\pi_g$ or $\pi^*2p_x)$

FIG. VI-9. (Continued). (*d*) Contour lines for an antibonding pi orbital. The electron density is largely compressed within the dashed areas; these contours represent lower density than for the other orbitals shown. (Based on Bates, Ledsham, and Stewart, *loc. cit.*)

applied to non-linear polyatomic molecules.   Even in diatomic molecules the shapes of the orbitals may be expected to vary with the number and states of the other electrons present.

A further approximate description that is often helpful is to divide orbitals into "bonding" and "antibonding" categories.   The prototype bonding σ orbital is that of the hydrogen molecule ion (Figs. VI-8 and

VI-9a). The corresponding antibonding orbital is shown schematically in Fig. VI-9c. The plane perpendicular to the internuclear axis is a nodal plane, with a change of sign of wave function across this plane. The probability of finding the electron on either side of this plane is the same. Such a state is sometimes interpreted, as suggested above, as one in which the electron oscillates from one extreme to the other. The antibonding π orbital is represented in Fig. VI-9d. This state has nodal planes passing through the nuclei and also cutting the internuclear axis. It is clearly antibonding, since the electrons tend to be outside, rather than between, the nuclei.[1] For homonuclear diatomic molecules the symbols σ_g, σ_u, π_u, and π_g designate bonding and antibonding orbitals. The g and u subscripts specify the behavior of these orbitals to the inversion operation.

In the bonding-antibonding mode of description the number of chemical bonds formed in a molecule is equal to the number of electrons in bonding orbitals, minus the number in antibonding orbitals, divided by two. For example, a single bond may consist of an equal number of "inner" electrons in bonding and antibonding orbitals (such "inner" orbitals are sometimes described as "non-bonding") plus two electrons in a σ orbital. A double bond may consist of such a σ bond plus two electrons in a π bond. A σ bond plus four electrons in a pair of degenerate π orbitals produces a triple bond, which, like the σ bond, has axial symmetry.

The description of electronic orbitals as σ and π orbitals is based on the assumption that the orbitals are similar to those in H_2^+ and H_2. For other diatomic molecules this is apparently a good approximation, and even polyatomic linear molecules can be treated in the same manner since the essential features of σ and π orbitals, the constant projection of the orbital angular momentum on the symmetry axis, must be applicable in so far as it is possible to talk of distinct electronic orbitals. For non-linear polyatomic molecules the approximation is more strained. It is nevertheless convenient to consider each chemical bond as if it were a diatomic molecule and to speak of σ and π orbitals in this sense. More accurate descriptions must then allow these orbitals to be combined. Particularly in conjugated systems, this classification is inadequate to distinguish between bonding electrons and the non-bonding, or "lone-pair," electrons of atoms such as oxygen, nitrogen, or the halogens. The non-bonding electrons are conventionally given the symbol n.

2.3 Electronic Spectra

All absorption of appreciable intensity in the visible region and at all higher frequencies, up to the level of nuclear reactions, is attributable to

[1] T. Berlin, *J. Chem. Phys.* **19**, 208 (1951).

transitions involving changes in the electronic structure of the substance. Since all matter contains bound electrons, all matter will show absorption in at least some part of this region. Certain molecules will absorb throughout virtually the entire region; others absorb only in the vacuum ultraviolet, a region inaccessible to most laboratories.

Many generalizations have been suggested for predicting the absorption spectra of compounds. Some of them are discussed in chapter VIII. All, however, are limited in reliability by the fact that the electronic absorption spectrum is not determined by the electronic state of the molecule at room temperature, but by the difference in energy between this ground state and the various excited states of the molecule. Thus molecules with seemingly very similar ground states may have very different spectra, or molecules with very different ground states may happen to have similar absorption spectra.

The standard chemical description often provides a reasonably accurate picture of the ground electronic state of a molecule, but excited states are not so easily predicted. Theoretical treatments are hampered by the failure of classical mechanics when applied to the motions of electrons and by the inseparability of the motions of the many electrons, which tend to be strongly coupled by their mutual coulombic interactions. Aside from the highly empirical generalizations, therefore, attempts to understand electronic spectra have been largely based on arguments dealing with molecular symmetries, with interpolations between limiting simplified forms (such as united-atom or separated-atom approximations), or on the results of approximate calculations.

Most molecules show only one or two electronic transitions, if any, in the visible and near ultraviolet regions. Small molecules in the vapor phase may show a great deal of structure in these bands, but it is typical of molecules in condensed phases that the absorption is broad and without structure or with half a dozen or fewer sub-bands. Interpretation is often based on absorption intensities almost as much as on the frequency of absorption or on the band shape.

A rather crude, but often helpful, semitheoretical method of predicting positions of electronic absorption bands can be derived from the Bohr model and the Correspondence Principle.[1] Quantization of electronic states becomes important for Bohr orbits of small radius; for large orbits the quantum mechanical results will approach the classical behavior. In the classical limit, however, the difference in energy between adjacent states becomes vanishingly small. If one could assign a size to the electronic orbitals in a molecule, it would seem that at least a rough correlation could be drawn between the size of the orbitals and the size of the

---

[1] See also problem V-4 and section X-2.3.

energy gap between orbitals; that is, larger orbitals should correspond to smaller energy differences and, therefore, lower absorption frequencies. Since only the lowest-frequency absorption band is sought, only the outermost electrons need be considered.

The hydrogen molecule represents a limiting case for small molecules, and the lowest-frequency transition of molecular hydrogen is found at 91,690 cm^{-1} (1090 Å), far into the vacuum ultraviolet. In saturated hydrocarbon molecules the electrons are not rigidly bound within a single chemical bond, and the absorption is accordingly moved to lower frequencies. At the same time, the isolation of electrons in the individual bonds suggested by chemical evidence is apparently not far wrong, since the absorption does not move very far from that of hydrogen. In particular, it is worth noting that the frequency does not depend strongly on the over-all molecular size. Long-chain paraffins are transparent throughout the visible and near ultraviolet regions.

Chemical, as well as spectroscopic, evidence suggests that electrons in π orbitals (double and triple bonds) are distributed over a larger volume than are electrons in σ orbitals (single bonds). The absorption in hydrocarbons containing one double bond occurs at the edge of the vacuum ultraviolet region, falling in the region of 50,000 to 60,000 cm^{-1} for most such compounds. Acetylenic molecules absorb in roughly the same region. Conjugation of multiple-order bonds, which is known from chemical reactions and bond lengths to be associated with an increased orbital size, tends to move the electronic absorption bands into the near ultraviolet.

A particular limiting form of conjugation of double bonds is to be found in the aromatic molecules. In them, the double and single bonds have completely lost their independent existence. Single-ring aromatics absorb in the vicinity of 40,000 cm^{-1} (2500 Å); naphthalenes in the vicinity of 33,000 cm^{-1} (3000 Å); anthracenes and phenanthrenes in the vicinity of 28,000 cm^{-1} (3600 Å); and larger fused-ring systems in the visible region.

Substitution of other atoms for carbon or hydrogen can cause remarkable changes in the spectrum. Alcohols and ethers, as well as saturated organic acids, are transparent in the near ultraviolet, but ketones and aldehydes absorb strongly in the vicinity of 36,000 cm^{-1} (2800 Å). Nitrogen, sulfur, and halogens tend to move absorption to lower frequencies.

A molecule containing two or more groups that would normally give rise to absorption in the near ultraviolet or visible region will show either of two patterns of behavior, depending on the relative positions of these groups. Unsaturated groups that are conjugated generally absorb at lower frequencies than would be predicted for either group alone. This is consistent with the picture of electrons moving freely between conjugated portions of the molecule and thus occupying larger orbitals. If the unsaturated groups are isolated by more than one carbon-carbon single bond, however, the absorption spectrum will tend to be very much the same as if two types of molecules were present, each containing one of the unsaturated groups.

The preceding discussion is extremely qualitative. With increasing understanding of molecular spectra it has become possible to distinguish between transitions of different types, depending on the orbitals initially and finally occupied by the electron responsible for the absorption. Particularly in conjugated systems, the lowest unoccupied orbital is most often a π orbital; the highest occupied orbitals are often π orbitals, with the non-bonding n orbitals of somewhat lower energy and the bonding σ orbitals of much lower energy. The most common transitions, therefore, are $\pi - \pi$ or $n - \pi$ transitions. They have different intensities and behave differently upon chemical substitution or change in molecular environment.

One might expect that $\pi - \pi$ transitions would be most sensitive to the size of the molecule, and especially to the size of the conjugated portion. Such transitions are often among the most intense, with oscillator strengths approaching (or exceeding) unity. Upper states of such transitions are given the symbol ^1B, so that a fully allowed $\pi - \pi$ transition from the ground state (given the symbol ^1A) is labeled a $^1B \leftarrow {}^1A$ transition. Not all $\pi - \pi$ transitions are this intense, however. The band may be weakened if a large change in linear or angular momentum is required (^1L upper state), if the transition violates the (weak) selection rule requiring a change of parity in molecules with a center of symmetry (^1C upper states), or if both a large change in angular or linear momentum and a violation of the parity selection rule is required (^1K upper state). Triplet upper states (^3B, ^3L, ^3C, ^3L, for example) may also be involved in the transition, with an additional loss of intensity over the other effects. Subscripts, a or b, are added to the symbols for the upper states to indicate the direction of the change in dipole moment in the plane of the molecule during the transition from the ground state. This can be determined in principle by measuring the absorption intensity with polarized radiation.

Transitions from non-bonding orbitals are expected only in molecules containing atoms such as N, O, or Cl (for example, heterocyclic aromatics). The intensity will depend more strongly on the immediate environment of the "hetero-atom" than on the length of the chain. For example, if the non-bonding electrons are exposed to polar solvent molecules the energy levels will be appreciably broadened and the transition may be moved to higher frequencies, disappearing in the limit of actual bonding between the hetero-atom and a proton in acid solution. The symmetry of the wave functions at the hetero-atom will also be of great importance; if the upper-state π orbital has a node at the hetero-atom the transition will be relatively unlikely ([1]U state, as contrasted with [1]W for the upper state of an allowed n — π transition). Additional symbols are available for labeling states within this system of notation,[1] and other independent notations have been employed. These are discussed in more detail in chapter VIII and in chapter X.

2.4   Franck-Condon Principle

It was pointed out above that for most molecules only one or two electronic transitions, at most, are directly observable (except in the vacuum ultraviolet), so that the ultraviolet-visible spectrum should be basically simple. Yet, for those polyatomic molecules that do exhibit electronic absorption in an accessible region, the superposition of vibrational transitions on the electronic transition leads to spectra that are not a single line or a group of lines but a complex combination of overlapping series of lines or a broad continuum.

Probably the most helpful rule in understanding the structure of electronic transitions is the principle first put forth by Franck and later placed on a firmer theoretical basis by Condon. The Franck-Condon principle is based upon the assumption that during an electronic transition the nuclei do not change their positions or their momenta. Consideration of the relative velocities of electrons and nuclei, or the low frequencies of vibrational motions compared to the Bohr orbital frequencies of electrons, strongly suggests the plausibility of the assumption, and the validity of the principle has been demonstrated by application to many observed spectra.

Considering only one of the possible modes of vibration of a polyatomic molecule, it is to be expected that the potential function corresponding to this mode of vibration will depend on the electronic state of the molecule. Specifically, it is quite likely that the equilibrium internuclear distance will differ in the upper electronic state from its value in the ground electronic state owing to a difference in bond strengths. In Fig. VI-10 vibrational potential energy curves are drawn for upper and lower electronic states under the assumption that the displacement of the minimum is zero, small, and large. It will be observed that the potential function is not a true parabola. It must continue to rise steeply as the nuclei approach, since they will strongly repel each other, but for larger separations the molecule will dissociate and the potential energy will no longer depend on the internuclear distances. As the curve begins to spread, approaching the dissociation energy, the vibrational energy levels tend to converge,

---

[1] J. R. Platt, *J. Opt. Soc. Am.* **43**, 252 (1953).

becoming continuous for the dissociated molecule. The deviation from parabolic form corresponds to an anharmonicity of the vibrations, which may be considered as due to the influence of the vibrations on the electronic energy. The potential curves for bending vibrations may be more nearly parabolic.

From the classical picture of the vibrations the nuclei would be expected to spend most of the time at the extremes of the motion (except in the "vibrationless" lowest vibrational state), with zero or very small momentum. According to the Franck-Condon principle, therefore, the molecule must go to a point on the upper-electronic-state curve where the internuclear distances are not significantly different and where the nuclei will

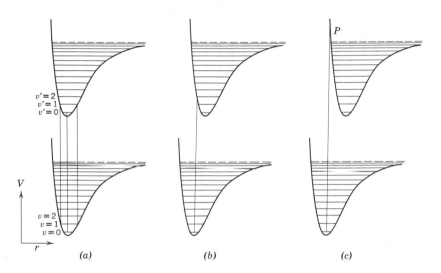

FIG. VI-10. Plot of a single vibrational mode in two electronic states. In (a) the equilibrium distance is the same in the upper state as in the lower; in (b) and (c) there is a change in the equilibrium distance. Vertical transitions, as shown, are most probable.

have little or no momentum. That is, the transition must be representable by a nearly vertical line and must start and end on or near the intersection of a horizontal line with the potential curve (or the midpoint of the lowest vibrational level). The spectrum will depend strongly on the relative positions and shapes of the vibrational potential wells.

If the potential curves lie directly above each other, as in Fig. VI-10a, the most likely transitions will be the 0-0, 1-1, ..., v-v jumps. At room temperature only the lowest vibrational state will have a significant population, except for very low-frequency vibrations (section V-4.1). The electronic absorption spectrum should therefore consist primarily of a strong line due to the 0-0 transition, with weaker lines trailing off to higher frequencies corresponding to the 0-1, 0-2, etc., jumps.

For polyatomic molecules there will be more than one mode of vibration and transitions corresponding to excitation of the other vibrations will also appear. The potential wells of different vibrational modes will, in general, have different curvatures, or force constants, but the minimum of the potential curve represents a common equilibrium point for all vibrations of the given electronic state. (The abscissa represents the normal coordinate for that vibration and all plots for a given electronic state coincide for zero displacement.)

Displacement of the upper curve with respect to the vibrational potential well of the ground electronic state will produce a more complex spectrum. In Fig. VI-10b the most intense lines should arise from the 0-2 transition, with 0-1, 0-3, and other transitions appearing more weakly. If the displacement of the upper curve is large, as in Fig. VI-10c, a very different appearance of the spectrum may be expected. The most likely transition is now from the $v = 0$ level of the lower state to the point P of the upper state. But from this point the molecule will spontaneously dissociate during the first vibrational cycle. The point P thus does not correspond to a quantized energy level. Transitions to all neighboring points are possible, giving rise to a continuum in the electronic absorption spectrum. The transition is from a well-defined vibrational level of the lower electronic state to the unquantized state of a dissociated molecule.

2.5 Dissociation and Ionization

In any electronic state it is possible for the molecule to dissociate if it acquires sufficient vibrational energy. The amount of vibrational energy required (the dissociation energy) will depend on the electronic state, since this determines the firmness of the chemical bonding, and on the particular mode of vibration. In some electronic states the molecule may be unstable, dissociating spontaneously into fragments. It is possible for dissociation to lead to ions, but more often uncharged radicals are produced.

It is also possible for a molecule to become ionized. To a first approximation this is equivalent to the process of ionizing an atom. An infinite number of electronic states exists for each electron in a molecule. Transitions to these states give rise to a Rydberg series,

$$\sigma = A - \frac{R}{(n + a)^2}$$

in which hcA is the ionization energy, n the principal quantum number of the electrons (or simply a running index), and a is a correction term

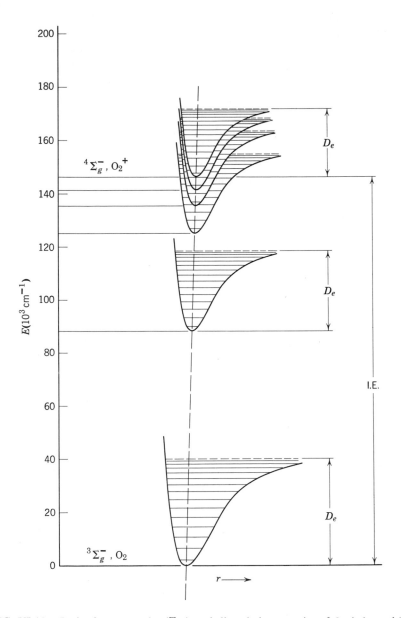

FIG. VI-11. Ionization energy (to $^4\Sigma_g^-$) and dissociation energies of O_2 (schematic). Vibrational frequencies and dissociation energies decrease as electron is removed from the bond. Additional electronic states lying just below that of the ion have been omitted for clarity.

required because of the increased complexity of the system as compared to a hydrogen atom. Such Rydberg series generally fall in the vacuum ultraviolet and are observed with difficulty if at all. Often they may be hidden by a continuum arising from dissociation of the molecule in one of the low-lying states. The first few terms of the series may deviate significantly from the formula, but for large values of **n** good agreement is to be expected.

The distinction between dissociation and ionization should be kept clearly in mind. For the particularly simple case of a diatomic molecule, such as oxygen, a series of levels such as those depicted in Fig. VI-11 might be observed. Along the left-hand side of the figure the electronic levels are represented by lines spaced according to the Rydberg formula. For each of these levels there will be a vibrational potential well. In the lowest electronic state the harmonic vibration wavenumber is 1580 cm^{-1}, the dissociation energy is equivalent to 41,000 cm^{-1}, and the internuclear distance is 1.2074 Å. The Rydberg series follows the equation $\sigma = 146,548 - R/(m + 0.32)^2$, with **m** assuming the values 3, 4, 5, ... The limiting state is the O_2^+ ion with a vibrational wavenumber of 1197 cm^{-1}, a probable dissociation energy equivalent to about 30–40,000 cm^{-1}, and an internuclear distance of 1.2795 Å. The vibrational wells for the series of Rydberg states will vary continuously between these limits.

Even in the simple diatomic molecule O_2 more than one Rydberg series has been observed, corresponding to the excitation and ionization of electrons originally in different orbitals of the O_2 molecule. For a polyatomic molecule a full representation of the energy states would require several Rydberg series and, for each of the electronic states of each series, $3N–6$ potential wells (for a non-linear molecule of N atoms) should be drawn in $(3N–6)$-dimensional space. Each of the potential wells would have its own dissociation energy and each Rydberg series would have its own ionization energy. In view of the tremendous complex of potential curves it is not surprising that they sometimes seem to interact, so that a molecule excited to one state may slip over into a different state. This can lead to "predissociation" in some molecules (section X-5.24).

Problems

1. Calculate the reduced mass, μ, for an electron and the nucleus, for the atoms

$\qquad\qquad$ (a) He^4 $\qquad$ (b) O^{16} $\qquad$ (c) U^{237}

From this calculate the Rydberg constant for these atoms.

2. Show that the frequency absorbed by a hydrogen atom when $\Delta n = 1$ falls between the classical frequencies for the electron in the initial and final states. Show that these classical frequencies approach each other for large **n**.

3. Find the statistical weight for the hydrogen atom level of energy $-hcR/n^2$. Write down the Boltzmann distribution for the hydrogen atom and differentiate to find what maxima or minima exist (evaluate the second derivative to distinguish between these). Calculate r for the state(s) of interest.   Interpret your result in terms of the physical quantities involved.

4. Give the electronic configuration for the ground states of the atoms

(a) O   (b) Mg   (c) Sc   (d) Cu

5. Acetophenone in water shows an absorption band at about 2480 Å, with a half-band width of 287 Å.   The peak absorptivity is 1.3×10^4 L/mole-cm.   Find the oscillator strength for this band.   What does this intensity say about the extent to which the band is allowed or forbidden?

6. The benzene absorption band in the vicinity of 40,000 cm^{-1} (2500 Å) shows an integrated absorption intensity of roughly 10^5 L/mole-cm^2.   What is the oscillator strength of this band?

7. The ground state of the molecule NO is given the term symbol $^2\Pi$.

(a) What is the value of Σ, the projection of spin on the axis?

(b) What is the value of Λ, the projection of orbital angular momentum on the axis?

(c) What are the possible values for the total projected electronic angular momentum along the axis?

8. The total kinetic and potential energies of a molecule must follow the virial-theorem equation $\bar{T}_t = -E_t = -\frac{1}{2}\bar{V}_t$, but for small displacements of the nuclei from equilibrium the kinetic energy of the nuclei will be related to the potential energy of vibration by the virial-theorem conditions $\bar{T}_v = \bar{V}_v = \frac{1}{2}E_v$.   The total kinetic energy is the sum of electronic and nuclear kinetic energies.   Show that the average kinetic energy of the electrons can be related to the energy, E_e, of the electronic state and to the vibrational energy, E_v.   Does the average kinetic energy of the electrons increase, decrease, or remain constant when the molecule is excited vibrationally?

VII

Molecular vibrations and rotations

For a molecule of N atoms, there are $3N$ degrees of freedom associated with the momentum coordinates. Of these, 3 will describe the translation of the molecule as a whole. Another 3, for a non-linear molecule, will be required to describe the rotation; for a linear molecule rotation about the axis is not possible (section V-2.5), so that only two coordinates are required. The remaining degrees of freedom, $3N-6$ or $3N-5$, correspond to vibrations of the molecule.

I Normal Modes

Consider a mass, m_1, on a spring with the force constant k_1. For small displacements this system will oscillate with the single frequency $\nu_1 = (1/2\pi)\sqrt{k_1/m_1}$. A second system, with mass m_2 and force constant k_2, will oscillate with the frequency $\nu_2 = (1/2\pi)\sqrt{k_2/m_2}$. If these two systems are weakly coupled, for example by connecting the masses with a third, very weak spring, each will continue to vibrate with its own frequency to a first approximation. If the first system is set into motion while the second remains at rest, the moving system will send periodic weak impulses to the second, but so long as these impulses do not have the frequency ν_2 there will be little tendency for transfer of energy from one system to the other.

In the event that ν_1 is equal, or nearly equal, to ν_2, the results will be quite different. The impulses transmitted from the first system to the second will have a cumulative effect which is described by saying that resonance is established between the two oscillators. Energy will flow from one to the other until the first has actually come to rest and the second is moving with the amplitude originally given the first; the process is now reversed and energy flows in the other direction. The transfer back and forth continues until frictional forces have brought the entire system to rest.

Experimentation will show that it is possible to set the two masses in motion in either of two ways so that the form of the motion will remain unchanged with time. In one of these modes of motion the two masses will be moving in phase; in the other they will be moving exactly out of phase. These forms of oscillation are called independent modes, or normal modes.[1]

As the number of degrees of freedom is increased, the difficulty of treating a vibrating system tends to increase. The actual forms of the vibrations then depend on the relative masses, force constants, and angles as well as the coupling force constants. It is easily shown, however, that there will be as many normal modes of vibration as there are degrees of freedom, since the frequencies of these modes correspond to the solutions to a system of linear equations, the number of equations being equal to the number of coordinates, or degrees of freedom. In a normal mode any number of the masses may move simultaneously, subject to two conditions. Each mass will move with the same frequency and each will have the same phase factor, so that all the masses will pass through the equilibrium configuration of the system simultaneously.[2]

Associated with each normal mode will be one, and only one, frequency, but the total number of distinct frequencies for a molecule is generally less than the number of normal modes. For example, in large molecules it is quite likely that there will be at least two methyl groups which are widely separated. Each of these units would be expected to give rise to the same frequencies and because of the large distance between them there is no mechanical interaction. In such a case the two units will act as if they are truly independent oscillators. This is called "accidental" degeneracy. It is extremely common, particularly in connection with C—H motions. Under high resolution it is sometimes found that the accidental degeneracy is only approximate, especially when the two non-interacting groups which have the same frequency are chemically different (for example, an N—H stretch and an O—H stretch might overlap under low resolution but show separate absorption bands under high resolution).

Degeneracy of normal modes also occurs as a consequence of symmetry. Any molecule with a three-fold, four-fold, or higher axis of

---

[1] The term "normal" is carried over from mathematical terminology. Vectors which are perpendicular, or normal, to each other are independent of each other.

[2] Degenerate vibrations need not satisfy the second requirement.

symmetry will exhibit such "necessary" degeneracy. For example, SF_6, CCl_4, NH_3, and all methyl groups (to the extent that interactions with the remainder of the molecule can be neglected) will have pairs of normal modes which are rigorously degenerate. In the first two, since there is more than one higher-than-two-fold axis, there will also be sets of three degenerate vibrational modes. Under these circumstances the normal modes are no longer uniquely defined. Any linear combination of the two (or three) vibrations which are degenerate will have the same frequency and will be an equally good normal mode. Experimentally it will be impossible to observe more than one frequency unless there is interaction between the molecule and some external field that has the effect of destroying the symmetry.

It is not possible to say exactly what form the normal modes of vibration will have, except in a few particularly simple cases, without detailed mathematical calculations. Approximate forms can be predicted on the basis of information provided by a few typical molecules, molecular symmetry, and observed values for characteristic vibrational frequencies. The most important consideration is that equivalent bonds must be treated in an equivalent manner. For example, if one of the C—H bonds of ethylene were to be stretched while the others were left unchanged, the oscillations of the one bond would be of the proper frequency to excite oscillations in each of the others. The condition of resonance would be established and the vibrational energy would flow from one bond to another and back. This obviously does not represent a stationary state; the initial form of motion was clearly not independent of the other motions of the system and was therefore not a normal mode.

More precise specification of the necessary properties of these approximate normal modes (or symmetry coordinates) will be given in section X-3.4.

When two oscillations are coupled, the normal modes will involve both oscillators, and the frequencies of these normal modes will differ from the original frequencies of the independent oscillators. One of the resultant frequencies will be higher than either of the original values, the other will be lower than either. This is a consequence of the resultant equations of motion, according to which the effective masses and the effective force constants will differ for the normal modes as compared to the original oscillators. Often, in referring to a complex system, it is convenient to imagine it broken down into simpler systems for which frequencies are at least approximately known. These simple systems are then imagined to interact to yield the complete assembly. Instead of calling this an interaction between independent oscillators, it is common practice to say that the frequencies, or energy levels, interact and split apart.

2   Valence and Bond Strength

In a comparison of the hydrogen molecule ion, H_2^+, and the hydrogen molecule, H_2, it was seen that the binding energy was nearly proportional to the number of electrons in the bond for this very limited sampling of compounds.   Although this simple rule has not been justified by the complex mathematical treatments of molecules, nor is it easily phrased in an exact manner for larger molecules, it appears to be part of a valid generalization of the properties of chemical bonds.

Table VII-I gives the vibrational wavenumbers, corrected to the reduced mass of the O_2 molecule, for several electronic states of various diatomic

TABLE VII-I[a]

Molecule	State	Number of Electrons	Observed Wavenumber[b]	Corrected Wavenumber[c]
H_2^+	$^2\Sigma_g^+$	1	2297	575
H_2	$^1\Sigma_g^+$	2	4395	1100
F_2	$^1\Sigma_g^+$	2	892	972
CN	$^2\Sigma^+$	5	2069	1860
	$^2\Pi$	5	1814	1630
CO	$^1\Sigma^+$	6	2170	2010
	$^1\Pi$	4	1516	1405
NO	$^2\Pi$	5	1904	1840
	$^2\Sigma^+$	7	2371	2290
	$^2\Pi$	3	1038	1002
O_2^+	$^2\Pi_g$	5	1876	1876
	$^4\Sigma_g^-$	3	1197	1197
	$^4\Pi_u$	3	1036	1036
	$^2\Pi_u$	3	900	900
O_2	$^3\Sigma_g^-$	4	1580	1580
	$^1\Delta_g$	4	1509	1509
	$^1\Sigma_g^+$	4	1433	1433
	$^3\Sigma_u^+$	2	819	819
	$^3\Sigma_u^-$	2	700	700
Na_2	$^1\Sigma_g^+$	2	159	191
Li_2	$^1\Sigma_g^+$	2	351	232
Cs_2	$^1\Sigma_g^+$	2	42	121
Cl_2	$^1\Sigma_g^+$	2	565	835

[a] Based on tabulations in Herzberg, ref. 43.   Notation is explained in chap. X.

[b] Harmonic wavenumber values, in reciprocal centimeters.

[c] Wavenumber values corrected to reduced mass of O_2 for purposes of comparison.

molecules. These wavenumbers are plotted in Fig. VII-1 against the number of electrons in the bond as determined by conventional approximate descriptions (number of electrons in bonding orbitals minus number

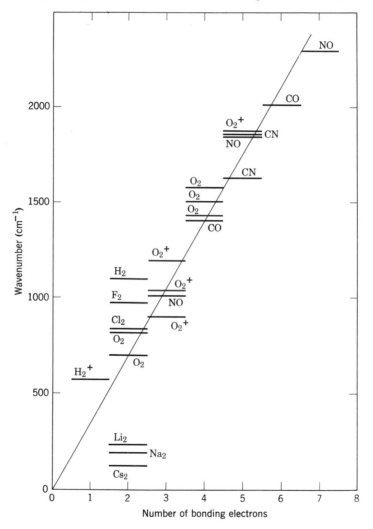

FIG. VII-1. Observed wavenumber for vibrational transitions, corrected for mass effect, of diatomic molecules, plotted against net number of bonding electrons.

in antibonding orbitals; see sections VI-2.2, X-2.2). There is a distinct dependence on the positions of the nuclei in the Periodic Table. For example, hydrogen and fluorine molecules fall above the carbon, oxygen, and nitrogen compounds, whereas the alkali metals fall increasingly far below with increasing atomic number. Apart from this effect, the correlation between vibrational frequency and number of electrons is quite striking, suggesting quite strongly that the differences in chemical bonds are essentially quantitative but not qualitative. This is supplemented by the observations that, for a given pair of nuclei, there is a unique relationship between bond distances and force constants.[1]

The positions of absorption bands due to vibrations involving primarily bond-stretching motions can be predicted with reasonable accuracy on the basis of the masses of the atoms involved, the type of bond (single, double, or triple), and the characters of the nuclei involved. In Table VII-II the

TABLE VII-II

Bond	Reduced Mass (H = 1)	σ (cm^{-1})
H—H	0.50	4160
O—H	0.94	3600
O—D	1.78	2700
N—H	0.93	3400
C—H	0.92	2900
C—D	7.71	2100
C—Cl	9.0	700
C—C	6.0	ca. 1000
C=C	6.0	1650
C≡C	6.0	2100
C—O	6.9	ca. 1200
C=O	6.9	1720
C≡O	6.9	2144

wavenumbers observed for several types of bonds are tabulated, along with the reduced mass (equation V-10) for the two nuclei. It will be observed that by far the greatest effect is that due to change in mass; the second largest effect is the difference between single, double, and triple bonds. Although there are distinct differences associated with the variation of atom (compare C—H, N—H, and O—H, each with nearly the same reduced mass), these differences are relatively small.

The constancy of the vibrational frequencies of a particular functional group as the molecular environment is changed has extremely important consequences. Examination of an infrared spectrum nearly always

[1] R. M. Badger, *J. Chem. Phys.* **2**, 128 (1934); Lippincott and Schroeder, *J. Chem. Phys.* **23**, 1131 (1955).

provides a rapid and accurate answer to such questions as "Is there a carbonyl group in the molecule?" or "Is the compound aromatic?" If the frequencies were completely unaffected by environment, this would be the limit to the type of information obtainable—it would not be possible, for example, to know whether the carbonyl group was a ketone, an aldehyde, an acid, or a quinone. Experience has shown that the bonds do show small variations in strength, which are reflected in small changes in the vibrational frequencies.

The variety of effects leading to shifts of vibrational frequencies may be broken conveniently into two groups, mechanical and electrical. Mechanical effects include changes in mass and changes in the form of the vibration resulting from variations in the coupling between motions of adjacent bonds. If a complete and accurate calculation of the force constants could be carried out, it would be found that these mechanical effects have no influence on the force constants of the bonds. Electrical interaction can also change the forms of the vibrations, but only through changes in the individual force constants. Such effects arise when electron densities are changed, as by conjugation or "induction". In a few instances the distinction between mechanical and electrical interactions becomes somewhat obscure—for example, hydrogen bonding seems to introduce a combination of the two forms of interaction, with the relative weights quite possibly varying with the amplitude of the motion—but normally they are quite distinct and should be kept clearly separate.

An example of mechanical interaction is the coupling of vibrations of the C—H bonds in a methyl or a methylene group. In CH_3D the stretching wavenumbers are 3030 and 2982 cm^{-1} for the C—H motions, in CH_2D_2 the values are 3020 and 2974 cm^{-1}. The difference in wavenumbers of nearly 50 cm^{-1} does not indicate a difference in the C—H bonds but rather a difference in frequency between symmetric and asymmetric, or symmetric and antisymmetric, vibrational modes.[1] Similar mechanical interaction is known to occur between the C—O—H bending motion and the C—O stretching motion in alcohols, between the C—N—H bend and C—N stretch in amides, and between the out-of-plane bending motions

[1] This "mechanical" interaction is, of course, electrical in nature in the sense that one atom knows where another atom is only by means of the changes in electric field produced by the displacements of the atoms. Stretching a chemical bond, during a vibration, is accompanied by an adjustment of the electronic states. The term "mechanical interaction" is still appropriate, however, since the interaction is a consequence of the vibrational motion, or displacement, and vanishes when the atoms are in their equilibrium positions. Such mechanical interactions can be observed if ball-and-spring models of the molecule are constructed. Interactions described here as being electrical in nature are present for the equilibrium configuration and are considered to be independent of vibrational displacements.

of the adjacent hydrogens on aromatic rings, as well as in many other types of molecular groupings. Isotopic substitution or replacement of one atom by another of similar electrical characteristics but different mass causes a change in vibrational frequency that is properly classified as mechanical in nature.

Electrical interaction is to be expected in molecules that have unsaturation or non-bonding valence-shell electrons. For example, an idealized carbon-carbon double bond has four bonding electrons while the adjacent C—H (or C—C) bonds have only two each. A net increase in stability

TABLE VII-III[a]

Compound Type	σ (cm^{-1})	Range
R—CH$_3$	2962 2872	
R$_1$—CH$_2$—R$_2$ (H above and below C)	2926 2853	2840–2970
R$_1$—CH(R$_3$)—R$_2$	2890 (?)	
If R = ϕ	2844–2969	
R—CH=CH$_2$	3085 ± 5	
R$_2$,R$_1$ / C=C \ H,H	3080 ± 5	3010–3090
R$_1$—CH=CH—R$_2$	3030 ± 10	
R$_1$—C(H)=CH—R$_2$	3025 ± 5	
R—C≡C—H	3270–3305 (liq.)	
H—C≡C—H	3287 and 3374	
ϕ—H	3000–3111	

[a] These numbers are taken in part from ref. 36.

TABLE VII-IV

Molecule	σ (cm^{-1})	Bond
H H CH$_3$CH$_2$—C=C H	1645	
H H ϕ—C=C H	1629	C=C
H H H H C=C—C=C H H	1592	
O ‖ CH$_3$—C—H	1720	
O ‖ ϕ—C—H	1696	
O ‖ CH$_3$—C—CH$_3$	1706	C=O
O ‖ ϕ—C—CH$_3$	1678	
O H H ‖ C=C—C—CH$_3$ H	1676 1619[a]	
R—C≡N	2250 ± 10	
ϕ—C≡N	2230	
H H C=C—C≡N H	2224 1607[a]	C≡N
CH$_3$CH$_2$—C≡C—H	2118	
H H C=C—C≡C—H H	2099 1600	C≡C
H—C≡C—C≡C—H	2024	

[a] C=C.

is achieved if the electrons of the double bond spend part of the time in the adjacent bonds. This "spilling over" of electrons causes a drop in strength of the double bond but an increase in the strength of the single bonds. The change in vibrational frequency of the C—H bonds is shown in Table VII-III.

The amount of delocalization that can take place in a molecule with an isolated double bond is severely limited. It is not possible to put additional electrons into the occupied orbitals, and the empty orbitals are of too high energy; the delocalization must therefore be considered to occur by a change in the shapes of the existing orbitals. (If complete and accurate descriptions of all the orbitals were available the various methods of approximating the true distribution would seem artificial and cumbersome, but with sufficient refinement they should all lead to the same, correct description in the limit.) Conjugated systems are more susceptible to the delocalization process, since in these molecules the increase in electron density in the intermediate single bond represents a shift of orbitals from one side of a carbon atom to the other without increasing the total number of filled orbitals in the vicinity of either of the carbon atoms. Evidence of this greater delocalization is found in the vibrational spectrum, as shown in Table VII-IV. Additional evidence is the well-documented shortening of the intermediate bond in such systems.

A very different type of electrical interaction is found in molecules containing the halogens or singly bonded oxygen. The "non-bonding" electrons in the valence shell of these atoms can contribute to the stability of the molecule if they are displaced toward the internuclear region. The extent to which these electrons can exist in the bonding region is limited by the electrons already present, but there seems to be some tendency for these bonding electrons, in turn, to move into immediately adjacent parts of the remainder of the molecule. (This motion of charge reduces the dipole moment, which is due to the asymmetrical distribution of the valence-shell electrons, but does not change its sign. The observed value

TABLE VII-V

Molecule	σ (cm^{-1}), C—H
H—CBr$_3$	3023 (liq.)
H—CCl$_3$	3033
H—CF$_3$	3062
H$_3$C—CH$_3$	2899, 2954, 2963, 2994
H$_3$C—CCl$_3$	2953, 3016
H$_3$C—CF$_3$	2975, 3035

of the dipole moment in bonds such as C—F is consistent with this interpretation.)

Examples of this effect in saturated molecules are given in Table VII-V. It will be observed that the C—H stretching vibrations in the haloforms are comparable to those in olefinic compounds, rather than saturated

TABLE VII-VI

Molecule	σ (cm^{-1}), C=O
$\underset{\text{H}_3\text{C}-\text{C}-\text{CH}_3}{\overset{\text{O}}{\overset{\|}{}}}$	1705
$\underset{\text{H}_3\text{C}-\text{C}-\text{H}}{\overset{\text{O}}{\overset{\|}{}}}$	1720
$\underset{\text{Cl}_3\text{C}-\text{C}-\text{H}}{\overset{\text{O}}{\overset{\|}{}}}$	1761
$\underset{\text{H}_3\text{C}-\text{C}-\text{Cl}}{\overset{\text{O}}{\overset{\|}{}}}$	1808
$\underset{\text{R}_1-\text{C}-\text{O}-\text{R}_2}{\overset{\text{O}}{\overset{\|}{}}}$	1730–1760
$\underset{\text{Cl}-\text{C}-\text{Cl}}{\overset{\text{O}}{\overset{\|}{}}}$	1827
$\underset{\text{H}_3\text{C}-\text{C}-\text{F}}{\overset{\text{O}}{\overset{\|}{}}}$	1840
$\underset{\text{F}-\text{C}-\text{F}}{\overset{\text{O}}{\overset{\|}{}}}$	1928

hydrocarbons. In carbonyl compounds the frequency shifts are sometimes extremely large, as shown in Table VII-VI. The observed shifts have been shown to be partially electrical in nature and partially due to mechanical coupling.[1]

The halo-olefins exhibit the competing influences of mechanical and electrical perturbations. Increasing the mass of substituents around a

[1] The difference between halogen and hydrogen or carbon substitution seems to be an electrical effect; the differences in carbonyl frequencies between the various halogen-substituted compounds is largely, if not entirely, due to differences in the mechanical coupling. See Overend and Scherer, *Spectrochim Acta* **16**, 773 (1960).

carbon-carbon double bond must lower the double-bond stretching frequency, although the change may be small.   On this basis the hydrogen, deuterium, fluorine, chlorine, bromine, and iodine compounds should have double-bond frequencies decreasing in that order.   The electrical interaction should increase the double-bond frequency and should be strongest for the most "electronegative" atom and should thus give double-bond frequencies which decrease in the order fluorine, chlorine, bromine, iodine, and hydrogen and deuterium.   The result should be, therefore, a decrease in the series fluorine, chlorine, bromine, and iodine, and a decrease from hydrogen to deuterium.   The relative positions of the two series will be determined by the relative magnitudes of the mechanical and electrical effects.   The observed values are given in Table VII-VII.

TABLE VII-VII

Molecule	σ (cm^{-1}), C=C	σ (cm^{-1}), C—H
$H_2C=CH_2$	1623	2990, 3010, 3106, 3108
$D_2C=CD_2$	1515	2200, 2251, 2304, 2345
$H_2C=CHF$	1650	3080, 3110, 3135
$F_2C=CF_2$	1872	
$H_2C=CHCl$	1610	3030, 3080 3130
$H_2C=CHBr$	1593	3014, 3076 3100
$H_2C=CHI$	1581	3000, 3060 3100
$H_2C=CBr_2$	1605	3023, 3108

A check on the interpretation of the preceding paragraph is to be found in the vibrational frequencies of the C—H bonds.   The mechanical interaction between the C—X vibrations and the C—H vibrations should be smaller than between the C—X and C=C motions because of the larger frequency separation.   The predominant influence should therefore be the electrical interaction, as in the saturated molecules.   Comparison of the relative values in Table VII-VII shows that this is the case.   As for the saturated molecules, this is further demonstration that the electrical interaction does not resemble the alternate-bond effects characteristic of conjugated systems.

The frequencies given in this section have all been bond-stretching frequencies.   The bending motions generally have much lower frequencies (often one half or less) but are equally valuable for purposes of identification of molecules.   Examples of these, along with some general procedures for interpreting the spectra of unknown materials, are given in chapter VIII.

3   Selection Rules

According to classical mechanics the requirement for absorption of radiation is that there be a change in dipole moment (or, if much weaker absorption is considered, a change in quadrupole moment or magnetic dipole moment).   For Raman scattering there must be a change of polarizability.   The frequency of the radiation absorbed, or the difference in frequency between incident and scattered radiation, is equal to the classical vibration frequency.

In treating the problem from the standpoint of quantum mechanics, emphasis is placed upon the initial and final states, described by the appropriate wave functions Ψ_i and Ψ_f, and on the difference in energy between these states.   The difference in energy between the two states must be equal to the energy of the photon absorbed, or the difference in energies of incident and scattered photons, in order that energy may be conserved.   In so far as the classical picture of vibrating molecules can be considered valid (and there is little reason to discard this assumption) the classical and quantum requirements can be shown to be equivalent in all but a few minor details.

Selection rules, which provide a means for deciding whether a particular transition will or will not occur under specified conditions, are conveniently divided into two categories.   The first applies to all systems of a given type, such as harmonic oscillators or rigid rotors.   It can be shown that, so long as the vibrations are harmonic, only the fundamental frequency will be absorbed or emitted (equation V-56) and the angular momentum will change in magnitude by one unit or remain unchanged, or by two units for Raman transitions (equations V-57 and V-58).   The second category deals with the symmetry properties of the system.

Powerful methods for deriving selection rules based on symmetry have been developed with the aid of group theory.   These methods are treated in chapter X.   For many purposes a more visual treatment has certain advantages.   The forms of the vibrations depicted in this connection will not necessarily be the correct vibrational forms but should be considered rather as schematic representations of vibrations for which the frequency of vibration and the symmetry are known.

3.1 Infrared: Change of Dipole Moment

Consider first the question of absorption of infrared radiation.   The requirement that there be a change in dipole moment during the vibration eliminates many vibrations that are symmetric in nature.   Four representative molecules will be considered, carbon dioxide, water, ethylene, and ethane.

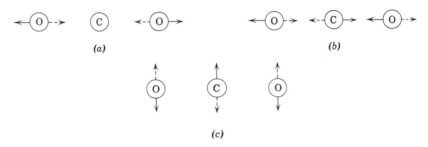

(a)   (b)

(c)

FIG. VII-2.   Normal modes of carbon dioxide.   (a) Symmetric stretch; (b) antisymmetric stretch; (c) bending motion.   An equivalent bending motion can be drawn at right angles to that shown; the actual motion will be any linear combination of the two. The dotted arrows show the motion in the alternate half of the vibrational cycle.

Carbon dioxide has four fundamental frequencies, two of which are identical.   The corresponding modes of vibration are shown in Fig. VII-2. There is no dipole moment in the equilibrium configuration, and none is produced by the vibration of frequency v_1.   This vibration must accordingly be inactive in the infrared.   The second vibration is antisymmetric and produces a dipole, which oscillates with the vibrational frequency. This motion is active in the infrared, giving rise to absorption at 2350 cm^{-1}. The third frequency arises from the bending motion.   This also produces a dipole moment and the corresponding absorption band is found at 667 cm^{-1}.

In Fig. VII-3 the vibrational modes of water are indicated.   The same figures would apply equally well to such molecules as H_2S, SO_2, or NO_2. The vibrational modes are closely related to those of CO_2.   In the symmetrical stretching vibration the natural dipole moment of the water molecule (directed along the axis bisecting the H-O-H angle) is modified in magnitude, though not in direction.   This is observed at 3652 cm^{-1} in the infrared.   The antisymmetric stretch produces a dipole moment perpendicular to the H-O-H axis.   As in the CO_2 molecule, the antisymmetric stretch occurs at a higher frequency than the symmetric stretch, but the spread is much smaller because of the smaller interaction in the bent systems   The antisymmetric stretch is observed at 3756 cm^{-1}, largely obscuring the 3652 cm^{-1} band.   The two bending motions of CO_2 be-

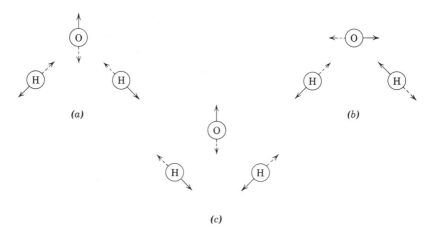

(a)

(b)

(c)

FIG. VII-3.   Approximate forms of normal modes of H_2O.   (a) Symmetric stretch; (b) antisymmetric stretch; (c) bend.   The symmetric stretch and bend will mix to an extent determined by masses and force constants.

come a bending motion (ν_2) and a pure rotation for the non-linear triatomic molecules.   The water bending motion changes the magnitude of the dipole moment and is observed at 1595 cm^{-1} in the infrared spectrum.

Ethylene has $(3 \times 6) - 6 = 12$ fundamental frequencies.   They are indicated in Fig. VII-4.   They are grouped according to the symmetry properties of the vibrations and are labeled accordingly (see section X-1). It should be emphasized that the true vibrations may be any combination of the forms shown within a given symmetry species, the exact form depending on the masses of the atoms and the strengths of the bonds.   The forms will accordingly differ somewhat as hydrogen atoms are replaced by deuterium, by halogens, or by alkyl groups.

Examination of Fig. VII-4 will show that for each of the vibrations listed as being infrared active (B_{1u}, B_{2u}, B_{3u}) there is a change in dipole moment during the vibration and for each of the other vibrations there is

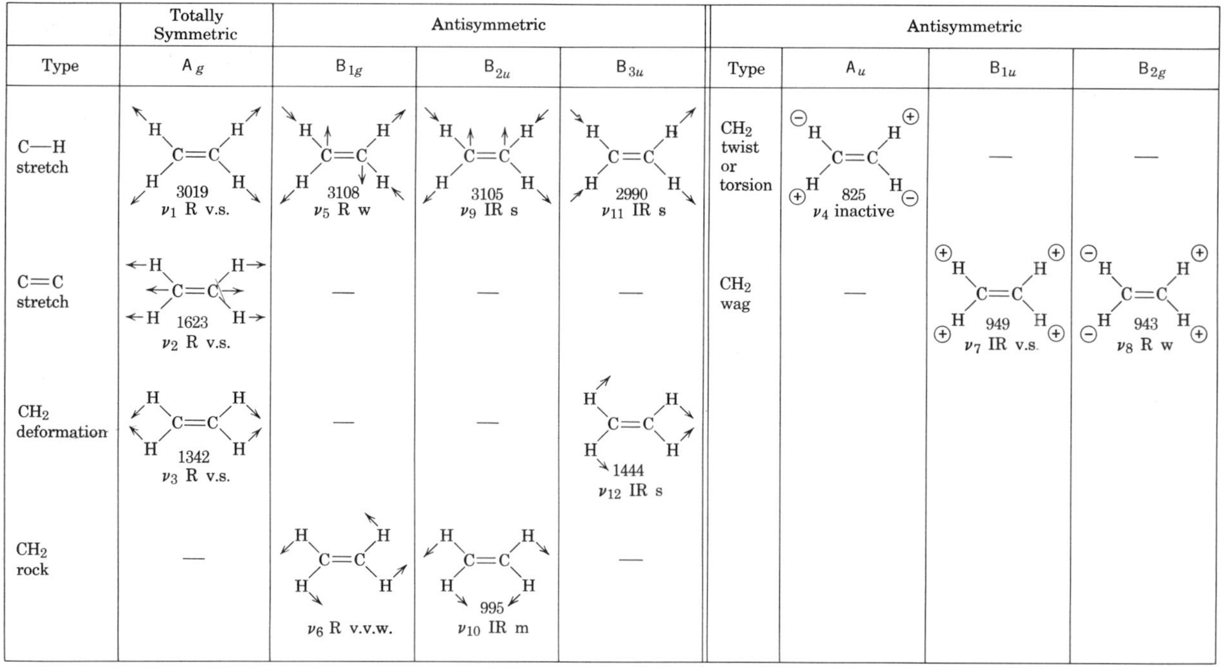

Type	Totally Symmetric A_g	Antisymmetric B_{1g}	Antisymmetric B_{2u}	Antisymmetric B_{3u}	Type	Antisymmetric A_u	Antisymmetric B_{1u}	Antisymmetric B_{2g}
C—H stretch	3019 ν_1 R v.s.	3108 ν_5 R w	3105 ν_9 IR s	2990 ν_{11} IR s	CH$_2$ twist or torsion	825 ν_4 inactive	—	—
C=C stretch	1623 ν_2 R v.s.	—	—	—	CH$_2$ wag	—	—	—
CH$_2$ deformation	1342 ν_3 R v.s.	—	—	1444 ν_{12} IR s			949 ν_7 IR v.s.	943 ν_8 R w
CH$_2$ rock	—	ν_6 R v.v.w.	995 ν_{10} IR m	—				

FIG. VII-4. Ethylene vibrations. The arrows represent the direction of motion during one phase of the oscillation; during the other phase all directions are reversed. Plus and minus signs, + and −, indicate motion up or down with respect to the plane of the molecule. Motions of the hydrogen atoms have been depicted as being strictly along or perpendicular to the bonds, without consideration of the mixing of modes falling in the same column. Compensating motions of carbon atoms have been omitted in some of the modes. For a more accurate representation see Herzberg, ref. 44, pp. 107, 325—328. Approximate observed intensities in the infrared (IR) or Raman(R) are indicated by s = strong, m = weak, v = very. Letter designations for symmetry (A_g, B_{1g}, etc.) are explained in chapter X. (Choice of axes and designations of symmetry are in agreement with ref. 44 but not with newer recommendations.)

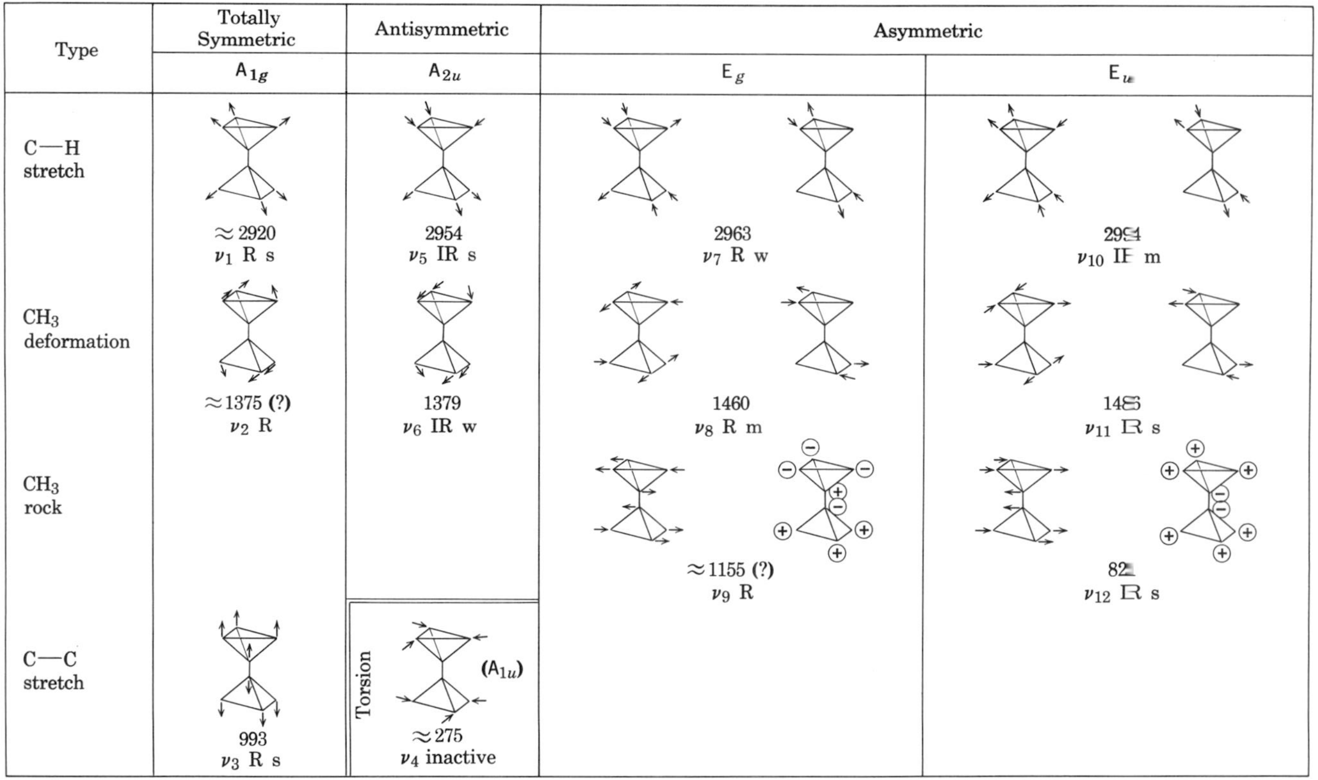

FIG. VII-5. Ethane vibrations. See Fig. VII-4 and Herzberg, ref. 44, pp. 110, 115, 344–345. (Numbering of degenerate vibrations differs from that in ref. 44.)

no change in dipole moment. It is necessarily true that each of the active vibrations destroys the center of symmetry [1] of the molecule.

Anticipating the discussion of chapter VIII, it may be mentioned that the C—H stretching vibrations near 3000 cm^{-1} and the deformations near 1400 cm^{-1} are the usual indications of C—H. The high value of the C—H stretch (above 3000) indicates unsaturation (or adjacent halogen), the very strong out-of-plane hydrogen motion (wag) in the 800–1000 cm^{-1} region is typical of olefinic compounds (if somewhat lower, it would be typical of aromatic compounds), and the 1623 cm^{-1} band, often weak or absent in the infrared, is an indication of C$=$C when it appears.

Ethane has a three-fold symmetry axis and thus exhibits degeneracies. The forms of the degenerate vibrations are indeterminate, in the sense that any mixture of the two forms shown would be as good. The approximate forms of the 18 fundamental modes of ethane are shown in Fig. VII-5. As in ethylene, only those vibrations that destroy the center of symmetry can produce an oscillating dipole moment. The 2850–3000 cm^{-1} and 1350–1500 cm^{-1} bands typical of compounds containing C—H are again observed.

3.2   Raman: Change of Polarizability

For the appearance of a band in the Raman spectrum the polarizability must differ at the two extremes of the motion when measured along some fixed axis. It is important to remember that polarizability is independent of the direction along such an axis. In Fig. VII-6 some of the Raman active motions from Fig. VII-2 through Fig. VII-5 are represented along with the directions in which a change in polarizability occurs. In contrast to the infrared selection rules it will be observed that in molecules with a center of symmetry (CO_2, C_2H_4, and C_2H_6) only those vibrations are Raman active that preserve the center of symmetry. It may also be noted that totally symmetric vibrations are always Raman active, with change of polarizability components α_{xx}, α_{yy}, and α_{zz}.

The classical interpretation of Raman scattering considers the incident frequency to be modulated by the oscillating dipole of the molecule. The compound signal is resolved by the spectrometer into two components, one higher and the other lower than the incident frequency by an amount equal to the vibrational frequency. The incident frequency will also

---

[1] If a molecule has a center of symmetry, a line drawn from any atom to the center of symmetry and extended an equal length beyond will encounter an identical atom. The process is called "inversion" and may also be described as a change of sign of all coordinates (x, y, z going to $-x$, $-y$, $-z$) or as a rotation by 180° followed by a reflection in a plane perpendicular to the axis of rotation (section X-1.1).

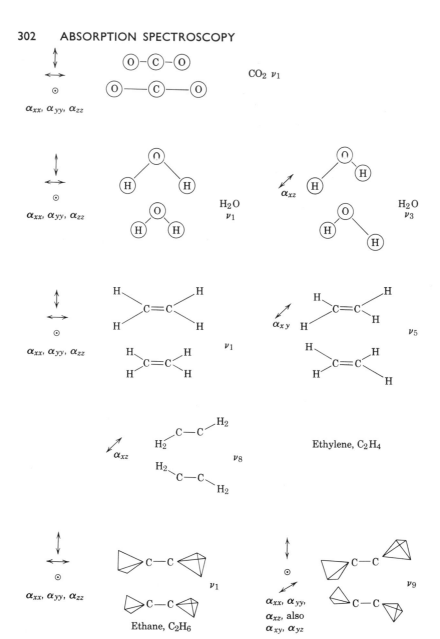

FIG. VII-6.   Raman-active vibrations.   Opposite phases, or extremes of the motions, are indicated, with the axes along which the polarizability changes.

appear since the magnitude of the modulating signal is small compared to the original intensity.   The difficulty with this purely classical picture is that the intensities of the high- and low-frequency components should be identical, whereas except for very small frequency shifts (low frequencies of vibration), the low-frequency components are observed to be much stronger.

Raman scattering may be treated by means of the wave functions and operators of quantum mechanics, or it may be considered as the absorption and re-emission of a photon. The photon striking the non-vibrating molecule is absorbed, causing a transition to an unspecified state[1] of high energy. A new photon, of slightly lower energy, is emitted as the molecule undergoes a transition to a state that differs from the original only in that the molecule is now vibrating. The resultant effect is similar to a quantized Compton scattering. The photon has been taken in, part of its energy removed to excite a vibration in the molecule, and the photon ejected with the remaining energy. Clearly this process must be one-way in the sense that the molecule must subtract from the energy of the photon, rather than add to it, unless the molecule was initially vibrating. The number of vibrationally excited molecules is small, as determined by the Boltzmann factor; consequently the number of photons observed which have acquired energy, compared to the number which have lost energy, is proportional to the Boltzmann factor for the particular vibrational mode.

The low- and high-frequency Raman lines are called, respectively, Stokes and anti-Stokes shifts owing to the superficial similarity of the Raman effect to fluorescence. Fluorescence is caused by the absorption of radiation to produce an excited (observable) electronic state, followed by re-emission of radiation at a different, usually lower, frequency. Stokes' law specifies that all fluorescence radiation should be of lower energy than the exciting radiation; hence fluorescence of higher energy is called anti-Stokes fluorescence. It must be remembered, however, that the resemblance between these effects is small. Fluorescence depends primarily on the electronic states of a molecule, with one or more vibrational modes contributing to the fine structure of the band. To put a molecule into the proper level from which it can fluoresce requires exciting radiation of the proper energy; below a certain critical energy the fluorescence will disappear entirely. A necessary condition for fluorescence is that the exciting radiation be of a frequency that will be absorbed. Raman scattering, on the other hand, does not disappear at a cut-off frequency but varies in intensity as a smooth function of the exciting wavelength. In practice, Raman scattering is observed in regions in which no electronic absorption occurs.

---

[1] Since the intermediate state is not directly observable, the transition to this state may be considered virtual, rather than real, and need not obey the law of conservation of energy even though the over-all, observable process is restricted by this law.

4   Rotational States and Transitions

The angular momentum of a rigid molecule may be expressed as the sum of the momenta about three mutually perpendicular axes, which for convenience are taken as the principal axes (section V-2.5).   The molecule as a whole can rotate about only one space-fixed axis at a time, of course, and this will in general not be one of the principal axes of the molecule. The resolution of the total motion into the sum of rotations about three axes is similar to resolving translational motion into motions along three perpendicular axes.

If a molecule has an axis of symmetry, every principal axis must either coincide with this axis or be perpendicular to it.   For molecules with a three-fold or higher axis of symmetry, the principal axes perpendicular to this axis are not unique.   The moment about any axis passing through the center of mass perpendicular to a three-fold or higher axis will be the same. Such molecules are called symmetric rotors, or symmetric tops.   Examples are ammonia, ethane, and benzene.   If the unique moment is larger than the equal moments, as in planar molecules, the molecule is an "oblate" symmetric rotor; if it is smaller, as in ethane, the molecule is a "prolate" symmetric rotor.

A molecule with more than one three-fold or higher axis of symmetry must be a spherical rotor.   Examples are CH_4, P_4, and SF_6.   For these molecules the moment of inertia is the same about any axis passing through the center of mass; there is no unique principal axis.

Linear molecules have one moment of inertia that is zero (or rather negligibly small) and two equal moments perpendicular to the axis of the molecule.   The molecule can possess an angular momentum about the molecular axis only for extremely large angular velocities.   This is impossible for molecular rotations at room temperature, but it can occur for electronic motions.   It will be assumed that no such electronic angular momentum exists in the molecules under discussion.

Absorption arising from a change in rotational energy will occur in the far infrared or microwave regions.   It is possible only if there is a change in dipole moment during the rotation; this means that it is possible only for molecules that have a permanent dipole moment.   Such transitions are observed only for gases; in liquids and solids the rotational states are no longer well defined and any absorption produces a continuum rather than discrete lines.[1]

[1] Rotational transitions are clearly seen in liquid and solid hydrogen.   Rotational structure in the absorption bands of other molecules has been reported but the evidence is less certain.   A condition for the observation of rotational fine structure is that the separation of rotational levels be larger than the half widths of the individual lines when these are broadened by collisions.

Absorption by a linear molecule requires that the quantum number of total angular momentum, $\mathbf{J}$, should increase by one unit. From the term values for linear molecules (equation V-38), the absorption frequency is given by

$$\nu = F(\mathbf{J}') - F(\mathbf{J}'') = B'\mathbf{J}'(\mathbf{J}' + 1) - B''\mathbf{J}''(\mathbf{J}'' + 1) \qquad \text{(VII-1)}$$

Assuming the moment of inertia to be constant (no centrifugal distortion) and setting $\mathbf{J}' = \mathbf{J}'' + 1$, the absorption frequency is

$$\nu = 2B\mathbf{J}' \qquad \text{(VII-2)}$$

Since $\mathbf{J}'$ takes on successive integral values, the pure rotation spectrum consists of a series of evenly spaced lines.

Exactly the same result is obtained for symmetric rotors (except those that are "accidental" symmetric rotors, for which the dipole moment might not coincide with an axis of symmetry). The only distinction possible between a linear molecule and a symmetric rotor arises through the difference to be expected in relative intensities of the lines or in the very small interactions between vibration and rotation.

A spherical rotor cannot have a permanent dipole moment and thus cannot exhibit a pure rotation spectrum in the infrared or microwave region. If the molecule, rather than being a spherical rotor because of symmetry, were an accidental spherical rotor, the spectrum would be similar, except in relative intensities, to those of the linear and symmetric rotor molecules.

Asymmetric rotors (including such molecules as H_2O and the dichlorobenzenes, as well as molecules with less symmetry) show no regularities in their pure rotational absorption spectra. Even the selection rules for such molecules are complex, since the angular momentum about the three principal axes may change in various ways depending on the properties of the molecule.

The pure rotational spectrum observed in the Raman effect is nearly identical with the infrared spectrum except that for linear molecules the spacing is $4B$. For symmetric rotors there are actually two series, one with spacing $2B$ and one with spacing $4B$, but, since alternate lines of the $2B$ series coincide with the lines of the $4B$ series, the result appears to be a single series with varying intensities. Spherical rotors do not exhibit a pure rotational Raman spectrum since the polarizability, like the moment of inertia, is independent of orientation. It should be remembered, however, that all other molecules do show rotational Raman spectra (whether or not it is experimentally resolvable) even though they have no permanent dipole moment.

The intensities of pure rotational spectra depend on the nuclei (statistical weights associated with nuclear spins) as well as on the value of the permanent dipole, or the polarizability variation along different axes in the molecule, and the statistical weights associated with the rotational quantum numbers.

Rotational transitions accompany vibrational or electronic transitions in order to satisfy the requirement of conservation of angular momentum. For diatomic molecules the rotational spacings of electronic bands are of immense value in identifying the natures of the states involved. For polyatomic molecules the rotational fine structure of the electronic bands is generally indiscernible, but the structure of the rotation-vibration bands in the infrared and Raman spectra are often resolvable and give important information about the vibrational states.

5   Rotation-Vibration Band Contours

Imagine a diatomic gas, such as CO, at such very low temperatures that all the molecules were in the lowest rotational state.[1] The molecules could absorb infrared radiation of wavenumber about 2144 cm^{-1}, equivalent to the vibrational frequency, ν_0, but in order to do so it would be necessary to change the angular momentum by one unit. The actual frequency absorbed would therefore be $\nu_0 + 2B$, rather than ν_0. Consider now a slight increase in temperature, such that some of the molecules are in the lowest rotational state and some in the first excited state ($\mathbf{J} = 1$). Those in the lowest state would still absorb at the frequency $\nu_0 + 2B$, but those in the excited state would absorb at the frequencies $\nu_0 + 4B$ and $\nu_0 - 2B$. Designating the quantities that describe the upper state with a prime (') and those describing the lower state with double prime ("), this result can be obtained by inserting appropriate values into equation VII-1.

$$\mathbf{J}'' = 1, \mathbf{J}' = 2: \quad \nu = \nu_0 + \nu_{rot} = \nu_0 + 2(2 + 1)B' - 1(1 + 1)B''$$
$$= \nu_0 + 4B$$
$$\mathbf{J}'' = 1, \mathbf{J}' = 0: \quad \nu = \nu_0 + 0(0 + 1)B' - 1(1 + 1)B''$$
$$= \nu_0 - 2B$$

It is assumed here that $B' = B''$, that is, that the average bond length is the same in the two vibrational states.

By an entirely equivalent process it can be shown that molecules originally in the state $\mathbf{J}'' = 2$ will absorb at the frequencies $\nu_0 + 6B$ and $\nu_0 - 4B$;

---

[1] In practice, gases generally condense before such a temperature is reached. An exception is H_2, for which no infrared absorption is observed.

those in the state $J'' = 3$ will absorb at the frequencies $\nu_0 + 8B$ and $\nu_0 - 6B$; and in general for the initial rotational state J'' the molecule will absorb at the frequencies $\nu_0 + 2B(J'' + 1)$ and $\nu_0 - 2BJ''$ (for $J'' > 0$). A representation of the various possible transitions, superimposed on the observed spectrum of CO at room temperature, is shown in Fig. VII-7.

The relative intensity of each line will be proportional to the Boltzmann factor, including degeneracy, for the initial state of that transition. The Boltzmann factor for a state of energy $hBJ(J + 1)$ is $(2J + 1) \exp(-hBJ(J + 1)/kT)$. Considering this as a continuous function of J, it may be differentiated with respect to J and the derivative set equal to zero to find the maximum population.[1] From this it can be shown that the separation between the two most intense peaks is

$$\Delta\nu_{PR} = \sqrt{8BkT/h} \qquad \text{(VII-3)}$$

For B expressed in reciprocal centimeters and for room temperature,

$$\Delta\sigma_{PR} = 40\sqrt{B} \qquad \text{(VII-3a)}$$

In Table VII-VIII the values of the rotational constants are given for several molecules. Since the resolution limit of most spectrometers is greater than 1 cm^{-1} and is often 5 cm^{-1} or much higher, it is apparent that the detailed structure will generally be resolved only for the lightest molecules. It is often necessary to deal with the contour of the band without benefit of seeing the individual rotational lines.

For non-linear molecules (or linear molecules with electronic angular momentum along the molecular axis) it is possible to have vibrational transitions in which the direction, but not the magnitude, of the total angular momentum changes. Absorption then is observed at the vibrational frequency, ν_0, as well as at higher and lower frequencies. The low-frequency lines ($\Delta J = -1$) are called the P branch of the rotation-vibration band, the absorption at the vibrational frequency ($\Delta J = 0$) is called the Q branch,[2] and the lines at higher frequencies ($\Delta J = 1$) constitute the R branch.

Approximate values of the rotational constants, and thus some estimates of molecular dimensions, can be obtained from measured separations of the maxima of the P and R branches when the band contour, but not the individual lines, can be resolved. For reliable application of this method it is necessary to know something of the nature of the transition and perhaps also some of the characteristics of the particular molecule, since the

[1] Gerhard and Dennison, *Phys. Rev.* **43**, 197 (1933).
[2] A Q branch is also observed for a linear molecule when a bending mode is excited.

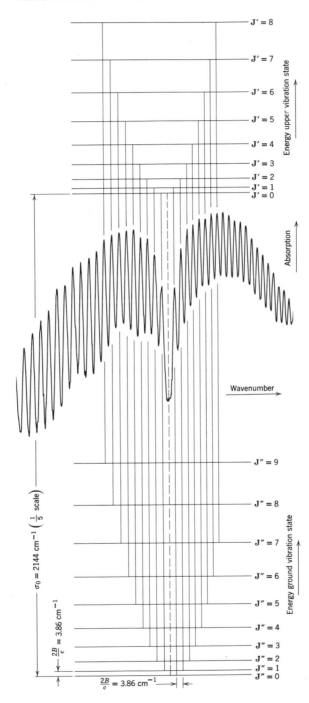

FIG. VII-7. Origin and appearance of rotational structure. P and R branches are shown to left and right, respectively, on the spectrometer tracing of the carbon monoxide fundamental absorption band at 2144 cm^{-1}. The Q branch (dotted line) is missing. Energy levels are shown to scale except that distance between upper and lower vibrational states (2144 cm^{-1}) should be about five times as great as in the figure.

band contour is subject to wide variations depending on the relative values of the moments of inertia and the amount of rotation-vibration interaction (Coriolis coupling). For example, failure to resolve P, Q, R structure does not mean that the moments of inertia are quite large, since the band shape may be such that the Q branch dominates the contour. Similarly a

TABLE VII-VIII

Rotational Constants[a] of Small Molecules

Molecule	A	B	C
H_2	∞	60.84	60.84
HCl^{35}	∞	10.44	10.44
DCl^{35}	∞	5.45	5.45
CO	∞	1.92	1.92
I_2	∞	0.037	0.037
CO_2	∞	0.39	0.39
HCN	∞	1.48	1.48
C_2H_2	∞	1.18	1.18
NH_3	9.94	9.94	6.31
CH_3F	5.10	0.85	0.85
CH_3Cl	5.10	0.49	0.49
C_2H_6	2.54	0.66	0.66
CH_4	5.25	5.25	5.25
CD_4	2.65	2.65	2.65
CF_4	0.18	0.18	0.18
H_3CCCCH_3	2.54	0.112	0.112
F_3CCCCF_3	0.095	0.020	0.020
BF_3	0.35	0.35	0.18
H_2O	26.64	14.40	9.16
H_2S	10.39	9.04	4.72
H_2CO	9.5	1.31	1.15
C_2H_4	4.83	1.00	0.83
C_3H_6	1.34	1.34	0.67
C_6H_6	0.38	0.38	0.19

[a] In cm^{-1}.

failure to observe a Q branch when the P and R branches are well resolved is not strong evidence that the Q branch is absent because of symmetry-induced selection rules. On the other hand, a measured P-R separation is likely to be approximately correct, even in the worst cases, and may provide a valuable clue to the particular molecule responsible for the absorption or to the configuration of a known molecule under investigation. Observed band contours for several molecules are shown in Fig. VII-8.

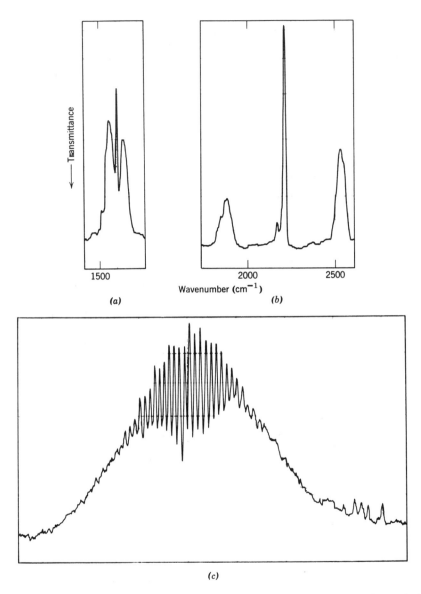

FIG. VII-8. Rotation-vibration bands of gases. (*a*) Spherical rotor, showing typical *P-Q-R* branches (CF$_4$, 1538 cm^{-1}; Coriolis constant -0.35, *P-R* separation 35 cm^{-1}). (*b*) Unresolved bands (CF$_4$; Coriolis constant of 2180 band is 0.84, *P-R* separation 4 cm^{-1}). (*c*) Partially resolved structure of a perpendicular band of a symmetric rotor, showing splitting of the *Q* branch (C$_2$H$_6$ 821 cm^{-1}). (*d*) Parallel band of a linear molecule, showing absence of a *Q* branch (CO$_2$, 2350 cm^{-1}). (*e*) Portion of a perpendicular band of a linear molecule, showing regularity of resolved structure (CO$_2$, 667 cm^{-1}, *Q* and *R* branches). (*f*) Portion of a band of an asymmetric rotor, showing irregular structure (H$_2$O, 1595 cm^{-1}). Band contour alone is seldom sufficient for deducing the symmetry properties of the molecule.

310

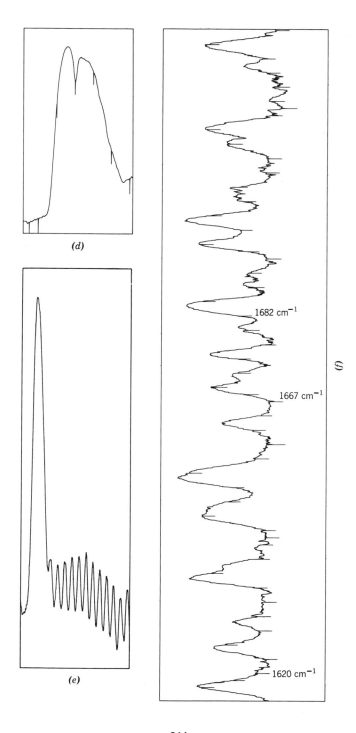

(d)

(e)

(f)

1682 cm⁻¹

1667 cm⁻¹

1620 cm⁻¹

Problems

1. The observed vibrational frequency (neglecting the correction for anharmonicity) of hydrogen chloride corresponds to a wavenumber of 2886 cm^{-1}.

   (a) Find the force constant for the hydrogen chloride molecule.

   (b) Find the shift in vibrational frequency for HCl^{37} compared to HCl^{35}.

   (c) Find the classical amplitude of the motion in the ground vibrational state (energy $\frac{1}{2}h\nu_0$) and in the first excited vibrational state. Express the displacement in Å and as a percentage of the normal bond length (1.275 Å).

2. Calculate the separation, in cm^{-1}, to be expected between rotational lines in the 2886 cm^{-1} HCl absorption band.

3. Absorption bands in liquids have half band widths of roughly 2.5 to 25 cm^{-1}. Find the average time between collisions for a molecule of CCl$_4$ at room temperature, assuming that the liquid can be treated as an ideal gas. From the Heisenberg uncertainty principle, $(\Delta E)(\Delta t) \geqslant h/2$, calculate the uncertainty in energy of the vibrational states and hence the absorption band half width, $\Delta\sigma_{1/2} = \Delta E/hc$. Use 4.75 Å, the height of the CCl$_4$ pyramid ($\frac{4}{3}$ times the sum of covalent radii and van der Waals radius), as the molecular diameter.

4. Aliphatic hydrocarbons show C—H stretching vibrations at approximately 2850 and 2950 cm^{-1}. Calculate where these vibrations would be observed if the compound were deuterated,

   (a) neglecting the motions of the carbon atoms

   (b) considering the C—H group as a diatomic molecule.

5. Calculate the shift to be expected in the benzene vibrations involving motions of the carbon atoms upon deuteration if the hydrogen atoms are considered rigidly attached to the carbons (that is, considering deuteration to increase the effective mass of the C from 13 to 14).

6. Benzene shows the following Raman-active vibrations: 606, 849, 992, 1178, 1596 (split by interaction with another band), 3047, and 3062 cm^{-1}. Deuterobenzene, C$_6$D$_6$, shows the bands: 577, 661, 867, 945, 1559, 2264, and 2292 cm^{-1}. On the basis of this evidence alone, which bands (in each molecule) would you assign to vibrations involving primarily motions of the hydrogen atoms and which to vibrations involving primarily motions of the carbon atoms?

7. CHCl$_3$, when irradiated with the Hg 4358 Å line, shows a Raman band at 5090 Å.

   (a) If the molecule were irradiated with the Hg 4047 Å line, where would this Raman band appear?

   (b) Where would this vibration be observed in the infrared spectrum?

   (c) What type of vibration is responsible for the band?

8. Indicate whether the following vibrations will be active or inactive in the infrared spectrum and whether they will be active or inactive in the Raman spectrum.

Molecule	Motion
(a) H$_3$C—CH$_3$	C—C stretch
(b) H$_3$C—CCl$_3$	C—C stretch
(c) C$_6$H$_6$	Rotation,

Molecule	Motion
(d) $C_6H_5NH_2$	Deformation, 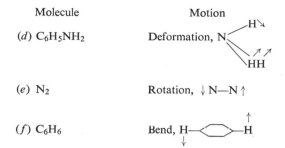
(e) N_2	Rotation, $\downarrow N—N \uparrow$
(f) C_6H_6	Bend, H—⟨ ⟩—H

9. Water vapor shows infrared absorption bands at 1595 cm⁻¹ and at 3652 and 3756 cm⁻¹. If the Raman spectrum is observed with the mercury green line (5461 Å) as the exciting line,
(a) at what wavelengths would you expect to find Raman lines?
(b) what color would each of the Raman lines appear to the eye?

10. Which of the following molecules will show microwave spectra?

(a) C_2H_2	(b) $CHCl_3$	(c) CCl_4
(d) SO_2	(e) CO	(f) CO_2

How could the same type of information be obtained for the others?

11. The generalized momentum conjugate to (that is, corresponding to) any co-ordinate q is defined to be $p = \partial L/\partial \dot{q}$ where $L \equiv T - V$ is the Lagrangian. The equations of motion in the Lagrangian notation are $(d/dt)(\partial L/\partial \dot{q}_i) - (\partial L/\partial q_i) = 0$. Solve the problem of the mass on a spring, using the Lagrangian notation. What is the momentum conjugate to the position variable x?

12. Solve the problem of a mass describing a circle at the end of a string, using the Lagrangian notation. What is the momentum conjugate to the position variable θ?

13. For a diatomic molecule free to move along its symmetry axis, $T = \frac{1}{2}m_1\dot{x}_1^2 + \frac{1}{2}m_2\dot{x}_2^2$; $V = \frac{1}{2}k[(x_1 - x_1°) - (x_2 - x_2°)]^2$.
(a) Let $q_1 = (x_1 - x_1°) - (x_2 - x_2°)$
    $q_2 = (x_1 - x_1°) + (x_2 - x_2°)$
    (i) Find p_1 and p_2 in terms of $\dot{q}_1$ and $\dot{q}_2$ and in terms of $\dot{x}_1$ and $\dot{x}_2$.
    (ii) Solve the equations of motion, in Lagrangian form, to find $q_1(t)$, $\dot{q}_1(t)$, $\ddot{q}_1(t)$ and $q_2(t)$, $\dot{q}_2(t)$, $\ddot{q}_2(t)$. Explain briefly the significance of these results in terms of the form of the motion and in terms of the conservation laws.
(b) Let $q_1 = \frac{1}{2}[m_1(x_1 - x_1°) - m_2(x_2 - x_2°)]$
    $q_2 = \frac{1}{2}[m_1(x_1 - x_1°) + m_2(x_2 - x_2°)]$
    (i) Find p_1 and p_2.
    (ii) Solve the equations of motion and discuss results.

14. The vibrational frequency of N_2 is equivalent to a wavenumber of 2360 cm⁻¹.
(a) Find the force constant of the N_2 bond.
(b) Assume that a mechanical spring is available with the same force constant. What would be the length of the scale of a spring balance, made from this spring, with a load capacity of 20 kg? Are such springs available?

15. Derive equation VII-3 for a parallel band of a symmetric rotor.

16. Derive an expression comparable to equation VII-3 applicable to a spherical rotor, remembering that the relative statistical weight is $(2J + 1)^2$ for a rotational state of quantum number J.

VIII
Qualitative analysis

Methods of chemical analysis have undergone a major revolution over the last few decades. Classical procedures are far from disappearing, but instrumental methods are taking over an ever increasing share of the expanding load of the analytical chemist. Especially prominent is the family of spectroscopic techniques, which have extremely wide variation in applicability.

Emission spectroscopy is especially suitable for metals. With arc or spark excitation most of the metals and many non-metals can be detected in trace amounts. The alkali and alkaline earth metals can be measured in parts per million by flame excitation. X-ray fluorescence is somewhat better for determining major components of a mixture than for finding traces.

Ultraviolet-visible absorption is particularly sensitive for unsaturated organic compounds, especially those containing aromatic or carbonyl groups. Many substances that would not normally absorb in a convenient region can be detected and quantitatively determined "colorimetrically" by forming suitable derivatives, for example, by combining an organic compound with a metallic ion in solution. Many organic molecules show strong fluorescence which permits identification of these substances in trace amounts.

The most nearly universal method of analysis is infrared spectroscopy. All organic compounds and all but a few inorganic compounds absorb within the range of the commercial spectrometers. Spectra of closely related compounds may be quite similar; this is of assistance in determining the type of compound or compounds present, but nearly always there will be sufficient individuality of the spectrum to permit identification of the exact compound by comparison with the spectrum of the known material. Exceptions arise primarily for complex mixtures and some inorganics. Raman spectroscopy should, in principle, be nearly as ver-

314

satile as infrared, but the field is still limited by experimental difficulties, especially for samples that are colored, cloudy, powdered, or fluorescent.

Nuclear magnetic resonance is particularly sensitive for hydrogen and fluorine compounds, although a number of other atoms can be examined. Mass spectroscopy is best suited to volatile, low-molecular-weight compounds which have been previously investigated by this technique. X-ray diffraction determines the distances between atoms or ions in a crystal, thus permitting a determination of the chemical nature of the crystal provided the constants for that substance are available in the literature. Inorganic compounds are usually readily identified by this means. Microwave spectroscopy is limited to volatile, polar compounds and has seen little application to chemical analysis.

In this chapter the application of ultraviolet-visible, infrared, and Raman spectroscopy to the identification of chemical compounds will be considered. The following chapter treats the adaptation of these methods to the quantitative determination of one or more components of a sample containing known compounds.

The absorption spectrum will depend on the structure of a compound, as discussed in earlier chapters. Accordingly, it provides a fingerprint of the molecule, so that if the spectrum of a known sample is available it is easily proved, in general, whether the unknown could be that same compound. It also provides information from which the structure of the molecule can be determined, often in great detail. Extensive calculations are usually required to extract the full amount of information about the structure of a molecule from the observed spectrum, and for many molecules these calculations are not yet feasible. But in many cases a surprisingly large amount of information on the structure of the compound can be obtained by a qualitative inspection of the spectrum. This not only enables the physicist or physical chemist to draw conclusions about the structure of a "known" substance; it also often makes it possible for the analyst to identify the class of compounds to which the unknown belongs or even specify the exact compound, even though the spectrum has not previously been observed. Particularly when such preliminary identification can be coupled with a comparison of the spectrum of an authentic sample of the suspected compound, an extremely powerful tool for qualitative identification is made available to the chemist.

I   Ultraviolet and Visible

Among the most obvious characteristics of a chemical compound is its color. The relationship between color and chemical constitution has been a topic of investigation for many years. These attempts have been successful to the extent that it is now usually possible to predict from the structural formula of a compound whether or not it will be colored and the general region of the ultraviolet or visible in which it will absorb. Predictions of exact positions of absorption bands have been somewhat less successful, except with families of similar compounds where the spectra of several members are known. Two approaches to the prediction of the position of electronic absorption will be treated briefly, the chromophore-auxochrome theory and the free-electron molecular-orbital theory (FEMO).

1.1 Chromophores and Auxochromes

In 1876 Witt called attention to the existence of certain chemical groups which appeared to be associated with the appearance of color in molecules. These he termed "chromophores," or color bearers. One cannot, however, draw a one-to-one correspondence between the chromophoric groups present and the colors observed. The color depends on the relative positions of the chromophoric groups in the molecule and also on certain other groups, which do not themselves produce color but which tend to shift the absorption associated with the chromophore. These have been termed "auxochromes," or color aids.

It is now known that the distinction between chromophores and auxochromes is largely a quantitative, rather than a qualitative, one, for molecules containing only auxochromic groups show absorption at lower frequencies than would be expected in the absence of such groups, though at higher frequencies than if a "chromophoric" group were present. One may arbitrarily classify as chromophores those groups that produce absorption in the region below 50,000 cm^{-1} (2000 Å) and as auxochromes those that produce absorption at higher frequencies, but this dividing line is based solely upon experimental convenience and has no theoretical justification.

1.11 Simple Chromophores

A listing of common chromophoric and auxochromic groups is given in Table VIII-I, along with the approximate regions in which they absorb when present by themselves or attached to a saturated hydrocarbon chain and the approximate intensity to be expected for the group. Most of them are unsaturated groups, in the sense that they are represented by Lewis structures (dashes or pairs of dots for bonds) containing multiple bonds. Some, however, are saturated groups which have "non-bonding," or "lone-pair," electrons in the valence shell of one of the atoms.[1]

The numbers given in Table VIII-I must be considered only as a rough guide to position and intensity. The absorption bands tend to be broad and often consist of multiple peaks or a main absorption band with weaker bands adjacent. The question of what constitutes appreciable absorption or where the band center of the lowest-frequency band is to be found is sufficiently subjective in many cases that values in the literature appear to be in violent disagreement, even for common compounds.

The spectra of molecules containing groups that are structurally similar often resemble each other. For example, alcohols and ethers absorb at the edge of the accessible ultraviolet region, the ethers showing stronger absorption. Mercaptans and thioethers absorb at somewhat lower frequencies, resembling in intensity the alcohols and ethers, respectively. Free amines also absorb in the approximate region of the sulfur compounds, but if the lone-pair electrons are engaged by the formation of the $-NH_3^+$ ion the absorption becomes more like that of the oxygen compounds. There are also some similarities between the spectra of carbonyl compounds and of substances containing $C\!=\!N$ or $N\!=\!O$ chromophores.

Chromophoric groups have been roughly divided by Burawoy into two classes, those giving rise to R bands and to K bands. The former are associated with isolated multiple order bonds, especially those involving oxygen or nitrogen, and with certain free radicals. The K chromophores are primarily conjugated multiple order bonds. When both types of chromophores are present in a single molecule, as in α,β-unsaturated carbonyl compounds, two bands are observed, one with the general characteristics of a K band, the other with the properties of an R band. These may be distinguished, among other methods, by the intensities; K bands are very intense, arising from allowed transitions (absorptivity values of roughly 10^4 L/mole-cm), R bands tend to be very weak (absorptivity values of the order of 10 to 1000), indicating that the transition is forbidden. The R and K band notation is only a rough, empirical system. It will be noticed, however, that those transitions classified as R bands by Burawoy have the general characteristics of n-π transitions and the K bands of Burawoy have properties associated with π-π transitions.

If ethylene is substituted with alkyl groups the position of the low-frequency absorption band moves progressively to lower frequencies with increasing substitution. The shift is not great (roughly 1000–2000 cm^{-1})

---

[1] Sometimes the unsaturated groups are called chromophores, the saturated groups auxochromes. Others prefer the equally valid, but generally less convenient, definition of a chromophore as any group that causes absorption in any region of the electromagnetic spectrum.

TABLE VIII-I
Chromophores and Auxochromes[a]

Group	Example	σ (10^3 cm^{-1});	λ (Å)	a (L/mole-cm)
C=C	$H_2C=CH_2$	55	1825	250
		57.3	1744	16,000
		58.6	1704	16,500
		62	1620	10,000
C≡C	$H—C≡C—CH_2—CH_3$	58	1720	2500
C=O	H_2CO	34	2950	10
		54	1850	strong
C=S	$CH_3—\overset{\overset{\text{S}}{\|}}{C}—CH_3$	22	4600	weak
—NO$_2$	$CH_3—NO_2$	36	2775	10
		47.5	2100	10,000
—N=N—	$CH_3—N=N—CH_3$	28.8	3470	15
		> 38.5	< 2600	strong
⬡		39	2550	200
		50	2000	6300
		55.5	1800	100,000
—Cl	CH_3Cl	58	1725	—
—Br	CH_3Br	49	2040	1800
—I	CH_3I	38.8	2577	—
		49.7	2010	1200
—OH	CH_3OH	55	1830	200
		67	1500	1900
—SH	C_2H_5SH	43	2320	160
—NH$_2$	CH_3NH_2	46.5	2150	580
		52.5	1905	3200
—S—	$CH_3—S—CH_3$	44	2280	620
		46.5	2150	700
		49.3	2030	2300
C=C—C=C	$H_2C=CH—CH=CH_2$	48	2090	25,000
⬡⬡		32	3110	250
		37	2700	5000
		45	2210	100,000
⬡⬡⬡		28	3600	6000
		40	2500	150,000

TABLE VIII-I (continued)

Group	Example	σ (10^3 cm^{-1}); λ (Å)		a (L/mole-cm)
O=⟨ring⟩=O		23	4400	20
		34	3000	1000
		40	2500	15,000
C=C—C=O	$H_2C=C-\overset{\overset{\displaystyle O}{\|}}{C}-H$	30	3330	20
		47.5	2100	12,000
⟨ring⟩-$\overset{\overset{\displaystyle S}{\|}}{C}$-CH$_3$		16.5	6000	—
⟨ring⟩-N=N-⟨ring⟩		22.5	4400	500
		31	3200	20,000
		43	2300	10,000

[a] Band positions and especially band intensities must be regarded as approximate. Values are taken largely from Kamlet and Ungnade, *Organic Electronic Spectral Data*, Interscience, New York, 1960, or from F. A. Matsen, ref. 47.

and depends on the resultant symmetry of the molecule, but it is independent of the length of the saturated chains. Nietzki had postulated (in 1879) that increasing the molecular weight of a compound led to a decrease in absorption frequency. Later investigators showed that such a broad generalization was unjustified, but the shift to lower frequency accompanying alkyl substitution is still called a "weighting" effect. The terminology was undoubtedly encouraged by the confusion that existed for some time between the electronic absorption and the vibrational properties of molecules.

1.12 Compound Chromophores

Two or more chromophoric groups in a molecule will produce the absorption characteristic of each isolated group if the chromophores are insulated by more than one carbon atom or more than one carbon-carbon single bond. If the groups are adjacent, either as a conjugated system (such as 1,3-butadiene) or as a cumulated system (such as allene), the spectrum may be strikingly different from that characteristic of the indi-

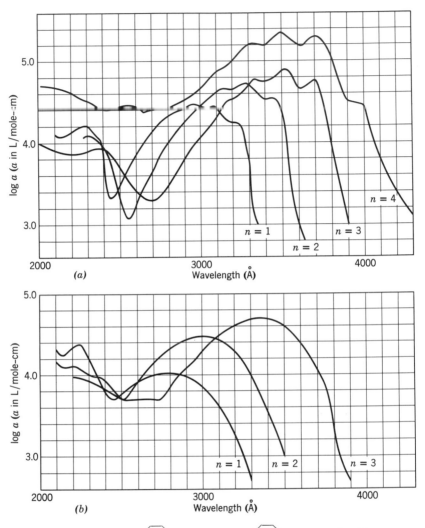

FIG. VIII-1.   Spectra of ⬡—(HC=CH)$_n$—⬡ compounds: (a) *trans* configuration; (b) *cis* configuration. [From Beale and Roe, *J. Chem. Soc.* **1953**, 2755;
Pinckard, Wille, and Zechmeister, *J. Am. Chem. Soc.* **70**, 1938 (1948); Lunde and
Zechmeister, *ibid.* **76**, 2308 (1954); and Hirshberg, Bergmann, and Bergmann, *ibid.*
72, 5120 (1950).]

vidual chromophores.   It was the magnitude of this effect, which generally
results in a shift of the absorption to lower frequencies, that led to the
early description in terms of auxochromes.[1]

   [1] The term auxochrome was originally applied in connection with dyes and carried
with it a connotation of improved dying characteristics as well as a "deepening" of the

The number of ways in which the groups listed in Table VIII-I can be combined in conjugated or cumulated systems is obviously extremely large. Each of these possibilities could give rise to a compound with a different spectrum. Three types of compounds that are important "building blocks" and have been extensively studied will be considered very briefly. They are the conjugated polyenes, the polycyclic aromatics, and the substituted benzenes.

The conjugated polyenes display a remarkable regularity with increasing length of the system. The position of the absorption moves to lower frequencies and the intensity increases, at least approximately linearly, as shown in Fig. VIII-1.

If the polyene chain is conjugated with a carbonyl group or with C=N, two bands appear. The very intense π-π transition (Burawoy's K band) appears in the vicinity of 48,000 cm^{-1} (2100 Å) for a compound such as acrolein (CH_2=CHCHO) but shifts to lower frequencies as the unsaturated chain is lengthened or when a group such as —OH or —OR is substituted for hydrogen. The lower-frequency absorption band appears about 32,000 cm^{-1} (3200 Å) in aqueous solution. This is interpreted as an n-π transition (Burawoy's R band); it moves to lower frequency as the unsaturated chain is lengthened but moves to higher frequencies upon substitution.

The "linear" polycyclic aromatics, such as benzene, naphthalene, anthracene, and naphthacene, show a regular progression toward lower frequencies with increasing size of the molecule. The appearance of these spectra is quite striking because of the sharp bands and their symmetrical pattern. It will be noted, from Fig. VIII-2, that the larger compounds absorb in the same region as benzene, but much more strongly. Other polycyclic aromatics, such as phenanthrene, benzanthracene, and pyrene, exhibit absorption curves that are similar in many respects to those of the "linear" ring systems but do not follow so simple a pattern.

Substitution of the benzene molecule with functional groups that are not themselves strong chromophores will cause a shift in the position of the benzene spectrum that can be correlated with the nature of the substituent, the number of substituents, and the relative positions of these around the ring. Not only the $^1L_b \leftarrow {}^1A$ transition[1] at 40,000 cm^{-1} color of the dye in solution. The ambiguity of meaning was aided by the fact that most of those groups considered auxochromes are polar in nature and thus do increase the binding between dye and fabric as well as change the color of the dye molecule.

---

[1] The notation given is that discussed in section VI-2.3 and is due to Platt. The upper states in benzene are probably B_{2u}, B_{1u}, and E_{1u}, respectively, in the notation of group theory. Other designations given to the transitions include, for example, the terms "secondary," "first primary," and "second primary," applied by Doub and Vandenbelt, *J. Am. Chem. Soc.* **69**, 2714 (1947); **71**, 2414 (1949); **77**, 4535 (1955).

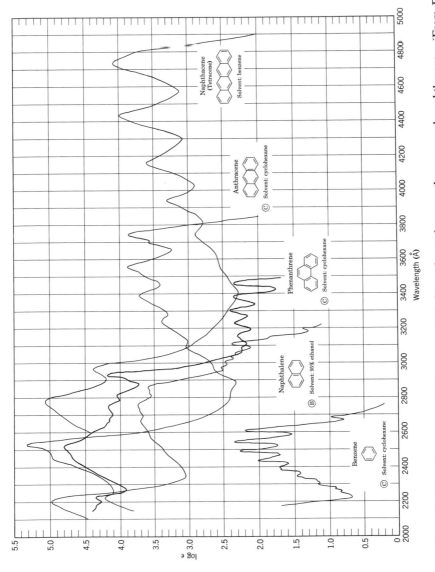

FIG. VIII-2. Electronic absorption spectra of benzene, naphthalene, phenanthrene, anthracene, and naphthacene. From Friedel and Orchin, *Ultraviolet Spectra of Aromatic Compounds*, John Wiley & Sons, Inc., New York, 1951.)

(2500 Å) but also the $^1L_a \leftarrow {}^1A$ band at 50,000 cm^{-1} (2000 Å) and the $^1B \leftarrow {}^1A$ band at 55,000 cm^{-1} (1800 Å) shift upon substitution.   The high-frequency bands are roughly 35 and 250 times as intense as the low-frequency group and in some cases appear to overtake and hide the

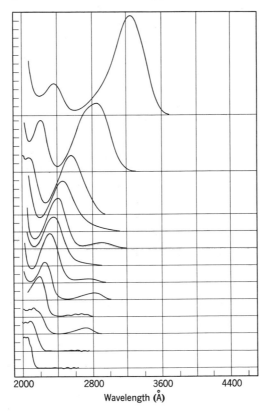

FIG. VIII-3.   Ultraviolet spectra of substituted benzenes.   High-frequency band moves to lower frequencies when ring is substituted.   Compounds are benzene, toluene, phenol, benzenesulfonamide, *p*-chlorophenol, benzoic acid, *p*-methylbenzoate ion, *p*-chloroaniline, *p*-hydroxybenzoate ion, *p*-hydroxybenzoic acid, *p*-hydroxybenzalde-hyde, and *p*-hydroxyacetophenone anion.   [From Doub and Vandenbelt, *J. Am. Chem. Soc.* **69**, 2714 (1947).]

low-frequency band altogether.   Figure VIII-3 shows a series of substituted compounds in which this shift is quite apparent.

A change in absorption frequency can be attributed to a change in the energy of the ground electronic state, a change in the upper electronic state, or a combination of the two.   Assuming the correlation of shifted bands with unshifted bands in Fig. VIII-3 is correct, the different rates of motion of the bands demonstrate that a significant part, at least, of the change in energy must occur in the excited states. Other spectroscopic evidence, based on investigations of the ground state, support this view. It is not surprising that there is some correlation between the effect of a substituent on the benzene spectrum and the effect on the rates of chemical reactions involving the benzene ring; it should also not be surprising that the relationship is not a trivial one, since the reaction kinetics depend on the energy of a transient state that need bear little resemblance to any of the three excited states associated with the three benzene absorption bands.

If substituents are ordered according to the magnitude of the shift they produce in the benzene bands, the order is found to parallel that found in many other types of experiments, including, for example, the ortho-para directing power of the substituent. An important difference, however, is that the magnitude of the frequency shift produced depends only on the magnitude of the difference in character between the substituent and hydrogen, without regard to the direction of this difference (ortho-para or meta directing). Positions of the $^1L_a - {}^1A$ bands for some monosubstituted benzenes are given in Table VIII-II.

TABLE V II-II

Wavenumber of ^1L_a Band of Substituted Benzenes

Substituent	Wavenumber[a]	Substituent	Wavenumber[a]
H	49.2	CN	44.7
NH_3^+	49.3	COO^-	44.7
CH_3	48.4	COOH	43.5
Cl	47.7	NH_2	43.5
Br	47.6	O^-	42.5
OH	47.5	Ac	40.7
CH_3O	46.1	CHO	40.1
Sa[b]	46.0		

[a] In 10^3 cm^{-1}.
[b] Sulfonamide, $-SO_2NH_2$.

To a first approximation, the shift produced upon disubstitution is the sum of the shifts to be expected for the individual substituents,[1] but some rather significant deviations from this generalization are found. A better correlation is obtained if compounds are grouped according to the types

[1] This is expected for small shifts for which first-order perturbation theory may be applied.

of substituents and the position of substitution.   Some examples of such relationships are shown in Tables VIII-III and VIII-IV and in Fig. VIII-4.

TABLE VIII-III

Wavenumber of ^1L_a Band of Para Disubstituted Benzenes

Substituents	Wavenumber[a]	Substituents	Wavenumber[a]
CH_3, NH_3^+	48.2	OH, COOH	39.2
Cl, NH_3^+	46.4	CH_3, Ac	39.1
Br, NH_3^+	45.8	CH_3O, COOH	39.0
OH, NH_3^+	45.8	Sa, NH_2	38.8
CH_3, Sa	44.3	Br, Ac	38.7
CH_3, CN	42.7	NH_2, COO^-	37.8
Cl, COO^-	42.5	NH_2, CN	37.0
CH_3, COO^-	42.5	OH, Ac	36.4
Cl, CN	42.1	CH_3O, Ac	36.2
Br, COO^-	41.8	O^-, COO^-	35.7
Cl, COOH	41.5	OH, CHO	35.3
CH_3, COOH	41.5	NH_2, COOH	35.2
OH, COO^-	40.8	NH_2, Ac	32.1
Br, COOH	40.7	Ac, O^-	30.8
CH_3O, COO^-	40.5	CHO, O^-	30.3

[a] In 10^3 cm^{-1}.

TABLE VIII-IV

Wavenumber of ^1L_a Band of Ortho and Meta Disubstituted Benzenes

Substituents	Wavenumber[a]		Substituents	Wavenumber[a]	
	Ortho	Meta		Ortho	Meta
Sa, CH_3	45.9	—	CHO, OH	39.1	39.3
CN, CH_3	43.7	43.6	NH_2, CN	—	42.3
COO^-, Cl	—	43.9	O^-, CN	41.7	—
COOH, Cl	43.6	43.2	NH_2, COO^-	41.7	41.5
COO^-, OH	43.4	43.1	O^-, COO^-	41.3	40.8
COOH, OH	42.2	42.3	NH_2, COOH	40.3	40.0
CN, OH	43.3	—	Ac, O^-	39.1	37.6
Ac, OH	39.6	39.9	CHO, O^-	37.8	37.4

[a] In 10^3 cm^{-1}.

A purely empirical expression relating the position of absorption of multiply substituted benzenes to a product function of parameters characteristic of the individual substituents has been reported by Doub

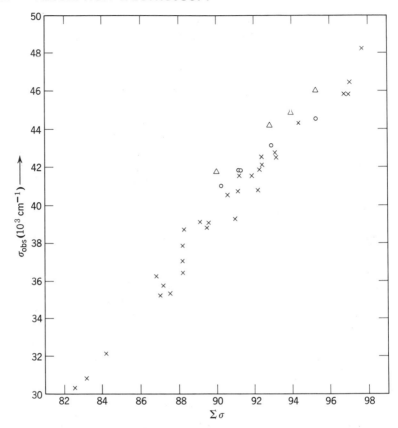

FIG. VIII-4a.   Observed wavenumbers of *p*-disubstituted benzenes plotted against sum of wavenumbers for corresponding monosubstituted compounds.   ○ = two ortho-para directing substituents; △ = two meta directing substituents; × = one ortho-para and one meta directing substituent.   (Based on Doub and Vandenbelt, *loc. cit.*   See Tables VIII-II and VIII-III.)

and Vandenbelt.[1]   They have provided, also, for the slight change to be expected on changing from water to ethanol as a solvent.

Significant changes are often found in comparing the spectra of a given compound observed in the vapor phase and in solution, or observed in two different solvents.   For example, in Fig. VIII-5 the spectra of benzene and acetone are shown for vapor and solution and the spectra of phenol and acetone are compared for polar and non-polar solvents.   The nature of the solvent may produce significant changes in the spectrum of a polar molecule, whereas molecules such as benzene which have no dipole

[1] *Loc. cit.*

moment are little affected by the nature of the solvent.   As the dielectric constant of the solvent is increased, the very intense π-π bands tend to move toward lower frequencies whereas the weaker n-π bands tend to move toward higher frequencies.

The appearance of an electronic absorption band depends on the vibrational frequencies, through the Franck-Condon principle, but often the only absorption is a broad, structureless band.   Acetone in solution shows

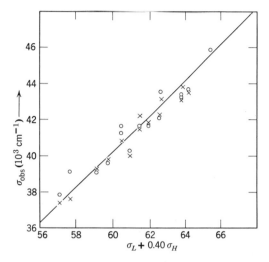

FIG. VIII-4b.   Observed wavenumbers of o-disubstituted ($\bigcirc$) and m-disubstituted ($\times$) benzenes plotted against a weighted sum of the wavenumbers for the corresponding monosubstituted compounds (wavenumber of lower-frequency monosubstituted compound plus 0.40 times the wavenumber of the higher-frequency monosubstituted compound). [Based on Doub and Vandenbelt, J. Am. Chem. Soc. 71, 2414 (1949).   See Tables VIII-II and VIII-IV.]

such broad absorption, whereas benzene gives a series of moderately narrow peaks (half width about 300 cm^{-1}).   Lewis[1] pointed out that the sharp absorption bands are characteristic of rigid molecules, the broad bands of compounds which are more flexible.   He termed this phenomenon the "loose bolt" effect.

The explanation of the "loose bolt" effect is to be found in the Franck-Condon principle.   If there is a low-frequency vibration which can be excited simultaneously with the electronic excitation, the spectrum should contain closely spaced lines differing by this small frequency.   There is also a significant probability of the upper vibrational levels being populated before the transition, causing a further very significant increase in the

[1] Lewis and Calvin, Chem. Rev. 25, 273 (1939).

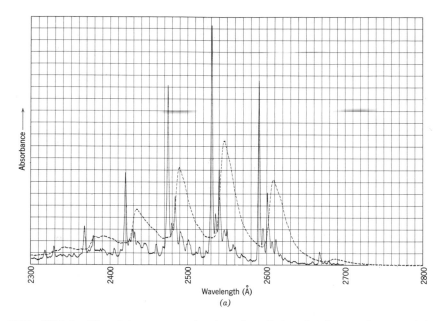

FIG. VIII-5. Ultraviolet spectra, showing the effects of solvents. Instrumental conditions are held constant for each sample but concentrations are only roughly comparable. (a) Benzene vapor (solid line) and solution in cyclohexane (dashed line).

complexity of the spectrum.   Under low resolution, or in solution where the lines become broadened by intermolecular effects, the complex spectrum will appear to be a continuous, broad band.

1.2 Free-Electron Model

Considerable success in predicting the appearance of the electronic absorption spectra of polyenes and aromatics has been achieved by means of the "free-electron" model.   If one considers the nuclei to be fixed in space, they will produce a strong potential field, or well, with dimensions approximately equal to the over-all size of the molecule.   Electrons will be firmly held within this well by the coulombic forces.   In saturated molecules the potential in which the electrons move will be highly non-uniform, so that to a first approximation one can often consider any particular electron to be bound to the vicinity of one or two nuclei.   Conjugated systems will contain certain orbitals that extend over the length of the conjugated portion of the molecule; within this region the electric field seen by the electrons in these enlarged orbitals will be somewhat uniform, though with a strong periodic nature imposed by the nuclear charges.

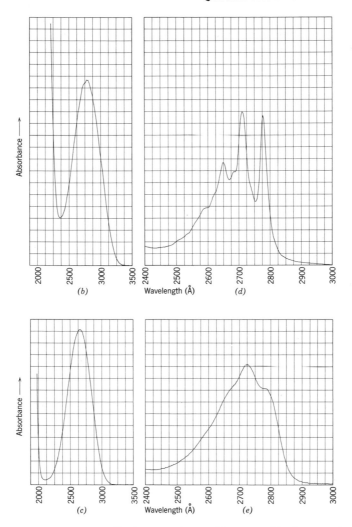

FIG. VIII-5 (*Continued*). (*b*) Acetone in cyclohexane. (*c*) Acetone in water. (*d*) Phenol in cyclohexane. (*e*) Phenol in 95% ethanol.

This picture of conjugated systems has suggested that the energy levels of the electrons might be calculated as if the electron were simply a particle in a box (section V-2.3). In simplest form, the calculation proceeds, for a molecule with N electrons in π orbitals, by determining the energy states for one electron and assuming that each of the lowest $N/2$ of these is filled with two electrons and that the energy levels above this are empty. Transitions from the highest filled orbital to one of the unfilled orbitals can occur.   The calculated energy for such a transition is compared with the lowest-frequency transitions observed in the electronic spectrum.

The length of the "box" for a conjugated system is somewhat indeterminate; in practice, this is usually chosen to extend about half a bond length beyond the last carbon nucleus on each end of the conjugated chain.   In benzene the diameter of the ring in which the electrons are considered to move is somewhat smaller than the diameter of the ring formed by the carbon nuclei.   This is an indication that there is some binding across the ring as well as around the circumference.

A serious difficulty is the neglect of electron-electron repulsion terms in assuming that the energy levels calculated for a single electron in a box are undisturbed when N electrons are put into these states.   If the repulsion terms are considered, the problem can no longer be solved exactly, but approximation methods can be applied to improve the agreement with experiment.   Despite the uncertainties and shortcomings of the simple free-electron molecular-orbital method, it has provided surprisingly good values for positions of the low-frequency absorption bands for many systems.

The fundamental applicability of the FEMO concept seems also to have been effectively demonstrated by some calculations made by Platt.[1]   He has calculated the free-electron wave functions for boxes of several sizes and shapes, corresponding to the external dimensions of aromatic hydrocarbons.   The points of maximum electron density are found to lie at those points corresponding to the normal positions of the carbon nuclei. Thus it is not only possible to consider a molecule to be formed by adding electrons to the potential field produced by nuclei in fixed, prearranged positions; it is equally valid, at least for certain types of molecules, to consider the nuclei to be added to the potential field produced by the electrons occupying the appropriate volume element in space.

2   Infrared and Raman

For diatomic molecules the frequency of vibration is given by $\nu = (1/2\pi)\sqrt{k/m}$, where k is the force constant of the bond and m is the reduced mass (equation V-10).   If potential energy of the bond is plotted against the internuclear distance, k will be a measure of the steepness of the sides of the parabola, or width of the potential well, since $v = \frac{1}{2}kx^2$.   The force constant represents the "strength," or "stiffness," of the bond in its equilibrium position.

[1] J. R. Platt, *J. Chem. Phys.* **22**, 1448 (1954).

Actual molecules are not truly harmonic oscillators. The correction terms which must be added to the expression for potential energy are quite unimportant in many respects, but they do have a very significant effect on intensities of combination and overtone bands and on the positions of these bands. The anharmonic correction terms are also important in that they show that the molecule will tend to dissociate at large vibrational amplitudes. The dissociation energy, or the height of the potential well at which it asymptotically becomes horizontal, is not in any obvious way connected with the force constant of the bond. Thus a bond that is strong in the sense that the force constant is large might be easily dissociated, or a weak bond might not give rise to dissociation except at very high energies.

In practice it is found that chemical bonds are sufficiently similar to each other that those bonds with large force constants also tend to have large dissociation energies and those with small force constants tend to have small values for the energy of dissociation. This still does not, however, mean that the bonds considered "weak," or "easily broken," by the chemist are necessarily weak in the sense of having a small force constant. A chemical reaction generally represents the breaking of certain bonds accompanied by the formation of new bonds. Thus attack at a double bond includes formation of new single bonds; loss of the hydrogen of acetylene occurs with the formation of a bond to a metal ion to produce, for example, silver acetylide; or ionization of an acid is a consequence of the formation of bonds between the resultant ions and the solvent. The term "bond strength" in the present context will always mean the strength of the bond, as defined by the force constant, in its equilibrium position. In this sense a double bond is roughly twice as strong as a single bond and an acetylenic C—H bond is stronger than an aliphatic C—H bond.

Calculation of the frequencies of vibration of a polyatomic molecule is a straightforward, if slightly tedious, procedure if the masses, bond lengths, bond angles, and force constants are known. For many molecules the bond lengths and angles, as well as the masses, are known, but the force constants are seldom known and must be approximated by one of several methods. This is often a helpful means for identifying observed frequencies with particular vibrational modes for small molecules; only very limited success has been achieved in applying such calculations to large molecules.

If the complete mathematical analysis of the vibrations of a polyatomic molecule has been carried out, the frequencies of vibration can be written in a manner that is formally similar to the equation for diatomic molecules. The effective force constant and the effective mass for each normal vibration will be complex expressions depending on the physical constants of the molecule. In any case one can be certain that as the effective force constant is increased the frequency must increase and as the effective mass is increased the frequency must decrease.[1]

The interpretation of vibrational spectra is based, in practice, on the assumption that the approximate vibrational modes are known and are essentially constant from one molecule to another containing chemically equivalent groups. In certain groups of molecules it has been found possible to demonstrate the constancy of a particular vibrational frequency without being certain of the form of the vibration responsible, but this is a much less satisfactory form of interpretation since it does not permit any predictions of the circumstances under which the correlation should be valid or would be expected to break down.

As a basis for correlating observed frequencies with specific vibrational modes, one often starts with the simplest possible vibrational forms in which equivalent atoms which are close together are treated in equivalent fashion. Examples of this process, for small molecules, are given in section VII-3. Essentially it means that the molecule is separated into a collection of methyl, methylene, carbonyl, hydroxyl, etc., groups. Each group is treated as if it were independent unless it is immediately adjacent to a group with similar frequencies. When two groups with similar frequencies (even though the groups are chemically very different) are close enough for mechanical interaction to occur (as when they involve a common atom), the vibrations are combined in phase and out of phase to give two new vibrations, one of higher frequency and one of lower frequency.

The presentation of accumulated information on the frequencies of vibration of bonds and groups may be approached equally well from either of two directions. The various types of chemical bonds can be considered in turn, with the probable positions in which they are likely to absorb, or the discussion can proceed from one region of the spectrum to another, listing those groups that are likely to cause absorption in each region. The second method will be followed here, since this is the manner in which one actually looks at a spectrum of an unknown compound. Also, the excellent monographs by Bellamy and by Jones and Sandorfy follow the former system. If one can guess, by looking at a certain region, that a band may be due to a particular functional group, these extensive discussions can be consulted for more complete information on the exact nature of the absorption to be expected for that group. A very convenient form of cross-indexing between the two alternative orders of presentation is pro-

[1] More generally, an increase in the force constant of any part of a vibrating system must increase, or as a limiting case leave unchanged, the frequency of every vibrational mode of that system.   Similarly an increase in mass in any part must decrease (or leave unchanged) every vibrational frequency.   See Rayleigh, ref. 28, pp. 110–111.

vided by the graphical summary of probable positions of absorption bands due to N. B. Colthup. A recent version of Colthup's chart is shown in Fig. VIII-6.

It would be a gross injustice to the novice not to point out that an accumulation of probable positions, with some indications of intensity and shape, will not suffice for the interpretation of very many infrared or Raman spectra in the absence of a thorough familiarity with the actual appearance of the bands and additional information about the samples. Other physical and chemical properties, such as appearance, boiling or melting point, reactivity, method of preparation or isolation, and empirical formula, should be combined with the observation of the spectrum to obtain the maximum amount of information from the spectrum. Whenever possible a suggested interpretation should be confirmed by comparing the spectrum of the unknown with that of an authentic known sample or, at very least, by comparing the spectrum with those of similar compounds.

Only in very exceptional cases will it be possible to assign all observed bands in the spectrum to particular modes of vibration or to the vibrations of particular chemical groups. The ratio of observed bands to useful bands is generally quite high. It is much better to draw only very limited conclusions from a few bands than to spend an excessive amount of time trying to assign bands that may have no (known) significance. Overinterpretation is a common difficulty among beginners.

In discussing the bands to be observed in a specific region only the fundamental frequencies will be considered, even though overtone or combination bands are likely to be found, except where the latter have been shown to be consistent and therefore helpful in interpretation. It is not always easy to decide whether some of the weaker bands are overtone or combination bands or are due to minor components of the sample. In this, as in all problems of interpretation, it is important that evidence from all regions of the spectrum should be correlated to see whether the entire spectrum is consistent with a tentative assignment made on the basis of a small region of the spectrum.

Some very remarkable changes in band positions and intensities due to a change in state of the sample have been observed, as in going from solution to solid or from one crystalline modification to another. It is very important to remember this in comparing unknowns with known materials. These effects will be specifically mentioned only for certain systems for which they are known to be particularly large or predictable. Apparent intensities, and particularly peak intensities, can change significantly with change of instrumental conditions. The area under a band is somewhat less sensitive to experimental procedures, but is less convenient. In

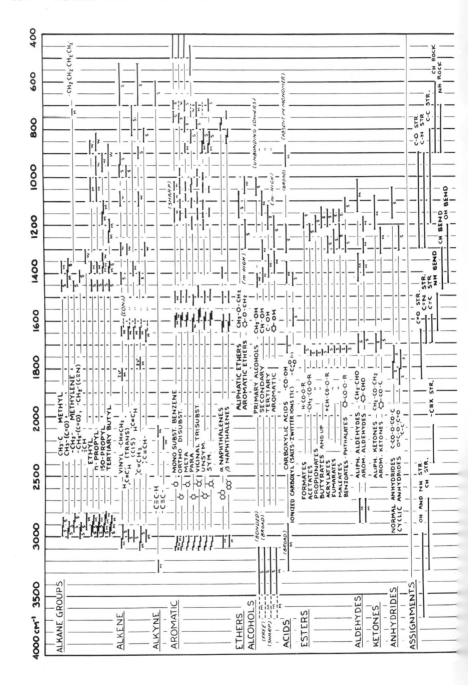

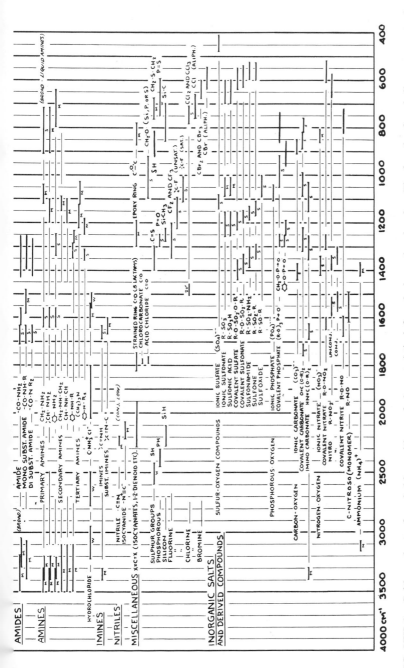

FIG. VIII-6. Colthup chart of probable positions of characteristic infrared absorption bands. The length of each line represents the wavenumber range within which the band center is expected to fall. Expected intensities (strong, medium, weak) and widths (sharp or broad) are indicated for some bands. Bands assigned as overtones are marked 2ν. (Courtesy N. B. Colthup and American Cyanamid Co.)

describing a band as strong or weak, the peak intensity under normal conditions will be understood unless otherwise stated.

2.1   Hydrogen Stretching Vibrations; 3700–2500 cm⁻¹

All fundamental vibrations observed above 2500 cm⁻¹ may be assigned with considerable certainty to a stretching of a bond between hydrogen and another atom. This is to be expected because of the very low mass of the hydrogen atom. Since the vibrational frequencies are much higher than for nearly all other chemical bonds, the amount of interaction between the hydrogen stretching motions and other vibrations is generally quite small.

The highest band to be expected is the "free" OH stretch, in the vicinity of 3600–3700 cm⁻¹. This is found only in dilute solutions in non-polar solvents or in certain solids and a few organic compounds in which hydrogen bonding is sterically hindered. Hydrogen bonding drops the frequency of the OH band by 300–1000 cm⁻¹ or more, simultaneously increasing the (integrated) intensity and causing the band to broaden. In extreme cases, such as the solid organic acids, the OH becomes so broad that it is lost beneath the CH stretching bands.

NH absorption also falls in the region of 3300–3400 cm⁻¹. The weak hydrogen bonding[1] of NH causes the frequency to drop only slightly, with little change in band width. The relative sharpness of the NH bands as compared to the hydrogen-bonded OH bands in the same region provides a convenient, if not totally reliable, criterion for distinguishing between NH and OH bands. Primary amines generally show some splitting due to interaction between the equivalent bonds of the NH₂ group. Such splitting is not expected for OH, except in some crystals, since equivalent OH bonds are seldom immediately adjacent. Amine hydrochlorides absorb at much lower frequencies.

Aliphatic CH vibrations fall in the region between 2850 and 3000 cm⁻¹. The CH absorption bands are moderately broad but much narrower than hydrogen-bonded OH. On a linear wavelength scale (or a compressed linear wavenumber scale) the CH bands appear quite narrow, but they are split into at least two peaks with even an NaCl prism.

The exact shape of the band envelope depends on the particular spectrometer and its resolving power in this region as well as on the nature of the compound. Most aliphatic samples have a sufficiently large number of CH bonds to make the absorption appear quite strong and to produce an "average" contour that remains reasonably constant from one compound to another. Under higher resolution it is often possible to separate the

---

[1] C. G. Cannon, *Spectrochim. Acta* **10**, 341 (1958).

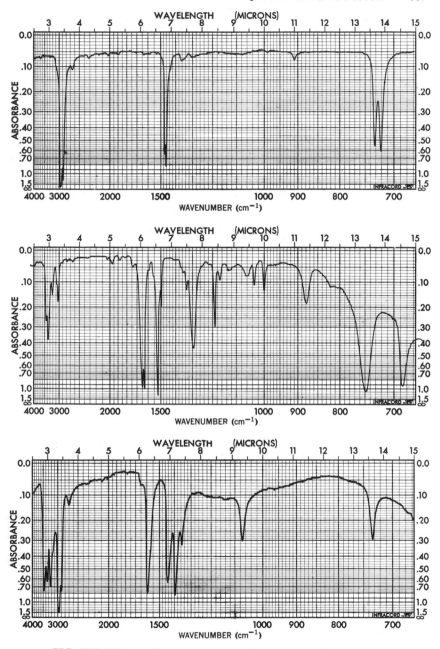

FIG. VIII-7 (Top).   Infrared spectrum of polyethylene film.
FIG. VIII-8 (Center).   Infrared spectrum of aniline.
FIG. VIII-9 (Bottom).   Infrared spectrum of thiourea (Nujol mull).

bands in this region and make a more detailed analysis of the structure, but there is considerable overlapping of the bands that cannot be eliminated by improved instrumentation.

Slightly different positions may be expected for CH, CH_2, and CH_3 (two bands). In addition, anything that significantly changes the strength of the CH bond will affect the position of the absorption band. For example, O—CH of an ether or alcohol will absorb near 3000 cm^{-1} (but generally very slightly below), Cl—CH will absorb just above 3000 cm^{-1}, and a strained-ring compound will show absorption at higher frequencies than acyclic or large-ring compounds. The CH of an aldehyde group is found at lower frequencies and is often split into two bands of roughly equal intensity near 2750 and 2850 cm^{-1}. This is probably an example of Fermi resonance with the overtone of the bending motion of the same CH bond.

A CH bond adjacent to a double bond or an aromatic ring is moved up to the region between 3000 and 3100 cm^{-1}. Since the intensity of CH absorption is small, the presence of a few olefinic or aromatic hydrogens may be hidden in the shoulder of the band caused by a much larger number of aliphatic CH bonds. A sharp band or shoulder above 3000 cm^{-1} is quite good evidence for an olefinic or aromatic group. Only small-ring compounds (especially a cyclopropane ring, at about 3100 cm^{-1}) and halogenated compounds are likely to interfere. Acetylenic CH is moved to higher frequencies. It appears as a very sharp, quite strong (for CH) band at about 3300 cm^{-1}.

As the size of the atom to which the hydrogen is attached is increased, the bond tends to become somewhat weaker and move to lower frequencies. Thus SH, PH, and SiH fall in the approximate regions of 2500, 2400, and 2200 cm^{-1}, respectively. This cannot be attributed to the change in mass since the reduced mass is effectively that of the hydrogen atom.

Substitution of deuterium for hydrogen in a molecule will produce a shift to lower frequencies. The ratio of the hydrogen frequency to the deuterium frequency is generally somewhat less than 1.41 (often 1.28 to 1.38); the discrepancy between the observed and calculated ratio is attributed to the failure of the approximation of independence of the vibrations. This will be true for bending motions as well as the stretches. Similarly, there will be a small shift in C—C vibrations upon deuteration (often 1.02 to 1.06) since the motion is usually not completely independent of the CH motion or mass.

2.2   Triple-Bond Region; 2500–2000 cm^{-1}

Two principal types of absorption fall in the region between 2500 and 2000 cm^{-1}, aside from the few hydrogen stretches mentioned above.

Triple-bond stretching vibrations fall in this region because of the large force constant of these bonds, and compounds of the allene type ($H_2C{=}C{=}CH_2$) have an absorption band falling in this region because of the small effective mass of the antisymmetric vibration of the cumulated double bonds (section VII-3.1). These two cases are completely distinct, since any given molecule must be in either the triple-bond or the cumulated double-bond form and the energy barrier for the transition between them will be large, involving the motion of hydrogens or other atoms from one position to another in the molecule. In particular, it is important that the fictitious "resonance" structures should not be confused with the actual configuration of the molecule; since the "resonance" forms do not exist, they cannot individually contribute in any way to the absorption spectrum.

Typical of the triple-bond absorptions are those of $C{\equiv}C$, between 2050 and 2300 cm^{-1}, and $C{\equiv}N$, near 2200–2300 cm^{-1}. The nitrile band is generally very strong and sharp. The $C{\equiv}C$ band is often very weak or totally absent from the infrared spectrum because of the symmetry or pseudosymmetry of the molecule. It is very intense in the Raman spectrum. Such compounds as the allenes and isocyanates fall in the diene class. The allene band is low, near 1900 cm^{-1}, and is sometimes split to form a doublet. A second band, near 1100 cm^{-1}, corresponding to the symmetric stretch, should be observed in conjunction with the 1900 cm^{-1} band but is not so readily identified. Carbon dioxide absorbs at 2350 cm^{-1}.

2.3   Double-Bond Region; 2000–1600 cm^{-1}

Certain carbonyl compounds, as well as dienes and amine hydrochlorides, may absorb above 1800 cm^{-1}. The principal absorption of interest in this upper region, however, is due to the combination bands of substituted aromatic compounds. They fall between 1650 and 2000 cm^{-1} and form an unusually reliable index to the position of substitution on the aromatic ring. If the substitution is primarily with nitro, fluoro, or ether groups the pattern may be atypical, leading to an absence of identification rather than to an incorrect conclusion. For other substituents the patterns are quite consistent, independent of the nature of the substituents, although weak compared to the carbonyl fundamental frequencies which may overlap and obscure them.

Carbonyl groups, $C{=}O$, whether they occur as ketones, aldehydes, acids, amides, or carbonates, have strong absorption in the vicinity of 1700 cm^{-1}. If the carbonyl group is adjacent to singly bonded oxygen (ester or acid) or halogen the frequency will be raised (see Table VII-V, section VII-2). Conjugation or hydrogen bonding will lower the frequency

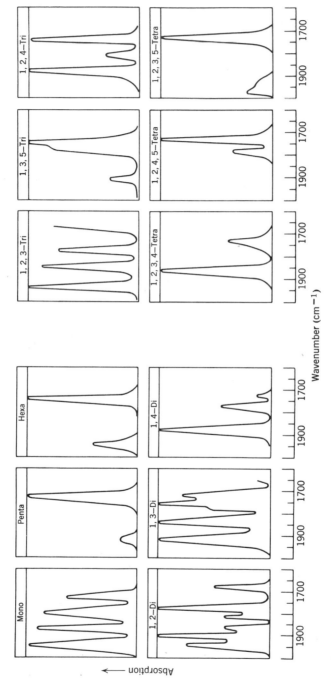

FIG. VIII-10.   Aromatic substitution bands, 1650–2000 cm⁻¹.   [From Jones and Sandorfy, ref. 36; based on Young, DuVall, and Wright, *Anal. Chem.* **23**, 709 (1951).]

by roughly 10 to 50 cm^{-1}.   If the carbonyl is adjacent to a strained ring the frequency will be raised.   Coupling of the carbonyl groups in acid dimers leads to a splitting of the vibrational frequencies into a symmetric mode, strong in the Raman effect, and an antisymmetric mode, strong in the infrared spectrum.   In amides in solution or in the solid phase the carbonyl vibration is lowered to the vicinity of 1650 cm^{-1} and probably is coupled to some extent with the CN stretch and NH bend.[1]   Very often the final position of a carbonyl bond must be predicted by taking the sum of several effects which may be in opposing directions.

Olefins show absorption due to the C=C stretch in the vicinity of 1650 cm^{-1}, but this band, like the acetylenic stretch, is often too weak to be observed, particularly in trans-substituted compounds since these compounds have at least an approximate center of symmetry.   Occasionally the band will be confused with the carbonyl band, especially if there is reason to believe the carbonyl band may be lowered by conjugation or if such a carbonyl is expected as an impurity.   The C=N group absorbs in approximately the same region, with variable intensity.

Bending of the NH bond gives rise to absorption between 1500 and 1650 cm^{-1} which tends to be fairly broad and moderate to strong in intensity.   It can often be distinguished from nearby carbonyl, olefin, or aromatic bands by its shape.   Especially if there are non-equivalent NH groups, or in primary amines, the band may be split.   In amides the NH and CN vibrations are mixed.

Organic nitrite and nitrate absorb in the vicinity of 1600 to 1650 cm^{-1}. Ionized carboxylic acids, both salts and zwitter ions, show an antisymmetric stretch of the relatively weak carbonyls around 1600 cm^{-1} or a little lower and a symmetric stretch around 1400 to 1450 cm^{-1}.

2.4   Single-Bond Stretch and Bend Region; 1500–700 cm^{-1}

Above 1600 cm^{-1} it is frequently possible to explain all bands of at least moderate intensity; in fact, if there is a moderately strong band in this region which cannot be explained there is reason to suspect that some important feature of the sample has been overlooked.   This is not true for the region below 1500 or 1600 cm^{-1}.   Many bands in this region depend significantly for their exact position on which member of a homologous series is being examined.   The low-frequency region has been called the fingerprint region because it is in this region that the differences arise between the spectra of similar molecules.

[1] The "NH bend" is, of course, really a change of the C—N—H angle, but because of the light mass of the hydrogen this involves primarily a motion of the hydrogen atom or the NH bond.

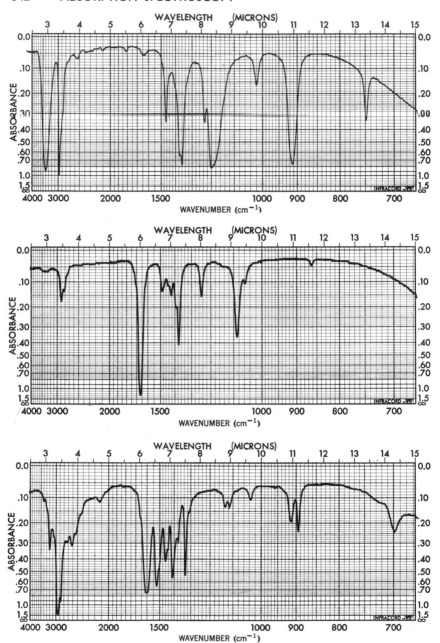

FIG. VIII-11 (Top).   Infrared spectrum of *t*-butyl alcohol (liquid).
FIG. VIII-12 (Center).   Infrared spectrum of dimethyl formamide.
FIG. VIII-13 (Bottom).   Infrared spectrum of glycine (Nujol mull).

Most single bonds will give rise to stretching vibrations of approximately the same frequency and hence the adjacent single bonds will mechanically interact. The observed frequencies will therefore depend on the "skeleton" of the molecule, and the observed bands will often be composite bands resulting from many different modes of oscillation of the skeleton or of the skeleton and the attached functional groups.   Considering also the possibility of interaction between the single-bond stretching modes and the bending vibrations, it is perhaps surprising how many, rather than how few, generalizations can be drawn about the infrared spectra of compounds in this region.

The presence of an aromatic ring usually gives rise to a pair of bands at 1500 and 1600 cm^{-1}.   They are generally quite sharp, but they may vary considerably in intensity and are sometimes missing or hidden.   Depending on the nature of the substitution on the ring, the bands may split, especially the upper member.   These bands are exceedingly helpful in confirming or suggesting the presence of aromatic rings.

Most compounds exhibit a series of absorption peaks in the region between 1300 and 1475 cm^{-1} owing to the bending motion of the hydrogens.   The exact positions depend on the nature of the group; it has been possible, for example, to carry out quantitative analyses for methyl, methylene, and CH groups.

A pair of strong symmetrical bands around 1375 and 1550 cm^{-1} is indicative of a nitro group.   The NH bend, which normally falls above 1500 cm^{-1}, drops to about 1400 in the NH_4^+ ion.   Carbon-fluorine bonds give rise to extremely strong, moderately sharp bands in the region of 1100 to 1300 cm^{-1}.   In some solid samples, however, in which fluorine is a minor constituent, the band seems to be weak and hard to identify.   The reason for this is not clear.

Both the C—O stretch and the OH bend fall in the general region of 900 to 1450 cm^{-1}.   Ethers, esters, acids, and alcohols show the former, usually quite intense and quite broad, and not too far from 1200 cm^{-1}. Alcohols and acids show the latter, generally in the vicinity of 1300 cm^{-1}. Both bands are subject to variation due to hydrogen bonding.

A very broad band, quite unsymmetrical and inherently very strong, at about 1000 to 1100 cm^{-1} is characteristic of Si—O.   The band is common to glass and silica, as well as organic silicones and inorganic silicates.   A strong but very sharp band at 1250 cm^{-1} is a good indication of silicone. It is especially common in residues from distillations.

The C—Cl bond absorbs in the general vicinity of 700 cm^{-1}.   It is quite intense, easily confused with the CH band of aromatics and olefins. Bromine and iodine compounds have characteristic absorption at lower frequencies than are permitted by an NaCl prism.

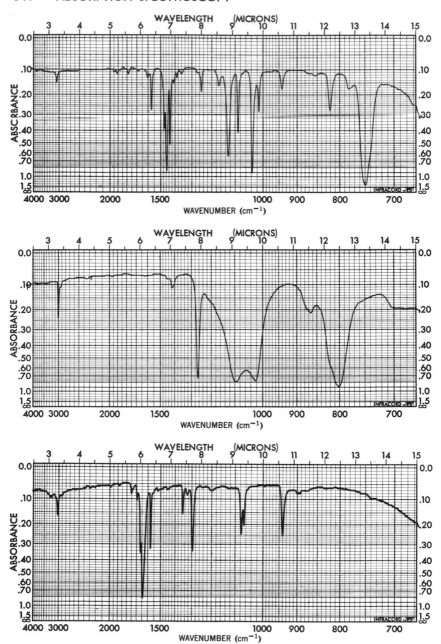

FIG. VIII-14 (Top).   Infrared spectrum of o-dichlorobenzene.
FIG. VIII-15 (Center).   Infrared spectrum of silicone grease.
FIG. VIII-16 (Bottom).   Infrared spectrum of p-benzoquinone (melt).

Among the most valuable characteristic bands appearing in the low-frequency range are the out-of-plane bending motions of olefinic and aromatic CH groups, occurring between 700 and 1000 cm^{-1}. The pattern depends on the substitution pattern around the ethylenic bond, thus making it possible to distinguish between cis, trans, and vinyl groupings. The aromatic substitution bands depend on the number of adjacent hydrogens remaining on the ring. Another group of bands above 1000 cm^{-1} provides similar information.

Inorganic compounds (except the gaseous elements) also show infrared absorption spectra. The purely ionic crystals, such as the alkali and alkaline earth halides, tend to give broad, structureless absorption which often falls beyond the low-frequency limit of the spectrometer. Compounds containing covalently bonded radicals, such as sulfate, nitrate, or carbonate, show absorption more typical of molecules, though generally with relatively few bands. There is a significant amount of overlapping of absorption regions due to different groups and the positions vary slightly depending on the cation present. It is thus advisable to draw conclusions concerning the interpretation of inorganics only on the basis of a direct comparison with reference spectra. Inorganic compounds often appear when they are not expected. The infrared spectrum is a powerful tool for identifying them, but the possibility of inorganics being present must be kept in mind; neglect of this may lead to error or frustration in interpreting an infrared spectrum.

Probably the most important rule to remember in interpreting spectra is that the whole curve must be considered. Interpretations suggested by one region may be confirmed or disproved by some other part of the spectrum. For example, water in liquid or solid samples gives a band at 1630 cm^{-1} but it also gives an OH stretch at about 3300 cm^{-1} (3600 in some crystals) and a very weak, broad band at 2200 cm^{-1}. Identification of water must consider the presence or absence and relative intensities of all three bands. A sample containing an aromatic ring should show the strong CH bands in the vicinity of 700–800 cm^{-1}, the 1500–1600 cm^{-1} pair, CH stretching bands above 3000 cm^{-1}, and the weak combination bands in the 1600–2000 cm^{-1} region. In addition there is a strong tendency for aromatic compounds to show very sharp bands throughout the spectrum.

It is often difficult to decide from position alone whether a carbonyl band is due to an acid, ester, ketone, or aldehyde. The remainder of the spectrum can provide this information, since the acid shows CO and OH, the ester CO but no OH, the ketone neither CO nor OH, and the aldehyde has a characteristically low CH band. The distinction between an acid and a ketone alcohol is more subtle but can be based on the amount of hydrogen

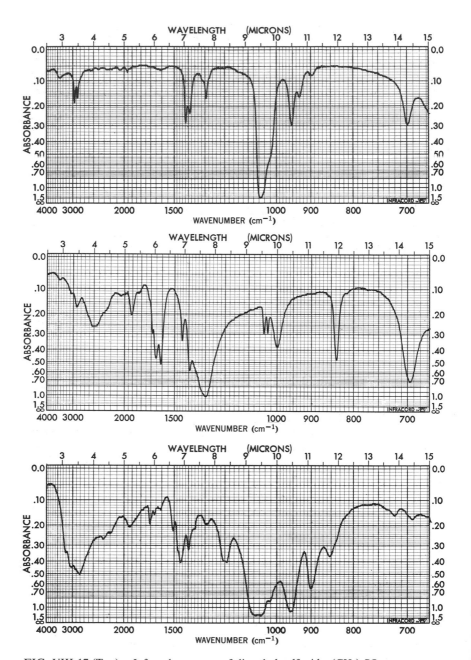

FIG. VIII-17 (Top). Infrared spectrum of dimethyl sulfoxide, $(CH_3)_2SO$.

FIG. VIII-18 (Center). Infrared spectrum of sodium bicarbonate, $NaHCO_3$ (Nujol mull).

FIG. VIII-19 (Bottom). Infrared spectrum of dihydrogen ammonium phosphate, $NH_4H_2PO_4$ (Nujol mull).

346

bonding shown by the OH, the position of the carbonyl, and, when necessary, the change in the spectrum when base is added.

These are only a few of many examples where the interpretation of one band depends on that of another. It is this necessity for examining the entire spectrum, even though only a few bands will be specifically assigned, that hampers the beginner at interpretation. Very often it is the appearance of a band, including shape and intensity, that is as important in its assignment as is its position. The appearance is affected also by sample thickness or concentration, especially on a linear transmittance recording. It is advisable, therefore, to be satisfied with rather limited interpretations at first, adding more details with growing experience.

3 Bibliographies and Indices

Characteristic frequencies provide a fast and convenient method for the identification and classification of unknown compounds and often provide sufficient information to decide the question at hand. For example, it should be possible to decide unambiguously between the keto or enol form of a compound, between ortho or para substitution of an aromatic ring, or whether a nitrile group has been added and if so whether in a conjugated or unconjugated position. But at times this type of information may not be sufficient.

Given a compound that is quite clearly an organic acid, it may be necessary to know precisely which acid it is, or, knowing that a compound is an aliphatic hydrocarbon, it may be required to know which it is of several that fall in the same boiling point range. Even when there seems to be sufficient evidence to determine the exact compound, it is advisable to confirm the identification by comparing the spectrum with that of an authentic sample. Other times, whether because more than one compound is present or for other reasons, it may not be possible to find a self-consistent interpretation of the spectrum.

To meet these needs there has been an extensive effort in recent years to accumulate bibliographies of spectra. Some of them include ultraviolet, infrared, and Raman, but most are limited to either the ultraviolet and visible or to the infrared. These collections have become so extensive that special indices are required to find the desired spectrum. Some of the collections have been put on edge-punched cards, and one very extensive index has been put onto IBM cards to permit rapid mechanical sorting.

The principal collections of spectra and indices to these are listed here, and a brief discussion of each is given.

3.1 Ultraviolet Spectra

1. American Petroleum Institute (API).   Ultraviolet-visible spectra are reproduced on $8\frac{1}{2} \times 11$ in. loose-leaf sheets.   Originally only hydrocarbon spectra were given but the coverage has been broadened considerably. Published by A.P.I. Research Project 44 and the Manufacturing Chemists Association.   Originally this group was under the direction of F. D. Rossini at the National Bureau of Standards and later at Carnegie Institute of Technology.   It is now at Texas A & M, College Station, Texas, under the direction of Bruno J. Zwolinski and Alfred Danti.

2. Friedel and Orchin, *Ultraviolet Spectra of Aromatic Compounds*, Wiley, New York, 1951.   A large number of spectra reduced to a common scale (log *a*) and published in loose-leaf form (spiral binder) so that spectra may be removed and directly superimposed for comparison purposes.

3. Hershenson, *Ultraviolet and Visible Absorption Spectra*, Academic Press, New York, 1956.   References to original literature from 1930 to 1954 for many compounds.   Listed by compound in alphabetical order. Selected journals, only.

4. *Organic Electronic Spectral Data*, Vol. I, 1946–1952, Vol. II, 1953–1955, Interscience, New York, 1960.   These volumes are the work of many volunteer abstractors, under the editorship of M. J. Kamlet and H. E. Ungnade.   It is expected that supplementary volumes will cover current literature.   For each compound, listed by empirical formula, are given the name, solvent, wavelengths of absorption maxima, approximate values for log *a*, and original reference.

5. American Society for Testing Materials (ASTM).   Operating under the direction of L. E. Keuntzel, of Wyandotte Chemical Co., volunteers working for the ASTM have undertaken the task of coding ultraviolet-visible spectra (as well as other regions) on IBM cards.   Spectra are taken from the API collection and from the original literature.   The system, especially as it applies to the more extensive infrared collection, is described in more detail below.   The cards are available from the ASTM, 1916 Race Street, Philadelphia, Pa.

6. C. Karr, Jr., *Appl. Spectroscopy* **13**, 15–25, 40–45 (1959); *ibid.* **14**, 146–153 (1960).   A tabulation of the lowest-frequency electronic absorption bands of 408 polycyclic aromatic hydrocarbons (three or more aromatic rings) and 204 polynuclear heterocyclic aromatics (three or more rings) as an aid to their identification.

3.2 Infrared Spectra

1. American Petroleum Institute.   Infrared spectra are reproduced on $8\frac{1}{2} \times 11$ in. loose-leaf sheets.   See under section 3.1.

2. National Research Council–National Bureau of Standards. Infrared spectra are reproduced on edge-punched cards. Cards also contain information about physical properties. A companion set carries abstracts of literature references to the field. These cards have been produced under the direction of E. C. Creitz.

3. Sadtler Standard Spectra, sold by Samuel P. Sadtler and Son, Inc., 2100 Arch Street, Philadelphia 3, Pa. This is by far the largest collection of infrared spectra now available. In addition to a wide assortment of compounds, the set includes certain industrial mixtures such as detergents. Originally the spectra were reproduced on large cardboard sheets which were edge punched for hand sorting. They are now available either in 7×18 in. cardboard (without edge punches) or in the Midget Edition which has three curves on each $8\frac{1}{2} \times 11$ in. page. An index arranged according to strongest bands, designed for rapid identification of any compound in the collection, is also available.

4. Documentation of Molecular Spectroscopy (DMS). Published by Butterworths Scientific Publications, 88 Kingsway, London, E.C.2, England, and by Verlag Chemie GMBH., Weinheim/Bergstrasse, West Germany, in cooperation with the Infrared Absorption Data Joint Committee, London, and the Institut fur Spektrochemie und Angewandte Spectroskopie, Dortmund. Spectra are reproduced on edge-punched cards. Literature cards are also issued, covering instrumentation, techniques, or theory. They include an abstract of the article and are coded for content. The publication schedule is 2000 cards a year, of which about 400 are literature cards and the remainder spectrum cards. The system may be expanded to cover other regions.

5. *Infrared Absorption Spectra of Steroids, An Atlas*, Vol I, Dobriner, Katzenellenbogen, and Jones, 1953; Vol. II, Roberts, Gallagher, and Jones, 1958; Interscience, New York. These volumes are an authoritative and important reference work for those working with biological materials.

6. Miller and Wilkins, *Anal. Chem.* **24**, 1253 (1952); Miller, Carlson, Bentley, and Jones, *Spectrochimica Acta* **16**, 135 (1960). The first of these gives infrared spectra in the rock-salt region of a large number of inorganic compounds, with a brief discussion of the application of the results. The second extends the survey to the cesium bromide region.

7. Landolt-Bornstein, *Zahlenwerte und Funktionen aus Physik, Chemie, Astronomie, Geophysik, und Technik*, Sechste Auflage, 1. Band, "Atom- und Molekular-Physik," 2. Teil, A. Eucken and K. H. Hellwege, eds. Springer, Berlin, 1951. This reference gives a number of spectra, a comprehensive compound and author index, and a discussion of the theory of vibrations.

8. American Society for Testing Materials. The indexing program of

the ASTM includes all spectra of the Sadtler, DMS, API, and NRC-NBS collections. In addition a literature search has been carried out to provide a rapid index to all spectra published. The initial program began with 1950 and worked forward; the earlier literature will be added as abstracting capacity permits. The positions of absorption bands are punched on the $3\frac{1}{4} \times 7\frac{3}{8}$ in. IBM cards with a one-to-one correspondence between holes and absorption bands. Each column represents a wavelength range of 1 micron and the ten numbers in the column represent the tenth-micron subdivisions. High-speed sorters will select those which have, or those which do not have, punches in any region or regions of the spectrum, thus making it possible to find the card representing a compound given only the spectrum of the compound. It is also possible to sort for specific compounds or for compounds of a given chemical classification. Unpunched, preprinted cards are available for coding spectra obtained in the user's laboratory.

9. Hershenson, *Infrared Absorption Spectra*, Academic Press, New York, 1959. References to original literature for 1945–1957.

10. *An Index of Published Infra-red Spectra*, a publication of the British government, is available from Her Majesty's Stationery Office. The first two volumes (published in 1961) give references to about 10,000 infrared spectra published up to 1957, with notations concerning the state of the sample, the range examined, and the instrument and dispersing element employed. The third volume, in preparation, will cover the literature since 1957.

Several other reference works deserve special mention. An early book by Barnes, Gore, Liddel, and Williams, entitled *Infrared Spectroscopy, Industrial Applications and Bibliography* (Reinhold, New York, 1944) presents spectra which are crude and incomplete by modern standards. It represents an important landmark in the development of infrared and gives a bibliography of early literature. A volume by Randall, Fuson, Fowler, and Dangl, published in 1949 (*Infrared Determination of Organic Structures*, D. Van Nostrand, Princeton, N.J.) reproduces spectra obtained on an early spectrometer. A catalog of infrared spectra of gases, by Pierson, Fletcher, and Gantz [*Anal. Chem.* **28**, 1218 (1956)] is convenient for identification of components of a gaseous mixture. A literature survey has been published by K. E. Lawson: *Infrared Absorption of Inorganic Substances*, Reinhold Publishing Corp., New York, 1961. In addition many references are given in the annual review articles in *Analytical Chemistry* and in the monographs by Bellamy (ref. 36) and by Jones and Sandorfy (ref. 38). A bibliography on the infrared region has been prepared by Brown for the Library of Congress.

3.3   Raman Spectra

1. American Petroleum Institute. Raman spectra are reproduced in bar-graph form, giving band positions and estimated intensities. See under section 3.1.

2. Hibben, *The Raman Effect and Its Chemical Applications*, Reinhold, New York, 1939.

3. Kohlrausch, *Ramanspectren, Hand- und Jahrbuch der Chemischen Physik*, Vol. 9, A. Euchen and Wolf, eds, Becker and Erler, Leipsig, 1943; Edwards Bros., Ann Arbor, Mich., 1945.

4. Landolt-Börnstein, *Zahlenwerte und Funktionen*, pp. 479–551. See section 3.2.

Many of the discussions of infrared spectra include Raman shifts, since the interpretation of one often depends on results from the other. The volume of published Raman spectra is much smaller than for the infrared because the instrumentation has not been so convenient nor, in recent years, has the analytical need been so pressing owing to the availability of infrared spectrometers.

3.4   Mechanical Sorting

The introduction of an index to infrared spectra on cards that may be sorted by high-speed mechanical sorters has provided an important new tool for the identification of unknown materials and for a correlation of absorption frequencies with molecular structure. Thus, if an adequate reference deck is available, it should be possible to make a positive identification of an unknown pure compound simply by sorting through the deck for those compounds which absorb at the observed frequencies. Even if a mixture is to be analyzed, it may be possible to identify the individual components by this method. If the compound under investigation has not been previously synthesized, the reference deck may be a fast and convenient method for finding the spectra of related compounds, thus establishing the nature of the spectrum to be expected for the postulated structure as an aid in confirming or refuting the structure.

With the ASTM index cards and an appropriate sorter a number of operations can easily be performed, such as locating a card for a given compound by means of the structure or the index number of the compound, or sorting for certain physical properties. By far the most important application, however, is the process of sorting for positions of absorption bands and especially in the infrared region for which large numbers of cards are available. The sorting process may be quite rapid if appropriate choices of procedure are followed; sorting by one who is not familiar with the interpretation of spectra may not only be slow but also can result in the rejection of the card being sought.

Consider the spectrum shown in Fig. VIII-20. From the appearance of the spectrum it would seem to be an alkyl-substituted aromatic, but it would be somewhat more difficult to decide exactly which one. Certain bands can be rejected immediately as being unsuitable for sorting. The bands at 2850–3100 cm^{-1} are due to CH stretching vibrations and will appear in the spectra of nearly all compounds in the deck. Similarly, the 1350–1500 cm^{-1} region is not likely to exclude very many cards, since this again is a region of CH absorption.

The bands at 700 and 760 would appear to be excellent choices, since these are strong and in a region of little or no absorption for many compounds. It would probably be best, however, to postpone sorting for these bands since an aromatic impurity can produce a strong band in this region. Excluding all compounds which do not have these bands could then exclude the major component of the sample. The preferable first sort will be a "negative sort," based on the transparent regions of the spectrum. (The hydroxyl impurity in this sample could be particularly misleading if it were made the basis for an initial sort.) For example, all compounds that absorb (at least moderately strongly) in the regions of 800–860 and 940–1000 cm^{-1} can be removed and set aside quite safely since an impurity cannot remove absorption bands from the major component. A similar sort could be carried out for 2000–2600 and 3500–4000 cm^{-1}, but this would probably be a waste of time (unless these sorts can be performed simultaneously with the first one) since few compounds absorb in either of these places.

After the initial negative, or "no-band," sorts have significantly reduced the size of the deck, those compounds can be selected that show specific absorption bands, such as 700, 760, 1500, 1600, and 1030 cm^{-1}. Discarded cards from these sorts should preferably be kept separate from the initial discards. The sort at 1600 cm^{-1} would probably discriminate against nearly all compounds that are not aromatic; 700 cm^{-1} would screen the aromatic compounds by substitution pattern, and further selection would be performed by sorts at 760 or 1030 cm^{-1}. Depending on the size of the remaining deck at each point, other sorting procedures may be preferable. There is some correlation between the 1500, 1600, 700, 760, and 1030 cm^{-1} bands; all monosubstituted benzenes will have bands falling near these positions, so it may be necessary to select another band not typical of aromatic compounds to obtain a drastic reduction in size of the working deck.

When the deck is reduced to a small handful it may be faster to look through these by hand, checking the chemical nature of each compound

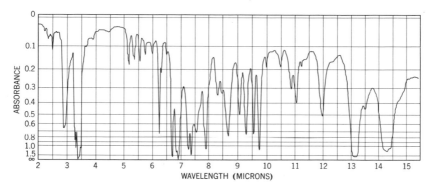

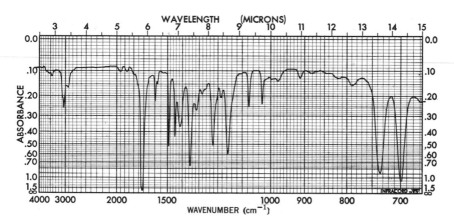

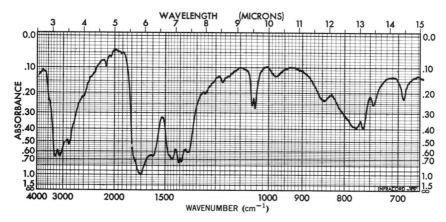

FIG. VIII-20 (Top).   Infrared spectrum of cumene, $(CH_3)_2$—CH—C_6H_5 (impure).

FIG. VIII-21 (Center).   See problem 4.

FIG. VIII-22 (Bottom).   See problem 5.

and perhaps one or more physical properties. The final step, whenever possible, should be a direct comparison of the unknown spectrum with an authentic curve for the known compound. If the authentic spectrum shows fewer bands, but otherwise seems to be the same, sorting for the extra bands may give the impurity. The detailed mechanics of the sorting procedure will depend on the sorter available, the cards to be sorted, and any initial segregation of the cards that may have been found advisable.

In principle, every point of the spectrum provides some information about the nature of the sample. For distinct pure compounds much less information than this is required for identification. Complex mixtures, however, require many more points for qualitative analysis, especially since a quantitative and qualitative analysis must be carried out simultaneously. Computer techniques have been developed sufficiently to make such analyses possible. A specialized instrument has been described[1] that will store the spectra of many compounds, feed variable amounts of them by an automatic trial-and-error procedure into a mixer for comparison with an unknown spectrum, and minimize the deviation between the synthetic and experimental curves. As such instruments become more abundant they may very significantly change the approach of the analyst to the interpretation of spectra.

Problems

1. In the ultraviolet and visible regions it is common practice to make routine measurements on solutions in 1-cm cells. In the infrared region, on the other hand, cell lengths commonly vary between 0.01 mm and 1.0 mm. Yet the absorptivities are frequently of the same order of magnitude or are much larger in the ultraviolet.

Why are shorter cells necessary for the infrared? What are the implications in terms of the utility of the infrared and ultraviolet regions?

2. How would you decide on the basis of ultraviolet or infrared spectra whether a particular sample, of typical commercial purity, was

    (a) 1,4 dioxane or anisole?
    (b) heptyl methyl ketone (2-nonanone) or heptanoic acid?
    (c) o-dichlorobenzene or p-dichlorobenzene?
    (d) octane or 1-pentanol?
    (e) CO_2 or CO?
    (f) di-n-propyl ether or pentanal?

Indicate specifically what features would be expected to be different in the ultraviolet, what features would be expected to be different in the infrared, and whether the ultraviolet or the infrared spectrum would be preferable for deciding between the two compounds.

3. What change would be expected in the ultraviolet spectrum and in the infrared spectrum if acid or base were added to the following compounds?

    (a) hexyl amine   (b) α-naphthol
    (c) t-butyl alcohol   (d) benzoic acid

[1] M. Rogoff, ref. 55, p. 27.

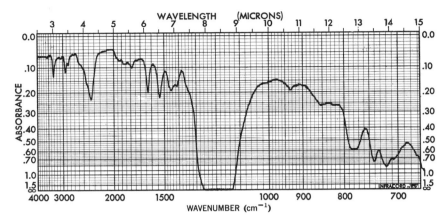

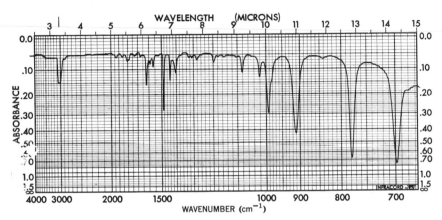

FIG. VIII-23 (Top).   See problem 6.
FIG. VIII-24 (Bottom).   See problem 7.

4. Fig. VIII-21 shows the spectrum of a liquid.   What assignment would you give for the band at 1715 cm⁻¹? for the bands at 700 and 735 cm⁻¹? for the bands just above and the bands just below 3000 cm⁻¹?   What is the simplest compound that could exhibit these features?

5. The spectrum of a Nujol mull of a white crystalline solid is shown in Fig. VIII-22. What two functional groups can be identified?   If these are the only groups present, what is the compound?

6. The spectrum shown in Fig. VIII-23 was obtained on a thin polymer film.   What was the polymer?

7. The spectrum shown in Fig. VIII-24 was obtained on a liquid.   What is the most probable explanation for the two strongest bands in the spectrum?   What is the most probable explanation for the two next strongest bands?   What bands can be found that confirm either or both of these assignments?

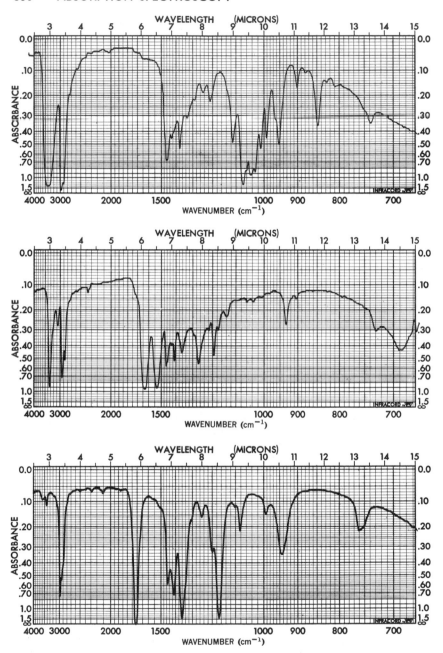

FIG. VIII-25 (Top).   See problem 8.
FIG. VIII-26 (Center).   See problem 9.
FIG. VIII-27 (Bottom).   See problem 10.

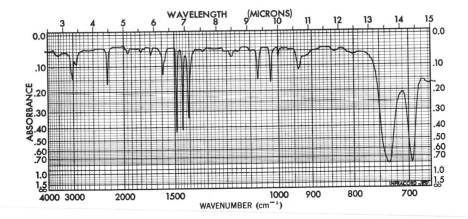

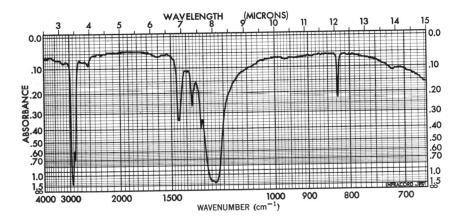

FIG. VIII-28 (Top).   See problem 11.
FIG. VIII-29 (Bottom).   See problem 12.

8. The spectrum shown in Fig. VIII-25 was obtained on a liquid with a boiling point of 118°C. What was the compound?

9. Fig. VIII-26 shows a spectrum of a film of a commercial polymer. What is the polymer?

10. The spectrum shown in Fig. VIII-27 was obtained on a colorless liquid with unpleasant odor and boiling point about 80°C. What was the compound?

11. The spectrum shown in Fig. VIII-28 was obtained on a colorless liquid. What was the compound?

12. The spectrum shown in Fig. VIII-29 was obtained on a Nujol mull of a white, crystalline, water-soluble compound. What was the compound?

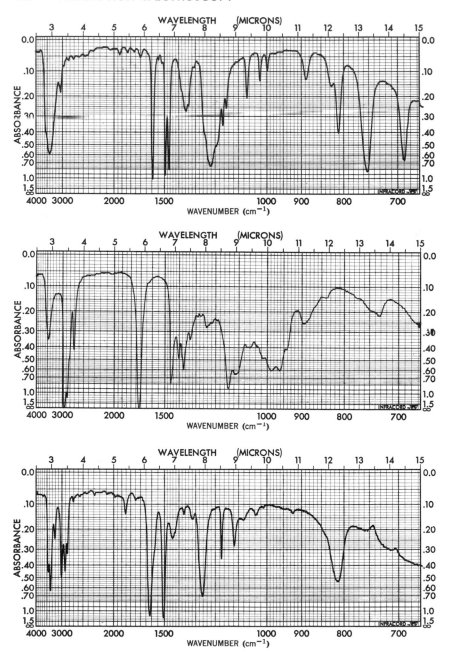

FIG. VIII-30 (Top).   See problem 13.
FIG. VIII-31 (Center).   See problem 14.
FIG. VIII-32 (Bottom).   See problem 15.

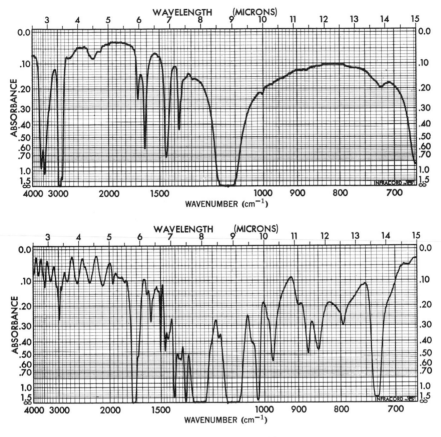

FIG. VIII-33 (Top).   See problem 16.
FIG. VIII-34 (Bottom).   See problem 17.

13. The spectrum shown in Fig. VIII-30 was obtained on a liquid that would crystal-lize at room temperature.   What was the compound?

14. The spectrum shown in Fig. VIII-31 was obtained on a liquid with a boiling point close to that of water.   What was the compound?   What type of impurity is clearly present?

15. The spectrum of Fig. VIII-32 was obtained on the molten form of a compound, under a heat lamp.   What was the compound?

16. The spectrum shown in Fig. VIII-33 was obtained on a Nujol mull of a white powder.   What was the compound?   (What causes the weak band at 2200 cm^{-1}?   Is the sample crystalline or amorphous?)

17. The spectrum of a commercial polymer film is shown in Fig. VIII-34.   What is the polymer?

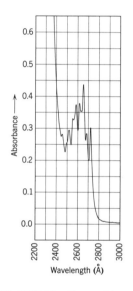

FIG. VIII-35. See problem 18.

18. The ultraviolet spectrum of a compound dissolved in cyclohexane (0.28 gm/liter) is shown in Fig. VIII-35.   What conclusions can be drawn about the compound?

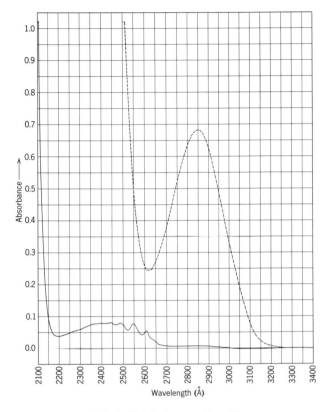

FIG. VIII-36.   See problem 19.

19. Figure VIII-36 shows the spectrum of a compound dissolved in ethanol (0.036 gm/liter) before (dotted line) and after (solid line) addition of a drop of concentrated HCl to the cell.   What is the compound?

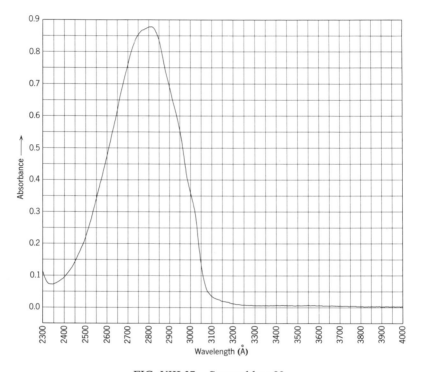

FIG. VIII-37.   See problem 20.

20. The ultraviolet spectrum of an aromatic aldehyde ($3.4 \times 10^{-5} M$) in 1 cm of cyclohexane is shown in Fig. VIII-37.   What is the absorptivity of the compound at the band maximum?   Is the carbonyl conjugated?

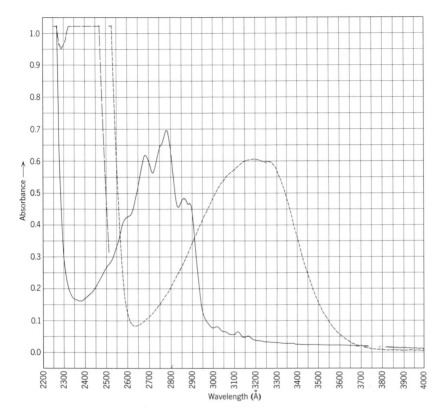

FIG. VIII-38.   See problem 21.

21. The ultraviolet spectrum of a white solid dissolved in ethanol (1.67 mg/liter) is shown in Fig. VIII-38 before (dotted line) and after (solid line) addition of a drop of HCl to the cell (1 cm).   What is the nature of the compound?

IX

Quantitative analysis

Spectroscopy laboratories would easily pay for themselves in most industries if they could only determine what compounds are present or absent in a given sample.   Yet the determination of how much of certain constituents is present is often a problem of at least equivalent importance, so much so that in many laboratories quantitative determinations are the chief application of spectroscopic instrumentation.   The theory and practice of quantitative analysis is largely independent of the region of the spectrum utilized, except for certain difficulties characteristic of the infrared region because of problems of sample preparation and cell-thickness determination.

I   Bouguer's Law

If homogeneous (that is, monochromatic) radiant energy strikes an absorbing medium, the amount absorbed will depend on the frequency of the radiation, the nature of the absorber, and the thickness of the absorber. Let the radiant power, or intensity, of a beam of parallel, homogeneous radiation striking an isotropic, homogeneous sample with smooth, plane surfaces at perpendicular incidence be represented by I.   The decrease in intensity in a thickness dx of the sample, due to absorption, may be written

$$-\frac{dI}{dx} = \mu I \tag{IX-1}$$

where μ is a constant characteristic of the sample material and the frequency.   For a finite path length, $\varDelta x$,

$$\int_{I_0}^{I} -\frac{dI}{I} = \ln \frac{I_0}{I} = \mu \, \varDelta x \tag{IX-2}$$

The ratio, I/I_0, of transmitted to incident intensities is called the transmittance.   The actual dimensions of the quantities I and I_0 are unimportant so long as they are proportional to the energy of the beam; in practice they will be observed as deflections of a galvanometer or displacements on a chart or dial.

Equation IX-2 states that the negative logarithm of the transmittance, or the logarithm of the ratio of incident to transmitted intensities, will be proportional to the thickness of the sample.   This law was put forward by Bouguer in 1729 and independently by Lambert somewhat later.   An experimental confirmation of the rule will not succeed unless the effects due to reflection, convergence, and spectral slit width, as well as possible scattering, fluorescence, chemical reaction, sample inhomogeneity, and sample anisotropy, are taken into consideration.

The fraction of incident intensity reflected upon perpendicular incidence depends on the relative values of the refractive index in the two media if these are non-absorbing.   For any other angle of incidence the components of the beam polarized in the plane of the incident and refracted rays and perpendicular to this plane must be treated separately.   Reflectance of an absorbing substance depends on the complex refractive index.   If the sample is a gas or a very dilute solution the refractive index of the sample will be essentially constant, or at least characteristic of the solvent and not the solute.   The refractive index of a concentrated solution will change significantly in the vicinity of each absorption band.

Reflection coefficients are also susceptible to trace contaminations of the surface.   If the refractive indices of the cell windows and solution (or of the sample if this is a homogeneous solid) are known, and the surfaces are clean, the reflection losses can be calculated.   In general, it is much simpler to measure these losses by comparing the transmittance of the sample with the transmittance of the same, or an equivalent, cell filled with solvent.   In the absence of complications, taking the ratio of the intensity transmitted by the sample to the intensity transmitted by the solvent is an exact method for correcting for reflection losses.

In many spectrometers the beam passing through the sample compartment is convergent or divergent.   Many of the rays within the beam then strike the cell windows at an angle, increasing the difficulty of calculating reflection losses.   A much more important consequence of this convergence, however, is that the rays passing through the sample at an angle travel a greater distance through the sample than those traveling parallel to the optical axis.   These angular rays are more strongly absorbed, so that the observed transmittance of the sample becomes a more complex function of the sample length than is indicated by equation IX-2.   Convergence error can be calculated, but it depends on the angle of convergence (and thus on the design of the spectrometer) and on the refractive index of the sample and the cell windows. The error can be particularly important when the beam is strongly convergent as in beam-condensing units and micro-illuminators, or microscopes.

The radiation emitted by a low-pressure gas discharge lamp in the ultraviolet and visible regions will generally consist of a small number of frequencies which may be isolated by filters or a monochromator to provide monochromatic radiation. For most purposes, however, it is necessary to start with the continuous emission from a hot source and to isolate from this, by filters or more elaborate monochromators, a band of radiation varying continuously in frequency over a range which may be loosely called the spectral slit width (see section III-5.5). The range of frequencies passed through the sample at any given setting is in general sufficiently large that the absorption constant, μ, will be different for different frequencies contained in the beam. Under these circumstances, frequencies corresponding to the greatest values of μ will be absorbed more strongly by the first layers of the sample and the beam will become relatively depleted of these frequencies. In any subsequent layer of the sample, less absorption will occur because the beam contains a higher fraction of the less absorbable frequencies. Although Bouguer's law applies to the intensity of each frequency within the beam, it will not apply to the total intensity of the band of frequencies.

The magnitude of the error introduced by the non-homogeneity of the beam depends on the width of the frequency band and the change of absorption coefficient of the sample over this frequency range. It is most serious for wide slits and narrow absorption bands, least important for broad bands and narrow slits. If the spectral slit width is comparable in magnitude to the half band width of the absorption band, or slightly smaller, the effect on intensities can be minimized by measuring at the absorption maxima and minima, since the absorption coefficient is changing least rapidly in these regions. Band areas also depend on slit widths but not quite so much as do peak intensities.

An associated source of error arises from the selective sensitivity of the spectrometer for various frequencies. For example, if the detector gives a greater signal for high frequencies than for low frequencies of the same intensity, a band of radiation will give rise to an average signal which may or may not be the correct signal for the average frequency. The error depends on the curvature of the spectral distribution reaching the detector, rather than on the slope.[1] The magnitude of this error is, in general, so much smaller than that arising from variation of absorbing power as discussed in the preceding paragraph (which gives rise to a dependence on the slope of the absorption curve) that it is usually neglected.

[1] See the discussion by Gibson on p. 253 of ref. 38.

It may be argued that no truly monochromatic source or signal exists. The "monochromatic" lines emitted by mercury, for example, can be broken into a series of lines by monochromators of high resolving power. Furthermore it is easily shown (by Fourier analysis or from the uncertainty principle) that any beam which is interrupted must contain many different frequencies. These distinctions are of no practical importance in absorption measurements since the bands to be measured are, in general, far wider than the half width of such nearly monochromatic lines. Even relatively broad distributions obtained by filters or by small prism or grating monochromators may be sufficiently monochromatic for certain analyses, particularly in the visible region.

The sources of deviations, or apparent deviations, from Bouguer's law listed above—reflection, convergence, and non-homogeneity of the incident radiation—are essentially characteristic of the spectrometer. The magnitude of these effects may change from one sample to another, but in principle they must always be considered. This is also true of errors arising from stray radiation, which is treated elsewhere (section III-5.3). Certain samples will introduce additional errors.

Small, non-conducting particles suspended in a sample will show Tyndall scattering, the amount of the scattering increasing with the fourth power of the frequency. The beam transmitted by a cloudy sample will be influenced by selective reflection and by reflection from the walls of the cell as well as by absorption processes. These effects may give rise to deviations from Bouguer's law, though the major error is likely to result from a lack of reproducibility of the sample.

If the particles of sample are large enough to make the sample appear inhomogeneous to the beam, or if the sample does not completely fill the beam, a very large deviation from Bouguer's law may be expected. Consider the transmission measurements indicated in Fig. IX-1 on four identical pieces of glass (edge effects are neglected). Each piece of glass transmits 40% of the radiant energy incident upon it and fills half the area of the beam. With one piece of glass in the beam (a), 70% of the beam will be transmitted: $0.40 \times 50 + 1.00 \times 0.50 = 0.70$. A second piece of glass placed behind the first (b) will transmit half of the radiation passed by the first, while all of the other half of the beam will pass unchanged. The net transmittance will be 58%: $0.40 \times 0.40 \times 0.50 + 1.00 \times 0.50 = 0.58$. If the second piece had been placed adjacent to the first (c), filling the entire beam, the transmittance would have been 40%: $0.40 \times 0.50 + 0.40 \times 0.50 = 0.40$. Addition of two more plates, keeping the beam uniformly filled (d), gives a transmittance of 16%, in agreement with Bouguer's law: $0.40 \times 0.40 \times 0.50 + 0.40 \times 0.40 \times 0.50 = 0.16$. Inhomogeneity is a very important problem for solid samples, including those dispersed in a liquid or in another solid.   This will be discussed at greater length in section 7.

Anisotropic solids may exhibit different indices of refraction and different absorption coefficients along different directions within the solid. Such solids may give rise to displacements of the beam and produce polarization of the radiation.   Deviations from Bouguer's law may occur for such samples.   Fluorescence by the sample or decomposition of the sample may also produce apparent deviations.   In microwave and radio-frequency spectroscopy saturation effects must be considered, since

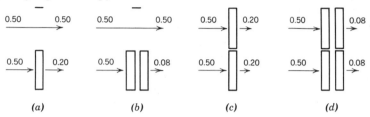

FIG. IX-1.   Effect of non-uniform distribution.   Observed transmittance (and absorbance) values for arrangements shown would be: (a) 70% (0.155); (b) 58% (0.237); (c) 40% (0.398); (d) 16% (0.796).

Bouguer's law does not hold if a significant fraction of the absorbing molecules become activated by absorption.   Saturation effects are not observed in the optical regions.

2   Beer's Law

In 1852 Beer observed that for a given sample thickness the transmittance depended exponentially on the concentration of the absorbing species. This relationship may be combined with equation IX-1 to give

$$-dI/dx = kcI \qquad \text{(IX-3)}$$

$$\ln I_0/I = kc \, \Delta x \qquad \text{(IX-4)}$$

A more convenient form, for most purposes, is obtained by converting to common logarithms.

$$\log I_0/I \equiv \log 1/T \equiv A = abc \qquad \text{(IX-5)}$$

In this equation, known as the Bouguer-Beer law or more commonly as Beer's law, I_0 is the incident intensity; I the intensity that will pass through a sample of thickness (or "breadth") b; c is the concentration of the sample; and a, the absorptivity, is the absorption constant characteristic of the sample and the frequency of the radiation.   The absorbance, $A = \log 1/T$, is more simply related to concentration than is the transmittance, and therefore many spectrometers plot directly in absorbance rather than transmittance.

Beer's law is subject to the same limitations as Bouguer's law.   Reflection, convergence, non-homogeneity of radiation or of the sample, scattering, fluorescence, decomposition, anisotropy, or saturation will give rise to deviations from ideality at least as large when absorbance is plotted against concentration as when absorbance is plotted against path length.

In addition, there are other effects that may be important experimentally when the concentration is varied.   They result from the possibilities for chemical or physical interaction between the molecules or ions which are responsible for the absorption.   Hydrogen bonding, ion pair formation, solvation, or other chemical reactions may take place, leading to an anomalous change of concentration of one component as the concentration of solute is changed.   Physical interactions are especially important among polar molecules in solution and are observable in gases even at moderate pressures.   In addition, a variation of absorptivity is to be expected as the refractive index, and hence the dielectric constant, of the solution is varied.   This effect is negligible for very dilute solutions (below about 10^{-3} M) but not necessarily so for concentrated solutions.

Whether those experimental situations in which the absorbance is not equal to the product of cell length, concentration, and absorptivity are called exceptions to Beer's law or only apparent exceptions is a question of personal preference.   It should be stressed, however, that such situations are not really exceptional but are quite common.   Deviations nearly always become significant at higher concentrations, so that the plot of absorbance $vs.$ concentration becomes concave toward the concentration axis.

An important extension of Beer's law is the "law of additivity," which states that the absorption of radiation by one species will be unaffected by the presence of other materials, whether they absorb or not.   In this more general form Beer's law may be written

$$A = \sum_i a_i b c_i \qquad \text{(IX-6)}$$

where the summation is over all substances present.   Nearly all quantitative analyses are dependent on the validity of this equation.   If it is not obeyed, quantitative determinations may still be possible but they will be more difficult (section 4.2).

3   Single-Component Quantitative Analyses

Quantitative analysis by absorption spectroscopy is based upon the principle that as one increases the amount of absorbing material in the beam the fraction of the incident radiant energy that is absorbed will increase in a reproducible manner.   If the relationship is strictly exponential, so that the absorbance is directly proportional to concentration, this is a considerable convenience, but this is most certainly not a necessary condition for the performance of a satisfactory analysis.

The procedure for quantitative analysis may be summarized briefly as follows: a series of known samples is compared with a reference absorber and the measured absorbance values of the known samples are plotted against the concentrations of the material or materials to be determined. The absorbance of an unknown sample, measured under the same conditions, is then compared with the curve and the concentration is read graphically or calculated by suitable algebraic methods.

3.1   Single-Beam Methods

Quantitative determination of the concentration of a single compound in the presence of other materials which do not interfere is a simple procedure that will afford insight into the methods of handling more difficult problems.   Single-beam methods, which are simplest from the standpoint of instrumentation rather than experimental procedure, will be discussed first, since this will more clearly demonstrate the principles upon which the other methods are based.   It will not be assumed that Beer's law is rigidly obeyed.   We shall assume, for the present, that the material under investigation is a liquid solution.

3.11   Procedure

The reference cell chosen for a particular analysis is filled with solvent and placed in the instrument.   The slit widths and amplifier gain (or the "sensitivity") are then adjusted to produce a suitable signal.   For a recording instrument linear in transmittance, this may mean a full-scale deflection; for an instrument employing a "densitometer" it may mean setting the transmittance knob to 100% and then adjusting to give a "zero" reading on the meter.   The choice of instrument settings is discussed below in section 3.16.

The sample cell, containing a known solution, is now placed in the instrument and the signal is measured, either as a deflection on the recorder or as the position of the transmittance scale required to balance the meter.   The transmittance of the solution is then the ratio of these two signals, either the ratio of the linear distances on the recorder chart or the ratio of distances on the potentiometer slide wire as read from the transmittance scale. The common logarithm of the ratio of reference signal to sample signal is the absorbance of the sample relative to that reference. $A = \log_{10} R/S$, where R and S are the readings, in any units chosen, for the signals obtained for reference and sample, respectively. If the instrument is calibrated directly in absorbance, it is of course sufficient to subtract the corresponding readings; then the absorbance of the sample relative to the chosen reference is $A = A_S - A_R$, where A_S and A_R are the absorbance values read from the instrument for sample and reference, respectively. The two methods are mathematically equivalent, since, if $A_S = \log C/S$ and $A_R = \log C/R$, where C is any arbitrarily defined constant reference signal,

$$A_S - A_R = \log C/S \cdot R/C = \log R/S \qquad \text{(IX-7)}$$

Unless one is quite certain of the stability of the instrument, it is advisable to repeat the above readings on the reference and sample cells, alternately. The reference signal is then taken as an average of the values obtained before and after the measurement on the sample, with instrument settings left unchanged. Of course, if the reproducibility is not quite high, the cause of the fluctuation must be found before proceeding.

At least two additional solutions of known concentration should be measured in the same manner and the absorbance value of each plotted against the concentration. If the experimental points and the origin lie on a straight line to within the accuracy desired for the analysis, the solution is said to obey Beer's law over the range of concentrations studied. Deviations from Beer's law may be expected to appear as the concentration is increased, and are more likely to appear in cases where the sample has sharp absorption bands or forms a non-ideal solution with the solvent. In nearly every case the deviations will be such as to make the curve concave to the concentration axis.

If Beer's law is followed, the slope of the line, determined by inspection or more accurately where necessary by a least-squares method, represents the product of the absorptivity of the solute and the cell length. The concentration of an unknown solution may be found by measuring the transmittance or absorbance of the unknown under precisely the same conditions and against the same reference. Then, if the slope was calculated, the concentration is calculated by dividing the measured absorbance by the slope. In many cases it is at least as simple to read the concentration from the graph that was drawn from the known solutions.

If Beer's law is not followed over the range of concentrations that one desires to investigate, it is necessary to determine the absorbance of sufficient known solutions so that a smooth curve may be drawn.   It is not advisable to assume that the curve will go through the origin without checking low concentrations to be sure that this is the case.   With an accurately drawn calibration curve of absorbance *vs*. concentration, it is then a straightforward procedure to determine the concentration of an unknown from this working curve.

3.12   Recording

If it is possible to record the spectrum over a range of frequencies about the absorption band chosen for the analysis, rather than simply to make all measurements at a single frequency, this has certain advantages.   Certainly the band should be scanned before starting the analysis to determine the width and shape of the band as well as the position of the maximum. Analyses should be avoided on bands that are extremely sharp, since it will be difficult to find the band maximum reproducibly and the peak intensity may vary markedly as slit widths change slightly.   Scanning each unknown has the additional advantage of indicating the presence of interfering constituents that may unexpectedly appear in the unknowns.

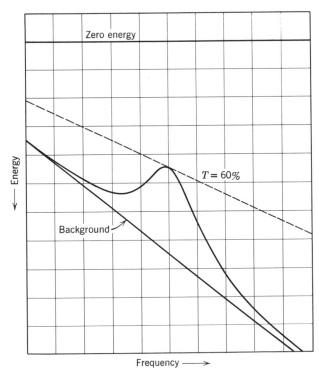

FIG. IX-2.   Location of band, maximum with sloping background.

In selecting the band maximum from the recorded curve, it should be kept in mind that a sloping background will lead to an apparent displacement of the peak. When the approximate background is known, the maximum can be found by drawing a tangent to the curve, at the peak, along a line of constant transmittance, as shown in Fig. IX-2. When the background is not known, it is in general not possible to find the maximum accurately. This may be less of a problem in a quantitative analysis than in qualitative applications.

3.13 Densitometers

The advantage of a single-point determination, with a "densitometer" attachment, lies in the improved signal-to-noise ratio obtainable. Very qualitatively, it is apparent that any reasonable rate of scanning will permit only a very short period of time for examination of the small part of the spectrum that will actually be measured. Random fluctuations, or noise, over this short period of time will seriously affect the measured value. It is always possible to greatly increase the damping applied to the measuring circuit and thus largely average out the statistical fluctuations. This greatly increases the response time, so that it may require half a minute or more for the system to reach equilibrium, but this is not a significant disadvantage when only one point is to be obtained.

3.14 Frequency Setting

Whether the measurement is made on a recorded curve or with a densitometer circuit, it is important that all measurements on a particular band be made at exactly the same frequency. If the band is recorded, one should be careful to read at a fixed frequency, rather than at the apparent band maximum, since the latter is subject to extraneous influences. The problem of reproducibility of the frequency setting is made less critical by operating at the absorption maximum, however, since the rate of change of absorbance with frequency is necessarily zero at this point. Actually this is in most cases the only reason for choosing the band maximum; if there is an optimum value for the absorptivity, it will generally not be precisely that of the band maximum. (Trace analysis would be the exception, since the largest absorptivity is then the most desirable.) The difficulties of accurately reproducing a frequency setting are sufficiently great that one should almost never attempt an analysis on any part of a band with appreciable slope.

3.15 Selection of Reference Absorber

In the ultraviolet and visible regions, one can readily obtain cells of glass or silica matched to better than 0.5% (or even 0.05%) and unaffected by normal usage.   Solvents are also plentiful which are transparent through-out all or nearly all of the region.   One may, therefore, with some assur-ance assume that transmission losses due to absorption, reflection, or scattering by the sample cell and the solvent can be measured by means of a companion reference cell filled with the solvent, provided the solution is quite dilute.   In fact, for dilute solutions in a transparent solvent, the matching of cell thicknesses is not at all critical.   A great deal of effort is often wasted on matching cells to 0.01 or 0.001 mm, when a difference of 5 mm out of 10 would not produce a measurable variation in absorbance.

If the solvent absorbs slightly, a correction must be made for any difference in amount of solvent in the sample and reference cells, although this may be minimized by working with dilute solutions and carefully matching cell thicknesses.   In some cases measurable variations may be produced by a difference in refractive index of pure solvent and the sample solution; this could show up as a change in reflection losses or, in some cases, as a difference in the efficiency of focusing.   Under the conditions of concentration, cell matching, and solvent transmittance normally en-countered in the ultraviolet and visible regions, these effects are quite negligible.   In the infrared region, however, all these difficulties may be expected to be more serious and should be considered potential sources of trouble.

Infrared cells are usually much thinner than those employed in the ultra-violet or visible, in order to minimize the absorption due to the solvents available, and they are most often made of sodium chloride or other water-soluble or flexible materials.   It is not often that one can obtain or main-tain a pair of cells matched to better than 1% in thickness.   Even if one had such cells, however, they would be of limited value since concentra-tions are generally high enough to cause significant differences in the amount of solvent present in sample and reference cells of equal thickness. Concentrations must be high (of the order of 5%, as an average) because solvent absorption makes it difficult to employ long-path-length cells; yet the solvent absorption makes matching of solvent in the two cells more important.

One fairly obvious method for circumventing this difficulty is to make the reference cell of continuously variable thickness.   Cells are com-mercially available that may be adjusted to produce the proper thickness of pure solvent to match the amount of solvent in the sample cell.   Un-fortunately, there are certain difficulties.   If one knew the concentration of solvent in the unknown, and knew that Beer's law was obeyed by the solvent, it would be a simple matter to calculate the thickness of the reference cell required.   In many cases the solvent concentration is un-known until the sample composition has been determined.   In this case one might find a solvent band elsewhere in the spectrum and adjust the reference cell thickness to cancel out this absorption band. Even if such a band can be found and the adjustment made, there is no assurance that the band that is adjusted to zero difference and the band that is interfering with the sample absorption will deviate to the same extent from Beer's law.

A second alternative is to let the same cell serve as both sample and reference cell, and to ignore the difference in effective solvent thickness. Thus the cell may be filled with solvent and the pen deflection determined (or slit widths and amplifier gain or "sensitivity" adjusted to give a 100% reading); the cell is then emptied and filled with the sample solution and the deflection or dial reading again noted.   The logs of the ratios of transmittance values obtained in this manner are then plotted against sample concentrations.   Quite apparently the values found in this method will not be the true absorbance values of the sample if the solvent absorbs, but any deviations will be in the form of systematic errors which will affect the calibration curve and the values read from the calibration curve in an equivalent manner.   Thus, although the deviations from Beer's law may be increased somewhat by this technique, the analysis will be no less precise or accurate.

Many of the older instruments were not sufficiently stable to allow measurements to be spread over the period of time required for emptying and refilling a cell. Amplifier drift (change in zero-energy level) is eliminated by reading with an opaque shutter in the beam before and after each transmittance measurement.   Errors due to variation in gain of the amplifier may be compensated by scanning the analytical region with a transparent object, such as a piece of rock salt, in the beam, or with no sample at all in the beam, before and after running the sample and before and after scanning the solvent.   The reading obtained for this blank disappears in the calculation of sample transmittance (equation IX-7). Recent instruments show exceptionally stable performance over long periods of time, so that for all but the most exacting analyses it should be quite adequate to measure reference energy before each group of unknown samples and again after examining the group.

Consideration of the way in which the results of these measurements will be treated will make it clear that the measurement of the cell filled with solvent plays no real part in the analysis, unless it is known that the cell filled with solvent represents the true absorbance for a sample of zero concentration.   Since the origin is then equivalent to an experimental point, the Beer's law plot will go through the origin; in the more general case it will be necessary to add a small arbitrary correction term to all readings if one wishes to make the plot pass through the origin.

Two different types of unknown can be treated by the methods already described. If the compound to be determined is the only constituent of the unknown that absorbs at the frequency chosen for the analysis, the addition of the unknown to a constant weight of solvent will result in a known background absorption due to the solvent. This may be compensated by a fixed-thickness or variable-thickness cell or by an arbitrary correction to make the curve pass through the origin, as described above. If the "solvent" is the remainder of the unknown sample, and if it is transparent at the frequency of the analysis, no correction will be required. On the other hand, if the "solvent" material has measurable absorption, this can quite obviously not be corrected for arbitrarily. In such a case it will be necessary to follow the procedures for a two-component or multicomponent analysis, as discussed in section 4.

3.16   Conditions for Minimum Concentration Error

An advantage of the single-beam instrument is that both reference- and sample-beam energy levels can be determined, and it is accordingly more obvious how each of these is changed as slit widths, amplifier gain, concentrations, or other variables are adjusted. But it is not immediately obvious which instrument settings will give the most accurate quantitative results. Certain principles are basic to all spectrometers but it must be recognized that the limiting factors will vary from one instrument to another. Thus it may be necessary for the individual operator to determine the best values for his own particular spectrometer.

We may start by drawing a somewhat arbitrary distinction between two limiting conditions of spectrometer operation. Throughout much of the ultraviolet and infrared regions, instrument performance is limited by the total amount of energy available in each range of frequencies. Increasing the intensity of the source or increasing the sensitivity of the detector will produce an increase in quality of performance. This situation is termed "energy-limited" operation. In the visible region somewhat different conditions prevail. The intensities of available sources and sensitivities of photoemissive detectors are sufficiently great that slit widths may be made very small. A limitation on instrument performance is then the combination of diffraction effects in the monochromator and the optical aberrations of the spectrometer.

In either case the instrumental limitation on quantitative accuracy, or photometric accuracy, is imposed by such factors as the linearity of the amplifier or the potentiometer slide wire (or optical wedge in optical-null double-beam instruments), the stability of the amplifier (freedom from drift of zero-energy level and from change in gain), and the noise level. In a modern, well-designed spectrometer the linearity and stability characteristics will be sufficient to throw most, if not all, of the responsibility for error on the noise level. The signal-to-noise ratio is thus the most important characteristic, and it becomes necessary to consider the quantitative accuracy as a function of the time required for the measurement. The signal-to-noise level can be improved in the energy-limited regions by increasing slit widths; it is therefore also necessary to specify the resolution conditions in order to compare photometric accuracies of two instruments or two different modes of operation of the same instrument.

Other errors arise from uncertainties of cell thickness, sample handling, and the "convergence error." In a given analysis, cell thickness and convergence errors, as well as such effects as refractive index, can nearly always be maintained constant and thus incorporated into the calibration curve. Sample-handling errors can usually be kept at a negligible level if sufficient attention is paid to calibration of glassware for non-aqueous solvents and other details. Non-linearity of the amplifier or slide wire can also be accommodated in the calibration curve if instrument conditions are kept constant. Effects of amplifier instability are minimized by reducing the time between measurement of sample and reference cells. Reproducibility of frequency setting is important for sharp absorption bands examined under moderately high resolution. Very high resolution will make the frequency setting less critical by increasing the apparent band width (relative to spectral slit width), but for quantitative measurements there is probably more justification for decreasing the resolution by increasing slit widths, since this will not only make the intensity less dependent on frequency but also at the same time will increase the available energy. Deviations from Beer's law may be larger, but this does not necessarily affect the accuracy of the determination.

Accuracy of reading the position of a pen line or of reading a dial is very seldom a significant limitation on over-all accuracy, although there are some instruments which have been shown to be slightly better than their read-out apparatus. In such a case straightforward scale expansion, by optical, mechanical, or electronic means, will produce a real improvement in photometric accuracy. The width of the pen line is not important if readings are always taken from the same side of the line. The rulings on strip-chart paper are often unreliable. Band intensities should be measured with a ruler rather than from chart paper calibrations in order to minimize this effect.

The optimum intensity range for measurement of intensities will depend on the net result of the various sources of error and accordingly may vary not only from one instrument to another but even from one operator to another. The best guess at present seems to be that the noise is the primary limiting factor in quantitative accuracy on modern instruments with skilled operators. The experimental evidence[1] now available appears to be in agreement with this conclusion. If this is the case, instruments with thermal detectors (thermocouple, bolometer, or Golay pneumatic cell) will show optimum accuracy in one range (about 35% T, or an absorbance of about 0.4), and spectrometers with photoemissive detectors (phototube or photomultiplier tube) will perform best in a somewhat different range (roughly an absorbance of 1.5 or 2). The method of arriving at such a prediction is of interest whether or not a valid connection can be drawn between the idealized cases treated and actual instruments operated under laboratory conditions.

Assume first that the error in a transmittance measurement is independent of the value of the transmittance. This should correspond to an instrument with thermal detector which is noise limited. The highest percentage accuracy in the transmittance measurement will then correspond to 100% T, but since this represents zero concentration it will not give accurate quantitative results. Assuming that Beer's law is obeyed,

$$c = \frac{1}{ab} \log \frac{I_0}{I}$$

$$dc = \frac{-1}{ab} \cdot \frac{dI}{2.3I}$$

or

$$\frac{\Delta c}{c} = \frac{-\Delta I}{2.3 A I} \tag{IX-8}$$

Thus the percentage error in concentration, $\Delta c/c$, depends inversely on the product of absorbance and transmitted intensity, which of course vary in opposite manner. Assuming ΔI, the error in intensity measurement, to be constant (Fig. IX-3), the minimum value for the percentage error is found by setting the derivative equal to zero.

$$\frac{d}{dI} \frac{\Delta c}{c} = \frac{-\Delta I}{2.3} \frac{d}{dI} \left(I \log \frac{I_0}{I} \right)^{-1} = \frac{\Delta I}{2.3} \left(I \log \frac{I_0}{I} \right)^{-2} \left\{ \log \left(\frac{I_0}{I} \right) - 0.4343 \right\} = 0$$

This will be satisfied if

$$A = \log \frac{I_0}{I} = 0.4343$$

$$\tag{IX-9}$$

$$T = \frac{I}{I_0} = \frac{1}{e} = 0.3679 = 36.8\%$$

[1] Slavin and Porro, "Measurement of Photometric Accuracy," Paper 61, Pittsburgh Conference on Analytical Chemistry and Applied Spectroscopy, March, 1960.

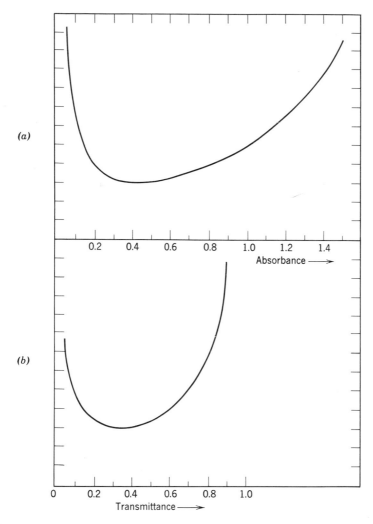

FIG. IX-3.   Relative error, $\Delta c/c$, for a constant transmittance error, plotted (*a*) against absorbance, (*b*) against transmittance.

An instrument with a photoemissive detector, operating under noise-limited conditions, should show a different behavior pattern, for in this case the noise is proportional to the square root of the intensity (equation II-13).   Assuming Beer's law,

$$\frac{\Delta c}{c} = \frac{-\Delta I}{2.3AI} \tag{IX-8}$$

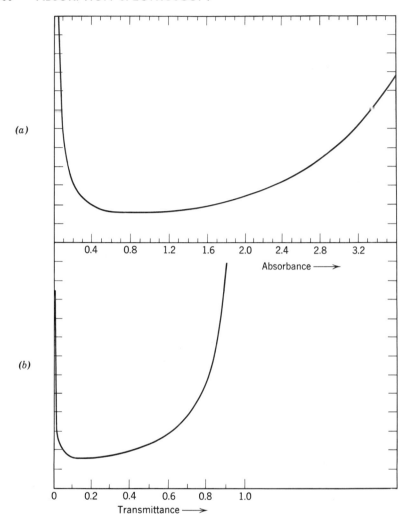

FIG. IX-4.   Relative error, $\Delta c/c$, for an error proportional to $I^{1/2}$, plotted (a) against absorbance, (b) against transmittance.

Replacement of ΔI by $hI^{1/2}$, where h is the constant of proportionality, yields the expression for percentage error in concentration (Fig. IX-4).

$$\frac{\Delta c}{c} = \frac{-h}{2.3}\left(I^{1/2}\log\frac{I_0}{I}\right)^{-1}$$

Then

$$\frac{d}{dI}\frac{\Delta c}{c} = \frac{h}{2.3}\left(I^{1/2}\log\frac{I_0}{I}\right)^{-2}\left\{\tfrac{1}{2}I^{-1/2}\log\frac{I_0}{I} - I^{1/2}(0.4343I^{-1})\right\} = 0$$

The minimum percentage error will occur for that concentration which gives an intensity satisfying the equation

$$A = \log I_0/I = 2 \times 0.4343 = 0.8686$$
$$T = I/I_0 = 0.135 = 13.5\% \tag{IX-10}$$

It is a simple matter to find the corresponding equations for other types of error functions; it is not so straightforward to know which of them, if any, is applicable to a particular instrument. Probably more realistic expressions would include a sum of terms. For example, if an ultraviolet spectrometer is limited by phototube shot noise and by mechanical noise in the pen mechanism on a linear transmittance scale (or more generally by any process which leads to transmittance error independent of the transmittance), one might expect that the optimum range would fall between the transmittance values of 37% and 14% calculated above, the exact position depending on the relative magnitudes of the two types of error. An ultraviolet spectrometer limited by shot noise and by a "constant absorbance" error, such as film or dust on the cell windows, would perform best at an absorbance higher than the 0.87 found above. The optimum value in this case would probably fall somewhere nearer an absorbance of 2, since the error curve for shot-noise limitation is quite flat.

3.17 Expanded-Scale Spectroscopy

In the derivations of the last section, the incident intensity, I_0, was considered a constant and was disregarded in finding the optimum conditions. Setting $(d/dI_0)(\Delta c/c) = 0$ shows that I_0 should be infinite. That is, the larger the incident intensity, I_0, the greater will be the measured intensity, I, for a given value of concentration and hence absorbance, and thus the smaller will be the percentage error in concentration (equation IX-8). Under normal operating procedures, the maximum value of I_0 is limited by the size of the potentiometer scale or recorder chart, since one end of the potentiometer slide wire corresponds to zero intensity and the other end to the full intensity at zero concentration, I_0. This is an artificial requirement, as is shown by the discussion of the selection of a suitable reference absorber for infrared measurements. In effect, we can have our cake and eat it, too—that is, we can have the greater accuracy of a higher incident intensity and still fit the region of interest onto the scale—by setting the full-scale deflection or "100% T" with a strong absorber in the beam. A sample slightly less concentrated than that to be measured or a "neutral density" filter, such as a wire screen, would be equally suitable. The only condition is that the reference absorber shall transmit more radiant power than the sample to be measured.

The distinction between this type of measurement, which has been called "differential spectroscopy" in the infrared region and (rather inappropriately) "precision colorimetry" for the ultraviolet and visible regions, and a simple expansion of scale, by either optical, mechanical, or electronic means, should be carefully noted. A scale expansion will not change the signal-to-noise ratio, and thus under ordinary conditions in which noise is one of the primary limitations, if not the most important, the accuracy of a determination will not be increased by this means. Only if the scale was initially too small for the spectrometer will such a scale expansion help, for it then permits more accurate reading of the value that was inherent in the original measurement. The scale expansion achieved by means of a reference absorber and artificial I_0 does increase the accuracy, for the important difference is the wider slit, and hence higher energy level, which leads to a greater accuracy in the measurement and thus justifies the expanded scale that automatically results.

It should be apparent that one of the side effects of this method will be to make the Beer's law plot miss the origin. A new scale has been chosen for the absorbance axis, such that zero absorbance would correspond to the concentration of sample in the reference sample or to the equivalent concentration for a screen or other absorber. This is no real disadvantage; neither is it any advantage in itself. One is now measuring a difference in concentration, from the reference point, but then that is precisely what is done with a calibration curve when the same "reference" sample corresponds to one of the points on this curve (Fig. IX-5). The process is still one of preparing a calibration curve and subsequently reading values from this curve. The only improvement in accuracy arises from the more advantageous instrument settings, which make a given ΔI less significant in terms of $\Delta c/c$.

One limitation of the method, which deserves emphasis, is that the wider slits required to increase the energy level will lower the resolution, and this may, in turn, mean that the radiant intensity measurements which are so carefully made have only limited significance in terms of the concentration that is sought. In extreme cases the wider slit widths may make it impossible to distinguish between the absorption due to the compound to be determined and other substances which have adjacent absorption bands. If loss of resolution is not important, and it is especially likely to be unimportant in the visible region where very broad bands are encountered, it may actually be possible to achieve as good or better accuracy with a filter photometer than with a much more expensive spectrometer that has severe mechanical limitations on the slit widths available.

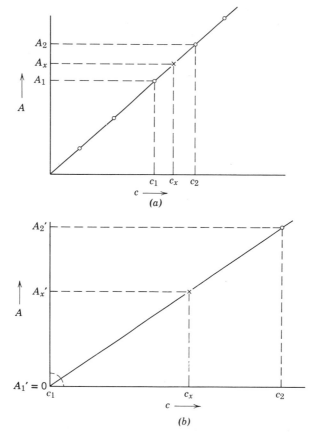

FIG. IX-5. Expanded scale analysis leaves the accuracy unchanged unless the slit width is increased. (a) In conventional method the unknown, c_x, is compared with the nearest calibration points, c_1 and c_2, $A_x = abc_x = \log 1/T_x$. (b) When the scale is expanded the value c_x is still read with respect to the nearest concentrations. $A_x' = ab(c_x - c_1) = \log 1/T_x'$. Unless the slits are changed, the absolute error increases in proportion to the scale expansion. (Calibration points are indicated by ◯, experimental points by ✕.)

The significance of the new "I_0" level is shown in Fig. IX-6. Assume the true absorbance of the sample is adjusted to 1.0 (10% T), with an uncertainty of measurement of $\pm 0.5\%$ T. The curve of transmittance vs. frequency will appear as in Fig. IX-6a. A screen with a transmittance of 11%, equivalent to an absorbance of 0.96, is selected for the new I_0 (we shall designate this I_0' to avoid confusion). The slits of the spectrometer are now opened, increasing the amount of energy transmitted by both the sample and the reference, until I_0' has reached the end of the scale. The

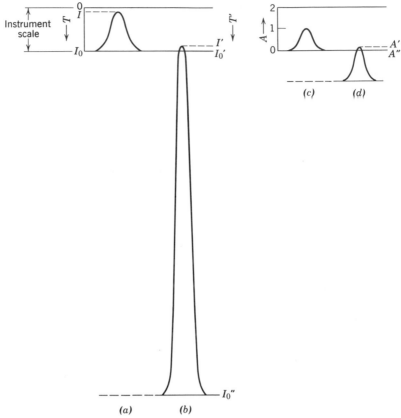

FIG. IX-6. Nine-fold scale expansion. (a) Appearance of band under normal conditions on transmittance scale. (b) Expanded transmittance scale. (c) Same band on normal absorbance scale. (d) Expanded absorbance scale. The expansion is achieved by setting the 100% T or zero absorbance line with an absorber of 11% ($A = 0.909$) in the beam, or in the reference beam for double-beam instruments.

true I_0, labeled I_0'', is now very much greater than the original and is off scale; it could not be measured directly since the instrument would go off scale if there were no absorber in the beam. The spectrometer will record the band as shown in Fig. IX-6b. The band will appear to transmit 90.9%, with an uncertainty of $\pm 0.5\%$. The accuracy has been increased by a factor of 9. For the initial conditions,

$$
\begin{aligned}
A &= abc = 1.0 \\
T &= 0.10 \\
\Delta T &= \pm 0.005 \\
\Delta A &= \pm 0.022 \\
\Delta c &= \pm 0.022/ab
\end{aligned}
\tag{IX-11}
$$

When the scale is expanded so that $11\% \, T$ equals full-scale deflection, the apparent transmittance, T', and absorbance, A', are

$$T' = 0.10/0.11 = 0.909$$
$$\begin{aligned}
A' &= \log I_0/I = \log I_0''/I' \\
&= \log (I_0'/I')(I_0''/I_0') \\
&= \log I_0'/I' + \log I_0''/I_0' \\
&= A' + A''
\end{aligned} \qquad \text{(IX-12)}$$
$$\varDelta T' = \pm 0.005$$
$$(\varDelta A)' = \varDelta(A') = \pm 0.0024$$
$$(\varDelta c)' = \pm 0.0024/ab$$

The equivalent curves as they would appear when plotted linearly in absorbance are given in Fig. IX-6c and d.   With a photoelectric detector the nine-fold scale expansion would improve the accuracy by a factor of three.

It will be noticed that no uncertainty is assigned to the quantity A''. This must be so since there can be no experimental uncertainty for a quantity that is not experimentally measured.   There is an uncertainty to be associated with adjusting the 11% level to full scale but this is the usual calibration error associated with any point on a calibration curve, decreased in this case by the scale expansion.

Determinations of trace quantities are limited by the total absorbance of the unknown, which at some point will no longer be as large as the uncertainty in reading the pen or dial.   This is shown in Fig. IX-7a.   Increasing the slit widths, and hence I_0, will not help in this case, since this would drive the entire absorption band off scale.   Increasing path lengths will help, of course, and if this leads to excessive interference it may be possible to subtract out the interference by choosing the same concentration and path length of interfering substance as the reference absorber. This effect is shown in Fig. IX-7b and c; it represents a particular form of differential spectroscopy.   (Note that we are still considering single-beam spectrometers at this point; the technique is of course equally adaptable to double-beam instruments but is certainly not unique to them.)   In this case, as is generally true with single-beam measurements, it will be necessary to adjust slit widths as one examines different frequencies to plot absorbance vs. frequency.   If the interfering absorber is placed in the reference beam when adjusting the "I_0" for each point measured, the background absorption will be corrected for in the same manner as changes in source intensity.

When the problem is a limited total amount of sample, rather than simply concentration of sample, it may not be possible to increase the cell

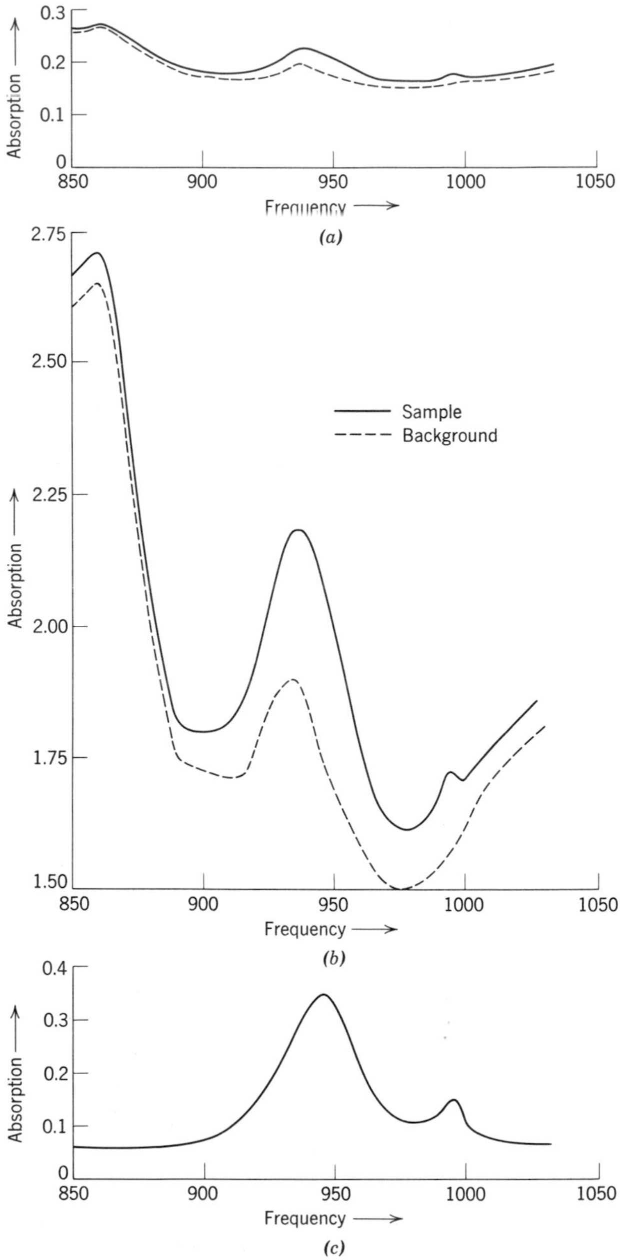

FIG. IX-7.   Differential spectroscopy for trace analysis.   (a) Sample plus background (solid line) and background absorption (dashed line) under normal instrumental conditions.   (b) Same spectra with ten-fold expansion of scale.   (c) Differential spectrum, sample including background against background, at same scale expansion as in (b).

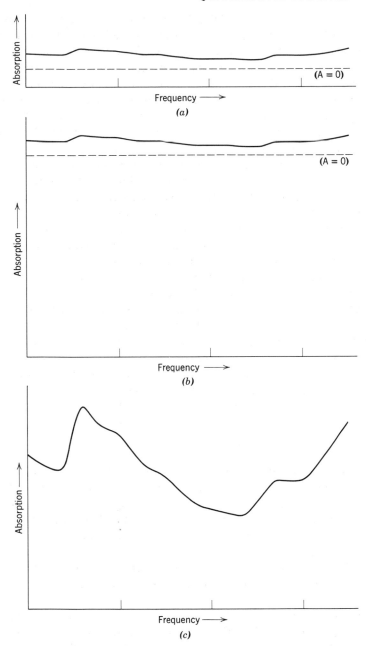

FIG. IX-8. Expanded scale spectroscopy for trace analysis. (*a*) Sample absorption
under normal instrumental conditions. (*b*) Same spectrum with scale shifted. (*c*) Same
spectrum, including scale shift as in (*b*), with the scale expanded. The 100% *T* or zero
absorbance line is off scale below the bottom of the figure.

length (see, however, section IV-4.5). In such cases it may be helpful to shift the scale. The zero energy is "faked" by placing in the beam a cell or screen which actually transmits a significant fraction of the incident radiation; this energy is set equal to zero on the transmittance scale (Fig. IX-8).

On the Beckman DU this is achieved by moving the transmittance dial to zero and adjusting the dark-current potentiometer to give a "zero" reading on the meter with the reference sample in place and the slit switch on. On other instruments such as the Beckman IR-2 or PE-12, there is a "zero control" or "balance" control which may be adjusted to give a reading of zero transmittance when the reference absorber is in position.

No direct advantage is gained from such a shift in zero-energy level, but it permits other changes to be made which can yield better accuracy. For example, since the scale has been shifted, it is now possible to increase the gain to move the I_0 level back to 100%, or to the corresponding edge of the chart, and thus produce a magnification of the band over the initial conditions. The noise will be correspondingly increased, but additional damping can often compensate for this at the price of an increased length of time to reach equilibrium. The accuracy may be increased by this method if it enables one to see a band which could not be seen under initial conditions. Alternatively, the slit widths may be increased to move the I_0 level to the 100% T position, with a net increase in accuracy (except that this may "wash out" weak bands which have a width comparable to the spectral slit width). The zero-suppression method seems less generally helpful than the expanded-scale method involving an increase in incident intensity, and it has been applied to fewer problems.

3.18   Least-Squares Approximations

One does not accept the absorptivity value determined from one known concentration; rather, several concentrations are prepared and the corresponding absorbance values plotted against the concentrations. In any real experiment there will be random errors arising from the limitations of the measurement. If there is a sufficiently large number of experimental points and one has reason to believe that the deviation of these points from a straight line can be attributed to random errors, a better value may be obtained by minimizing the squares of the deviations from the "straight-line" values.

In the equation $A = abc$, it is customarily assumed that the concentrations are known "exactly" (that is, more accurately than the absorbance values). The deviation of experimental values from the equation may then be written $A - abc_i = e_i$. The deviations, e_i, are squared and the sum of them taken for all the experimental points. It is required that this sum of the squares of the deviations be a minimum.   This is achieved by setting the derivative with respect to the adjustable parameter, a or ab, equal to zero.

$$\frac{\partial \sum_i e_i^2}{\partial ab} = \frac{\partial \sum_i}{\partial ab} [A_i^2 - 2abc_iA_i + (abc_i)^2] = 2\sum_i (abc_i^2 - c_iA_i) = 0$$

$$(\text{IX-13})$$

The least-squares condition is therefore that

$$ab = \frac{\sum_i A_ic_i}{\sum_i c_i^2} \qquad (\text{IX-14})$$

To find the best value of the absorptivity (by this criterion) one should therefore multiply each absorbance value by its corresponding concentration and find the sum of these products.   The sum is divided by the sum of the squares of the concentrations.

In some cases it is not plausible to assume *a priori* that the straight line should go through the origin.   This is especially true in the infrared because of uncertainty in locating the I_0 line.   Beer's law should then be written

$$A = abc + A_0 \qquad (\text{IX-15})$$

Again assuming the concentration term to be exact, the deviation is

$$e_i = A_i - (abc_i + A_0) \qquad (\text{IX-16})$$

Two variables must now be found, a (or ab) and A_0, and they are evaluated by setting the derivative of $\sum_i e_i^2$ with respect to each of these parameters equal to zero.   Consider first the value of the intercept, A_0.

$$0 = \frac{\partial \sum_i e_i^2}{\partial A_0}$$

$$= \frac{\partial \sum_i}{\partial A_0} (A_i^2 - 2A_iabc_i - 2A_iA_0 + (abc_i)^2 + 2abc_iA_0 + A_0^2)$$

$$= \sum_i -2[A_i - (abc_i + A_0)] \qquad (\text{IX-17})$$

This shows that the sum of the deviations must be zero to obtain the best value for A_0.   A considerable simplification in finding the absorptivity is achieved by transforming to "center-of-gravity" coordinates.   The average of the concentration values and the average of the absorbance values are found and subtracted from each of the corresponding original numbers.

$$\bar{A} = \frac{\sum_i A_i}{n}; \quad \bar{c} = \frac{\sum_i c_i}{n}; \quad A_i' = A_i - \bar{A}; \quad c_i' = c_i - \bar{c} \quad \text{(IX-18)}$$

Now, since the sum of the deviations is required to be zero, the straight line must go through the new origin ($A' = c' = 0$), so that Beer's law may be written, for this general case, $A' = abc'$. Applying the results obtained earlier, the best value is

$$ab = \frac{\sum_i A_i' c_i'}{\sum_i c_i'^2} \quad \text{(IX-19)}$$

Two advantages are gained by the transformation of coordinates. The new variables are small numbers, and thus there is a slight simplification in the ensuing calculations, and the equation for the absorptivity is much simpler than if we had proceeded by brute force. In the original co-ordinate system the corresponding equation would be

$$ab = \frac{\sum_i c_i \sum_i A_i - n \sum_i A_i c_i}{\left(\sum_i c_i\right)^2 - n \sum_i (c_i^2)} \quad \text{(IX-20)}$$

The method of equations IX-15 to IX-20 is not limited to problems involving Beer's law. In a more general case the reduction to center-of-gravity coordinates also helps to show which variable is known more exactly, and this is important since the subsequent equations depend on this point.

3.19   Increment Method

Occasionally one is more concerned with determining changes in concentration of a particular compound than with determining the true concentration. This may be accomplished by means of a log A vs. log c plot.

Assume that over a certain range of concentration the absorbance varies linearly with concentration. Then $A = abc + A_0$, where A_0 may have any of several interpretations, as discussed below. Add to the original unknown, of concentration c, a known additional amount, Δc, of the pure substance to be determined. Then $c' = c + \Delta c$ and $A' = abc' + A_0$. The observed ratio, A'/A, is given by

$$r \equiv \frac{A'}{A} = \frac{c' + A_0/ab}{c + A_0/ab}$$

$$= \frac{c + \Delta c + A_0/ab}{c + A_0/ab}$$

and solving for c or for Δc will give

$$c = \frac{\Delta c}{r-1} - \frac{A_0}{ab} \qquad \text{(IX-21)}$$

or

$$\Delta c = (r-1)\left(c + \frac{A_0}{ab}\right) \qquad \text{(IX-21a)}$$

These equations have two potential applications.   If Beer's law is known to be obeyed, so that $A = abc$ and $A_0 = 0$, equation IX-21 gives the value of c directly.   In such a case, however, the present method will probably not offer any real advantage over the conventional procedure.   If $A_0 \neq 0$, equation IX-21 or IX-21a may be solved, for a particular value of Δc and r, for the sum $(c + A_0/ab)$; substitution of this into equation IX-21a gives

$$\Delta c = (r-1)\left(\frac{(\Delta c)_1}{r_1 - 1}\right) \qquad \text{(IX-22)}$$

where $(\Delta c)_1$ and r_1 are known.   Any subsequent increment, Δc, is determined by simply measuring the ratio of absorbance values, r, upon the addition of that Δc.

In Fig. IX-9 are shown two types of unknown sample behavior which might be treated by this procedure.   In one case, there is a constant interfering background which produces the additive absorbance value, A_0.   In the other example, Beer's law is not obeyed, but over the operating region the curve is sufficiently linear to permit the incremental method to be applied.   In the latter case the constant term, A_0, represents the intercept of the extrapolated tangent.   Both types of deviation from Beer's law may occur simultaneously, as in Fig. IX-9c.   These figures should make it clear why in the general case one cannot determine an absolute value of the concentration by this procedure.   But, if the only object of the analysis is to determine small changes in concentration from some arbitrary (and quite possibly unknown) initial concentration, the incremental method will achieve this with a minimum of effort.

In the simplified case where $A_0 = 0$, taking the logarithm of each side of the equation gives $\log A = \log c + \log ab$, which is the equation of a straight line of unit slope.   In this case, therefore, one may plot A as ordinate, arrange the points along any line at $45°$, and the abscissa will be in units of $\log c$ with, however, an unknown additive constant.   That is, zero concentration must correspond to $-\infty$ along the abscissa and $c = +\infty$ will correspond to $+\infty$ along the axis, but one has no way of knowing where the point $c = 1$, or $\log c = 0$, falls, since the absolute value is assumed unknown.   Linear distance along the abscissa between $\log c$ and $\log c'$ will give the ratio of c' to c.   As was shown algebraically above,

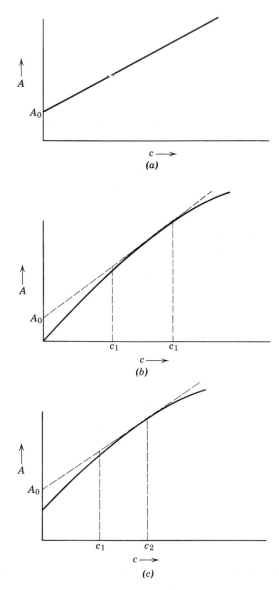

FIG. IX-9.   Application of Beer's law to non-ideal systems.   In spite of (*a*) background absorption, (*b*) non-linear behavior, or (*c*) a combination of these, it may be possible to describe the curve, at least over a limited range ($c_1 - c_2$), by the equation $A = A_0 + abc$.

this permits a determination of c, and therefore c', if Δc is known. In the more general case, placing the points along a straight line of unit slope will give a plot of $\log A$ *vs.* $\log (c + A_0/ab)$.

3.2 Double-Beam Methods

Analytical methods with double-beam spectrometers are exactly the same in principle as those with single-beam instruments. There is no operation or analysis that can be performed on a double-beam instrument that cannot also be carried out on a single-beam instrument. The primary difference, therefore, is one of convenience, for the double-beam instrument will, in effect, run the sample and reference cells simultaneously, subtract the corresponding absorbances (or divide the transmittances), and report only the relative values. In some instances where the reference curve has an erratic shape, the operation of comparing the two curves obtained from a single-beam spectrometer would be extremely tedious and necessarily inaccurate. If the stability of the single-beam spectrometer is not very high, the double-beam instrument may give more accurate comparisons since there is no time lag. On the other hand, the double-beam spectrometer provides less information, since only the relative values, and not the absolute values, are recorded. This can lead to severe difficulties if it is not constantly kept in mind, especially in optical-null spectrometers.

3.21 Procedure

A sample of known concentration is placed in a cell of suitable thickness, and this is placed in the appropriate holder in the sample beam of the spectrometer. Another cell filled with solvent, a salt plate, a screen, or some other absorber is placed in the reference beam (frequently no reference absorber will be employed, especially in the infrared). It may be necessary at this stage to adjust the balance or beam trimmer to ensure that the $100\% T$ or zero absorbance line will be on scale at all points along the chart. The spectrum is then recorded. At least two additional solutions of known concentrations should be scanned in the same manner against the same reference. Unless the absorption curve of the solvent (or other reference absorber) is definitely known, the reference cell should be placed in the sample beam in place of the sample cell and, with no absorber in the reference space, the spectrum recorded. This is always good practice, although it can sometimes be eliminated by an experienced operator with an electronic-null spectrometer by simply observing the slit widths as the spectrum is scanned. In many cases it will also be desirable to fill the cell in which the known solutions were run with pure solvent and record the spectrum of this against the same reference absorber.

Unknown samples can be scanned in the same manner as the knowns after the calibration curve has been drawn and found satisfactory.

Interpretation of the curves will vary depending on whether the spectrometer is of the electronic-null, linear-absorbance, or electronic-null, linear-transmittance, or optical-null, linear-absorbance, or optical-null, linear-transmittance type. These types will accordingly be treated separately.

3.22 Electronic-Null, Linear-Absorbance Spectrometer

If the spectrum is recorded on a scale that is linear in absorbance (not to be confused with linear-transmittance records on non-linear paper), quantitative analyses are especially simple since it is only necessary to

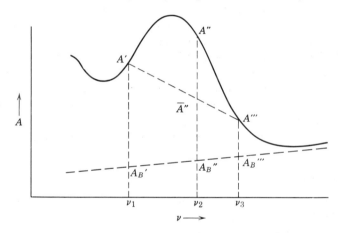

FIG. IX-10. Hill-and-valley method. If the absorbance of the background, A_B'', at some intermediate frequency lies on the straight line $A_B' - A_B'''$, the concentration of the sample will be proportional to the length $A'' - \bar{A}''$, provided that the sample obeys Beer's law.

measure, with a good ruler, the distance from the zero absorbance line to the point of interest on the spectrum. The scale factor can be obtained from the chart paper, but the chart paper is in general not sufficiently reproducible in dimensions for the more accurate quantitative analyses.

The zero absorbance line can be chosen in either of two ways. The sample cell, filled with pure solvent, may be considered the reference level. In the ultraviolet, where concentrations are low and solvents transparent, this is usually the most satisfactory and simplest method. Alternatively, any other reasonably transparent substance would be suitable, since such a substitution will be equivalent to a displacement of the zero absorbance line. This may cause the Beer's law plot to miss the origin but will not affect the linearity of the plot. If there is interference by some other absorbing material, the "hill-and-valley" method, shown in Fig. IX-10, will be preferable. One assumes that between two arbitrarily chosen frequencies the background is linear, but not necessarily horizontal. A straight line is drawn between the points of the curve corresponding to these two frequencies, and the absorbance at any frequency within this range is measured from this somewhat arbitrary line. The proof of the validity of the method is straightforward.

Three frequencies along the absorption curve, ν_1, ν_2, and ν_3, are selected arbitrarily, as shown in Fig. IX-10. The point A_B'', the absorbance of the background at the intermediate frequency, is assumed to lie on the straight line connecting A_B' and A_B''' (although we do not know the values of A_B', A_B'', or A_B''') and the absorbances of the sample and background are assumed to be additive. That is,

$$A_B'' = \frac{\nu_2 - \nu_1}{\nu_3 - \nu_1}(A_B''' - A_B') + A_B' \tag{IX-23}$$

and

$$A' = A_S' + A_B'$$
$$A'' = A_S'' + A_B'' \tag{IX-24}$$
$$A''' = A_S''' + A_B'''$$

It is to be proved that $A'' - \bar{A}'' = kc$, where k is a constant and c is the concentration of the sample.

$\bar{A}''$ is, by definition, on the straight line between A' and A'''. Therefore

$$\bar{A}'' = A' - \frac{\nu_2 - \nu_1}{\nu_3 - \nu_1}(A' - A''') \tag{IX-25}$$

$$= A_S' + A_B' + \frac{\nu_2 - \nu_1}{\nu_3 - \nu_1}(A_S''' + A_B''' - A_S' - A_B')$$

$$= A_B' + \frac{\nu_2 - \nu_1}{\nu_3 - \nu_1}(A_B''' - A_B') + A_S' + \frac{\nu_2 - \nu_1}{\nu_3 - \nu_1}(A_S''' - A_S') \tag{IX-26}$$

Now, since Beer's law is obeyed by the sample,

$$A_S' = k_1 c$$
$$A_S'' = k_2 c \tag{IX-27}$$
$$A_S''' = k_3 c$$

The first two terms of equation IX-26 may be replaced by A_B'' (equation IX-23). Then, writing $f(\nu) = (\nu_2 - \nu_1)/(\nu_3 - \nu_1)$,

$$\bar{A}'' = A_B'' + k_1 c + f(\nu)(k_3 c - k_1 c) \tag{IX-28}$$

and therefore, from equations IX-24 and IX-28,

$$A'' - \bar{A}'' = A_S'' + A_B'' - A_B'' - (k_1 + f(\nu)k_3 - f(\nu)k_1)c$$
$$= [k_2 - k_1 - f(\nu)k_3 + f(\nu)k_1]c \tag{IX-29}$$

The quantity in brackets is a constant which may be represented by k. Hence

$$A'' - \overline{A}'' = kc \qquad \text{(IX-30)}$$

Note that the choice of frequencies is completely arbitrary, but one must always use the same three frequencies or the proportionality constant, k, will be changed.   It is often most convenient to select maxima and minima of the absorption curves for the points of measurement, since at the minima the baseline will be tangent to the curve and at the maximum the baseline will be approximately parallel to the curve, so that in each case a small frequency shift will lead to little or no error.   But, having once chosen these frequencies, it is necessary to keep the same frequency values in further work even though they may not correspond, in the later samples, to maxima or minima of the absorption curves.

The assumption that the background is linear over the frequency interval chosen is not necessarily a safe one.   Inspection of the equations will show that, if it is not valid, an additive term appears on the right-hand side of equation IX-23 and is carried over to IX-28, IX-29, and IX-30.   The magnitude of this term may be expected to vary with the total absorbance of the background and with the composition of the sample.   The hill-and-valley method should therefore be followed only when there is some prior knowledge of the background absorption or when adequate empirical investigation of the system has shown that the method is sufficiently good for the intended analysis.[1]

Expanded-scale spectrometry may be carried out on an electronic-null spectrometer, regardless of the scale on which the spectrum is plotted, in essentially the same manner as described above for single-beam instruments. The reference absorber, which may be a known solution or an arbitrary type of filter, is placed in the reference beam and the sample is compared automatically to this absorbance level.   The true absorbance of the sample, as measured against the transparent solvent, should be adjusted according to the error characteristics of the spectrometer; generally, for ultraviolet instruments, the absorbance should be between 1 and 2.   It is most important, of course, to watch the slit widths, since they must be reproduced for all samples that will be compared to a particular calibration curve, and also to be certain that the slits remain below the limiting value set by the mechanical stops, since this is necessary for proper instrument operation.   If stray radiation is not negligible a lower absorbance value will be required.

3.23 Electronic-Null, Linear-Transmittance Spectrometer

When the spectrum has been recorded on a scale that is linear in transmittance, it is necessary to locate not only the 100% transmittance line

[1] See, for example, Hazlett, Hannan, and Wells, *Anal. Chem.* **22**, 1132 (1950).

(zero absorbance) but also the 0% T line.   For an electronic-null spectrometer this involves nothing more than inserting an opaque object in the
sample beam.   If the 100% T line can be satisfactorily found by running
the sample cell filled with solvent against the reference absorber, the
absorbance of the sample is calculated by measuring the distance, I, between the zero energy line and the sample curve and the distance, I_0,
between the zero-energy line and the 100% T line (Fig. IX-11).   The
absorbance is $A = \log I_0/I$.   Note in particular that one cannot substitute the percentage absorbed for the percentage transmitted in finding

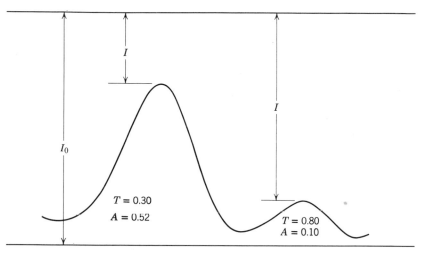

FIG. IX-11.   Measurement of band intensity on a linear-transmittance plot.   The
transmittance values, I_0/I, for the bands shown are 30% and 80%; the absorbance
values, $\log I_0/I$, are 0.52 and 0.10.

absorbance.   The percentage absorbed is $(I_0 - I)/I_0 = 1 - T$.   Neither
$\log (1 - T)$ nor $\log 1/(1 - T)$ is simply related to the concentration of the
sample.
    The 100% T, or I_0, line may well be indefinite in this case, just as in
linear-absorbance recording or in single-beam operation.   Any arbitrary
choice of the I_0 will be suitable, subject to a possible displacement of the
Beer's law plot.   The proof of this is indicated in Fig. IX-12, which shows
the intensity, I, transmitted by the sample solution; the true 100% line,
I_0, which may be unknown; and an assumed 100% T line, I_0'.   The
calculated absorbance will be

$$A' = \log I_0'/I$$
$$= \log (I_0'/I_0)(I_0/I)$$
$$= A + \text{constant}$$

where the constant is simply log I_0'/I_0. If Beer's law is obeyed, this gives the equation $A' = abc +$ constant, which is still the equation of a straight line.

The case of interfering absorption is not quite so simply treated when the recorded curve is linear in transmittance. In particular, it is not possible to assume the background to be linear on the transmittance plot and draw in an arbitrary baseline, as can be done for linear-absorbance plots. The equations derived above are still applicable, but the $\bar{A}''$ can no

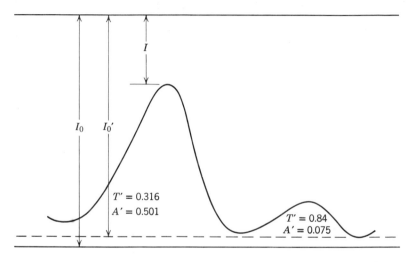

FIG. IX-12. Choice of I_0 line. Intensities measured relative to the broken line, I_0', will be shifted by a constant absorbance increment (0.022) with respect to those measured relative to the solid line, I_0. Absorbance will vary linearly with concentration for any assumed I_0 line.

longer be located by drawing a straight line between two points on the curve. This difficulty can be circumvented in either of two ways.

The quantities A', A'', and A''', the absorbance values of sample plus background, can be read from the curve by measuring I_0/I at each of the three frequencies and finding the logarithms. The distances $\nu_2 - \nu_1$ and $\nu_3 - \nu_1$ can also be measured, and $\bar{A}''$ can then be evaluated algebraically from equation IX-25. The concentration will be proportional to $A'' - \bar{A}''$, as before.

Quite apparently the equation will be very much simplified if $A' = A'''$, that is, if the baseline is horizontal. It was pointed out in the derivation that the choice of frequencies, ν_1, ν_2, and ν_3, was completely arbitrary. It is therefore always possible to choose the line to be horizontal, at least for an "average" sample. If the deviations in other samples are not great, the error introduced by this assumption should be small and can always be calculated if desired.   More serious difficulties may arise from errors in locating the frequencies ν_1 and ν_3 when the corresponding portions of the curve have an appreciable slope.

3.24 Optical-Null, Linear-Absorbance Spectrometer

There is little or no difference in procedure between an electronic-null and an optical-null spectrometer if they both record on a linear-absorbance scale.   One may expect the optical-null instrument to show a higher noise level at high absorbance values, since the optical-null system is characteristic of spectrometers operating under a less favorable signal-to-noise ratio; more specifically, optical-null instruments are generally designed for the infrared region and accordingly employ thermocouple or other heat-sensitive detectors, which show different characteristics from photo-emissive detectors.

At very high absorbance values the optical-null system will tend to go dead, but since this will correspond to an off-scale reading it is not likely to cause trouble.   The exception would be the case in which the reference sample absorbs strongly and the slit program is independent of reference signal, but since this problem is more pronounced in the linear-transmittance instruments it will be treated in connection with them.

3.25 Optical-Null, Linear-Transmittance Spectrometer

Throughout the previous sections the uncertainty of the 100% T, or I_0, line in many types of analyses has been emphasized.   In an optical-null spectrometer there is an additional difficulty, for it is no longer possible to determine accurately the zero-energy level.   A very brief review of the operating principle of the optical-null system will demonstrate the cause of this uncertainty.   Figure IX-13 shows a schematic representation of an optical-null spectrometer.   Radiant energy from the source passes through the sample and reference compartments and then through the mono-chromator and onto the detector.   A chopper mirror causes the two beams to pass alternately through the monochromator and strike the detector. The unbalance signal is amplified and sent to a servomotor, which drives an optical wedge into or out of the reference beam to produce a balance at the detector.   The pen is mechanically or electrically linked to the optical wedge.

To measure the zero-energy level one would naturally be inclined to insert an opaque object into the sample beam and note the position to which the pen moves.   But as the pen moves toward a lower transmittance value the optical wedge is moving into the reference beam.   There is no optical signal being passed during the sample half cycle, and there is progressively less and less energy transmitted in the reference beam. Eventually, as the pen reaches a value such as 1% or 0.1% T, the unbalance signal will have become so small that it can no longer actuate the servo-motor. Both beams are blocked, no energy is being passed, and the spectrometer has no way of knowing how close it is to the correct transmittance value.

The effect of this may be seen experimentally by blocking off the sample beam very slowly and noting the rest position. This will represent the true 0% T line plus the smallest intensity level to which the instrument will respond. The pen is then returned to the opposite edge of the chart by removing the opaque object and the sample beam blocked very rapidly, again noting the final pen position. This may represent the position of

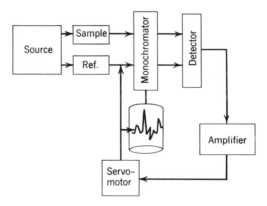

FIG. IX-13.   In an optical-null spectrometer the pen records the position of an optical wedge that is moved into or out of the reference beam to eliminate fluctuations in signal at the detector.

the mechanical stop, for the inertia of the pen mechanism will carry it beyond the true 0% T line. In scanning a spectrum, sharp absorption bands will appear to absorb more strongly than very broad absorption bands, even though both should be totally absorbing, simply because inertia plays a more important part in one case than in the other.

Various methods of overcoming this difficulty have been proposed. Most involve some type of "up-scale signal." For example, one may intentionally produce a very small unbalance signal in the amplifier. This will have no appreciable effect during normal operation, for the signal from the detector will over-ride this signal. But when the unbalance signal from the detector disappears, the amplifier unbalance signal will drive the pen toward higher transmittance values until the amplifier unbalance just matches the true signal from the detector. Quite clearly this will not give a true $0\%\ T$ line, but it will tend to give a more reproducible line (with a larger systematic error) and may produce somewhat better-looking spectra. In some cases the unbalance signal is only applied when the pen goes below a certain transmittance value. In other cases a mechanical signal, such as a spring against which the pen will ride at the zero-energy end of the scale, achieves the same result. A somewhat different technique applies an a-c signal to the pen at low transmittance values. This does not produce any net displacement of the pen but serves to overcome the static friction that makes the pen mechanism less sensitive to small signals coming from the detector. The inherent non-linearity of the optical wedge (see section III-5.2) should also be taken into consideration.

Fortunately the uncertainty in the $0\%\ T$ line is not very important in terms of quantitative accuracy. Modern instruments are sufficiently sensitive that the error is not large (probably about 1% to 0.1% or perhaps even less). Also, if the transmittance of the sample is kept within a suitable range, the error will have very little effect on the measured intensity. If the measured zero-energy line is in error by an amount δI, the absorbance error will be

$$\delta A = \log \frac{I_0 - \delta I}{I - \delta I} - \log \frac{I_0}{I}$$

$$= \log \frac{1 - \delta I/I_0}{1 - \delta I/I} \qquad \text{(IX-31)}$$

The error δI will be small compared to I_0 and for most values of I the ratio $\delta I/I$ will also be small. If, for example, the concentration has been adjusted to give a transmittance of 37% and the uncertainty in the $0\%\ T$ line is 0.5%, the absorbance error will be

$$\delta A = \log \frac{1 - 0.005/1}{1 - 0.005/0.37} = \log \frac{0.995}{0.9865} = \log (1.01)$$

$$= 0.004$$

A closely related problem arises in regions where the reference sample absorbs strongly. This is particularly important in the infrared region, for which most optical-null spectrometers have been designed, because infrared solvents have strong absorption bands and the presence of solvent in the reference beam gives rise to these difficulties. It is also important in differential spectroscopy, either in cases of expanded-scale measurements or for the detection of trace impurities.

Consider the extreme case in which an opaque object is placed in a position to block both beams simultaneously. The detector will receive no signal and will therefore show no unbalance. Wherever the pen, and optical wedge, may be, they will tend to stand still, thus accurately reporting that the two beams are balanced for that position of the optical wedge. If there is even a very slight unbalance in the amplifier this will cause a drift of the pen which will bear no relation to the optical signal.

To avoid such a "dead" region, it is necessary to increase the available energy. A simple test to determine whether there is sufficient energy being passed by the reference beam is to insert quickly an opaque object in the sample beam (a hand will do) and observe the response of the pen. If the pen seems sluggish, or if there is no response, it will be necessary to decrease the absorbance of the reference material or increase the incident intensity, generally by opening the slits. A particularly insidious type of dead region is that which arises in regions of atmospheric absorption. Over a rather narrow region it is quite possible to have virtually no energy available in either beam because of absorption of CO_2 (2350 cm^{-1} and 667 cm^{-1}) or water vapor (sharp bands distributed around 3700 cm^{-1} and 1600^{-1}), and yet the recorded spectrum will appear normal because the inertia of the pen mechanism tends to produce a smooth trace (with no real significance in many cases). Similar effects have been observed in cases where gases or volatile liquids are placed in the cell compartment and leak into the spectrometer housing. To avoid this situation it is a rather simple operation to equip the monochromator housing with a nozzle and inlet hose for flushing with dry nitrogen. This should be done on every instrument, before the need specifically arises, since otherwise there is a strong tendency to get by without it in each individual case and hope that no error results. It is not necessary to flush the entire optical path (although for some measurements it would be preferable to do so), since the double-beam principle will effectively cancel out the absorption effect provided at least 10% or 20% of the energy is passed (or even less for slower rates of scan). The lifetime of a Nernst glower can be shortened significantly by continually flushing the source housing with a gas containing no oxygen.

The corresponding difficulty for electronic-null spectrometers is the situation in which the slits open to their mechanical stop, in which case the operation of the instrument is so completely upset that the recorded spectrum has no significance at all. In the ultraviolet region it is most likely to happen at the high-frequency (short-wavelength) cut-off for the particular solvent or optical materials employed. Two significant differences may be noted between the performance of the electronic-null and the optical-null spectrometers in this connection. First, if the reference absorbs strongly, the electronic-null instrument will automatically open the slits to maintain maximum photometric accuracy, with a subsequent loss in resolution. This prevents gross errors due to the instrument going dead, but, of course, if the change in slit widths goes unnoticed, this can lead to a very serious quantitative error in comparing measurements made under different conditions of reference absorption. Secondly, the electronic-null instrument will display the slit width on a dial, and this will provide a visible warning of increasing reference absorption if the operator watches the slit widths during operation. The optical-null instrument operates on a fixed slit schedule, and there is no visible warning to the operator of increasing reference absorption unless it happens to produce a characteristic peculiarity on the recorded curve.

4   Multicomponent Analyses

Systems containing more than one substance in unknown concentration can be treated by precisely the same methods as have been outlined under single-component analyses if an absorption band can be found for each constituent that does not overlap absorption bands of other unknowns in the sample. When overlapping of absorption bands does occur the experimental procedure is only slightly changed, but it becomes necessary to resort to somewhat more involved methods of calculating concentrations from measured absorbances. A set of simultaneous equations is obtained; if the system is nicely behaved they will be linear equations, but in some cases the equations may be non-linear and graphical or successive-approximation procedures may be required. The ideal and non-ideal cases will be treated separately, to emphasize more clearly what changes in method are required when Beer's law is not obeyed by all constituents.

4.1   Ideal Systems

Assume four substances to be present in unknown concentrations in a liquid or in a solid that is soluble in a transparent solvent. It is desired to find four pieces of information—the four concentrations—and thus it is necessary to make at least four experimental measurements. Some care is required in selecting the measurements to be performed (that is, at what frequencies absorbance values are to be determined) since the four measurements must be independent in the mathematical sense. It would be of little help, for example, to measure four bands due entirely, or even principally, to the same compound.

The absorbance due to the jth compound at the ith frequency will be

$$A_{ij} = a_{ij}bc_j \qquad \text{(IX-32)}$$

where a_{ij} is the absorptivity of compound j at the frequency i; b is the cell thickness; and c_j is the concentration of the jth compound. Assuming the absorbances due to different compounds to be additive, the total observed absorbance at the ith frequency should be

$$A_i = \sum_j A_{ij} = \sum_j a_{ij}bc_j \equiv \sum_j k_{ij}c_j \qquad \text{(IX-33)}$$

where $k_{ij} \equiv a_{ij}b$.

More explicitly,

$$\begin{aligned}
A_1 &= k_{11}c_1 + k_{12}c_2 + k_{13}c_3 + k_{14}c_4 \\
A_2 &= k_{21}c_1 + k_{22}c_2 + k_{23}c_3 + k_{24}c_4 \\
A_3 &= k_{31}c_1 + k_{32}c_2 + k_{33}c_3 + k_{34}c_4 \\
A_4 &= k_{41}c_1 + k_{42}c_2 + k_{43}c_3 + k_{44}c_4
\end{aligned} \qquad \text{(IX-34)}$$

If each absorption band were due solely to one component, the sum in equation IX-33 would consist of a single term and the calculation of the concentration would be trivial. Each of the four equations (IX-34) could be solved independently to find one concentration from each equation. When it is not possible to find absorption bands involving no mutual interference, it is often possible to approximate this situation by finding bands for which the interference is small. One of the absorptivity terms in each equation will then be significantly larger than the others. By suitable choice of numbering of components and frequencies it is then possible to make the large absorptivity terms the diagonal elements (k_{11}, k_{22}, k_{33}, and k_{44}). Methods of solution will not depend on the diagonal terms being largest and in many cases it will not be possible to choose them to be so, but when approximation methods are required for solution of the equations it is a decided advantage to have the diagonal terms large compared to the other values.

A great simplification of notation is possible by writing the linear equations in matrix form (see Appendix I). The first equation is written

$$\mathbf{A}_1 = [k_{11} \quad k_{12} \quad k_{13} \quad k_{14}] \begin{bmatrix} c_1 \\ c_2 \\ c_3 \\ c_4 \end{bmatrix} \equiv \sum_j k_{ij}c_j$$

or

$$\mathbf{A}_1 = [k_{1j}][c_j] \equiv \mathbf{K}_1\mathbf{C} \qquad \text{(IX-35)}$$

The first term in the row is multiplied by the first term in the column, to this product is added the product of the second term in the row by the second term in the column, and so on for the third and fourth terms. The other equations are written in similar form, then combined to give

$$\begin{bmatrix} A_1 \\ A_2 \\ A_3 \\ A_4 \end{bmatrix} = \begin{bmatrix} k_{11} & k_{12} & k_{13} & k_{14} \\ k_{21} & k_{22} & k_{23} & k_{24} \\ k_{31} & k_{32} & k_{33} & k_{34} \\ k_{41} & k_{42} & k_{43} & k_{44} \end{bmatrix} \begin{bmatrix} c_1 \\ c_2 \\ c_3 \\ c_4 \end{bmatrix}$$

or

$$[A_i] = [k_{ij}] [c_j]$$
$$\mathbf{A} = \mathbf{KC} \tag{IX-36}$$

4.11   Methods of Solution

If only one or two unknown mixtures are to be analyzed, it will be most convenient to solve the equations by means of Cramer's rule. The first column of the absorptivity matrix ($\mathbf{K}$) is replaced by the column of measured absorbance values ($\mathbf{A}$). The determinant of the new matrix is divided by the determinant of the original absorptivity matrix to find the value of c_1. Concentrations of other components are found in a similar manner; the jth column of $\mathbf{K}$ is replaced by $\mathbf{A}$ and the determinant of this matrix is divided by the determinant of $\mathbf{K}$ to give c_j.

When several unknown samples are to be analyzed by means of the same absorptivity matrix, the extra time involved in finding the inverse matrix will be well worth while. Multiplying equation IX-36 on the left by $\mathbf{K}^{-1}$,

$$\mathbf{K}^{-1}\mathbf{A} = \mathbf{K}^{-1}\mathbf{KC} = \mathbf{C} \tag{IX-37}$$

or

$$c_j = \sum (k^{-1})_{ji} A_i \tag{IX-38}$$

Thus, if the matrix $\mathbf{K}^{-1}$ is known, any concentration, c_j, can be found by multiplying together four pairs of numbers and adding the products.

The following example will illustrate the details of the procedure. Figure IX-14 shows the spectra of o-xylene, m-xylene, p-xylene, and ethyl-benzene in cyclohexane, a mixture of all four compounds in cyclohexane, and pure cyclohexane. Four frequencies were chosen for a quantitative analysis. Table IX-I lists the absorptivity values of the four pure compounds, as measured in cyclohexane solution at several different concentrations. The measured absorbance values of the unknown are also given.

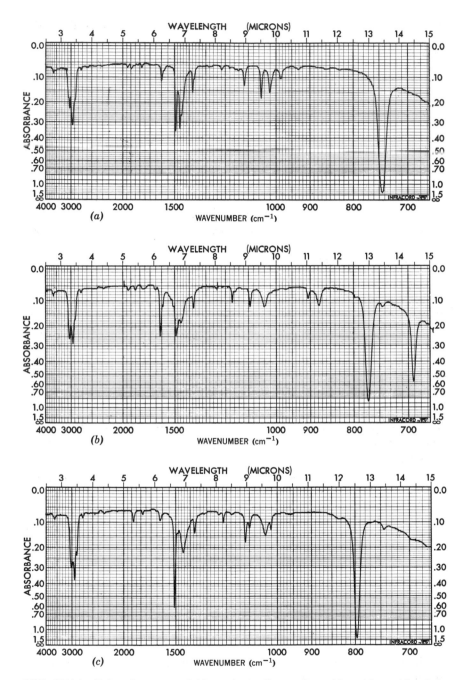

FIG. IX-14. Infrared spectra of (*a*) *o*-xylene; (*b*) *m*-xylene; (*c*) *p*-xylene; (*d*) ethyl-benzene; (*e*) cyclohexane; and (*f*) a mixture of the xylenes and ethylbenzene in cyclohexane.

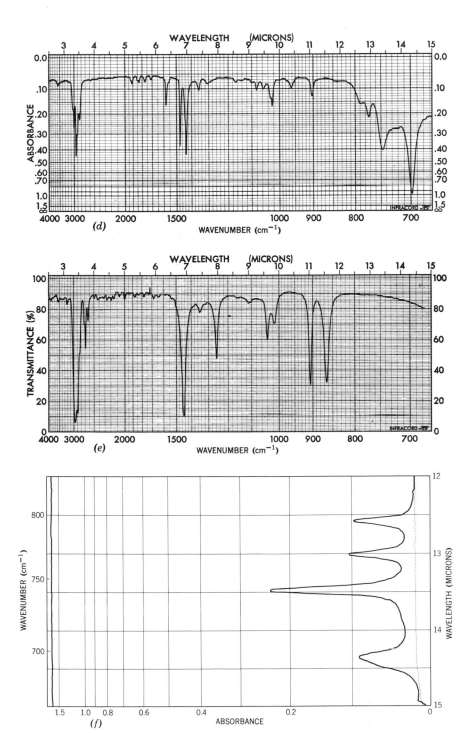

(d)

WAVELENGTH (MICRONS)

(e)

(f)

407

TABLE IX-I[a]

Wavenumber (cm^{-1})	Absorptivity × Length (L/gm) × 0.2				Absorbance × 10 Mixture
	p-Xylene	m-Xylene	o-Xylene	Ethyl-benzene	
795.2	2.8288	0.0968	0.0000	0.0768	0.7721
768.0	0.0492	2.8542	0.0000	0.1544	0.8676
741.2	0.0645	0.0668	4.7690	0.5524	2.2036
696.3	0.0641	0.1289	0.0000	1.6534	0.7386

[a] Absorbance and absorptivity values are probably accurate to no better than ±0.05 in the units given. The extra digits, obtained by dividing measured distances, are carried throughout to avoid introduction of error in the calculations. The absorbance values are below the optimum values to avoid deviations from Beer's law.

The first equation of IX-34 would read as follows.

$$0.7721 = 2.8288c_1 + 0.0968c_2 + 0.0000c_3 + 0.0768c_4 \quad \text{(IX-39)}$$

The matrix equation IX-36 in explicit form is

$$
\begin{bmatrix} 0.7721 \\ 0.8676 \\ 2.2036 \\ 0.7386 \end{bmatrix}
=
\begin{bmatrix}
2.8288 & 0.0968 & 0.0000 & 0.0768 \\
0.0492 & 2.8542 & 0.0000 & 0.1544 \\
0.0645 & 0.0668 & 4.7690 & 0.5524 \\
0.0641 & 0.1289 & 0.0000 & 1.6534
\end{bmatrix}
\begin{bmatrix} c_1 \\ c_2 \\ c_3 \\ c_4 \end{bmatrix}
\quad \text{(IX-40)}
$$

The concentrations are found by means of Cramer's rule, evaluating the determinants by the method of pivotal condensation (Appendix I, section 1.1).

$$
c_1 = \frac{
\begin{vmatrix}
0.7721 & 0.0968 & 0.0000 & 0.0768 \\
0.8676 & 2.8542 & 0.0000 & 0.1544 \\
2.2036 & 0.0668 & 4.7690 & 0.5524 \\
0.7386 & 0.1289 & 0.0000 & 1.6534
\end{vmatrix}
}{
\begin{vmatrix}
2.8288 & 0.0968 & 0.0000 & 0.0768 \\
0.0492 & 2.8542 & 0.0000 & 0.1544 \\
0.0645 & 0.0668 & 4.7690 & 0.5524 \\
0.0641 & 0.1289 & 0.0000 & 1.6534
\end{vmatrix}
}
$$

$$= \frac{\dfrac{1}{(0.7721)^2} \begin{vmatrix} 2.11974 & 0.00000 & 0.05258 \\ -.16173 & 3.68214 & 0.25727 \\ 0.02803 & 0.00000 & 1.21987 \end{vmatrix}}{\dfrac{1}{(2.8288)^2} \begin{vmatrix} 8.06920 & 0.00000 & 0.43300 \\ 0.18272 & 13.49055 & 1.55768 \\ 0.35843 & 0.00000 & 4.67222 \end{vmatrix}}$$

$$= \frac{\dfrac{1}{0.59614 \times 2.11974} \begin{vmatrix} 7.80518 & 0.55385 \\ 0.00000 & 2.58433 \end{vmatrix}}{\dfrac{1}{8.00211 \times 8.06920} \begin{vmatrix} 108.85795 & 12.47609 \\ 0.00000 & 37.54759 \end{vmatrix}} = \frac{15.96245}{63.30051}$$

$$= 0.252(16) \frac{\text{gm}}{50 \text{ ml}} \; p\text{-xylene} \tag{IX--41}$$

$$c_2 = \frac{\begin{vmatrix} 2.8288 & 0.7721 & 0.0000 & 0.0768 \\ 0.0492 & 0.8676 & 0.0000 & 0.1544 \\ 0.0645 & 2.2036 & 4.7690 & 0.5524 \\ 0.0641 & 0.7386 & 0.0000 & 1.6534 \end{vmatrix}}{63.30051}$$

$$= \frac{\dfrac{1}{(2.8288)_2} \begin{vmatrix} 2.41628 & 0.00000 & 0.43300 \\ 6.18374 & 13.49055 & 1.55767 \\ 2.03986 & 0.00000 & 4.67222 \end{vmatrix}}{63.30051}$$

$$= \frac{\dfrac{1}{8.00211 \times 2.41628} \begin{vmatrix} 32.59695 & 1.08623 \\ 0.00000 & 10.40613 \end{vmatrix}}{63.30051} = \frac{17.54342}{63.30051}$$

$$= 0.277(14) \frac{\text{gm}}{50 \text{ ml}} \; m\text{-xylene} \tag{IX--42}$$

$$c_3 = \frac{\begin{vmatrix} 2.8288 & 0.0968 & 0.7721 & 0.0768 \\ 0.0492 & 2.8542 & 0.8676 & 0.1544 \\ 0.0645 & 0.0668 & 2.2036 & 0.5524 \\ 0.0641 & 0.1289 & 0.7386 & 1.6534 \end{vmatrix}}{63.30051}$$

$$= \frac{\dfrac{1}{(2.8288)^2} \begin{vmatrix} 8.06920 & 2.41628 & 0.43300 \\ 0.18272 & 6.18374 & 1.55768 \\ 0.35843 & 2.03986 & 4.67222 \end{vmatrix}}{63.30051}$$

$$= \frac{\dfrac{1}{8.00211 \times 8.06920} \begin{vmatrix} 49.45633 & 12.47609 \\ 15.59397 & 37.54759 \end{vmatrix}}{63.30051} = \frac{25.74096}{63.30051}$$

$$= 0.406(64) \frac{gm}{50 \ ml} \ o\text{-xylene} \qquad\qquad (IX\text{-}43)$$

$$c_4 = \frac{\begin{vmatrix} 2.8288 & 0.0968 & 0.0000 & 0.7721 \\ 0.0492 & 2.8542 & 0.0000 & 0.8676 \\ 0.0645 & 0.0668 & 4.7690 & 2.2036 \\ 0.0641 & 0.1289 & 0.0000 & 0.7386 \end{vmatrix}}{63.30051}$$

$$= \frac{\dfrac{1}{(2.8288)^2} \begin{vmatrix} 8.06920 & 0.00000 & 2.41628 \\ 0.18272 & 13.49055 & 6.18374 \\ 0.35843 & 0.00000 & 2.03986 \end{vmatrix}}{63.30051}$$

$$= \frac{\dfrac{1}{8.00211 \times 8.06920} \begin{vmatrix} 108.85795 & 49.45633 \\ 0.00000 & 15.59397 \end{vmatrix}}{63.30051} = \frac{26.28946}{63.30051}$$

$$= 0.415(31) \frac{gm}{50 \ ml} \ \text{ethylbenzene} \qquad\qquad (IX\text{-}44)$$

It should be noted that nearly all numbers appear at least twice during the evaluation procedure.   This means that a significant fraction of the time can be saved by recognizing the pattern of repetition and writing down these numbers from earlier results.   Alternatively the repetition will serve as a check on the accuracy of the calculations.

To evaluate the inverse of the absorptivity matrix, each element of the original matrix is replaced by its cofactor, the resultant matrix is transposed, and the determinant is divided into the new matrix.   This involves the evaluation of sixteen 3×3 determinants; as in the calculations above, much of this work is unnecessary since the same terms reappear.

The evaluation of the first column of the inverse matrix and the final inverse matrix are given below.

$$(k^{-1})_{11}D = \frac{1}{2.8542} \begin{vmatrix} 13.61168 & 1.56635 \\ 0.00000 & 4.69923 \end{vmatrix} = 22.41062$$

$$-(k^{-1})_{21}D = \frac{1}{0.0492} \begin{vmatrix} 0.23463 & 0.01722 \\ 0.00000 & 0.07145 \end{vmatrix} = 0.34073$$

$$(k^{-1})_{31}D = \frac{1}{0.0492} \begin{vmatrix} -0.18081 & 0.01722 \\ -0.17661 & 0.07145 \end{vmatrix} = -0.20076$$

$$-(k^{-1})_{41}D = \frac{1}{0.0492} \begin{vmatrix} -0.18081 & 0.23463 \\ -0.17661 & 0.00000 \end{vmatrix} = 0.84223$$

$$\mathbf{K}^{-1} = \frac{\begin{bmatrix} 22.41062 & -0.71606 & 0.00000 & -0.97411 \\ -0.34073 & 22.28182 & 0.00000 & -2.06492 \\ -0.20076 & -0.10442 & 13.27416 & -4.41581 \\ -0.84223 & -1.70935 & 0.00000 & 38.48617 \end{bmatrix}}{63.30100}$$

When the inverse has been found (this represents roughly an hour and a quarter of work, including checking), the concentrations of all four components of any unknown mixture can be evaluated by a single matrix multiplication.

$$\begin{bmatrix} c_1 \\ c_2 \\ c_3 \\ c_4 \end{bmatrix} = \begin{bmatrix} & & & \\ & \mathbf{K}^{-1} & & \\ & & & \\ & & & \end{bmatrix} \begin{bmatrix} 0.7721 \\ 0.8676 \\ 2.2036 \\ 0.7386 \end{bmatrix} = \begin{bmatrix} 0.252(16) \\ 0.277(14) \\ 0.406(68) \\ 0.415(35) \end{bmatrix} \tag{IX-45}$$

Concentrations (by synthesis) of the mixture were 0.248, 0.271, 0.398, and 0.420 gm/50 ml.

Another method for solution of the simultaneous equations has been described by Crout.[1] It requires roughly the same number of steps as the solution by Cramer's rule as carried out above.

4.12 Least-Squares Approximation

The optimum value for the absorptivity of a single compound at some point in the spectrum is found by plotting absorbance against concentration, determining the region over which this line is straight, and finding the slope of the straight line by a least-squares treatment (equations IX-14, IX-19). This is applicable, for example, in evaluating absorptivities for a multicomponent analysis, as in Table IX-I, or for a simple one-component analysis.

For essentially the same reason—to minimize the effects of random experimental errors—it is desirable to overdetermine the concentrations in a multicomponent system, then find the optimum concentrations by minimizing the sum of the squares of the deviations between the observed absorbance values and the calculated absorbance values.

An example is given below. The calibration values are taken from Table IX-I. These values, along with the observed absorbance values for a mixture, are shown in equation IX-46. The problem becomes the solution of three equations in two unknowns. This cannot be carried out by any exact procedure, but the "best" solution, by the least-squares criterion, is found by multiplying through by the transpose of the absorptivity matrix. This gives two equations in two unknowns, such that the solution to these two equations is also the optimum solution to the three (or more) original equations.

$$\mathbf{A} = \mathbf{KC}$$

$$\begin{bmatrix} 0.9416 \\ 0.1593 \\ 0.4047 \end{bmatrix} = \begin{bmatrix} 0.0768 & 2.8288 \\ 0.1544 & 0.0492 \\ 0.5524 & 0.0645 \end{bmatrix} \begin{bmatrix} c_1 \\ c_2 \end{bmatrix} \qquad \text{(IX-46)}$$

$$\mathbf{K'} = \mathbf{K*K}$$

$$\mathbf{K'} = \begin{bmatrix} 0.0768 & 0.1544 & 0.5524 \\ 2.8288 & 0.0492 & 0.0645 \end{bmatrix} \begin{bmatrix} 0.0768 & 2.8288 \\ 0.1544 & 0.0492 \\ 0.5524 & 0.0645 \end{bmatrix} = \begin{bmatrix} 0.33488 & 0.26048 \\ 0.26048 & 8.00825 \end{bmatrix}$$

$$\text{(IX-47)}$$

[1] P. D. Crout, *Trans. Am. Inst. Elec. Engrs.* **60**, 1235 (1941).

$$\mathbf{A'} = \mathbf{K} * \mathbf{A}$$

$$\mathbf{A'} = \begin{bmatrix} 0.0768 & 0.1544 & 0.5524 \\ 2.8288 & 0.0492 & 0.0645 \end{bmatrix} \begin{bmatrix} 0.9416 \\ 0.1593 \\ 0.4047 \end{bmatrix} = \begin{bmatrix} 0.32047 \\ 2.69754 \end{bmatrix} \qquad \text{(IX-48)}$$

$$\mathbf{A'} = \mathbf{K'C}$$

$$\begin{bmatrix} 0.32047 \\ 2.69754 \end{bmatrix} = \begin{bmatrix} 0.33488 & 0.26048 \\ 0.26048 & 8.00825 \end{bmatrix} \begin{bmatrix} c_1 \\ c_2 \end{bmatrix} \qquad \text{(IX-49)}$$

This is quickly and easily solved by multiplying through by $\mathbf{K'}^{-1}$.

$$\mathbf{C} = \mathbf{K'}^{-1}\mathbf{A'} = \frac{1}{2.61395} \begin{bmatrix} 8.00825 & -0.26048 \\ -0.26048 & 0.33488 \end{bmatrix} \begin{bmatrix} 0.32047 \\ 2.69754 \end{bmatrix} \qquad \text{(IX-50)}$$

$$\begin{bmatrix} c_1 \\ c_1 \end{bmatrix} = \begin{bmatrix} 0.713(00) \\ 0.313(65) \end{bmatrix}$$

The concentrations (by synthesis) were 0.704(4) and 0.311 gm/50 ml. A slightly better value for the first one would have been obtained in this system by including the band at 696.3 cm^{-1} because of the smaller relative error associated with the larger k value for ethylbenzene.

It must be borne in mind that the solutions found by this method are no better than the equations.   That is, it is explicitly assumed that only small, random errors cause the inconsistency of the equations and therefore the optimum concentrations are a compromise achieved by distributing the deviation among the various equations.   If there is a systematic error in the measurements or a serious error in any one equation, the least-squares method will not overcome this difficulty.   By examination of the deviations between observed absorbance values and the sum of products of absorp- tivities and concentrations a check is available on whether the errors are small or are due largely to one equation.

4.2 Non-ideal Systems

Deviations from Beer's law are not much of a handicap in single-com- ponent unknowns or in multicomponent unknowns in which the overlap is so small that they can be solved as several single-component analyses. When overlapping of bands is combined with marked deviations from Beer's law, the procedures for quantitative analysis become considerably more complex.   The difficulties are essentially mathematical in character, for as long as the absorbance of each constituent is independent of the presence of the other constituents equations analogous to IX-33 can be written down in principle.   The equations will not be linear, since the absorptivity values vary with concentration, but the (reasonable) solutions will still be unique for most systems.   For the present it will be assumed that the law of additivity applies rigorously.

For single-component unknowns there is little difference in accuracy or convenience between algebraic and graphical solutions if Beer's law is obeyed; if the calibration curve is non linear the graphical method is simpler.   In multicomponent systems the speed of solution of simultaneous equations by matrix methods produces a strong preference for this type of algebraic solution where applicable.   But, again, if the systems are non-ideal, it may be advisable to perform some part, at least, of the solution by graphical means.

The problems involved in non-ideal systems are so varied that only a few of the possible methods can be mentioned.   It is hoped that they will be sufficiently suggestive of the required approach to permit extrapolation and combination of these techniques and the initiation of entirely new procedures to handle specific systems in the simplest manner.

4.21   Solution over Limited Concentration Range

Often small variations in concentration of one or more components will be expected.   It may then be possible to approximate the portion of the Beer's law plot that is applicable by a straight line, as shown in Fig. IX-9.   The equation is then

$$A = abc + A_0$$

or

$$A' = A - A_0 = abc \qquad \text{(IX-51)}$$

That is, the known value of A_0 is applied as a correction term to observed absorbance values before these values are put into the matrix equations. If the concentration found in any particular sample falls outside the pre-scribed range, the absorptivity value and absorbance correction should be redetermined and the calculation repeated.   An approximate calculation, assuming Beer's law, will often give a value for each concentration suffi-ciently good that this procedure can be applied to find exact concentrations in a second calculation.   If the concentrations will vary between zero and some known maximum, the best choice for the absorptivity may be the slope of the chord running from the origin to the maximum value.

4.22   Iteration Procedures

A general characteristic of non-ideal multicomponent systems is a necessity for successive approximations.   Often the consecutive steps will be of different type.   The examples considered are: (a) successive graphical single-component calculations, with feedback; (b) approximate algebraic solution, followed by successive graphical single-component calculations; (c) approximate algebraic solution, followed by graphical corrections to the concentrations; and (d) approximate algebraic solution followed by non-linear single-component calculations.

In the abbreviated algebraic statement of each procedure following the discussions, a superscript ° will indicate a value assumed before any calculations are made on the individual sample.   First and second calculated values, or numbers based directly on them, will be designated by ′ and ″ respectively.

(a) When the interference between components is small, equivalent to large diagonal elements and small off-diagonal elements in the absorptivity matrix, a graphical solution will be relatively simple.   A plot of absorbance vs. concentration is made for each component at each frequency. An approximate concentration is determined for compound one by assuming that all the absorption at one of the four frequencies is due solely to this substance.   On the basis of this calculated concentration, the absorbance due to compound one at another frequency can be calculated and subtracted from the observed absorbance.   The remaining absorbance at the second frequency is assumed due entirely to compound two.   Absorbance contributions by compounds one and two at a third frequency can be estimated, then by compounds one, two, and three at the fourth frequency.   At the completion of this process the absorbance value at the first frequency due to all compounds other than the first can be estimated. Assuming the residual absorption to be due to compound one gives a better estimate for this concentration, which can be carried forward with the first-approximation values for the third, etc., compound concentrations to determine the second, and so on till repetition does not change the values.   To ensure rapid convergence the compound that interferes most strongly with the other constituents should be approximated first.

The successive graphical method has several advantages.   Since each step requires nothing more than reading a value from a graph, the total time consumed in a cycle should be quite small.   The extent of deviation from Beer's law is not at all important since all concentrations are read from the calibration curves.   If the interference is large the values may converge slowly.

Summary:

$$A_1 = k_{11}'c_1'$$
$$A_2 - k_{21}'c_1' = k_{22}'c_2'$$
$$A_3 - (k_{31}'c_1' + k_{32}'c_2') = k_{33}'c_3'$$

(IX-52)

$$A_1 - (k_{12}'c_2' + k_{13}'c_3' + \cdots) = k_{11}''c_1''$$

(IX-53)

etc.

(*Note.* The k_{ij} are not explicitly evaluated since concentrations (right-hand side of equations) or partial absorbance values (subtracted on left-hand side of equations) are read from the corresponding absorbance or concentration values, respectively, on the non-linear graphs.)

(*b*) An algebraic preliminary solution is generally most effective when the deviations from Beer's law are small or can be made small by substitution of an effective absorptivity (section 4.21). The amount of interference between components is unimportant in this step, since the approximate linear equations can be quickly solved by matrix methods. The calculated concentrations could serve as the basis for a similar calculation with better values for the effective absorptivities, but it may be more convenient at this stage to switch to a graphical iteration procedure, especially since the graphs will have been prepared as a necessary part of the calibration process. If the graphical method is followed, the peak that is most nearly due to a single component should be selected first, so that the best possible values of concentrations will be available for the more sensitive determinations. Note that this is not necessarily the same order of operation as in method (*a*).

Summary:
$$[A] = [k^\circ][c']$$ (IX-54)

$$A_1 - (k_{12}'c_2' + k_{13}'c_3' + \cdots) = k_{11}''c_1''$$
$$A_2 - (k_{21}''c_1'' + k_{23}'c_3' + \cdots) = k_{22}''c_2''$$ (IX-55)

[The note following method (*a*) applies also to equations IX-55 but not to IX-54.]

(*c*) If a large number of analyses on closely similar mixtures are to be carried out, it may be advantageous actually to plot correction curves. They could give the correction to the concentration of one compound that will be introduced by various concentrations of another compound. Following an initial estimate of all concentrations by solution of a matrix equation, corrections on the concentration of the first compound due to the estimated amounts of each of the other compounds could be read from the graphs and then summed to give the total correction to the concentration of the first compound.

Summary:
$$[A] = [k^\circ][c']$$ (IX-56)

$$\varDelta_2(c_1) = f_{12}(c_2'); \quad \varDelta_3(c_1) = f_{13}(c_3'); \quad \varDelta_4(c_1) = f_{14}(c_4')$$ (IX-57)

$$\varDelta_1(c_1) = f_{11}(c_1') \quad \text{(correction for non-linearity and}$$
$$\text{wrong initial choice of absorptivity)}$$ (IX-58)

$$\varDelta(c_1) = \sum_i \varDelta_i(c_1) \qquad c_1 = c_1' + \varDelta(c_1)$$ (IX-59)

where $\varDelta_i(c_1)$ represents a correction to c_1 due to the presence of the *i*th compound and f_{1i} is some function of c_i determined empirically.

(*d*) Sometimes it is possible to fit the non-linear curve by an approximate equation. For example, in a particular case it may be found that the absorbance is given reasonably accurately by an expression such as $A = abc + dbc^2$. If the deviation is "instrumental" or from some other source that causes it to behave as a deviation from Bouguer's law as well as from Beer's law, the form $A = abc + db^2c^2$ would be more appropriate. For a fixed cell length either equation may be written

$$A = kc + dc^2$$

or

$$A_i = \sum_j k_{ij}c_j + \sum_j d_{ij}c_j^2 \qquad \text{(IX-60)}$$

It is assumed that the d_{ij} values are small compared to the k_{ij} values and that the off-diagonal values (d_{ij} where $i \neq j$) can be neglected.

Approximate values of the concentrations can be found by solving approximate linear equations,

$$[A] = [k°][c'] \qquad \text{(IX-61)}$$

with absorptivity values, $k_{ij}°$, that are not necessarily the same as the k_{ij} values in equation IX-60. Those components that involve the non-linear behavior are subsequently redetermined by means of equation IX-60, inserting the first-approximation values for the other concentrations and, in part, for the concentration to be calculated. This is equivalent to assuming that equation IX-61 is capable of properly dividing the total absorbance among the individual compounds, so that it is only necessary to recalculate the concentration, the absorbance due to that compound being known.

Summary: $$[A] = [k°][c'] \qquad \text{(IX-61)}$$

Define the terms A_{ii} such that, for example,

$$A_{11} \equiv k_{11}°c_1' = A_1 - (k_{12}°c_2' + k_{13}°c_3' + \cdots)$$

Then

$$A_{11} = (k_{11} + d_{11}c_1')c_1''$$
$$A_{22} = (k_{22} + d_{22}c_2')c_2'' \qquad \text{(IX-62)}$$
$$\text{etc.}$$

If the interaction between compounds is too great to permit the equations IX-62 to converge rapidly, the system of linear equations could be solved again by matrix methods, setting

$$[A] = [k'][c''] \qquad \text{(IX-63)}$$

where $k_{ij}' = k_{ij} + d_{ij}c_j'$.

4.23   Non-additive Samples

If the absorbance of a mixture is not equal to the sum of the absorbance values of the separate components, whether or not these components follow Beer's law independently, analysis is not impossible but much greater care must be taken in finding a suitable procedure.   Certainly the first rule is to look hard for bands or experimental conditions for which the absorbances will be additive.

Deviations of this type are normally caused by chemical interactions, such as hydrogen bonding or other concentration-dependent chemical equilibria.   It may therefore be possible to avoid the difficulty by changing solvent, by changing concentration and path length, or by finding a band which is due to a part of the molecule unaffected by the chemical reaction. An isosbestic point (see section 5.1) will occasionally be suitable for avoiding changes in absorptivity due to changes in concentration.   Formation of a chemical derivative of the substance to be determined or separation of the mixture into non-interacting fractions may also be plausible in certain situations.   In any case the cause of the deviation should be determined, since otherwise the fluctuation may be due to an unsuspected variable that could make the results meaningless.   Only if such efforts fail should an analysis be attempted on non-additive bands.

Quite obviously it will not be easy to plot absorbance as a function of two or more independent concentrations.   If the deviations from additivity are small, it may be that fairly accurate values can be found by conventional procedures, assuming additivity, and correction curves may be plotted as a function of the concentration of one compound or as a sum of concentrations, whichever is more applicable in a particular situation [compare method (c) in section 4.22].

For some routine samples the total variation in concentration of one or more constituents may be relatively small.   The absorbances may then be approximately additive over this small range of concentrations.   Beer's law plots can be drawn for each component, assuming this approximate value of the concentration for the other compounds.   The incremental method (section 3.19) should be considered for such a system.   In other situations, even though no frequency can be found at which absorbance values will be additive, it may be possible to find bands that will vary to different extents.   In such a case simultaneous equations, in excess of the number of components, may provide a unique solution.

A particularly powerful technique for systems with strong concentration dependence is the differential titration procedure described by Jones, Clark, and Harrow.[1]   A circulating system connects a reference cell with

---

[1] Jones, Clark, and Harrow, *J. Assoc. Offic. Agri. Chemists*, **34**, 135 (1951).

a reservoir of solvent. The components of the solution are added, from burets, to the solvent reservoir until the differential spectrum between the sample and reference cells disappears at all points. The attainment of a balance between the two solutions will be greatly facilitated if it is possible to assign the absorption at certain frequencies to individual compounds (corresponding to an approximately diagonal matrix with variable absorptivity elements). Systems in which hydrogen bonding is important or, for example, a pH-sensitive compound in the presence of an absorbing weak acid, might be particularly amenable to this method. Even when severe overlapping of absorption bands is found, it should be possible to converge rapidly on the final solution by undertitrating (say by 10% or 50%) at each frequency in rotation.

5 Chemical Equilibrium

Absorption spectroscopy is ideally suited for determinations of the equilibrium point of chemical reactions, since the measurement need not disturb the system and it is often possible to determine, with one spectrum, the concentrations of two or more compounds participating in the reaction.[1]

For example, a keto-enol equilibrium may be followed in the infrared by observing the disappearance of the carbonyl and the appearance of the hydroxyl and $C\!\!=\!\!C$ or, more likely, the C—H adjacent to the double bond (especially evident in the low-frequency region). The disappearance of the ketone group will also be evident in the ultraviolet region. In the ultraviolet and visible regions equilibrium shifts of indicators and other dyes are often studied as the pH of the solution is varied. Especially relevant to measurements on indicators and complexes are the isosbestic point and the method of continuous variations.

5.1 Isosbestic Point

When only two compounds, which are in chemical equilibrium with each other, are responsible for all the absorption in a given region, it can be easily shown that there must exist at least one point in the spectrum at which the absorbance will be independent of the ratio of the two concentrations. If the bands do not overlap, this "point" will include the region

[1] This ability to determine concentrations on one or both sides of an equilibrium point is a necessary and sufficient condition for the application of the method to chemical titrations. For a discussion of these procedures see Meites and Thomas, ref. 37, sec. 8-13.

of zero absorptivity between them; if the bands do overlap and if the stoichiometry is one-to-one, the frequency will be that for which the absorptivities of the two species are equal (Fig. IX-15). This frequency, at which the absorbance is dependent only on the total number of "equivalents" of the two species, without regard to the equilibrium position of the

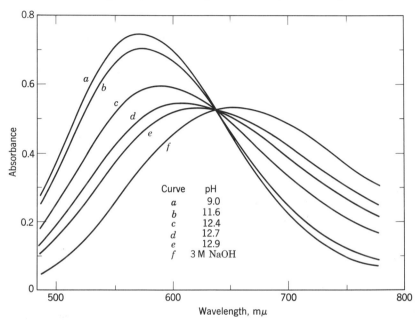

FIG. IX-15. Isosbestic point for copper triethylenetetramine. (Courtesy Joseph Steigman and David Gaskill.)

reaction between them, is called the isosbestic point (also sometimes isobestic).

The isosbestic point can be of assistance in both qualitative and quantitative analysis. The existence of such a point is not proof of the presence of only two compounds, since the third might very well have zero absorptivity at this particular frequency; but the absence of an isosbestic point is definite proof of the presence of a third constituent, if the possibility that the effect is caused by deviations from Beer's law for one form different from that for the other can be excluded. The isosbestic point provides, in one respect, a uniquely satisfactory frequency for quantitative determinations of the total amount of the two species present. The isosbestic point may also form a convenient reference point, or internal standard, to which the absorbance of one or the other of the species may be referred in order to find the ratio of the two compounds. In any particular case one must decide whether the advantages to be gained may not be offset by the disadvantages inherent in working on the sides of the absorption bands.

5.2   Continuous Variations

Two techniques which have been successfully applied in many studies of complex formation involve measurement of the absorbance of a solution as the ratio of two reactants is varied.

In the molar ratio method the concentration of one reactant is held fixed

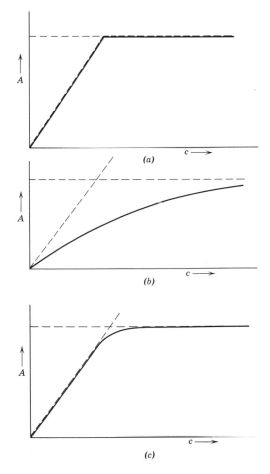

FIG. IX-16.   Molar ratio method.   (a) Dissociation constant very small.   (b) Dissociation constant very large.   (c) Intermediate stability.   Amount of one reagent is fixed; concentration of the other is plotted as the abscissa.   The intersection of the limiting slopes gives the stoichiometric concentration for formation of the complex.

and the concentration of the second is increased stepwise.   Assume that all the absorption at the given frequency setting is due to one compound, which is a product.   The initial absorbance will then be zero; as the second reactant is added, the absorbance will increase until eventually, at infinitely large concentration of the second compound, all the first compound will have reacted and the absorbance will have climbed to a value characteristic of the equivalent amount of product which has been formed. (If the absorption were due to a reactant present originally, the absorbance would drop from an initial high value to zero.)   The behavior of the plot of absorbance *vs.* concentration of the second compound may be approached from two limiting conditions.   If the equilibrium constant for the formation of the product were infinitely large, the final absorbance

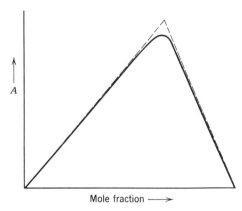

FIG. IX-17.   Job's method.   The sum of the molarities is kept constant.   The intersection of the limiting slopes gives the stoichiometric ratio in the complex and the deviation of the curve from this limiting absorbance is a measure of the dissociation constant.

value would be reached when just enough of the second compound had been added to react completely with the compound initially present.   The plot obtained would be two straight lines, as shown in Fig. IX-16*a*.   If the equilibrium constant were extremely small, on the other hand, the slope of the absorbance *vs.* concentration-added curve would be very small, as shown in Fig. IV-16*b*.   In a real case one may expect an intermediate situation, such as that of Fig. IX-16*c*.   The intersection of the extrapolated linear segments will indicate the equivalence point for the reaction, so that it is possible to distinguish, for example, between one-to-one and one-to-two complexes.   Furthermore, from the shape of the curve one can deduce at least an approximate value for the equilibrium constant.   In practice it may be more convenient to maintain the total amount (rather than concentration) of the first component constant as the second reactant, in reasonably concentrated form, is added; this will change the nature of the curve only slightly.

An alternative method of accomplishing the same ends, in a somewhat more accurate and time-consuming form, is the method of continuous variations due to Job.   In this case the sum of the molar concentrations of the two reactants is kept constant as their ratio is varied.   This will result in a curve such as that of Fig. IX-17, in which the abscissa of the extra-polated peak will correspond to the ratio present in the complex and the deviation of the curve at the apex will be an indication of the magnitude of the equilibrium, or dissociation, constant.

In either of these methods deviations from Beer's law will cause an error in the direction of a larger dissociation constant.   The effects may be separated by varying the path length and concentrations independently or by varying the total concentration of reactants for a given ratio of con-centrations.   The choice will depend in part on the suspected source of the deviation from Beer's law.

6   Chemical Kinetics

The application of spectroscopic techniques to problems of chemical kinetics has increased markedly over recent years and promises to con-tinue this expansion for some time to come.   Not only can measurements of the absorption (or emission) spectra as a function of time give quantita-tive analyses for several compounds which are participating in the reaction, but also the reaction mixture can often be left essentially undisturbed during the sampling, thus eliminating many of the problems inherent in taking aliquots or in establishing a large number of simultaneous reactions which may be stopped at various intervals.

The lower limit to the values of rate constants which can be determined spectroscopically is determined only by the patience of the operator, but the upper limit is still determined primarily by the instrumentation avail-able.   As a very rough estimate, one may consider an arbitrary limit of, say, 1 second per quantitative determination.   Assuming that at least four points are necessary to determine the rate constant, this will permit measurement of a half life as small as 4 or 5 seconds.   With special tech-niques and instrumentation, this limit can be pushed downward by many powers of 10.

Two distinct methods of carrying out the measurements of time-dependent concentrations may be mentioned.   The simpler of the two is to fix the monochromator at the frequency of the absorption band of one of the products or reactants and simply observe the transmittance or absorbance as a function of time.   This can be done either with a recorder or by repeated manual observations, although the former is generally considerably faster and more reliable.   The information obtained is limited to that of the single frequency—there is no check, for example, on whether extraneous reactions are occurring—but the method is inherently capable of following fast reactions.

By means of appropriately positioned microswitches on the frequency drive or recorder drum it is possible automatically to rescan repeatedly any desired portion of a spectrum.   Most commercial instruments are now equipped for this type of operation, either as a standard accessory or at small extra cost.   For kinetic studies which are suitably slow it may be desirable to follow the concentrations by means of repetitive scanning, since in this case one can obtain a check on the qualitative composition of the reaction mixture as well as the absorbance at a single frequency.

It is assumed above that the reaction can be carried out in an absorption cell positioned in the sample space of the spectrometer.   If this is not feasible, one may still follow the kinetics by periodic sampling of the reaction mixture, by following the evolution of a gas which is passed through an absorption cell, or by determining the qualitative composition of a reaction mixture where relative rates of two competitive reactions are to be determined.

Other topics that should be mentioned, although they will not be discussed here, include the studies of flames and explosions by following the emission from the hot gases, investigations of unstable and metastable electronic states by observations of fluorescence and phosphorescence, the detection of unstable chemical species present during chemical reactions or produced by electrical discharges, and the exploration of chemical reactions produced by the absorption of radiation.

7   Sample Preparation for Quantitative Analysis

General considerations involved in the preparation of samples for spectroscopic analysis have been presented in chapter IV, so that it is only necessary in this section to reiterate certain of the problems and pitfalls and indicate, where possible, the manner in which they can be avoided. The discussion will be limited to those cases in which the sample cannot be dissolved in a reasonably transparent solvent, since otherwise there is really no problem of sample preparation.

Liquids very seldom give trouble, since by their very nature they tend to mix with other liquids.   In some cases it may be possible to place the original liquid directly into the absorption cell, but often the uncertainty of cell thickness would be sufficiently great, percentage-wise, that it is preferable to add a diluent.   Although it is often not necessary to know the absolute thickness of a cell, most infrared cell-window materials are susceptible to erosion, with consequent change in cell thickness, and all extremely thin cells will be limited in utility by the problems of cleanliness of the surfaces and sample introduction and removal.

For purposes of qualitative identification, gases are easy to handle, although the techniques of handling a vacuum system are required.   In quantitative determinations special attention must be paid to the pressure of the gas, since pressure broadening may cause severe deviations from Beer's law.[1]   It is also necessary to reproduce slit widths accurately, since the intensities may be strongly dependent on spectral slit width.   In some routine analyses it may be sufficient to hold the total gas pressure constant, although this should be checked before attempting to prepare calibration curves.   Deviations may be expected to be greatest in gases which show strong intermolecular interaction.   Cells of 5 or 10 cm length are most common; for detecting very weak absorption or for picking up trace quantities longer-path-length cells, with mirrors for obtaining multiple traversals, are commercially available.

The real problems of quantitative analysis are the solids that cannot be put into a suitable solvent.   In the ultraviolet region the possibilities are very limited.   Reflection from the solid will give a characteristic spectrum which is closely related to the absorption spectrum.   The method of attenuated total reflection seems quite promising, especially since the intensity measured is independent of sample thickness.   Suspension in a pressed alkali halide pellet will give a more direct indication of the absorption spectrum, although the applicability for quantitative measurements is probably poorer in the ultraviolet than in the infrared.

Possibilities for sample preparation of solids in the infrared include examination in the form of a single crystal; mulling in mineral oil, perfluorokerosene, or other liquid; suspension of the solid in a liquid; or examination of a thin film prepared by sublimation onto the surface, casting from solution, or microtoming.   In addition, the reflectance and pressed pellet methods are applicable in the infrared as well as in the ultraviolet.

The most promising method has seemed to be the KBr pellet, for although it is comparatively time consuming it combines wide applicability to sample types with the possibility of accurately knowing the total amount of sample in the beam.   Somewhat reluctantly, however, it has been recognized by more and more spectroscopists that the technique tends to be non-reproducible.

[1] See Altschuller and Wartburg, *Appl. Spectroscopy* **15**, 67 (1961).

The absorbance observed for any non-homogeneous system, such as a pressed pellet containing an entrapped sample (as contrasted with a true solution) will depend not only on the concentration of sample in the pellet and the thickness of the pellet, but also quite strongly on the size of the sample particles. Variations in apparent absorptivity by a factor of 2 or more have been observed in controlled experiments. Mortar-and-pestle grinding, either manual or automatic, is the most convenient process for preparing the mixture to be pressed but is seldom adequate for reproducible quantitative results. Certain types of shakers are considerably more effective, although there seems to be considerable disagreement concerning their adequacy. At present it appears that the best procedure for preparing samples for quantitative determination in pressed pellets is freeze-drying. Results reported thus far on samples handled in this manner seem to indicate that, if one is willing to take the time and trouble to freeze-dry samples, the problem of particle size can be overcome.

The spectrum obtained from a sample in KBr is usually very nearly the same as that obtained from a Nujol mull or from a solution. True chemical reactions have been reported, but they seem to be rare. On the other hand, polymorphism induced by the pressing operation seems to be more common than had been suspected. In some cases, the changes are very slight, leading to small changes in frequency or to changes in relative band intensities. In other cases that have been reported, the spectra of two KBr pellets prepared in the same way from the same sample were so different that one would be forced to conclude that the substances were quite different.

The significant point to be kept in mind is not that the spectrum in KBr may differ from that in Nujol or in solution, for neither is inherently a "better" spectrum and such differences would be circumvented by the calibration procedure. The real difficulty lies in our lack of control over the pressing process at the microscopic level, which leads to the lack of reproducibility. In those cases where it is deemed necessary to make quantitative (or even qualitative) analyses in KBr pellets, this uncertainty should be kept in mind and as a minimum precaution the entire spectrum should be observed carefully for evidence of changes in sample due to the pressing operation.

It should be a warning to the neophyte spectroscopist that (with, of course, some important exceptions) the popularity of alkali halide pellets seems to vary inversely with the experience of the spectroscopist.

Of the alternative methods of preparation for solid samples, the most common is the Nujol mull. Although the mull shares the difficulties of sample polymorphism (even before grinding) with all other methods for scanning solids, and has the additional danger of sample orientation, very few cases of non-reproducibility of mull spectra, from equivalent samples, have been reported.   Since the method has been extensively employed for many years, this may be taken as an indication that sample transformations during the grinding process are not likely.   For quantitative determinations with mulls it is necessary to have an internal standard, since neither the sample concentration nor the mull thickness can be accurately known.   The chief requirements for an internal standard are a strong absorption band, so that low concentrations of the standard in the mixture will be adequate, and an absence of absorption bands that will interfere with the region of interest.   Chemical stability is also necessary, of course. Inorganic compounds, such as a pure chalk ($CaCO_3$), are among the more common choices.

Some solids which are insoluble in CS_2 or CCl_4 can be prepared in the form of suspensions in these liquids.   If such suspensions are put into a fixed-thickness cell a quantitative analysis can be carried out directly. Relatively little has been done with this technique, though it is not a new one.   Accuracy should be high, if the solid is sufficiently fine, since gravimetric determination of the amount of non-volatile sample in the suspension is possible.

In any of the procedures based on fine powders the restrictions on particle size discussed earlier are applicable.   In general, it seems that particle size should be comparable to the wavelength of the radiation, although larger particles are satisfactory if they can be uniformly produced and if they are bathed in a medium of comparable refractive index so that scattering is largely eliminated.   Contamination of samples by materials ground from the mortar and pestle has been reported, for shaker types as well as conventional styles, and seemingly with virtually every composition of mortar-and-pestle materials.

Many of the substances that are insoluble in transparent solvents are high-molecular-weight polymers which are soluble in other liquids.   In such a case it is often possible to cast a film of the material on a rock salt or fluorite crystal, glass, mercury, or other surface.   If it is possible to determine the thickness of the film, or to add an internal standard, such a film can be quite satisfactory for a quantitative analysis.   It is important that the film thickness be uniform; otherwise Beer's law will not be obeyed.

The best solution to the problem of examining the infrared spectra of solids would be the discovery of a polar liquid containing only heavy atoms, which would dissolve a large number of substances but would not have many interfering absorption bands.

8 Summary

Spectroscopic analyses are fundamentally of an empirical nature. Beer's law must be regarded as a limiting law that is satisfied rigorously only for infinitely dilute solutions or gases at low pressures with ideal instrumentation. It is not yet possible to calculate the absorptivity of any molecule to the accuracy with which it can be measured experimentally, but the observed value is itself so dependent on experimental conditions that without elaborate corrections it must be considered a mutual property of the compound and the spectrometer.

Accordingly, the analyst is not only justified in resorting to any procedure that can be shown to give accurate results, as determined by an independent method of analysis or synthesis, but he is also justified in employing any procedure only when it can be thus shown, by independent means, to be valid for the particular system under investigation. If it works, it is a good method, but that which is perfectly satisfactory for one sample may fail miserably for another. Only those analyses that have been carefully checked may be considered safe.

A few basic rules will help to increase the number of analyses that work. Although these rules have been implied or explicitly stated in the preceding discussion, they bear repeating.

1. Instrument conditions must be kept rigorously constant between the first measurement of the calibration procedure and the last measurement of an unknown based on that calibration. This does not mean, of course, that the knobs must be unmoved, but rather that the characteristic controlled by the knob must be maintained at the same level during operation on the series. In particular, the following should be held constant.

(a) *Slit widths*. The spectral slit width at each frequency must be unchanged throughout the analysis; barring any change in the monochromator optics, this means that the mechanical slit widths must be the same. In an instrument without automatic slit servo, this will be accomplished with only a minimum of attention, provided the operator resists the temptation to change slit widths in order to bring a particular band onto the scale or to expand the scale for an opaque sample. Instruments with automatic slit servomechanisms, and especially those in which the slit widths are dependent on reference signal, must be watched constantly. In these instruments the deterioration of components, including detector, source, optics, or vacuum tubes, may produce a change in slit width for a given setting of the slit-width control. Furthermore, since the change will generally be a function of frequency, it may often happen that an analysis initiated with one setting of the slit control for the entire region scanned may eventually require a different setting of that control for each frequency at which measurements are to be made.

(*b*) *Gain and response.*   In a single-beam instrument a change in gain may be corrected for by running an I_0 determination with each sample; in a double-beam spectrometer this is accomplished automatically.   The response or damping controls do not change the equilibrium position of the pen in either type of instrument, but in recording a spectrum the pen is seldom truly at equilibrium and hence changes in gain, response, or speed of scanning will change the observed absorbance.   These effects will be minimized by a densitometer.   For purposes of quantitative analysis it is preferable to operate without an automatic speed-suppression device, since their action is not sufficiently reproducible.

(*c*) *Frequency setting.*   Even more than slit settings, the frequency settings can cause marked changes in observed absorbance if they are not accurately reproduced.   Frequencies should always be approached from the same direction and with the same type of motivation, by hand or by motor, to avoid effects due to play or backlash in the mechanism.   *One should not assume that the absorption maxima, or the adjacent minima, represent reproducible reference points for setting the frequency!*   If the maximum appears to have shifted slightly during an analysis, one should be skeptical and investigate the possible causes; it is not safe simply to move to the maximum.

(*d*) *Other variables.*   Source characteristics, detector sensitivity, window transmittance, optical alignment, and electronic circuit performance can all produce measurable variations in absorbance readings.   In terms of the ultimate accuracy attainable, the difference between that achieved by the analyst who only occasionally operates a particular instrument and that achieved by a person who is constantly aware of the performance characteristics of the spectrometer and maintains them at a constant high level may well be more than a factor of 10.   The operator may be considered one of the most important variables in the analysis.

2. The effect of variations in slit widths may be minimized by keeping the spectral slit width narrow with respect to the band width or by making the spectral slit width large compared to the band width.   The latter would be more suitable in the case of isolated bands, and it can give substantially higher signal-to-noise ratio and therefore better accuracy than can be achieved with narrow slits.   Deviations from Beer's law may be more noticeable.   Measurement of band areas will generally lead to more accurate analyses than will determination of absorbance values at a single frequency.   Great care must be taken that the area is approximated

in a consistent fashion, since the portion of the total band area under the "wings" of the band may well be 10% or more.   Band areas are thus most meaningful for isolated bands.   Spectral slit widths are significantly larger in the ultraviolet than in the infrared region, ranging from about 15 cm^{-1} at 40,000 cm^{-1} (2500 Å) for very good commercial instruments to ten times this value or more.   In the infrared region it is possible with commercial instruments to operate in the vicinity of 1 cm^{-1} (or even lower with research-type grating instruments) spectral slit width, although 5 cm^{-1} is probably more common and with a rock salt prism in the 3000 cm^{-1} region the value will be very much larger.   Absorption bands are generally much narrower in the infrared region, however, so that the effects of spectral slit width are often more noticeable in the infrared than in the ultraviolet.

3. Deviations from Beer's law will be minimized by narrowing slits and by working with low concentrations.   Relatively reactive groupings, such as hydroxyl or amine groups, tend to show strong intermolecular interactions and should therefore be dissolved in as inert a solvent, at as low a concentration, as possible.   Because of this susceptibility to environment, infrared absorption bands arising from these groups are generally unsatisfactory for quantitative analysis.   Such effects are less common in the ultraviolet and visible regions, in part because much lower concentrations are feasible, but they are certainly not unknown.

4. Small temperature variations can cause shifts in the frequency passed by the monochromator.   The effect is especially important with CsBr and with NaCl and KBr prisms, less important for CaF$_2$ and LiF, and least important for glass, silica, and quartz.   The effect is largely overcome in commercial instruments by built-in temperature compensators which correct the angle of a mirror on the prism table with a bimetallic strip.   It is further reduced by thermostating the entire monochromator somewhat above room temperature.   In spite of these precautions the effect remains, probably due in part to the heating effect of the beam of radiation.   The uncertainty of frequency settings is important in preventing satisfactory quantitative measurements from being made on the sides of absorption bands.   Regardless of the instrument or the prism material, reproducible measurements of absorbance can be expected only if the rate of change of absorbance with frequency is small at the analytical frequency.

5. The concentration of the sample is important to the percentage accuracy.   The optimum range has been the subject of some controversy, but for each spectrometer there will be a range of transmittance or absorbance values for which the errors of measurement should be minimized.   There are reasons to expect that for infrared spectrometers this should be about 35 to 40% T, whereas for ultraviolet and visible instruments the best

choice should be nearer an absorbance of 1 or perhaps even 2. In optical-null spectrometers the uncertainty in the zero-energy level must be considered as well as the inherent uncertainty in measuring the transmittance. Expanded-scale methods can increase the accuracy of a determination if instrument conditions are simultaneously adjusted to improve the signal-to-noise ratio or if the original scale was too small to display the full accuracy built into the instrument.

6. Stray radiation must be eliminated or, if necessary, corrections for it must be made. Estimation of stray radiation is always subject to some uncertainty, so that it is much better to eliminate the stray by double-monochromator or double-pass design or by suitable filters.

7. Solid samples which cannot be put into solution must be ground very fine. Analyses on solids directly, either as mulls or in KBr pellets, should be avoided whenever possible. Gases must be analyzed under controlled pressures.

8. Regardless of the method of calculation, the calibration data should be plotted, generally in the form of absorbance *vs.* concentration, as a check on internal consistency of the values and of deviations from ideality. Before spending the time required for compilation of complete calibration curves, however, it is advisable to check a known mixture to be sure that the law of additivity is actually obeyed. Any analysis which is repeated over an extended period of time must be checked occasionally by means of known mixtures to guard against subtle changes in spectrometer performance, cell thickness, or other variables.

9. The sample must be protected from extraneous changes. For example, a change in the equilibrium constant of a complex can be expected when the sample compartment is warmed by the adjacent source housing; adsorption of solute onto the walls and windows of the absorption cells has been observed; the aromatic compounds reportedly form complexes with oxygen which show markedly different absorptivity values in the ultraviolet than do the pure hydrocarbons.

Problems

1. Show that, if y is known more accurately than x, so that deviations from the equation $y - ax + b$ are given by $\delta_i = x_i - (y_i - b)/a$, then the criterion to minimize the sum of the squares of the deviations is $a = \sum y_i'^2 / \sum x_i' y_i'$. The primed quantities refer to center-of-mass coordinates, $x_i' = x_i - \bar{x}$ and $y_i' = y_i - \bar{y}$. (Compare equation IX-19.)

2. Find the ratio of the absorptivities, a_1/a_2, for two species at their isosbestic point when the stoichiometry is

(a) 2 to 1   (b) n to m

3. Show that, for small values of the absorbance, A is proportional to $1 - T$. What is the proportionality constant?

4. The radiant power striking the detector of a spectrometer may be written

$$P = \int_{\nu_1}^{\nu_2} I F(\nu) \, d\nu = \int_{\nu_1}^{\nu_2} I_0(I/I_0) F(\nu) \, d\nu$$

where I is the intensity (or radiant power) passed by the sample at each frequency, $I = I(\nu)$; $I_0 = I_0(\nu)$ is the incident intensity; and $F(\nu)$ is (primarily) the exit slit function of the spectrometer. Assume that for a double-beam spectrometer with very wide $(\nu_2 - \nu_1 \gg \Delta\nu_{1/2})$ or very narrow $(\nu_2 - \nu_1 \ll \Delta\nu_{1/2})$ slits $I_0(\nu)$ and $F(\nu)$ may be replaced with constants over the band width or over the spectral slit width, respectively. Show that in the limit of small concentrations the slope of absorbance (or transmittance) against concentration will be constant for either wide slits or narrow slits. How does the slope depend on the spectral slit width, $\nu_2 - \nu_1$?

5. A certain spectrometer operates with an uncertainty in the transmittance of $\pm 0.5\%$. Find the percentage uncertainty in the concentration

(a) when the concentration has been adjusted to give about 37% T (0.43 absorbance)

(b) when the same concentration as in (a) is measured with the scale expanded to give 40% T equal to full scale

(c) when the concentration has been adjusted to give about 10% T (1.0 absorbance)

(d) when the same concentration as in (c) is measured with the scale expanded to give 11% T equal to full scale.

Calculate the percentage uncertainty in the concentration under the same conditions except that the uncertainty in the spectrometer is $\pm(0.001 \text{ absorbance} + 0.003\sqrt{T})$.

6. A mixture of o-, m-, and p-xylenes and ethylbenzene showed the following absorbance values:

σ (cm^{-1})	795.2	768.0	741.2	696.3
$A \times 10$	1.6608	0.0650	0.1213	0.2931

Assuming Beer's law to be valid for this solution and applying the values from Table IX-I, calculate the concentrations of these compounds,

(a) employing all four data

(b) employing only two of the four data and assuming only p-xylene and ethylbenzene to be present

(c) employing all four data to find the best value by the least-squares criterion, assuming only p-xylene and ethylbenzene to be present.

7. A solid sample is powdered and placed in the beam of a spectrometer, but examination with a microscope reveals that the coating is non-uniform.

(a) Plot the absorbance that would be observed against the true absorbance of the sample if 65% of the area were uniformly coated and the remaining 35% were completely clear.

(b) Plot the transmittance that would be observed against the true transmittance of the sample for the same conditions.

8. Find the integrated absorptivity, $\int a \, dv$, of the band (at 912 cm^{-1}) of styrene shown in Fig. VIII-24.   (Integrate between the arbitrary limits of 860 and 950 cm^{-1}.)   Compare with the value obtained from the peak absorptivity and half band width, $\int a \, dv = \frac{1}{2}\pi \hat{a} \, \Delta v_{\frac{1}{2}}$.

9. In the equation $y = ax + b$ there are two parameters, a and b.   Show by direct application of the least-squares condition that the best value of b is that which makes the straight line go through the center of mass of the points.

X

Principles of molecular spectroscopy

In earlier chapters the experimental aspects of spectroscopy—instrumentation, sample handling, and quantitative measurement—have been summarized and the principles underlying the absorption process have been briefly outlined and applied to the qualitative identification of compounds from their spectra. In the present chapter a more rigorous introduction to the theory is developed.

The intent in this chapter is not to give an exhaustive treatment of the theory of molecular spectroscopy as it is now understood. Monographs larger than this volume are available covering specialized areas of this topic. The purpose is rather to discuss some of the more important problems, such as the anharmonic oscillator, transitions from excited states, and the effects of statistical weights on intensities, and to introduce the broad assumptions and the nomenclature that will enable the reader to follow the meaning of the more advanced monographs and the current literature in the field.

I   Group Theory and Molecular Symmetry

Exact treatments of the states of molecules begin with an analysis of the symmetry properties of the molecule. The theorems by which these symmetry properties are utilized belong to a branch of mathematics known as the theory of groups. It is difficult to describe the extent to which group theory has permeated modern physical science; early quantum mechanics was largely expressed in the language of group theory and modern applications lean heavily upon symmetry properties; solid state physics and modern structural inorganic chemistry incorporate group theory in the form of crystal field theory; the electronic, vibrational, and rotational states of molecules are classified according to symmetry properties and the corresponding representations of group theory.

Fortunately the volume of literature on group theory has been growing rapidly over recent years.   In addition to the treatises written by and for mathematicians, several comprehensive discussions which emphasize the applications as well as the formalism are now available.   These works should be consulted for proofs of the results quoted here.

1.1 Symmetry Operations

A symmetry operation is any process, such as a rotation, that will transform a molecule into a form indistinguishable from its initial state.   It is convenient to assign arbitrary numbers to the equivalent atoms.   Then any operation that has only the effect of renumbering the atoms is a symmetry operation for that molecule.   The five types of symmetry operations are illustrated in Fig. X-1.

1.11   p-fold Rotation C_p

A rotation by an angle of $2\pi/p$, where p is an integer, is given the arbitrary symbol C_p.   If such a rotation is a symmetry operation of the molecule, the axis of rotation is said to be a p-fold axis of symmetry.

Water has a two-fold axis bisecting the H—O—H angle.   Ethylene has three mutually perpendicular two-fold axes, one passing through the two carbon atoms, one perpendicular to the plane of the molecule, and one perpendicular to the double bond in the plane of the molecule.   Benzene has a six-fold symmetry axis perpendicular to the plane of the molecule, three two-fold axes lying in the plane of the molecule and passing through opposing carbon atoms, and three two-fold axes lying in the plane and bisecting opposing carbon-carbon bonds.

All symmetry axes must pass through the center of mass of the molecule; if there is more than one symmetry axis they must all intersect at the center of mass.   For convenience, the axis of highest symmetry is conventionally taken as the z axis.   For water this is the two-fold axis, for benzene the six-fold axis.   When the choice is not unique, as in ethylene, it is necessary to state explicitly how the axes have been chosen.   (More elaborate rules for such molecules have been proposed[1] and should be followed whenever feasible, but it is still advisable to state how the axes have been assigned.)

[1] R. S. Mulliken, *J. Chem. Phys.* **23**, 1997 (1955).

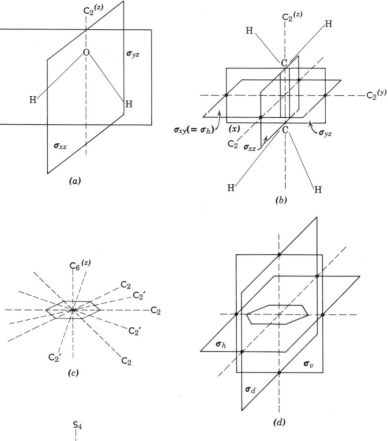

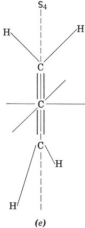

FIG. X-1. Symmetry operations. (a) Water has a two-fold axis and two mutually perpendicular planes of symmetry. (b) Ethylene has three mutually perpendicular two-fold axes and three mutually perpendicular planes. (c) In addition to the six-fold axis (which is also a two-fold and three-fold axis) benzene has $3C_2$ and $3C_2'$ axes. (d) The seven planes of symmetry in benzene are divided into one $\sigma_h(\sigma_{xy})$, three σ_v containing the C_2 axes, and three σ_d containing the C_2' axes. (e) Allene has an S_4 operation, which rotates the CH_2 groups by $2\pi/4$ about the vertical axis, then reflects them through the horizontal plane. Ethylene and benzene have a center of symmetry $i \equiv S_2$. Benzene has S_3 and S_6 axes (product of C_3 or C_6 with the σ_h).

1.12   Identity, **I**

A particular case of rotation is that by 0° or 360°. This leaves the molecule completely unchanged. Every molecule must have this operation, known as the identity operation, as a symmetry operation; it is included to meet certain requirements of group theory. The identity will be given the symbol **I** in this discussion. In much of the literature it is designated **E**, from the German *einheit*.

1.13   Reflection, **σ**

Another possible symmetry operation is that of reflection in a plane. For example, if the water molecule is reflected in a plane perpendicular to the plane of the molecule and bisecting the H—O—H angle, H_1 and H_2 will be interchanged. This achieves the same result as the two-fold rotation so far as the final positions of the atoms are concerned, but the configuration has been reached in a different way. (In a larger molecule, with the same symmetry elements, these operations would lead to distinguishable configurations.)

The plane of the water molecule is also, necessarily, a plane of symmetry. Each of these planes in water is designated σ_v, since they are "vertical" planes that include the z axis. A plane of symmetry perpendicular to the highest-fold axis of symmetry, such as the plane of the benzene molecule, is called a horizontal plane, designated σ_h. In some molecules there are two-fold axes perpendicular to the highest axis of symmetry. Any vertical planes that include one of these axes (and the highest axis) are designated σ_v planes, but any planes of symmetry that bisect the angle formed by the C_2 axes (and include the highest axis) are distinguished by the label σ_d. Sometimes the distinction between the σ_v planes and the σ_d planes becomes completely arbitrary, as in benzene.

1.14   Rotation-Reflection, S_p

In some molecules it is possible to reach an equivalent configuration by a rotation of $2\pi/p$ followed by a reflection in a plane *perpendicular to the axis of the rotation*. If there is a p-fold rotation axis and a plane of symmetry perpendicular to it, the rotation-reflection operation must necessarily be a symmetry operation, but some molecules which do not have the combination of axis and plane of symmetry do have a rotation-reflection axis of this type. For example, allene has a linear carbon chain with the CH_2 groups at opposite ends perpendicular to each other. A rotation by $2\pi/4$ is not a symmetry operation, nor is a reflection in a plane perpendicular to the axis of the molecule. The combination of these is a valid operation, designated S_4. Methane also has an S_4 axis which can be seen most easily by imagining the carbon chain of allene to be collapsed to a point. In general, if the rotation is by an angle of $2\pi/p$, the operation is called a p-fold rotation-reflection, or rotary-reflection, or improper rotation, and is designated S_p.

1.15 Inversion, i

A special case of the rotation reflection operation is the two fold axis, S_2. The net effect of this operation is to "reflect" each point through the origin, or to carry out the operation commonly known as inversion. Each point in the molecule not at the center of mass is carried along a straight line passing through the center of mass to an equal distance on the opposite side. The inversion operation is particularly helpful in classifying molecular configurations. It is given the symbol i. A pure reflection can be considered as a rotation-reflection of zero degrees. The S_p, σ, and i operations are called "improper rotations" in contrast to the "proper rotations," C_p and I.

These five types of operations, rotations, reflections, rotation-reflections, inversion, and the identity operation, are sufficient to take any configuration of a molecule into any equivalent configuration. In many cases, of course, only certain of these are required and appropriate.

1.2   Group Properties

Consider the four symbols, $\triangle$, $\square$, $\bigcirc$, and $*$. The "product" of any pair of them will be arbitrarily defined by a multiplication table, Table X-I. The collection of four symbols may be said to form a "group," for these quantities satisfy the following conditions.

TABLE X-I

	$\triangle$	$\square$	$\bigcirc$	$*$
$\triangle$	$\triangle$	$\square$	$\bigcirc$	$*$
$\square$	$\square$	$\triangle$	$*$	$\bigcirc$
$\bigcirc$	$\bigcirc$	$*$	$\triangle$	$\square$
$*$	$*$	$\bigcirc$	$\square$	$\triangle$

1. There is an "identity," I, such that $IX = XI = X$ for any member of the group, X.

2. The product of any two members of the group is a member of the group.

3. For each element, X, there is an element X^{-1}, which is also a member of the group, such that $XX^{-1} = X^{-1}X = I$.

4. The associative law of multiplication is obeyed.   If A, B, and C are any three members of the group, then $A(BC) = (AB)C$.

This particular group is "abelian," or "commutative," since for any two elements, A and B, $AB = BA$.

1.21   Symmetry Operations as Group Elements

Application of a symmetry operation to a molecule puts the molecule in a form equivalent to its original configuration, so that other symmetry operations may be subsequently applied.   Successive operation on a molecule with two symmetry elements is said to be identical with an operation by the "product" of these elements.   That is, if $\mathbf{C}_i$ and $\mathbf{C}_j$ are two symmetry operations which can operate on a molecule, M, then the product $\mathbf{C}_i\mathbf{C}_j$ is defined by the relation

$$(\mathbf{C}_i\mathbf{C}_j)M \equiv \mathbf{C}_i(\mathbf{C}_jM)$$

and the triple product, $\mathbf{C}_i\mathbf{C}_j\mathbf{C}_k$ is similarly defined by the statement

$$(\mathbf{C}_i\mathbf{C}_j\mathbf{C}_k)M \equiv \mathbf{C}_i[\mathbf{C}_j(\mathbf{C}_kM)]$$

The significance of the product is, however, independent of the object on which it will operate, so that multiplication tables may be constructed to show quickly the effect of successive operation with two or more elements.   For example, the symmetry elements of the water molecule are $\mathbf{I}$, $\mathbf{C}_2$, σ_v, σ_v'.   They obey the multiplication table in Table X-II.

TABLE X-II

	$\mathbf{I}$	$\mathbf{C}_2$	σ_v	σ_v'
$\mathbf{I}$	$\mathbf{I}$	$\mathbf{C}_2$	σ_v	σ_v'
$\mathbf{C}_2$	$\mathbf{C}_2$	$\mathbf{I}$	σ_v'	σ_v
σ_v	σ_v	σ_v'	$\mathbf{I}$	$\mathbf{C}_2$
σ_v'	σ_v'	σ_v	$\mathbf{C}_2$	$\mathbf{I}$

It is often convenient, when determining such a multiplication table, to set up a numbered model and see how the numbers are permuted.   A general model for these symmetry elements is a saw horse, as in Fig. X-2. It will be observed that the symmetry elements of the water molecule follow the same multiplication table as the four symbols of Table X-I. These are said to be different "realizations" of the same abstract group.

There are limitations on the number of symmetry operations that can be simultaneously applicable to any geometric figure.   The sets of elements that can occur together are called "point groups" (in each of them one point, the center of mass of the system, is left unmoved).   The designations of these point groups arise from the principal elements as follows.

1. If the only symmetry element is a C_p axis, the point group will be designated C_p.

2. If the point group contains a C_p axis and a vertical plane of symmetry, it must have p such vertical planes. If these are the only symmetry elements, the point group is called C_{pv}.

3. A C_p axis combined with a horizontal plane gives the point group C_{ph}.

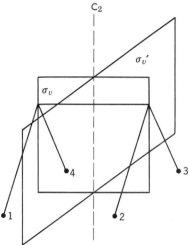

FIG. X-2.   Model for C_{2v} point group.

4. A particularly important combination of symmetry elements is a C_p axis with p two-fold axes perpendicular to the p-fold axis. (As in the case of planes of symmetry, the presence of one of these two-fold axes implies the presence of the others.) If these are the only elements, the point group is D_p (for dihedral). The dihedral groups of even p are sometimes called $V_{p/2}$ (for German *Vierergruppe*).

5. The addition of a horizontal plane of symmetry to a D_p group gives the point group D_{ph}. Other elements necessarily result.

6. The dihedral group D_p with p diagonal planes, σ_d, bisecting the angles between the p two-fold axes, produces the point group D_{pd}. These elements imply the presence of others, including the inversion operation, i (and, if p is even, a horizontal plane, σ_h, giving the group D_{ph}).

7. The point group S_p has only the symmetry operation S_p (and powers of this operation). This is possible only if p is even. If $p = 2$, the group is also called C_i.

The point groups discussed thus far, C_p, C_{pv}, C_{ph}, D_p, D_{ph}, D_{pd}, and S_p, can be constructed from an axis of symmetry plus two-fold axes perpendicular to it, combined with vertical and horizontal planes.   They are called the "axial" point groups and are the only groups of importance except for molecules with a single central atom, such as methane or SF_6.   The tetrahedral and octahedral (and icosahedral) point groups are characterized by more than one axis of symmetry higher than two-fold.   The following are called the "cubic" point groups.

8. Four three-fold axes, combined with three mutually perpendicular two-fold axes, produce the relatively unimportant tetrahedral group, T.

9. Addition of three planes of symmetry, containing the three mutually perpendicular two-fold axes, to the group T produces the point group T_h, which is also unimportant.

10. "Tetrahedral" molecules, such as methane, belong to the point group T_d, which may be constructed from the tetrahedral group, T, by the addition of mutually perpendicular planes of symmetry containing the

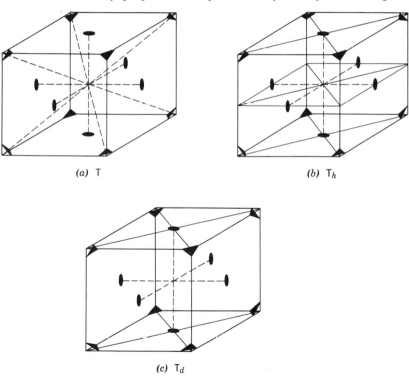

(a) T

(b) T_h

(c) T_d

FIG. X-3.   Tetrahedral point groups.   Only the "necessary" symmetry elements are shown; for the point groups T_h and T_d others arise as a consequence of these.   Also, dotted lines along three-fold axes have been omitted for clarity in these figures.

two-fold axes and the three-fold axes, or from the point group T_h by removing the plane of symmetry, σ_h, which does not contain any three-fold axis.   Figure X-3 shows the relationship between the groups T, T_d, and T_h.   Both the T_d and T_h groups have additional symmetry elements as a result of those listed.

11. Four three-fold axes, combined with three mutually perpendicular four-fold axes (taking the place of the two-fold axes of the group T), imply the presence of six additional two-fold axes.   This set of elements forms the unimportant octahedral group, O.

12. Figure X-4 shows the necessary symmetry elements of the octahedral group with a horizontal plane of symmetry, σ_h, added to produce the point group O_h.   This is the symmetry of a cube, of an octahedron,

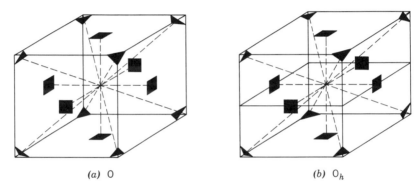

(a) O   (b) O_h

FIG. X-4.   Octahedral point groups.   Additional elements are implied by the presence of those shown.

and of XY_6 molecules in their most symmetrical arrangement (such as SF_6).   Additional planes of symmetry and rotation-reflection axes, including a center of symmetry, are necessary consequences of the $4C_3$, $3C_4$, and σ_h operations.

1.22 Stereographic Projection

A graphic method of representing a group of symmetry operations is called stereographic projection.   The axes and planes of symmetry are imagined fixed in space, their common intersection coinciding with the center of a sphere.   The intersections of the elements with the surface of the sphere are projected onto the equatorial plane.   This provides a unique and adequate description of the symmetry operations.

The following notation identifies the various elements in this system.

1. A plane of symmetry produces a continuous intersection and is there-

fore represented by a solid line.   If the system has a σ_h, the circumference of the circle will be a solid line; otherwise it is dotted.

2. The intersection of an axis of symmetry with the surface of the sphere is represented by a solid ellipse, triangle, square, or higher polygon as the axis is two-, three-, four-fold, or higher.   The z axis will be represented by such a symbol at the center of the circle; a two-fold axis perpendicular to the z axis will be represented by two such symbols along the circumference of the circle,[1] connected by a dotted line.

If the symmetry axis is neither along the z axis nor perpendicular to it, the projections of the intersections will fall within the circle.   In this case a dotted curve is added to indicate the projection, on the horizontal plane, of a great circle that passes through the intersections.   The great circle is drawn to intersect the horizontal plane along a line perpendicular to the projection of the axis.

3. A rotation-reflection axis is indicated by an open ellipse or polygon, at each intersection, connected by a dotted line.   A rotation axis cannot be indicated in the presence of a rotation-reflection axis of the same order, but its presence will be implied by the elements that are indicated.

Figures X-5 and X-6 give the stereographic projection representations of the most important finite point groups.   As an aid in following the significance of the symmetry elements, an arbitrary point that is not on any of the symmetry elements has been marked with an x.   The symmetry operations of the point group will take this point into each of the other points, x, also above the plane of projection, and into the points marked o below the plane.   For the axial point groups, all points will be equidistant from the plane; for the cubic groups a point x on the sphere will be carried into other points x, also above the equatorial plane but at other latitudes.   The projections of these points will accordingly fall at different distances from the center of the horizontal circle.   The points o, below the plane, will be the same distance from the plane of projection as the corresponding x points that appear at an equal distance from the center of the circle.   Either the symmetry elements (and only part of these are "necessary," as mentioned above) or the sets of equivalent points would be sufficient to define the respective point groups.

With the assistance of the stereographic projections or suitable models it is a simple matter to construct, for each point group, a multiplication table, such as Table X-II for the group C_{2v}.   By means of such a table it is possible to divide the elements uniquely into "classes," which will not be mixed by pre- and post-multiplication with other elements.   That is,

---

[1] All symmetry axes perpendicular to $C_p^{(z)}$ must lie in the same horizontal plane, which will include the center of mass of the system.

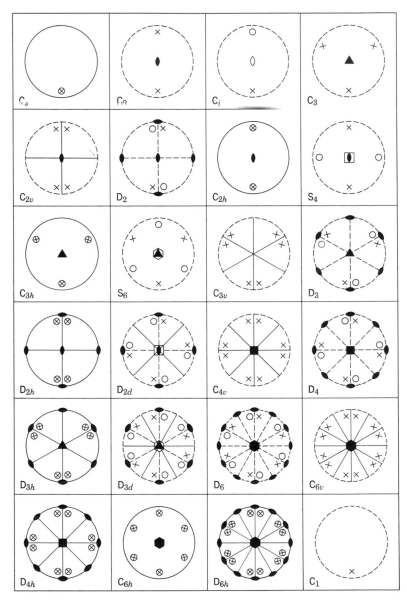

FIG. X-5.   Stereographic projections for some axial point groups.   The number of equivalent points, under the symmetry operations of the group, is equal to the order of the group (the number of symmetry elements).

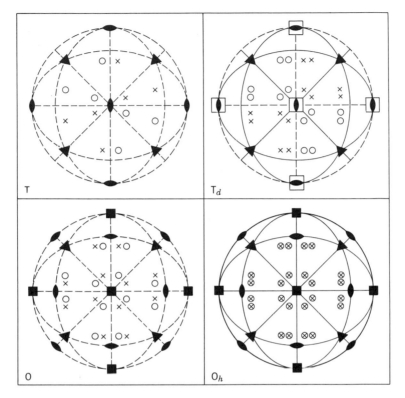

FIG. X-6. Stereographic projections for some cubic point groups. Points at equal distances from the center lie equal distances above or below the plane of the paper.

C_i and C_j are members of the same class if, and only if, $X C_i X^{-1} = C_j$, where X is another symmetry element of the group. (C_i and C_j are equivalent under a similarity transformation.)

1.3   Representations

A group is defined by its multiplication table, and the applications of group theory depend also on these multiplication properties.   It is possible to find certain simple quantities that will obey the same multiplication table as the elements of the group.   These quantities have been shown to have great utility.

Consider a trivial example.   If each of the four symbols of Table X-I is replaced by the number 1, the multiplication table will certainly still be obeyed.   The collection $+1$, $+1$, $+1$, $+1$ may be said to "represent" the abstract group of Table X-I (and Table X-II).   Three other "representations" can be found which consist only of the quantities $+1$ and -1. They are given in Table X-III, with the individual quantities listed under the elements they represent. The numbering of the representations, Γ_i, is at present to be considered completely arbitrary.

TABLE X-III

Group				
Elements:	I	C_2	σ_v	σ_v'
Γ_1	1	1	1	1
Γ_2	1	1	-1	-1
Γ_3	1	-1	1	-1
Γ_4	1	-1	-1	1

Actually there is an infinite number of representations for any group. Those given in Table X-III are particularly simple; it can be shown that all other representations can be written as combinations of these four. Since these are the simplest set they are called "irreducible representations." We shall later encounter representations that can be reduced.

Not all point groups have representations that are all as simple as those for C_{2v}. If there is a symmetry axis higher than a two-fold axis, one or more of the irreducible representations will consist of two-by-two matrices. If there is more than one non-coincident three-fold or higher axis, there will also be irreducible representations consisting of three-by-three matrices. The 1 and -1 may be considered one-dimensional matrices; all irreducible representations for the point groups then consist of matrices of dimensions 1, 2, or 3.

There are straightforward, if tedious, methods of constructing the irreducible representations of point groups. With just a little practice it is possible to write them down by inspection or with the assistance of models, but even this is unnecessary since they are given in many reference works. It is often convenient, however, to know how many of these representations there will be. This number is just equal to the number of different "types" of symmetry operations or, more specifically, just equal to the number of "classes" of elements or symmetry operations. Furthermore, the sum of the squares of the dimensions of the irreducible representations is just equal to the number of elements in the group.

An example of a point group containing two-dimensional representations is the group C_{3v}, appropriate to such molecules as ammonia, chloroform, and 1,1,1-trichloroethane. The symmetry operations are I, C_3, C_3^2, σ_v, σ_v', σ_v''; they form three classes and may thus be written

I, 2C$_3$, 3σ$_v$.   Since there are three classes, there must be three representations; and, in order that the sum of the squares of the dimensions of these should equal six (the number of elements), there must be one two-dimensional and two one-dimensional representations.

One set of irreducible representations for the point group C$_{3v}$ is given in Table X-IV.   In examining them it will be helpful to define six vectors which may be imagined to be attached to the hydrogen atoms of the ammonia molecule, as in Fig. X-7.   The unit vectors x_1, x_2, and x_3 lie in the

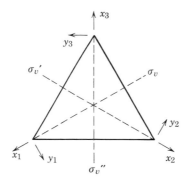

FIG. X-7.   Coordinate system for NH$_3$.   The x vectors should be collinear with the N—H bonds, the y vectors perpendicular to these, but for symmetry purposes the vectors may be taken as coplanar.

planes formed by the N—H bonds and the three-fold axis; the unit vectors y_1, y_2, and y_3 are perpendicular to these planes.   Linear combinations of these vectors can form the "basis" of a representation.

Consider the four coordinates defined as follows.

$$q_1 = (1\sqrt{3})(x_1 + x_2 + x_3)$$
$$q_2 = (1/\sqrt{3})(y_1 + y_2 + y_3)$$
$$q_3 = [(1 + i)/\sqrt{6}](x_1 + \omega x_2 + \omega^2 x_3)$$
$$q_4 = [-(1 + i)/\sqrt{6}](x_1 + \omega^2 x_2 + \omega x_3)$$

(X-1)

TABLE X-IV

Group Elements:	I	C$_3$	C$_3{}^2$	σ$_v$	σ$_v{}'$	σ$_v{}''$
Γ_1	1	1	1	1	1	1
Γ_2	1	1	1	-1	-1	-1
Γ_3	$\begin{bmatrix} 1 & 0 \\ 0 & 1 \end{bmatrix}$	$\begin{bmatrix} \omega^2 & 0 \\ 0 & \omega \end{bmatrix}$	$\begin{bmatrix} \omega & 0 \\ 0 & \omega^2 \end{bmatrix}$	$\begin{bmatrix} 0 & -1 \\ -1 & 0 \end{bmatrix}$	$\begin{bmatrix} 0 & -\omega^2 \\ -\omega & 0 \end{bmatrix}$	$\begin{bmatrix} 0 & -\omega \\ -\omega^2 & 0 \end{bmatrix}$

The quantity $(1 + i)/\sqrt{6}$ appearing in front of q_3 and q_4 is simply a normalizing factor of no immediate significance. The symbols ω and ω^2 represent two of the cube roots of 1.

$$\omega = -\tfrac{1}{2} + i\sqrt{3}/2$$
$$\omega^2 = -\tfrac{1}{2} - i\sqrt{3}/2$$

Any symmetry operation will simply interchange the vectors x_1, x_2, and x_3. This will leave q_1 unchanged; thus any symmetry element operating on q_1 has the effect of multiplying q_1 by $+1$. The rotations will similarly interchange the vectors y_1, y_2, and y_3; hence the effect of the rotations on q_2 will also be that of multiplication by $+1$. The reflections, however, will interchange the y vectors and change the sign of each, so that a reflection will be equivalent to multiplication of q_2 by -1. The reflection σ_v operating on q_3 gives $-q_4$, and the same reflection operating on q_4 gives $-q_3$. This is equivalent to multiplying the column matrix

$$\begin{bmatrix} q_3 \\ q_4 \end{bmatrix} \text{ by the square matrix } \begin{bmatrix} 0 & -1 \\ -1 & 0 \end{bmatrix}$$

as shown in Table X-IV. The rotations have the effect of multiplying q_3 and q_4 by ω or ω^2.

Neither the coordinates nor the matrices are unique, but the matrices are members of a family which are equivalent under a similarity transformation. That is, any other satisfactory representation can be found from these matrices by multiplying each matrix, **M**, of this representation by a transforming matrix, **H**, in the manner $\mathbf{HMH}^{-1}$. A specific example is the transformation by the matrix

$$\mathbf{H} = \begin{bmatrix} \dfrac{1-i}{2} & \dfrac{-(1-i)}{2} \\ \dfrac{1+i}{2} & \dfrac{1+i}{2} \end{bmatrix}$$

(Since this particular matrix is unitary, the inverse is equal to the transpose conjugate and can be written down by inspection.) The new coordinates,

$$\mathbf{H} \begin{bmatrix} q_3 \\ q_4 \end{bmatrix}$$

are

$$q_3' = (1/\sqrt{6})(2x_1 - x_2 - x_3) \tag{X-2}$$

and

$$q_4' = (1/\sqrt{2})(x_2 - x_3)$$

The new representation is

$$\begin{bmatrix} 1 & 0 \\ 0 & 1 \end{bmatrix} \begin{bmatrix} -\dfrac{1}{2} & -\dfrac{\sqrt{3}}{2} \\ \dfrac{\sqrt{3}}{2} & -\dfrac{1}{2} \end{bmatrix} \begin{bmatrix} -\dfrac{1}{2} & \dfrac{\sqrt{3}}{2} \\ -\dfrac{\sqrt{3}}{2} & -\dfrac{1}{2} \end{bmatrix}$$

$$\begin{bmatrix} 1 & 0 \\ 0 & -1 \end{bmatrix} \begin{bmatrix} -\dfrac{1}{2} & \dfrac{\sqrt{3}}{2} \\ \dfrac{\sqrt{3}}{2} & \dfrac{1}{2} \end{bmatrix} \begin{bmatrix} -\dfrac{1}{2} & -\dfrac{\sqrt{3}}{2} \\ -\dfrac{\sqrt{3}}{2} & \dfrac{1}{2} \end{bmatrix}$$

Although the two-dimensional representation is not uniquely determined, those properties that are invariant under a similarity transformation are fixed. Among them is the trace, or character (the sum of the diagonal elements). Since the trace of a one-dimensional representation is the entire representation, such representations are fixed. For many purposes it is adequate to know only the characters of the matrices of the higher-dimension representations. It is the characters that are most often tabulated. Since the character is the same for each member of a class, it is sufficient to enter each class only once.

1.4   Direct Products

The coordinate q_1 defined above may be said to transform under the symmetry operations of the point group C_{3v} according to the irreducible representation Γ_1. Similarly the coordinate q_2 and the pair of coordinates q_3 and q_4 transform according to the irreducible representations Γ_2 and Γ_3, respectively. In the literature of molecular spectroscopy these representations are often called "symmetry species." The symbols A_1, A_2, and E are given to the species Γ_1, Γ_2, and Γ_3.

If a function f transforms according to the species Γ_i (or a pair of functions, f_a and f_b, if Γ_i is two-dimensional) and another function g transforms according to the species Γ_j, it is possible to predict how the product fg [or $(c_a f_a + c_b f_b)g$] will transform under the symmetry operations of the group. It can be shown that the product of the functions will transform as the direct product[1] of the representations.

The direct product of two irreducible representations is also a representation of the group, although it may be a reducible representation. The direct product (or, more accurately, the characters of the direct product) can be obtained by taking the ordinary product of the characters of

[1] The direct product is defined in Appendix I, section 2.7.

the two representations, multiplying together the characters occurring in the same column (hence belonging to the same class). Thus, if $\chi_k{}^i$ is the character under the kth symmetry operation for the ith representation and $\chi_k{}^j$ is the character under the kth symmetry operation for the jth representation, then the character, under the kth symmetry operation, for the direct product of the ith and jth representations is the product $\chi_k{}^i\chi_k{}^j$. It must be remembered, however, for certain applications, that each character should appear as many times as there are members in that class.

The characters for the point group C_{3v} are shown in Table X-V. The direct products for these irreducible representations are given in Table X-VI. It should be clear that $A_1 \times \Gamma_i = \Gamma_i$, since the characters of any representation Γ_i are just multiplied by unity. Similarly the direct product $A_2 \times E$ must be E since the characters of the direct product are 1×2, $1 \times (-1)$, and -1×0. The direct product $E \times E$ gives the characters 4, 1, 0. Since these are not the characters of any one of the irreducible representations, the representation must be reducible. By inspection it can be seen that $A_1 + A_2 + E$ gives the desired characters.

TABLE X-V

C_{3v}	I	$2C_3$	$3\sigma_v$
A_1	1	1	1
A_2	1	1	-1
E	2	-1	0

There is a systematic way of reducing representations into their constituent irreducible representations. Let

χ_k = the character of the reducible representation corresponding to the class k, which contains h_k elements

$\chi_k{}^j$ = the character of the irreducible representation Γ_j corresponding to the class k

n_j = the number of times Γ_j should be added in to give the reducible representation

g = the number of elements in the group (the "order" of the group).

Then

$$n_j = \frac{1}{g}\sum_k h_k\chi_k{}^*\chi_k{}^j \qquad \text{(X-3)}$$

(If the characters are complex, the complex conjugate of χ_k is required, as indicated.) For example, the representation with the characters 4, 1, 0 contains the irreducible representation A_1 just once.

$$n_{A_1} = \tfrac{1}{6}[1(4)1 + 2(1)1 + 3(0)1] = 1$$

It contains the irreducible representations A_2 and E once apiece, also.

$$n_{A_2} = \tfrac{1}{6}[1(4)1 + 2(1)1 + 3(0)(-1)] = 1$$
$$n_E = \tfrac{1}{6}[1(4)2 + 2(1)(-1) + 3(0)0] = 1$$

Equation X-3 and the concept of direct products will find frequent application.

TABLE X-VI

	A_1	A_2	E
A_1	A_1	A_2	E
A_2	A_2	A_1	E
E	E	E	$(A_1 + A_2 + E)$

1.5   Designation of Species

The irreducible representations describe the symmetry properties of a function, or the way the function will transform under the symmetry elements of the group.   It has been found possible to summarize most of the necessary information in the symbol employed for the representation so that one need not constantly refer to character tables.   The notation is common to all the finite groups.   (The infinite groups $C_{\infty v}$ and $D_{\infty h}$ will be discussed in section X-2.21.)

The axis of highest symmetry is designated the z axis.   Any species that is symmetric with respect to this axis of rotation (that is, containing a $+1$ in this column) is labeled A.   If there is no rotational axis, all species are called A.

All symmetry species that are antisymmetric (containing a -1 in this column) to the highest-fold symmetry axis are labeled B.   Two-dimensional representations are neither symmetric nor antisymmetric to the highest axis; they are given the designation E.   These species correspond to doubly degenerate functions.   Three-dimensional species, which describe the triply degenerate functions associated with the cubic point groups, are given the symbol F, or sometimes T.

Further classification is generally necessary to distinguish between different species that have the same letter symbol.   If there is a center of symmetry (inversion operation), the subscripts g and u (for German *gerade* and *ungerade*, or even and odd) are added to the capital letter to indicate species that are symmetric or antisymmetric, respectively, to the center of symmetry.

When they are required, numerical subscripts, 1 or 2, are added to distinguish between states that are symmetric to a second axis of symmetry or antisymmetric to the second axis, respectively.   In the absence of a second axis of symmetry a rotation-reflection axis, $\mathbf{S}_p$ ($p > 2$), or sometimes a plane of reflection, will serve.   A final distinction can be made between states that are symmetric or antisymmetric with respect to a plane of symmetry by marking them ′ and ″.

These rules may be summarized as follows.

1. A indicates symmetry with respect to the principal axis.

2. B indicates antisymmetry with respect to the principal axis.

3. E indicates a two-dimensional representation (doubly degenerate state).

4. F indicates a three-dimensional representation (triply degenerate state).

5. Subscripts g and u indicate symmetry or antisymmetry with respect to a center of symmetry.

6. Subscripts 1 and 2 indicate symmetry or antisymmetry with respect to a rotation (or rotation-reflection) axis other than the principal axis, or in some point groups in which there is no second axis, with respect to a plane of symmetry.

7. Prime and double prime superscripts indicate symmetry or antisymmetry with respect to a plane of symmetry.

The order of these rules is significant.   Each designation is added only if the previous symbols fail to distinguish between all the irreducible representations of the point group.   The nomenclature is, of course, quite arbitrary and modifications are sometimes found.

One generally accepted variation that is important for the discussions to come arises for the point group D_2, consisting of the symmetry elements $\mathbf{I}$, $\mathbf{C}_2{}^z$, $\mathbf{C}_2{}^x$, $\mathbf{C}_2{}^y$.   Since there is no unique method of deciding which axis is the principal axis, the "normal" labels of A_1, A_2, B_1, B_2 are replaced by the symbols A_1, B_1, B_2, B_3.   For purposes of mapping this group onto another or for deducing direct products it will often be convenient to think in terms of the former set, although the latter terminology has become so well established that it should be followed.   The difficulty is carried over to the point group D_{2h}.

The convenience of the terminology just described is displayed, in part, by an analysis of the direct products of these representations.   The direct product of any two representations can generally be written down by inspection with the aid of the following rules.   The bases for these rules can be easily found by examination of the character tables.

1. The product of two A species will be an A species;
   the product of two B species will be an A species;
   the product of an A species with a B species will be a B species.

2. The product of two g species will be a g species;
   the product of two u species will be a g species;
   the product of a g and a u species will be a u species.
3. The product of two 1 species will be a 1 species;
   the product of two 2 species will be a 1 species;
   the product of a 1 species and a 2 species will be a 2 species.
4. The dimension of the direct product will be the product of the dimensions of the two irreducible representations (the dimensions are necessarily the same as the character under the identity operation).

If these rules break down as a consequence of variations in notation (as in D_2 and D_{2h} point groups, or when the subscripts are applied on the basis of two different criteria within the same group), equivalent rules can be constructed on the same principles or a table of direct products can be obtained by multiplying together the characters and reducing the representations by means of equation X-3.

1.6 Applications of Character Tables

Given some knowledge of group theory it is possible, for a given molecular model, (a) to determine the appropriate point group and therefore the possible symmetry species, (b) to assign each of the normal modes of vibration (or the approximate normal modes) to one of the symmetry species, (c) to determine the selection rules for transitions between the various electronic and vibrational states, and therefore (d) to predict the general appearance of the infrared and Raman spectra of the molecule. Some features of the ultraviolet spectrum can also be predicted. By comparison of the predicted spectra with those observed it is possible, for many molecules, to determine whether the original model had the same symmetry properties as the real molecule and thus to determine the true shape of the molecule.

1.61 Selection Rules

Selection rules have been discussed in earlier chapters in terms of (a) the classical model for resonance between the frequency of the exciting radiation and the frequency of the motion, (b) the quantum mechanical formula for the transition moment, and (c) the classical picture of oscillating dipoles or changing polarizabilities, involving the symmetry of the vibration. The selection rules based on the symmetries of the initial and final states can now be stated more precisely by employing the language of group theory.

The intensity of absorption or emission is proportional to the expression (section V-4.3)

$$\left| \int \Psi_f{}^* \mathbf{O} \Psi_i \, d\tau \right|^2$$

where Ψ_f and Ψ_i are the wave functions for the final and initial states, respectively, and $\mathbf{O}$ is the operator representing the mechanism (dipole moment, polarizability, quadrupole moment, etc.) responsible for the change of state of the molecule. Any symmetry operation must leave the molecule in a state indistinguishable from the original; it is equivalent to a renumbering of the atoms. Carrying out a symmetry operation can therefore have no effect[1] on the transition moment, $\int \Psi_f{}^* \mathbf{O} \Psi_i \, d\tau$. This requires that the product $\Psi_f \mathbf{O} \Psi_i$ transform according to the totally symmetric irreducible representation.

The ground vibrational state of any molecule is totally symmetric and the ground electronic state is totally symmetric for most common molecules. If the initial state is totally symmetric, the product $\Psi_f \mathbf{O}$ must be totally symmetric, or at least contain a totally symmetric component, in order for the transition moment to be unchanged by a symmetry operation. A necessary and sufficient condition for the direct product of two irreducible representations to contain the totally symmetric representation is that the two irreducible representations be identical. $\Gamma_i \times \Gamma_j$ can contain the totally symmetric representation only if $i = j$. Therefore transitions can occur from a symmetrical initial state only to those states that have the same symmetry properties as the transition operator, $\mathbf{O}$.

1.611 DIPOLE RADIATION

Transitions that occur as a consequence of a change in dipole moment are often said to absorb or give rise to "dipole radiation." (The radiation, or radiant energy, itself consists of photons that carry no memory of the mechanism for their origin.) The operator for emission or absorption of dipole radiation is the dipole moment operator (section V-4.3), which is a vector quantity and has the same symmetry properties as any other (polar) vector.

The transformation properties of a vector under any point group can be

---

[1] The transition probability is an experimentally observable quantity and must be independent of the coordinate system. Since $|\int \Psi_f{}^* \mathbf{O} \Psi_i \, d\tau|^2$ must be unchanged by a renumbering of particles, the integral $\int \Psi_f{}^* \mathbf{O} \Psi_i \, d\tau$ must be unchanged or at most change sign under the symmetry operation. But, if the integrand changes sign under a symmetry operation, it will have a value in one part of space equal and opposite to that in an equivalent portion of space. The integral over all space would then be zero. Hence the transition moment, $\int \Psi_f{}^* \mathbf{O} \Psi_i \, d\tau$, must be unchanged by a symmetry operation.

found in a general way.   Let a vector have the coordinates x, y, z, and arrange them in the form of a column matrix.   Then square matrices of dimension 3 can be found which will transform this vector in the same way as each of the symmetry operations.   If the operation is a pure rotation, by an angle ϕ about the z axis,[1] the corresponding matrix will be

$$\begin{bmatrix} \cos \phi & -\sin \phi & 0 \\ \sin \phi & \cos \phi & 0 \\ 0 & 0 & 1 \end{bmatrix}$$

and if the operation is a rotation-reflection, or a pure reflection, the corresponding matrix will be

$$\begin{bmatrix} \cos \phi & -\sin \phi & 0 \\ \sin \phi & \cos \phi & 0 \\ 0 & 0 & -1 \end{bmatrix}$$

The character for the transformation of a vector under each symmetry operation will therefore be

$$\chi_{\vec{M}} = \pm 1 + 2 \cos \phi \qquad \text{(X-4)}$$

The characters of the representation of a vector are calculated for the point group C_{3v} in Table X-VII.   Application of equation X-3 will reduce this representation into the sum $A_1 + E$.   Thus only transitions to states of symmetry A_1 and E can take place, by a dipole mechanism, in a molecule initially in a totally symmetric state of the point group C_{3v}.

TABLE X-VII

C_{3v}	I	$2C_3$	$3\sigma_v$
ϕ	0	120°	0
$2 \cos \phi$	2	−1	0
± 1	1	1	−1
$\chi_{\vec{M}}$	3	0	1

It is possible to be somewhat more specific than the last statement.   In Table X-VIII the transformation properties of the vector components x, y, z are given.   Thus rotation about the z axis of a vector directed along the z axis will not change this vector, nor will the vector be changed by reflection in either of the planes in which it lies.   The representation of the z component is clearly the totally symmetric representation.   Rotation by 120° will mix the x and y components as shown.   The characters of

[1] The assumption of the z axis as the axis of rotation is unnecessary but convenient. It will not affect the trace, which will be invariant under a rotation of coordinate axes.

TABLE X-VIII

C_{3v}	I	$2C_3$	$3\sigma_v$
z	z	z	z
x	x	$\left(-\dfrac{1}{2}x - \dfrac{\sqrt{3}}{2}y\right)$	x
y	y	$\left(\dfrac{\sqrt{3}}{2}x - \dfrac{1}{2}y\right)$	$-y$
χ_z	1	1	1
$\chi_{x,y}$	2	-1	0

this representation will be recognized as being identical with the characters of the E irreducible representation of the C_{3v} group. It is therefore possible to state that any transition from a totally symmetric state to another totally symmetric state under C_{3v} must be accompanied by a change in the dipole moment *along the z axis*; any transition from a totally symmetric state to a state of symmetry E must be accompanied by a change in dipole moment *perpendicular to the z axis* (in the x, y plane).

The selection rules for dipole radiation are included in the character tables of the point groups in Appendix III by placing the symbols T_x, T_y, T_z, or modifications of them alongside the appropriate symmetry species. The translations, which are also vector quantities, belong to these same species.

1.612   RAMAN EFFECT

Selection rules for Raman scattering are determined by finding the symmetry of the polarizability, α. Ordinarily it is convenient to represent the polarizability tensor by a square matrix,

$$\boldsymbol{\alpha} = \begin{bmatrix} \alpha_{xx} & \alpha_{xy} & \alpha_{xz} \\ \alpha_{yx} & \alpha_{yy} & \alpha_{yz} \\ \alpha_{zx} & \alpha_{zy} & \alpha_{zz} \end{bmatrix} \tag{X-5}$$

If the induced dipole moment, $\vec{\mu}$, and the impressed electromagnetic field, $\vec{\mathscr{E}}$, are then written as column matrices,

$$\vec{\mu} = \begin{bmatrix} \mu_x \\ \mu_y \\ \mu_z \end{bmatrix} \quad \text{and} \quad \vec{\mathscr{E}} = \begin{bmatrix} \mathscr{E}_x \\ \mathscr{E}_y \\ \mathscr{E}_z \end{bmatrix} \tag{X-6}$$

the equation $\vec{\mu} = \boldsymbol{\alpha}\vec{\mathscr{E}}$ takes the form

$$\begin{bmatrix} \mu_x \\ \mu_y \\ \mu_z \end{bmatrix} = \begin{bmatrix} \alpha_{xx} & \alpha_{xy} & \alpha_{xz} \\ \alpha_{yx} & \alpha_{yy} & \alpha_{yz} \\ \alpha_{zx} & \alpha_{zy} & \alpha_{zz} \end{bmatrix} \begin{bmatrix} \mathscr{E}_x \\ \mathscr{E}_y \\ \mathscr{E}_z \end{bmatrix} \tag{X-7}$$

The polarizability tensor, expressed in this form, is a symmetric matrix. That is, $\alpha_{xy} = \alpha_{yx}$; $\alpha_{xz} = \alpha_{zx}$; $\alpha_{yz} = \alpha_{zy}$. This is a consequence of the physical significance of the polarizability; it is essentially an expression of the fact that the polarizability along any given axis is independent of direction. In considering the transformation properties of α this limitation must be considered. There are only six independent components of the polarizability tensor and it is the behavior of these components, under a transformation of coordinates, that will be of interest. Finding this behavior will require two steps, or two distinct approaches to the transformation characteristics of α.

If $\vec{\mu} = \alpha\vec{\mathscr{E}}$ in a coordinate system x, y, z, then in another coordinate system, x', y' z', the corresponding equation will be $\vec{\mu}' = \alpha'\vec{\mathscr{E}}'$. The matrices of the second equation are related to those in the first by the equations

$$\vec{\mu}' = \mathbf{R}\vec{\mu}$$
$$\vec{\mathscr{E}}' = \mathbf{R}\vec{\mathscr{E}} \qquad \text{(X-8)}$$
$$\alpha' = \mathbf{R}^{-1}\alpha\mathbf{R}$$

where $\mathbf{R}$ is the transforming matrix, corresponding in the situations of interest to the proper or improper rotation associated with a symmetry operation. The transformation matrix has been given earlier,

$$\mathbf{R} = \begin{bmatrix} \cos\phi & -\sin\phi & 0 \\ \sin\phi & \cos\phi & 0 \\ 0 & 0 & \pm 1 \end{bmatrix} \qquad \text{(X-9)}$$

the plus sign to be taken for a proper rotation, the minus sign for an improper rotation.

The multiplication $\mathbf{R}^{-1}\alpha\mathbf{R}$ gives the matrix α' with the elements

$$\alpha_{11}' = \alpha_{xx}\cos^2\phi + 2\alpha_{xy}\cos\phi\sin\phi + \alpha_{yy}\sin^2\phi$$
$$\alpha_{12}' = \alpha_{21}' = -\alpha_{xx}\cos\phi\sin\phi + \alpha_{xy}(\cos^2\phi - \sin^2\phi) + \alpha_{yy}\cos\phi\sin\phi$$
$$\alpha_{13}' = \alpha_{31}' = \pm(\alpha_{xz}\cos\phi + \alpha_{yz}\sin\phi) \qquad \text{(X-10)}$$
$$\alpha_{22}' = \alpha_{xx}\sin^2\phi - 2\alpha_{xy}\cos\phi\sin\phi + \alpha_{yy}\cos^2\phi$$
$$\alpha_{23}' = \alpha_{32}' = \pm(-\alpha_{xz}\sin\phi + \alpha_{yz}\cos\phi)$$
$$\alpha_{33}' = \alpha_{zz}$$

It is the transformation properties of these six independent components of α that are important. The transformation given by equations X-8 and

X-10 may be rewritten in terms of a transforming matrix $\mathbf{T}$ and a column matrix, $\overline{\alpha}$, of the polarizability components as follows.

$$\overline{\alpha}' = \begin{bmatrix} \alpha_{xx}' \\ \alpha_{xy}' \\ \alpha_{xz}' \\ \alpha_{yy}' \\ \alpha_{yz}' \\ \alpha_{zz}' \end{bmatrix} = \mathbf{T}\overline{\alpha} =$$

$$\begin{bmatrix} \cos^2\phi & 2\cos\phi\sin\phi & 0 & \sin^2\phi & 0 & 0 \\ -\cos\phi\sin\phi & (\cos^2\phi - \sin^2\phi) & 0 & \cos\phi\sin\phi & 0 & 0 \\ 0 & 0 & \pm\cos\phi & 0 & \pm\sin\phi & 0 \\ \sin^2\phi & -2\cos\phi\sin\phi & 0 & \cos^2\phi & 0 & 0 \\ 0 & 0 & \mp\sin\phi & 0 & \pm\cos\phi & 0 \\ 0 & 0 & 0 & 0 & 0 & 1 \end{bmatrix} \begin{bmatrix} \alpha_{xx} \\ \alpha_{xy} \\ \alpha_{xz} \\ \alpha_{yy} \\ \alpha_{yz} \\ \alpha_{zz} \end{bmatrix}$$

$$\text{(X-11)}$$

(The matrix $\mathbf{T}$ can be written down by inspection of the equations X-10.) The trace of $\mathbf{T}$ is

$$\begin{aligned} \chi_\alpha &= 3\cos^2\phi - \sin^2\phi \pm 2\cos\phi + 1 \\ &= 2\cos\phi(\pm 1 + 2\cos\phi) \\ &= 2\cos\phi\chi_{\vec{M}} \end{aligned} \quad \text{(X-12)}$$

The transformation properties of the polarizability tensor, χ_a, under the point group C_{3v} are given in Table X-IX. This representation can be reduced, by application of equation X-3, to the sum $2A_1 + 2E$.

In Table X-IX, the characters χ_α are determined by multiplying $\chi_{\vec{M}}$ (from Table X-VII) by $2\cos\phi$. This provides the information that two components of α transform according to A_1 and two pairs of components transform according to E, but does not tell which ones. Multiplying together the appropriate rows of Table X-VIII gives the second section of Table X-IX, showing how the individual components xx, xy, etc., transform. By inspection these can be rearranged as shown in the third section of the table. Thus z^2 and $(x^2 + y^2)$ each transform according to A_1, and the other components, in the combinations shown, transform according to E.

TABLE X-IX

C_{3v}	I	$2C_3$	$3\sigma_v$
χ_α	6	0	2
xx	x^2	$\left(\frac{1}{4}x^2 + \frac{3}{4}y^2 + \frac{\sqrt{3}}{2}xy\right)$	x^2
yy	y^2	$\left(\frac{3}{4}x^2 + \frac{1}{4}y^2 - \frac{\sqrt{3}}{2}xy\right)$	y^2
zz	z^2	z^2	z^2
xy	xy	$\left(\frac{\sqrt{3}}{4}x^2 - \frac{\sqrt{3}}{4}y^2 - \frac{1}{2}xy\right)$	$-xy$
xz	xz	$\left(-\frac{1}{2}xz - \frac{\sqrt{3}}{2}yz\right)$	xz
yz	yz	$\left(\frac{\sqrt{3}}{2}xz - \frac{1}{2}yz\right)$	$-yz$
$[x^2+y^2]$	1	1	1
$[z^2]$	1	1	1
$\begin{bmatrix} xz \\ yz \end{bmatrix}$	$\begin{bmatrix} 1 & 0 \\ 0 & 1 \end{bmatrix}$	$\begin{bmatrix} -\frac{1}{2} & -\frac{\sqrt{3}}{2} \\ \frac{\sqrt{3}}{2} & -\frac{1}{2} \end{bmatrix}$	$\begin{bmatrix} 1 & 0 \\ 0 & -1 \end{bmatrix}$
$\begin{bmatrix} (x^2-y^2) \\ -2xy \end{bmatrix}$	$\begin{bmatrix} 1 & 0 \\ 0 & 1 \end{bmatrix}$	$\begin{bmatrix} -\frac{1}{2} & -\frac{\sqrt{3}}{2} \\ \frac{\sqrt{3}}{2} & -\frac{1}{2} \end{bmatrix}$	$\begin{bmatrix} 1 & 0 \\ 0 & -1 \end{bmatrix}$

1.613   OVERTONES AND COMBINATION BANDS

The wave function of a composite state, consisting of two independent states Ψ_j and Ψ_k, is the product of the two wave functions; $\Psi_f = \Psi_j\Psi_k$. This method of describing real states in terms of simpler states has many applications. The constituent states may describe, for example, two electrons, a molecular electronic state and a vibrational state, or two independent (normal) vibrational states. To find the selection rules for the transition $\Psi_i \rightarrow \Psi_f$, where Ψ_f and Ψ_i are composite states that may be written as a product of independent wave functions, is little more difficult than if the initial and final states are simple. The requirement is that the integrand (or some additive part of the integrand) shall transform as the totally symmetric representation of the point group of the molecule, and the transformation properties are determined by taking the direct products of the representations of the independent states involved.

This problem would not often arise if the customary idealizations were rigorously applicable. By the Born-Oppenheimer approximation the selection rules for an electronic transition should be independent of the vibrational states of the molecule and to the harmonic oscillator approximation the vibrational state will change by only one quantum in one vibrational mode. In practice, however, overtone and combination bands are observed in the vibrational spectrum and forbidden electronic transitions appear as a consequence of non-totally-symmetric vibrational states.

The product of any number of non-degenerate states will give a non-degenerate state; consequently the product of one-dimensional representations will be a one-dimensional representation and will be an irreducible representation. The product will have a degeneracy equal to the product of the degeneracies of the individual states, so that if two or more of the states are degenerate the resultant representation will not be an irreducible representation but can be reduced into a sum of irreducible representations. The resultant symmetries for multiple excitation of an A_1 vibration, an A_2 vibration, and a combination of E vibrations, in which no one of the E vibrations is multiply excited, are given in Table X-X. The last column gives the resultant states for multiple excitation of a single E vibration.

TABLE X-X

Vibration Quantum Number	Symmetry of Resultant State or States for Vibration of C_{3v} Symmetry			
	A_1	A_2	E[a]	E[b]
0	A_1	A_1	A_1	A_1
1	A_1	A_2	E	E
2	A_1	A_1	$A_1 + A_2 + E$	$A_1 + E$
3	A_1	A_2	$A_1 + A_2 + 3E$	$A_1 + A_2 + E$
4	A_1	A_1	$3A_1 + 3A_2 + 5E$	$A_1 + 2E$
5	A_1	A_2	$5A_1 + 5A_2 + 11E$	$A_1 + A_2 + 2E$

[a] Assuming no vibration occurs twice.
[b] One vibration multiply excited.

The cause for the marked difference between simultaneous excitation of two or more independent degenerate vibrations and multiple excitation of a single degenerate vibration will be apparent if the two component states of the degenerate level are explicitly considered. Let Ψ_{1a} and Ψ_{1b} be a pair of degenerate states and Ψ_{2a} and Ψ_{2b} be another pair of degener-

ate states.   (That is, Ψ_{1a} is a single state but has the same energy as Ψ_{1b}.)
The quantum numbers for excitation of these two degenerate vibrations
will be v_1 and v_2, respectively.   The first excited level for the first vibration,
$v_1 = 1$, can be realized in either of two ways, which can be written Ψ_{1a}
and Ψ_{1b} or $(v_{1a} = 1, v_{1b} = 0)$ and $(v_{1a} = 0, v_{1b} = 1)$.   The level in which
the two vibrations are each singly excited can be realized in four distinct
ways, $(\Psi_{1a}\Psi_{2a})$, $(\Psi_{1a}\Psi_{2b})$, $(\Psi_{1b}\Psi_{2a})$, and $(\Psi_{1b}\Psi_{2b})$, or $(v_{1a} = 1, v_{2a} = 1)$,
etc.   The multiple excitation of a single vibration, on the other hand, can
occur in only three ways, $(v_{1a} = 1, v_{1b} = 1)$, $(v_{1a} = 2)$, and $(v_{1b} = 2)$.

The degeneracy of an upper level of a doubly degenerate vibration varies
linearly, rather than exponentially, with the quantum number.   For a
given value of v_i $(v_i = v_{ia} + v_{ib})$, the degeneracy is $v_i + 1$.   For similar
reasons, the degeneracy of a level of a triply degenerate vibration with
quantum number v_j $(v_j = v_{ja} + v_{jb} + v_{jc})$ is $\frac{1}{2}(v_j + 1)(v_j + 2)$.

Two types of degeneracy appear in Table X-X.   Consider, for example,
the case of three independent doubly degenerate vibrations each singly
excited.   This gives states of symmetry A_1 and A_2 and three states of symmetry E.   To the harmonic oscillator approximation the level has an
eight-fold degeneracy.   Anharmonicity can split this degeneracy, as can
interactions with rotations or other perturbations arising solely within the
molecule.   Effects of this type cannot, however, split the degeneracies of
the individual E levels; they can be split only by a perturbation that lowers
the symmetry of the potential field of the molecule.   For the free molecule
a maximum of five closely spaced levels may arise, three of these sublevels
being doubly degenerate.

1.614   TRANSITIONS FROM NON-TOTALLY-SYMMETRIC STATES

In previous sections it has been assumed, for convenience, that the
initial state of the transition was totally symmetric.   Under these circumstances the condition for a transition to take place is that the final state
shall have the same symmetry as the operator causing the transition, or at
least some one component of the operator.   Transitions in the infrared or
ultraviolet can thus take place from a totally symmetric state only to a
state with symmetry corresponding to one or more of the three dipole
moment components; transitions in the Raman effect can occur from a
totally symmetric state only to a state with symmetry corresponding to
one or more of the polarizability components.

When the initial state is not totally symmetric, the selection rules are
found in the same manner except that the product of the initial and final
states must have the symmetry of one of the components of the appropriate
operator.   For example, dipole-induced transitions are possible for a C_{3v}
molecule between the pairs of states having the following symmetries:

$A_1 - A_1$, $A_1 - E$, $A_2 - A_2$, $A_2 - E$, $E - E$.   The dipole-moment components responsible for these transitions will be M_z, $M_{x,y}$, M_z, $M_{x,y}$, and M_z or $M_{x,y}$, respectively.

An important rule for infrared and Raman selection rules can now be deduced.   The dipole-moment components must change sign upon inversion, so that for any point group that includes the inversion operation the dipole-moment components must transform according to one of the u species (section 1.5).   The polarizability is independent of direction along any axis (or independent of "sense") and will be invariant to inversion. The polarizability components therefore transform according to g species. When a center of symmetry is present, every state is either g or u and the product of two states will be either g or u depending on whether the factor states are of the same type (g and g or u and u) or of opposite type (g and u). Taking the product of several wave functions will never lead to a mixture of g and u states.

It follows from the conditions above that a necessary (though not a sufficient) condition for infrared activity of a transition is that an odd number of odd (u) states must enter the transition moment; a necessary (but not sufficient) condition for Raman activity is that an even number of odd states must enter the transition moment.   This is the basis of the *Rule of Mutual Exclusion*: no vibrational transition that is active in the infrared can be active in the Raman; no vibrational transition that is active in the Raman can be active in the infrared.   It is thus impossible to have "coincidences" (vibrations of the same frequency) in the infrared spectrum and Raman spectrum except by accident when two different vibrations, of different symmetry, happen to have the same frequency. This rule applies *only* to molecules that have a center of symmetry.

1.62   Distribution of Vibrations

Symmetry properties of any vibrational mode can be determined by sketching the displacements and visualizing the effects of the symmetry operations.   If the vibrational displacements are unchanged by a symmetry operation the trace will be $+1$; if the vibrational modes are changed in phase by 180° the trace will be -1.   Degenerate pairs of vibrations will be mixed by most symmetry operations (but never by $\mathbf{I}$ or $\mathbf{i}$).   Their transformation properties will be described by matrices such as those shown in Table X-IV or in Table X-IX.

The total number of vibrations is $3N - 6$ for a non-linear molecule or $3N - 5$ for a linear molecule, but this tells nothing about the symmetries of the individual vibrations.   It is helpful, in writing down the normal modes, to know how many should fall into each irreducible representation. The distribution among symmetry species can be determined by finding the character of the representation for all vibrations, then reducing this to find the constituent irreducible representations.

It is necessary first to find the representation for rotations of the molecule. An infinitesimal rotation about the z axis can be represented by the differential of the vector product $\vec{x} \times \vec{y}$. (Finite rotations are not commutative and cannot be represented in this manner. See section V-3.2.)

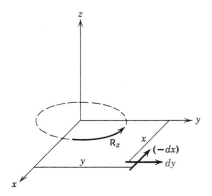

FIG. X-8.   Representation of an infinitesimal rotation. $(d\vec{R})_z = \mathbf{k} \cdot d(\vec{x} \times \vec{y}) = \mathbf{k} \cdot (\vec{x} \times d\vec{y} + d\vec{x} \times \vec{y}) = x\, dy - y\, dx$.

For a right-handed coordinate system, as shown in Fig. X-8, the components of any infinitesimal rotation may be written

$$(d\vec{R})_x = \mathbf{i} \cdot d(\vec{y} \times \vec{z}) = y\, dz - z\, dy$$
$$(d\vec{R})_y = \mathbf{j} \cdot d(\vec{z} \times \vec{x}) = z\, dx - x\, dz \qquad \text{(X-13)}$$
$$(d\vec{R})_z = \mathbf{k} \cdot d(\vec{x} \times \vec{y}) = x\, dy - y\, dx$$

Under a proper rotation about the z axis by an angle ϕ (finite) the components of the infinitesimal rotation will transform according to the matrix

$$\begin{bmatrix} \cos \phi & -\sin \phi & 0 \\ \sin \phi & \cos \phi & 0 \\ 0 & 0 & 1 \end{bmatrix}$$

which has the trace

$$\chi_{\vec{R}} = 1 + 2 \cos \phi \qquad \text{(X-14)}$$

Under an improper rotation the components will transform according to

$$\begin{bmatrix} -\cos \phi & \sin \phi & 0 \\ -\sin \phi & -\cos \phi & 0 \\ 0 & 0 & 1 \end{bmatrix}$$

which has the trace

$$\chi_{\vec{R}} = -(-1 + 2\cos\phi) \qquad (X\text{-}15)$$

Since $\chi_{\vec{M}} = \pm 1 + 2\cos\phi$, where the positive sign refers to a proper rotation,

$$\chi_{\vec{R}} = \pm\chi_{\vec{M}} \qquad (X\text{-}16)$$

with the same sign convention.

The total representation for the motions of N particles is found by writing the $3N$ coordinates, x_i, y_i, z_i where i takes on N values, as a column matrix, of dimension $3N$. Each symmetry operation will be expressed in the form of a square matrix of dimension $3N$. For the identity operation this will be the identity matrix, which is diagonal; for all other operations there must be off-diagonal elements that have the effect of interchanging certain atoms.

Consider two atoms, j and k, which are exchanged by the operation **C**. The pertinent portions of the matrices will appear as follows:

$$\mathbf{X'} = \mathbf{CX} = \begin{bmatrix} \cdots & \cdots & \cdots & \cdots \\ \cdots & \cdots & \cdots & \cdots \\ \cdots & 0\,0\,0 & x\,x\,x & \cdots \\ \cdots & 0\,0\,0 & x\,x\,x & \cdots \\ \cdots & 0\,0\,0 & x\,x\,x & \cdots \\ \cdots & x\,x\,x & 0\,0\,0 & \cdots \\ \cdots & x\,x\,x & 0\,0\,0 & \cdots \\ \cdots & x\,x\,x & 0\,0\,0 & \cdots \\ \cdots & \cdots & \cdots & \cdots \\ \cdots & \cdots & \cdots & \cdots \end{bmatrix} \begin{bmatrix} \cdot \\ \cdot \\ x_j \\ y_j \\ z_j \\ x_k \\ y_k \\ z_k \\ \cdot \\ \cdot \end{bmatrix} \qquad (X\text{-}17)$$

Any atom that is moved by the operation **C** will thus contribute nothing to the character of the corresponding matrix.

An atom that is left in place will, in general, undergo a transformation of coordinates due to the symmetry operation. The submatrix multiplying the coordinates of this atom will have the form, for the proper or improper rotation about the z axis,

$$\begin{bmatrix} \cos\phi & -\sin\phi & 0 \\ \sin\phi & \cos\phi & 0 \\ 0 & 0 & \pm 1 \end{bmatrix}$$

and will contribute to the character of **C** the quantity $\pm 1 + 2\cos\phi$.

Letting U be the total number of atoms in the molecule which are left in place by the operation **C**, the character of the representation of the coordinates of the atoms will be given by

$$\chi = U(\pm 1 + 2 \cos \phi) \qquad \text{(X-18)}$$

but this will include translations and rotations as well as true vibrations. The vibrational character is obtained by subtracting the sum of the translational and rotational characters, which were found above to be $\pm 1 + 2 \cos \phi \pm (\pm 1 + 2 \cos \phi)$, or $2(1 + 2 \cos \phi)$ for a proper rotation and zero for an improper rotation. The character of the representation of the true vibrations of any molecule will accordingly be given by

$$\chi_{\text{vib}} = (U - 2)(1 + 2 \cos \phi) \quad \text{for a proper rotation}$$

$$\text{(X-19)}$$

$$\chi_{\text{vib}} = U(-1 + 2 \cos \phi) \quad \text{for an improper rotation}$$

The problem may be treated in quite a different manner by considering the molecule to consist of bonds and bond angles. The transforming matrix will then operate on these. If a particular bond is left in place, it will contribute 1 to the trace of the transforming matrix; if it is not left in place, it will contribute nothing to the trace. Thus U_q, the number of coordinates of the type q left in place by the symmetry operation, will give directly the character of the representation of the vibrational motion in terms of these bond lengths and bond angles. This will, upon reduction with equation X-3, tell the number of vibrations involving a particular type of coordinate belonging to any particular irreducible representation. Some of them may turn out to be invalid vibrations if too many coordinates are included. The translations and rotations are automatically excluded in this method.

2   Electronic Spectra

Within the limits of the Born-Oppenheimer approximation, the total wave function is the product of the wave functions that describe the electronic, vibrational, and rotational[1] properties of the molecule.

$$\Psi = \Psi_{\text{el}} \Psi_{\text{vib}} \Psi_{\text{rot}} \qquad \text{(X-20)}$$

The total energy of the system is the sum of the energies attributed to the component states.

$$E = E_{\text{el}} + E_{\text{vib}} + E_{\text{rot}} \qquad \text{(X-21)}$$

[1] Additional factors should appear to account for smaller effects such as nuclear spin or quadrupole orientations.

These energy values are converted to term values, with dimensions of frequency or wavenumber, by dividing by Planck's constant or by hc. The frequencies absorbed are then the differences in these term values

$$\nu_{\mathrm{abs}} = E_f/h - E_i/h$$
$$= T_f - T_i \tag{X-22}$$

This is, of course, the fundamental equation proposed by Bohr. The individual term values, though they have the dimensions of frequency, do not necessarily correspond to any "real" frequency in either the classical or the quantum mechanical picture. Equation X-21, divided by Planck's constant, is written

$$T = T_e + G(\mathbf{v}) + F(\mathbf{J}) \tag{X-23}$$

Initial discussions in this chapter will retain the separation between electronic, vibrational, and rotational energy levels and transitions. In section X-5 the effects of superposition of vibrational transitions on electronic transitions and of rotational transitions on vibrational and electronic transitions will be considered.

2.1   Atoms

There seems to be no reason to believe that quantum mechanics, in essentially the form in which it is now known, is not adequate to explain in minute detail the structures of individual atoms and hence the nature of observed spectra.[1]   In spite of this, much of our present knowledge of atomic spectra must be regarded as semiempirical, simply because we have been unable to extract from the equations the information that is desired. This may be compared with the difficulty encountered in the more classical problem of a gas near its condensation point.   Although equations can be written that express the energy of an individual molecule and its interaction with a neighboring molecule, very limited progress has been made toward solution of these equations of motion to find the critical temperature in terms of known properties of the molecules.   Rather, the critical temperature must be determined experimentally.

2.11   Hydrogen Atom

The fundamental difficulty in the solution of the Schroedinger equation for atoms lies in the interaction potential between electrons.   This potential, given by Coulomb's law, can be put into the equations without

---

[1] Serious complications arise when one attempts to adapt quantum mechanics to the requirements of the theory of relativity.   The effect on atomic energy levels is sufficiently small that it may be neglected here.

difficulty, but it makes the equations insoluble. The equation for the
hydrogen atom contains no such electron-electron repulsion term and can
be solved exactly. The solutions are of particular importance since they
form the basis of many qualitative, as well as quantitative, discussions of
chemical structure.

The Schroedinger equation (section V-2.2) may be written

$$\sum_i - (\hbar^2/2m_i) \nabla_i^2 \Psi + v\Psi = E\Psi \tag{X-24}$$

The first term represents the sum of the kinetic energies of all particles
present. The mass of the proton is so much greater than that of the electron that the kinetic energy of the proton can be neglected without significant error. (Even this slight error can be eliminated by replacing the
mass of the electron by the reduced mass of the electron and proton.)
The second term represents the potential energy of the assembly,

$$v = \sum_{i>j} \frac{q_i q_j}{r_{ij}}$$

and the right-hand side represents the total energy. The appearance of
the equation is simplified if the unit of length is taken to be $\hbar^2/me^2$, the
unit of mass to be m (the mass of the electron), the unit of charge to be e
(the charge of the electron), and the unit of time to be $\hbar^3/me^4$. The constant $\hbar$ then has the value 1. These are called "atomic units." Equation X-24 for the hydrogen atom becomes

$$\nabla^2\psi + 2(E - v(r))\psi = 0 \tag{X-25}$$

with $v(r) = -1/r$. Since only the equilibrium states, or stationary states,
of the atom are sought, the time-dependence factor, $\exp(iEt/\hbar)$, has been
omitted from each term.

Expressed in polar coordinates, equation X-25 takes the form

$$\frac{1}{r^2} \frac{\partial}{\partial r} r^2 \frac{\partial}{\partial r} \psi + \frac{1}{r^2 \sin\theta} \frac{\partial}{\partial\theta} \sin\theta \frac{\partial}{\partial\theta} \psi + \frac{1}{r^2 \sin^2\theta} \frac{\partial^2}{\partial\phi^2} \psi + 2(E - v)\psi = 0$$

In this coordinate system r is the distance of the electron from the proton,
θ is the angle between the vector $\vec{r}$ and the z axis, and ϕ measures the angle
of rotation of $\vec{r}$ about the z axis (Fig. X-9).

From the nature of the physical problem it might be suspected that the
motions described by the three coordinates would be largely independent.
This suggests that a product of three functions,

$$\psi(r, \theta, \phi) = R(r) \, \Theta(\theta) \, \Phi(\phi) \tag{X-27}$$

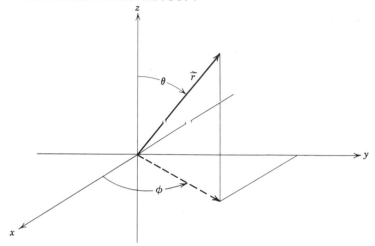

FIG. X-9. Spherical coordinates. Rotation about the vector $\vec{r}$ is described by the third of the Eulerian angles, χ.

be chosen as a trial solution. Substitution, followed by rearrangement of the terms, puts equation X-27 into the form

$$\Phi''/\Phi = -r^2 \sin^2 \theta \{R''/R + 2R'/Rr$$
$$+ 1/r^2 \sin \theta (\sin \theta \Theta''/\Theta + \cos \theta \Theta'/\Theta) + 2(\mathrm{E} - \mathrm{v})\} \quad \text{(X-28)}$$

The left-hand side depends only on the coordinate ϕ, whereas the right-hand side is independent of ϕ. This is possible only if each side is constant. It is convenient to call this constant $-\mathbf{m}^2$.

The equation in ϕ can now be solved:

$$\Phi''/\Phi = -\mathbf{m}^2$$

and therefore

$$\Phi = A \exp im\phi \quad \text{(X-29)}$$

The function Φ, since it depends only on ϕ, must repeat itself[1] after each full rotation. That is, $\Phi(\phi) = \Phi(\phi + 2\pi)$. This will be true if, and only if, $\mathbf{m}$ is an integer.

$$\mathbf{m} = 0, \quad \pm 1, \quad \pm 2, \ldots \quad \text{(X-30)}$$

The right-hand side of equation X-28 is also set equal to the constant $-\mathbf{m}^2$ and is then rearranged to give

$$\Theta''/\Theta + \sec \theta \Theta'/\Theta - \mathbf{m}^2/\sin^2 \theta = -\{r^2 R''/R + 2r R'/R + 2r^2(\mathrm{E} - \mathrm{v})\}$$
$$\text{(X-31)}$$

---

[1] For a more rigorous discussion, leading to the same results, see M. Leichter, *Am. J. Phys.* **27**, 281 (1959).

The left-hand side of equation X-31 is a function of θ only; the right-hand side is a function of r only, since the potential energy depends only on r. As before, each side must be constant. Calling the constant β and rearranging the equation in θ gives rise to the equation

$$\Theta'' + \sec\theta\,\Theta' + \left(\beta - \frac{\mathbf{m}^2}{\sin^2\theta}\right)\Theta = 0 \qquad (\text{X-32})$$

known as the "associated Legendre equation." (This reduces to the Legendre equation if $\mathbf{m}$ is set equal to zero.) The solutions to the associated Legendre equation are known to be power series of the form

$$\Theta(\theta) = \sin^{|\mathbf{m}|}\theta \sum_{\mu} \alpha_\mu \cos^\mu \theta \qquad (\text{X-33})$$

which terminates at some finite value of μ. It can be shown that the maximum value of μ is just $1 - |\mathbf{m}|$, where l is the quantum number of total angular momentum and $\mathbf{m}$, the quantum number appearing in the solution of the equation in $\Phi(\phi)$, is the projection of the angular momentum on the unique axis. The constant β is equal to $l(1 + 1)$.

From equation X-31 is obtained also an equation in $R(r)$ for which exact solutions are known. The form of the solutions will depend on the value of β, and thus on the value of l, since β appears as a constant in the separation of equation X-31.

It should be noted in particular that the solution of the Schroedinger equation for the hydrogen atom is conditional on the fact that the potential energy is a function only of r and not of θ or ϕ. If it should depend in any way on these other variables, it is unlikely that the equation could be separated or that an exact solution could be found.

The wave functions for the low-lying states of the hydrogen atom are given in Table X-XI. Of particular interest are the symmetry properties of these wave functions. The radial function, R, depends only on the variable r, which is the distance from the nucleus. This function is therefore totally symmetric.

The function Θ is the product of $\sin^{|\mathbf{m}|}\theta$ and a polynomial consisting of a power series in $\cos\theta$ that contains only even or only odd powers, depending on whether $1 - |\mathbf{m}|$ is even or odd. Under the inversion operation the variable θ goes over to $\pi - \theta$; $\sin\theta$ goes to $\sin\theta$ and $\cos\theta$ goes to $-\cos\theta$. The parity of Θ is therefore determined by the quantity $1 - |\mathbf{m}|$. If this is even, the function Θ is symmetric to inversion; if this is odd, Θ is antisymmetric to inversion.

Inversion takes the variable ϕ to $\pi + \phi$. The function $\Phi(\phi)$ goes over to $\Phi(\phi + \pi) = \Phi(\phi)\exp i\mathbf{m}\phi$. This is symmetric or antisymmetric with respect to the center of symmetry as $\mathbf{m}$ is even or odd. The total wave

TABLE X-XI

Wave Functions for the Hydrogen Atom

$$\psi_{1s} = \left(\frac{Z}{a_0}\right)^{3/2} e^{-\rho/2}/\sqrt{\pi}$$

$$\psi_{2s} = \left(\frac{Z}{a_0}\right)^{3/2} e^{-\rho/2}(2 - \rho)/4\sqrt{2\pi}$$

$$\psi_{2p(m=1)} = \left(\frac{Z}{a_0}\right)^{3/2} e^{-\rho/2}e^{i\phi}\rho/8\sqrt{\pi}$$

$$\psi_{2p(m=0)} = \left(\frac{Z}{a_0}\right)^{3/2} e^{-\rho/2}\rho \cos\theta/4\sqrt{2\pi}$$

$$\psi_{2p(m=-1)} = \left(\frac{Z}{a_0}\right)^{3/2} e^{-\rho/2}e^{-i\phi}\rho/8\sqrt{\pi}$$

$$\psi_{3s} = \left(\frac{Z}{a_0}\right)^{3/2} e^{-\rho/2}(6 - 6\rho + \rho^2)/18\sqrt{3\pi}$$

$$\psi_{3p(m=1)} = \left(\frac{Z}{a_0}\right)^{3/2} e^{-\rho/2}e^{i\phi}(4 - \rho)\rho \sin\theta/36\sqrt{\pi}$$

$$\psi_{3p(m=0)} = \left(\frac{Z}{a_0}\right)^{3/2} e^{-\rho/2}(4 - \rho)\rho \cos\theta/18\sqrt{2\pi}$$

$$\psi_{3p(m=-1)} = \left(\frac{Z}{a_0}\right)^{3/2} e^{-\rho/2}e^{-i\phi}(4 - \rho)\rho \sin\theta/36\sqrt{\pi}$$

$$\psi_{3d(m=2)} = \left(\frac{Z}{a_0}\right)^{3/2} e^{-\rho/2}e^{2i\phi}\rho^2 \sin^2\theta/72\sqrt{\pi}$$

$$\psi_{3d(m=1)} = \left(\frac{Z}{a_0}\right)^{3/2} e^{-\rho/2}e^{i\phi}\rho^2 \sin\theta \cos\theta/36\sqrt{\pi}$$

$$\psi_{3d(m=0)} = \left(\frac{Z}{a_0}\right)^{3/2} e^{-\rho/2}\rho^2 (3\cos^2\theta - 1)/36\sqrt{6\pi}$$

$$\rho \equiv \frac{2Z}{na_0} r$$

function, $\psi = R(r)\,\Theta(\theta)\,\Phi(\phi)$, will accordingly remain unchanged or will change sign upon inversion depending on whether the quantum number l is even or odd.   For s, d, g, ... orbitals the wave functions will be symmetric to inversion, whereas the wave functions for p, f, h, ... orbitals will be antisymmetric to inversion.

2.12   Heavier Atoms

The Schroedinger equation for an atom containing Z electrons can be written explicitly as follows.

$$\sum_{i=1}^{z} \frac{-\hbar^2}{2m} \nabla_i^2\psi - \sum_{i=1}^{z} \frac{Ze^2}{r_i} \psi + \sum_{i>j} \frac{e^2}{r_{ij}} \psi = E\psi \qquad \text{(X-34)}$$

The first term is the sum of the kinetic energies of the electrons, the second is the coulombic attraction between each electron and the nucleus, and the third is the repulsive energy between electrons. Additional terms—representing the relatively weak interactions between the electronic spin magnetic moment and the orbital magnetic moment, as well as spin-spin and nuclear quadrupole effects—are required for exact agreement with experiment.

Several methods for the approximate solution of equation X-34 have been developed. A very brief examination of the result of one of them, the perturbation method, on the helium atom will illustrate the nature of certain of the difficulties. In atomic units the Schroedinger equation for helium reduces to

$$\nabla_1^2 \psi + \nabla_2^2 \psi + 2\left(E + \frac{Z}{r_1} + \frac{Z}{r_2} - \frac{1}{r_{12}} \right)\psi = 0 \qquad \text{(X-35)}$$

with $Z = 2$. This is identical with the sum of two equivalent hydrogen atoms (equation X-25) except for the term $1/r_{12}$ and the value of Z. As a first approximation, therefore, the equation can be broken into two parts.

Let H represent the kinetic and potential energy operators in equation X-35. This equation can then be written

$$\text{H}\psi = \text{E}\psi \qquad \text{(X-35')}$$

Now let

$$\text{H} = \text{H}_0 + \text{H}_1 = \text{H}_0 + 1/r_{12} \qquad \text{(X-36)}$$

and

$$\text{H}_0\psi_0 = \text{E}_0\psi_0 \qquad \text{(X-37)}$$

In equation X-37 the wave function of the helium atom is assumed to be the product of the two hydrogen wave functions with Z set equal to 2. The energy, E_0, is accordingly $-Z^2$, or -4, as compared with the value $-\frac{1}{2}Z^2$, or $-\frac{1}{2}$, for a single electron in a hydrogen atom. This is expected to be too large, since the repulsive energy has been ignored.

With the approximate wave function, ψ_0, it is possible to calculate the repulsive energy of the two electrons, since ψ_0 describes the positions of the electrons and the repulsive energy depends on mutual positions. The value obtained is $5Z/8$, or $5/4$. To this approximation, then, the energy of the helium atom is -2.75. Subtracting the known energy for the ion He^+, $\frac{1}{2}Z^2$, gives a predicted ionization energy for He of 0.75 atomic unit. The observed value is 0.904.

Two major sources of error contribute to the discrepancy between calculated and observed values and make interpretation of the results somewhat uncertain. First, the calculated value of $5Z/8$ or $5/4$ must not be assumed to be the repulsive energy for the electrons, but rather an upper bound on this, because it is calculated for the wave function ψ_0. Clearly, ψ_0 will bring the two electrons much closer to the nucleus than they should be, since it does not take into account the repulsive energy that would tend to enlarge the orbits. The very quantity that is being sought forces an error in the calculation. The second difficulty, which is related to the first, has received the name "correlation energy." Imagine that an exact wave function could be written down for each electron. A calculation of the repulsive energy by standard methods would still give a value that is too large because these calculations employ an "average" electron position. In reality the electron repulsion will tend to make the two electrons occupy different regions of space at any given time, since this gives a minimum repulsive energy and thus a minimum energy for the system.

One of the most important consequences of the calculational difficulties encountered is that there is no way of determining the exact form of the true wave functions. Accurate values for the energy of the helium atom can be obtained (better, in fact, than the approximation implied by equation X-34), but the wave functions that give good values of the energy cannot be written in terms of integral values of the hydrogen atom quantum numbers.

The success of the extrapolation of hydrogenic orbitals to larger atoms in predicting the properties of the elements is well known. The Periodic Table is interpreted on the explicit assumption that electrons can be assigned to hydrogenic orbitals. On the other hand, it is known that the number of valid quantum numbers must be $4Z$ for an atom with Z electrons and among the valid quantum numbers must be total energy, total angular momentum, and projection of total angular momentum on the axis of an applied field; experimental evidence suggests that total orbital angular momentum and total spin angular momentum will also be good quantum numbers for light atoms. This leaves an insufficient supply of quantum numbers to assign **n**, **l**, **m**, and **s** to each electron. Furthermore, observed spectra show that the spin of an electron is not a valid quantum number for an electron in an atom as heavy as mercury.

The conclusions to be drawn from this conflicting evidence are essentially as follows. The *number of states* is determined by the number of valid quantum numbers and can therefore be found by assuming pure hydrogenic orbitals. The *energies* will change from those of the hydrogen atom, aside from the scale factor arising from larger nuclear charge, as the number of electrons is varied. In addition to the periodicity to be expected (Fig. VI-6) within each shell, the s subshells tend to become more stable than the corresponding p, d, and f shells as the size of the atom is increased. This leads to a cross-over in energy levels and to the transition metals and the rare earths. The *selection rules* are the most sensitive test of the validity of the assigned quantum numbers. Experimental intensities vary from strict conformance to the predicted rules, in hydrogen and helium, to only a very rough agreement with the hydrogenic rules in heavy atoms.

2.13 Pauli Exclusion Principle

For purposes of the *aufbau* principle it is sufficient to state the Pauli Exclusion Principle in the form "No two electrons can exist in the same state," where the state is determined by the four hydrogenic quantum numbers. A broader statement is necessary in many applications. For the electron, or for any other particle with half-integral spin, the total wave function must be antisymmetric with respect to the exchange of any two electrons (or other particles, as the case may be). This cannot be satisfied if the two electrons that are exchanged are in identical states; hence the first statement of the rule follows from the second.

The total orbital angular momentum of two electrons will be the vector sum of the orbital angular momenta of the individual electrons and can take any integral value between $l_1 + l_2$ and $|l_1 - l_2|$. The energy will be least for those states in which the electrons are in different orbitals and will depend slightly on the total angular momentum, but states will exist corresponding to all of these possible values of $\mathbf{L}$. For each of these states the value of the total spin may be restricted by the Pauli principle if the principal quantum numbers of the electrons are the same.

Consider the specific instance of two equivalent p electrons—that is, two electrons with $l = 1$ and the same value of $\mathbf{n}$. The possible values of $\mathbf{L}$ will be 0, 1, and 2, giving S, P, and D states, respectively. With two electrons the total spin is 1 or 0. In the absence of the exclusion principle, or if the values of $\mathbf{n}$ are different for the two electrons, the resultant states would be ${}^1S$, ${}^1P$, ${}^1D$, ${}^3S$, ${}^3P$, ${}^3D$, for a total of 36 states including the spin sublevels. For the equivalent p electrons only 15 of these, corresponding to the states ${}^1S$, ${}^3P$, and ${}^1D$, will exist.

The permissible states can be determined by assuming the hydrogenic quantum numbers are valid. In Table X-XII the possible values of $\mathbf{m}$ for each electron and the resultant values of $\mathbf{M_L}$ are given. The equivalent quantities for the spin moment are shown in Table X-XIII.

TABLE X-XII			
m_2 \ m_1	-1	0	1
-1	-2	-1	0
0	-1	0	1
1	0	1	2

TABLE X-XIII		
s_2 \ s_1	$-\frac{1}{2}$	$\frac{1}{2}$
$-\frac{1}{2}$	-1	0
$\frac{1}{2}$	0	1

The states appearing along the diagonals of the tables are clearly symmetric with respect to the two electrons. The off-diagonal terms are neither symmetric nor antisymmetric, but linear combinations can be found that will be symmetric and antisymmetric. For example, the four spin states may be written $(\frac{1}{2})(\frac{1}{2})$, $(-\frac{1}{2})(-\frac{1}{2})$, $(\frac{1}{2})(-\frac{1}{2}) + (-\frac{1}{2})(\frac{1}{2})$, and $(\frac{1}{2})(-\frac{1}{2}) - (-\frac{1}{2})(\frac{1}{2})$, the first three representing the three symmetric states (triplet), the last the antisymmetric (singlet) state. The numbers of symmetric and antisymmetric states and the M_L and M_S values corresponding to these are given in Table X-XIV.

TABLE X-XIV

Orbital Functions		Spin Functions	
Symmetric	Antisymmetric	Symmetric	Antisymmetric
2	1	1	0
1	0	0	
0	-1	-1	
0			
-1			
-2			

The D state must include states with $M_L = 2$ and $M_L = -2$; they are found only among the symmetric orbital states, from which it may be concluded that the D orbital function must be symmetric with respect to interchange of the two electrons. The five orbital functions of the D state, M_L equal to 2, 1, 0, -1, and -2, can be subtracted from the symmetric orbital functions. These five symmetric orbital functions must be combined with an antisymmetric spin function, hence the singlet spin state. The P state must include M_L values of 1, 0, and -1; only in the column of antisymmetric orbital functions are such values still available. The P state is thus antisymmetric to exchange and must be combined with the symmetric spin functions. The only remaining orbital state is the $M_L = 0$ state of the symmetric column, which can be combined only with the antisymmetric spin function. Thus the only possible states are ^1S, ^3P, and ^1D. The same conclusion can be reached by means of a table in which possible spin values are listed under the various m_l categories.[1]

2.14 Selection Rules

Two selection rules can be deduced without regard to the internal structure of an atom. They are accordingly valid for all free atoms (but may be violated if the atom is disturbed by external forces, as in a crystal

---

[1] See, for example, Herzberg, ref. 42, p. 134.

lattice). From the requirements of conservation of angular momentum, the absorption or emission of a photon must produce a change in the angular momentum of the atom of one unit ($\hbar$). This is a change by a unit vector and may cause a change by 0 or ± 1 in the magnitude of the total angular momentum if it was initially non-zero. Conservation of parity (valid in this type of experiment) requires that g states combine with u states: $g \leftrightarrow u$, $g \leftrightarrow\!\!\!\!\!\!\!| \; g$, $u \leftrightarrow\!\!\!\!\!\!\!| \; u$. This is LaPorte's rule.

The parity of the wave function for a single electron is even or odd as l is even or odd. For several electrons the wave function is the product of one-electron wave functions and the parity is even or odd as $\sum_i l_i$ is even or odd. (The one-electron functions in this product are not hydrogenic orbitals, but the parity is not changed by the internal coupling.) Closed shells are always symmetric to inversion so that only electrons outside of closed shells need be considered.

Other selection rules will depend on the structure of the atom and in particular on the extent of coupling between the electrons. In light atoms the interaction between the spin magnetic moment and the orbital moment is negligible. A total orbital angular momentum, $\mathbf{L}$, which is the vector sum of the orbital angular momenta of the individual electrons, can then be defined; similarly a total spin, $\mathbf{S}$, which is the resultant of the spins, is defined. The total angular momentum of the atom, $\vec{\mathbf{J}}$, is the resultant of the vectors $\vec{\mathbf{L}}$ and $\vec{\mathbf{S}}$. This is known as Russell-Saunders coupling.

For heavier atoms a better approximation may be the so-called "j-j coupling," in which the orbital and spin angular momenta of each electron are assumed to be coupled to form a resultant, $\vec{\mathbf{j}}$. The total angular momentum, $\vec{\mathbf{J}}$, is then the sum of the $\vec{\mathbf{j}}$ vectors for the individual electrons.

In a magnetic field the projection of the total angular momentum along the axis of the field will be quantized, leading to the restriction that $\Delta \mathbf{M_J} = 0, \pm 1$ (but $\mathbf{M_J} = 0 \leftrightarrow\!\!\!\!\!\!\!| \; \mathbf{M_J} = 0$ if $\Delta \mathbf{J} = 0$). In a strong field, however, the Russell-Saunders coupling of $\mathbf{L}$ and $\mathbf{S}$ may be destroyed; $\mathbf{L}$ and $\mathbf{S}$ each couple with the imposed magnetic field and the restrictions become $\Delta \mathbf{M_L} = 0, \pm 1$ and $\Delta \mathbf{M_S} = 0$. The quantum number $\mathbf{J}$ no longer has any real meaning. This is known as the Paschen-Back effect. In very strong fields the coupling between electrons may also be destroyed; then $\mathbf{L}$ and $\mathbf{S}$ lose significance and the selection rules become $\Delta \mathbf{m_l} = 0, \pm 1$ and $\Delta \mathbf{s} = 0$.

To the approximation of Russell-Saunders coupling, states differing only in multiplicity (spin quantum number) would seem to be degenerate, since the energy depends only on the orbital state. This degeneracy is removed by the coulombic interaction between the electrons, which gives rise to a splitting of the two levels (this has been called "Heisenberg resonance"). The true orbital functions will be linear combinations of the first-approximation functions; one will be symmetric, the other antisymmetric, with respect to interchange of electrons and they must accordingly have different spin functions in order that the total wave function will be antisymmetric in each case. This makes it appear as if the different spin values caused a difference in energies.

2.2   Diatomic Molecules

The high symmetry of diatomic molecules as compared with most polyatomic molecules, as well as the smaller number of nuclei and electrons, simplifies the problems greatly.   Much of the theory and terminology applied to polyatomic molecules is based on an extrapolation from diatomic molecules.

2.21   Symmetry

The axial symmetry of a diatomic molecule allows a factorization of the wave equation into a function dependent only on the angular position about the axis and a function dependent on position along the axis and radial distance away from the axis.   The first is the same as that found in solving the Schroedinger equation for the hydrogen atom (equation X-29). The wave function for an electron in a diatomic molecule is therefore

$$\psi = Z\Phi = Ze^{\pm i\lambda\phi} \tag{X-38}$$

where λ is an integer.   The functions with positive and negative exponents must have the same energy; thus all diatomic wave functions except those with $\lambda = 0$ must be doubly degenerate, unless this degeneracy can be split by an external perturbation or by interaction with some other form of angular momentum in the molecule that is not symmetric with respect to the axis. Z is a function of the other variables.

The wave function $\Phi(\phi)$ can serve as the basis for the representations of the point groups of diatomic molecules.   Consider first a heteronuclear molecule, such as HCl or CO.   Such molecules will have the symmetry operation **I** (the identity), a rotation by an arbitrary angle $\Delta\phi$, rotations by all multiples of this angle, and an infinite number of vertical planes of symmetry.

Let the pair of degenerate wave functions, $e^{i\lambda\phi}$ and $e^{-i\lambda\phi}$, be acted on by a symmetry operation, **C**, which includes a rotation by $\Delta\phi$ about the z axis. The effect must be to change the angle ϕ by the amount $\Delta\phi$.   Therefore,

$$\mathbf{C}\begin{bmatrix} e^{i\lambda\phi} \\ e^{-i\lambda\phi} \end{bmatrix} = \begin{bmatrix} e^{i\lambda(\phi+\Delta\phi)} \\ e^{-i\lambda(\phi+\Delta\phi)} \end{bmatrix} = \begin{bmatrix} e^{i\lambda\,\Delta\phi} & 0 \\ 0 & e^{-i\lambda\,\Delta\phi} \end{bmatrix}\begin{bmatrix} e^{i\lambda\phi} \\ e^{-i\lambda\phi} \end{bmatrix} \tag{X-39}$$

The trace of the operation **C** is $e^{i\lambda\,\Delta\phi} + e^{-i\lambda\,\Delta\phi} = 2\cos\lambda\,\Delta\phi$.

To find the trace of the reflection operators it is convenient to consider the special plane passing through the origin plane, such that $\phi = 0$ or π at any point in the plane. This operation changes ϕ to $-\phi$.

$$\sigma_v \begin{bmatrix} e^{i\lambda\phi} \\ e^{-i\lambda\phi} \end{bmatrix} = \begin{bmatrix} e^{-i\lambda\phi} \\ e^{i\lambda\phi} \end{bmatrix} = \begin{bmatrix} 0 & 1 \\ 1 & 0 \end{bmatrix} \begin{bmatrix} e^{i\lambda\phi} \\ e^{-i\lambda\phi} \end{bmatrix} \tag{X-40}$$

The character of this operation is zero; the character must therefore be zero for all members of the class and thus for all the reflections in vertical planes.

The exceptional functions are those with $\lambda = 0$. There must be two of them. Both are symmetric with respect to any rotation about the axis, but one is symmetric, the other antisymmetric, with respect to a reflection in a vertical plane. The characters for the group are shown in Table X-XV.

TABLE X-XV

λ	$C_{\infty v}$	I	$2C_{2\pi/\Delta\phi}^{(z)}$	$2C_{2\pi/2\Delta\phi}^{(z)}$	—	$\infty\sigma_v$
0	Σ^+	1	1	1	—	1
0	Σ^-	1	1	1	—	-1
1	Π	2	$2\cos\Delta\phi$	$2\cos 2\,\Delta\phi$	—	0
2	Δ	2	$2\cos 2\,\Delta\phi$	$2\cos 4\,\Delta\phi$	—	0
3	Φ	2	$2\cos 3\,\Delta\phi$	$2\cos 6\,\Delta\phi$	—	0

The direct products for this point group can be easily deduced from the condition that the degeneracy of the product is the product of the degeneracies, and from the trigonometric formula, applicable to the characters under the infinite-fold rotation,

$$\chi_1\chi_2 = \cos(\lambda_1\,\Delta\phi)\cos(\lambda_2\,\Delta\phi) = \cos[(\lambda_1 + \lambda_2)\,\Delta\phi] + \cos[(\lambda_1 - \lambda_2)\,\Delta\phi] \tag{X-41}$$

The direct products for the most important representations are given in Table X-XVI.

Homonuclear molecules, such as H_2, C_2, or O_2, have a center of symmetry, a horizontal plane of symmetry, an infinite number of two-fold rotational axes perpendicular to the plane, and an infinite number of rotation-reflection axes coincident with the infinite-fold rotational axis of the molecule. Any one of these added to the symmetry operations of the heteronuclear molecule would ensure the presence of all the others. It is convenient to consider the center of symmetry the important additional element. All functions will be either symmetric or antisymmetric with respect to the center of symmetry. Each representation is therefore split

TABLE X-XVI

$C_{\infty v}$	Σ^+	Σ^-	Π	Δ	Φ
Σ^+	Σ^+	Σ^-	Π	Δ	Φ
Σ^-	Σ^-	Σ^+	Π	Δ	Φ
Π	Π	Π	$(\Sigma^+, \Sigma^-, \Delta)$	(Π, Φ)	(Δ, Γ)
Δ	Δ	Δ	(Π, Φ)	$(\Sigma^+, \Sigma^-, \Gamma)$	(Π, H)
Φ	Φ	Φ	(Δ, Γ)	(Π, H)	(Σ^+, Σ^-, I)

Direct products for the point group $D_{\infty h}$ are obtained from the table by adding the appropriate g or u subscripts.   If the factors have the same parity, all terms of the product will be g; if different parity, all terms of the product will be u. The symbols H and I are meant to denote the representations corresponding to $\lambda = 5$ and $\lambda = 6$, respectively.   The Σ states are non-degenerate; all others are doubly degenerate.

into two, which are labeled g or u.   The designation of these two point groups as $C_{\infty v}$ and $D_{\infty h}$ follows from the rules discussed earlier.

2.22   Quantum Numbers

An electron moving in a circular path inclined to the direction of an electric field may be compared with the motion of a mass in a circular orbit inclined with respect to a gravitational field.   The electronic orbit will undergo a precessional motion about the direction of the field similar to the motion of the gyroscope.   The angular momentum vector will accordingly not be a constant, but the projection of this vector on the axis will be constant and an integral multiple of $\hbar$.

In addition to the orbital angular momentum of the electrons, there will be an angular momentum arising from the electron spin and an angular momentum arising from the rotation of the diatomic molecule in space. The orbital angular momentum can couple with the axis of the molecule, as discussed above, or couple with the spin or with the molecular rotation. Each of these possibilities has been considered by Hund in his treatment of the coupling rules for diatomic molecules.

2.221   HUND'S COUPLING RULES

The total orbital angular momentum will be designated $\mathbf{L}$, as in atoms, and the total spin angular momentum, $\mathbf{S}$.   The projections of these momenta on the internuclear axis are given the symbols $\mathbf{\Lambda}$ and $\mathbf{\Sigma}$, respectively.   The total angular momentum of the molecule is $\mathbf{J}$, and that portion of the angular momentum arising from the over-all molecular rotation will be indicated by $\mathbf{R}$.

In Hund's case (a), it is assumed that L is strongly coupled to the internuclear axis, giving a constant projection, Λ, on the axis. The projection of S is similarly defined; Σ is positive if it is in the same direction as Λ, negative if it is in the opposite direction. The total electronic angular momentum is then given the symbol $\vec{\Omega}$ and is the algebraic sum of Λ and Σ, directed necessarily along the axis. The molecular rotation, $\vec{R}$, is perpendicular to the axis, and therefore $\vec{J}$, the resultant of $\vec{\Omega}$ and $\vec{R}$, will in general form some acute angle with the internuclear axis. The axis of the molecule will precess about this constant vector $\vec{J}$, as shown in Fig. X-10. The highest precessional frequency is associated with the strongest coupling, in this instance that of L to the internuclear axis. The weaker coupling of S to the axis arises from the magnetic field due to the orbital motion. This causes a splitting into $2S + 1$ levels for any $\Lambda > 0$. (In an atom there are only $2L + 1$ levels if $0 \leqslant L \leqslant S$.)

Hund's case (b) arises when the coupling of S to the internuclear axis is very small, so that S may be ignored in the first approximation. A quantum number N may be defined from the vector sum of $\vec{\Lambda}$ and $\vec{R}$. This vector will couple weakly with S to give the total angular momentum vector $\vec{J}$. This weak interaction will give $2S + 1$ levels for $N > S$ or $2N + 1$ levels for $N < S$.

Heavier atoms show relatively strong spin-orbit coupling, leading to Hund's case (c). The vector sum of $\vec{L}$ and $\vec{S}$, $\vec{J}_a$, is coupled with the internuclear axis.[1] This projection, denoted by $\vec{\Omega}$, couples with $\vec{R}$ to give the total angular momentum $\vec{J}$.

In Hund's case (d), the orbital angular momentum, $\vec{L}$, is coupled directly to the rotational motion, $\vec{R}$, to give a resultant designated $\vec{N}$; compare case (b). The resultant of $\vec{N}$ and the spin gives the constant vector $\vec{J}$. If the coupling between $\vec{N}$ and $\vec{S}$ is extremely weak, $\vec{N}$ will be nearly constant (the precessional frequency of $\vec{N}$ and $\vec{S}$ about $\vec{J}$ will be very small). In this event $\vec{J}$ and $\vec{S}$ may be disregarded for many purposes. This is called case (d').

Hund's case (e) would occur if $\vec{L}$ and $\vec{S}$ were strongly coupled to give J_a [compare (c)], which in turn would be coupled directly to $\vec{R}$, rather than to the internuclear axis.

Each of these examples is to be considered a limiting form. Real molecules may not exactly fit any one of them or may correspond to different cases as one or another of the momenta varies in magnitude. The first two are the most important; the last one has not been observed. The coupling rules are summarized in Table X-XVII.

---

[1] In classical physics this would be the same as in case (a) since the projection of the sum is the sum of the projections. The distinction in quantum mechanics occurs because Λ and Σ must be integral in one case, but not necessarily in the other.

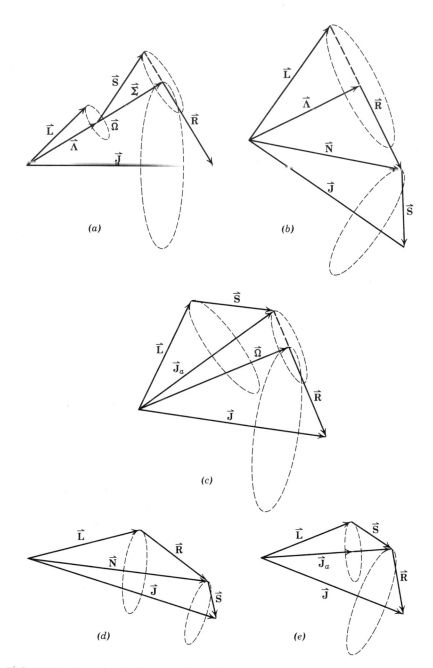

FIG. X-10. Hund's classification of coupled angular momenta. The total momentum, $\vec{J}$, is fixed in space and the rotation about $\vec{J}$ is relatively slow. The speed increases as the strength of the coupling is increased. For example, in case (c), **L** and **S** are tightly coupled, the coupling of $\mathbf{J}_a$ to the axis is weaker, and the coupling of Ω to **R** is weakest.

480

For singlet states the first three and the last two reduce to the equations

$$\vec{J} = \vec{\Lambda} + \vec{R} \quad \text{(cases a, b, c)}$$

and $\qquad\qquad\qquad\qquad\qquad\qquad\qquad\qquad\qquad$ (X-42)

$$\vec{J} = \vec{L} + \vec{R} \quad \text{(cases d, e)}$$

respectively. If $\mathbf{L} = 0$ a similar simplication results, giving

$$\vec{J} = \vec{\Sigma} + \vec{R} \quad \text{(cases a, c)}$$
$$\vec{J} = \vec{S} + \vec{R} \quad \text{(cases b, d, e)}$$

$\qquad\qquad\qquad\qquad\qquad\qquad\qquad\qquad\qquad$ (X-43)

TABLE X-XVII

Hund's Case	Equations
(a)	$\Omega = \lvert \Lambda + \Sigma \rvert$ $\vec{J} = \vec{\Omega} + \vec{R}$
(b)	$\vec{N} = \vec{\Lambda} + \vec{R}$ $\vec{J} = \vec{N} + \vec{S}$
(c)	$\Omega = (\vec{L} + \vec{S}) \cdot \vec{z} \equiv \vec{J}_a \cdot \vec{z}$ $\vec{J} = \vec{\Omega} + \vec{R}$
(d)	$N = \vec{L} + \vec{R}$ $\vec{J} = \vec{N} + \vec{S}$
(e)	$\vec{J}_a = \vec{L} + \vec{S}$ $\vec{J} = \vec{J}_a + \vec{R}$

2.222 TERM SYMBOLS

Designations of states of diatomic molecules must depend, to some extent, on the coupling rules followed by the molecule. If Λ is defined, the state is given a term symbol based on the value of Λ in the same way that the term symbols of atoms depend on the value of $\mathbf{L}$. Thus, if $\Lambda = 0, 1, 2, 3, \ldots$, the states are designated, respectively, $\Sigma, \Pi, \Delta, \Phi, \ldots$. These states may be correlated with the representations of the point groups $C_{\infty v}$ and $D_{\infty h}$ and, in fact, they provide the symbols for the irreducible representations of these point groups. The Σ states, and representations, are designated Σ^+ or Σ^- to indicate the symmetry or antisymmetry with respect to the σ_v planes.

The multiplicity is added to the term symbol as a left superscript, as for atoms. The parity forms a right subscript for homonuclear molecules. The value of the total angular momentum, $\mathbf{J}$, will depend on the rotational angular momentum, $\mathbf{R}$. In general, the molecules will be distributed among many values of $\mathbf{R}$, and hence also of $\mathbf{J}$, so they are not included in the term symbol. The value of Ω is added as a right subscript when this represents additional information.

When the coupling between $\mathbf{L}$ and $\mathbf{S}$ is sufficiently strong that neither is well defined, it may be necessary to designate the states by the value of Ω. The numerical value of Ω becomes the primary symbol; to this may be added the right subscript to show the parity of the wave function (for homonuclear molecules only) and, for the non-degenerate states ($\Omega = 0$), a right superscript showing symmetry with respect to the vertical planes of symmetry. Half-integral, as well as integral, values are possible, since the spin may be half integral. Typical symbols would be $0_g{}^+$, $\frac{1}{2}_u$, and 1_u.

2.223 SELECTION RULES

According to the selection rules for the point groups $C_{\infty v}$ and $D_{\infty h}$, dipole transitions can only occur, from the totally symmetric $\Sigma_g{}^+$ ground state, to states of symmetry $\Sigma_u{}^+$ or Π_u (where subscripts are to be ignored for $C_{\infty v}$). From the direct products of these groups this can be restated as three rules. Transitions between non-degenerate levels must obey the restriction $+ \leftrightarrow +$, $- \leftrightarrow -$, $+ \nleftrightarrow -$. For all transitions, the condition $g \leftrightarrow u$, $g \nleftrightarrow g$, $u \nleftrightarrow u$ will apply. Also $\Sigma \leftrightarrow \Sigma$, $\Pi \leftrightarrow \Pi$, $\Delta \leftrightarrow \Delta$, $\Phi \leftrightarrow \Phi$ and $\Sigma \leftrightarrow \Pi$, $\Pi \leftrightarrow \Delta$, $\Delta \leftrightarrow \Phi$, but $\Sigma \nleftrightarrow \Delta$, $\Pi \nleftrightarrow \Phi$. The second of these rules is LaPorte's rule, the third may be recognized as the condition that the projection of angular momentum along the axis of the molecule can change by zero or $\pm$ one unit.

The selection rule $\Delta \mathbf{J} = 0$, ± 1, $\mathbf{J} = 0 \nleftrightarrow \mathbf{J} = 0$, must apply to diatomic molecules in order that total angular momentum will be conserved. Since this includes changes in the quantum number of molecular rotations, it is important in the pure rotational or rotation-vibrational spectrum as well as in the rotational structure of electronic transitions.

Many of the selection rules will depend on the coupling within the molecule. For example, $\Delta \Lambda = 0$, ± 1 when Λ is defined; when Λ is not defined, the equivalent restriction will be $\Delta \Omega = 0$, ± 1. When the spin quantum numbers are defined, these will be unchanged; $\Delta \mathbf{S} = 0$ or $\Delta \Sigma = 0$. If the initial and final states follow different coupling rules, only those conditions applicable to both will apply. Within any spectral band it is possible that the coupling may change with increasing values of the rotational quantum number $\mathbf{R}$. This tends to cause a shift from case (a) to case (b) for both states.

2.23 Detailed Description of States

It would be desirable to be able to characterize uniquely the state of every electron in a molecule and to know what part the electron might play in the

chemical binding.   More realistically, we know that the individual electrons are indistinguishable and that the electrons will strongly interact,
so that the electronic state must be characterized by a set of orthogonal
wave functions involving the coordinates of more than one electron.
Even this would be satisfactory, but such information is not yet available
to us and probably will not be in the forseeable future, except possibly for
relatively simple molecules.   It is therefore necessary to resort to partial
and approximate descriptions.

The two basic approximations underlying most discussions of the electronic structure of diatomic molecules are the following.   It is assumed
that the hydrogen atom quantum numbers are meaningful in first approximation, so that it is possible to describe the orbitals in molecules as roughly
equivalent to one or a combination of two (but not ten or a hundred)
hydrogenic orbitals.   It is also assumed that the actual orbitals will
resemble the orbitals of the hydrogen molecule and the hydrogen molecule
ion or, for inner electrons, the hydrogen atom.   The projection of the
electronic orbital angular momentum on the internuclear axis is designated
λ.   The orbitals are called σ, π, or δ as λ is 0, 1, or 2.

2.231   MAPPING OF ORBITALS

In any procedure in which molecules are to be constructed from atoms,
the problem arises of mapping atomic orbitals into molecular orbitals and
atomic states into molecular states.   In Fig. X-11 the possible projections

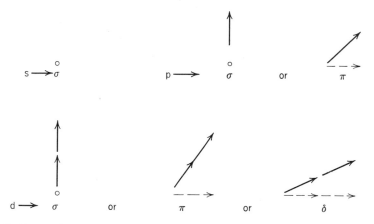

FIG. X-11.   Projection of s, p, or d orbitals onto an axis can give rise to σ, π, or δ
orbitals as shown.

of s, p, and d orbitals onto an axis are shown.   The atomic s orbital can
give rise only to σ orbitals, the atomic p orbital can give either σ or π

orbitals.   A "molecular" state can be ascribed to an atom on the basis of a similar projection of the atomic total orbital angular momentum onto the axis as shown in Table X-XVIII.

TABLE X-XVIII

Atomic Orbitals	"Molecular" Orbitals	Atomic States	"Molecular" States
s	σ_g	S_g	Σ^+
		S_u	Σ^-
p	$\sigma_u + \pi_u$	P_g	$\Sigma^- + \Pi$
		P_u	$\Sigma^+ + \Pi$
d	$\sigma_g + \pi_g + \delta_g$	D_g	$\Sigma^+ + \Pi + \Delta$
		D_u	$\Sigma^- + \Pi + \Delta$

The molecular states that can be created by the joining of two atoms, each of which is in one of the "molecular" states obtained by projecting the atomic angular momentum onto the internuclear axis, can be determined by finding the direct product of the representations of the two "molecular" states.   For example, an atomic S_g state gives only a Σ^+ state; two atoms initially in S_g states must form a Σ^+ molecular state.   An atomic P_u state, however, can give either a Σ^+ or a Π state, and the combination of one of these with the Σ^+ state from an atomic S_g state gives the possibility either of Σ^+ or Π as the resultant molecular state.   The number of states (including degeneracies) possible for the molecule will be the product of the degeneracies of the two atomic states.   For example, atomic P and D states (degeneracies of 3 and 5) will give 15 possible molecular states.

$$S_g + S_g = \Sigma^+ \times \Sigma^+ = \Sigma^+$$
$$S_g + P_u = \Sigma^+ \times \{\Sigma^+ + \Pi\} = \Sigma^+ + \Pi$$
$$P_g + D_g = \{\Sigma^- + \Pi\} \times \{\Sigma^+ + \Pi + \Delta\} \qquad \text{(X-44)}$$
$$= (\Sigma^- \times \Sigma^+) + (\Sigma^- \times \Pi) + (\Sigma^- \times \Delta) + (\Pi \times \Sigma^+)$$
$$+ (\Pi \times \Pi) + (\Pi \times \Delta)$$
$$= (\Sigma^-) + (\Pi) + (\Delta) + (\Pi) + (\Sigma^+ + \Sigma^- + \Delta)$$
$$+ (\Pi + \Phi)$$
$$= \Sigma^+ + 2\Sigma^- + 3\Pi + 2\Delta + \Phi$$

If the nuclei are identical, a degeneracy appears between states that differ only in the exchange of states between atoms.   That is, the state achieved by bringing together atom A in state 1 and atom B in state 2 must have an identical energy with the state achieved by combining atom A in state 2 with atom B in state 1.   These resultant states may be considered to mix and split apart, forming two sets of states, one even and one odd. For example, if atom A is in an S_g state and atom B in a P_g state, the possible resultant states will be Σ_g^-, Π_g, Σ_u^-, and Π_u.   These are the same states that would be possible if atom A were in the P_g state and atom B in the S_g state; hence the total number of states is not different from the case of unlike atoms [in this case, four states, two Σ^- and two Π, from $S_g(A)$ + $P_g(B)$ and $S_g(B)$ + $P_g(A)$].   This must be true since small changes in the nature of the nuclei cannot produce abrupt changes in the number of states.   If the atoms are in equivalent states (same symmetry and same energy), the mixing described above cannot take place and the available states will simply be divided between g and u states.

Each of the states found by taking the direct products of the equivalent atomic states can occur with $2S_A + 1$ different multiplicities, where S_A is the total spin quantum number of one of the atoms and $S_A \leqslant S_B$, the spin quantum number of the other atom.   Each of these $2S_A + 1$ multiplets, with multiplicities varying in integral steps from $S_B - S_A$ to $S_B + S_A$, will consist of a number, equal to the multiplicity, of nearly coinciding energy levels.   Each multiplet will be considered a single energy level and state unless otherwise specified.

The total number of states, including the splitting into levels of different multiplicities, can be readily calculated by multiplying together the total number of states associated with each of the atomic states, and multiplying this, in turn, by the number of possible multiplicities, $2S_A + 1$. For example, two atoms, one of which is in a ^3P state and the other in a ^2P state, will give a total of 9 states excluding spin, but 18 if multiplicities are included (but still counting a $^3\Sigma^+$ state, for example, as one state). The Pauli Exclusion Principle will not affect this total number, but it will have a profound influence on the relative energy values of the states by limiting the number of states belonging to any given shell (that is, with a given $\mathbf{n}$, assuming this has at least approximate validity as a quantum number).

For example, two equivalent p electrons ($\mathbf{n}_1 = \mathbf{n}_2$, $\mathbf{l}_1 = \mathbf{l}_2 = 1$) in a π orbital ($\lambda = 1$) will have the same value of $\mathbf{n}$ and $\mathbf{l}$ and must therefore differ in $\mathbf{m_l}$ or in $\mathbf{m_s}$.   (Even if these are not the proper quantum numbers, they must yield the proper number of states.)   For the two equivalent π electrons, the direct product $\Pi \times \Pi$ allows the possible states Σ^+, Σ^-, and Δ.   In the Δ state, the $\mathbf{m_l}$ values of the two electrons must be the same and therefore the $\mathbf{m_s}$ values must be different, leading to $S = 0$ and the state $^1\Delta$.   For a Σ state, the spins must be parallel or antiparallel, but the Pauli exclusion principle requires that the total wave function shall be antisymmetric to exchange of the electrons.   Since the triplet state is symmetric in electron spin it must be antisymmetric in the orbital momentum, whereas the singlet state is antisymmetric in the spin and must be symmetric in the orbital function.   The Σ^+ state is symmetric with respect to exchange of the electrons, the Σ^- state is antisymmetric with respect to exchange.[1]   Thus only the states $^3\Sigma^-$ and $^1\Sigma^+$, in addition to the $^1\Delta$ state, can arise from the two equivalent π electrons.   The lowest-energy state will be the one in which the electrons are in different orbitals, the $^3\Sigma^-$ state.   The other states ($^3\Delta$, $^3\Sigma^+$, $^1\Sigma^-$) that can be formed from the two π states must have a different value of $\mathbf{n}$ for one of the electrons.   These states will have very much greater energies.

2.232   UNITED-ATOM APPROXIMATION

The greatest body of knowledge that can be brought to bear for the interpretation of molecular structure is our understanding of the structures of free atoms.   It will be helpful to consider two extreme cases of molecule formation, the limiting case of very large internuclear distance, where the atoms will act approximately like free atoms in an electrostatic field of axial symmetry, and the limiting case of very small internuclear distance, such that the electrons will behave as if they belonged to a "united" atom, of atomic number equal to the sum of the atomic numbers of the two original atoms, but with a sufficiently large internuclear separation to retain the axial electrostatic field.   Real molecules fall somewhere between these extremes.   Their properties can often be determined by interpolation.

In the united-atom approximation, two atoms of atomic numbers Z_1 and Z_2 are considered to form a new atom of atomic number $Z = Z_1 + Z_2$. The order in which the orbitals of an atom with atomic number Z will be filled is known; it is assumed that the synthetic atom will follow the same pattern.   The atomic orbitals are then designated by the value of $\mathbf{n}$ and $\mathbf{l}$ in the usual manner, followed by the appropriate symbol for the value of λ, the projection of $\mathbf{l}$ on the internuclear axis.

Two hydrogen atoms, each with the configuration 1s, ^2S_g, can combine to give only Σ^+ states.   The most stable configuration would be $(1s\sigma)^2$, $^1\Sigma_g^+$, comparable to the ground state of helium.   This is in agreement

---

[1] An electron with a wave function containing the factor $\exp(i\phi)$ has an angular momentum on the axis of $\hbar$; with the factor $\exp(-i\phi)$ it has a projected angular momentum of $-\hbar$.   A Σ state can be obtained from two π electrons by writing the wave function with the factor $\exp(i\phi_1)\exp(-i\phi_2)$ or $\exp(-i\phi_1)\exp(i\phi_2)$.   Since these are equivalent, the most general function will be a linear combination.   Of the two orthogonal combinations $\exp[i(\phi_1 - \phi_2)] + \exp[-i(\phi_1 - \phi_2)]$ and $\exp[i(\phi_1 - \phi_2)] - \exp[i(\phi_1 - \phi_2)]$, the first is proportional to $\cos(\phi_1 - \phi_2)$, the second to $\sin(\phi_1 - \phi_2)$. The first is symmetric to reflection ($\phi_1 \rightarrow -\phi_1$, $\phi_2 \rightarrow -\phi_2$) and to exchange ($\phi_1 \leftrightarrow \phi_2$); the second is antisymmetric to reflection and to exchange.   In the $^3\Sigma^-$ state the electrons have the same spin quantum number.   The electrons are therefore in different orbitals.

with experiment.   Hydrogen, in its ^2S_g ground state, can combine with a sulfur atom, in the ^3P_g state, to give states of symmetry Σ^+ and Π.   The lowest-energy state of HS would be expected to be, by analogy with chlorine, the $^2\Pi$ state with the configuration

$$(1s\sigma)^2(2s\sigma)^2(2p\sigma)^2(2p\pi)^4(3s\sigma)^2(3p\sigma)^2(3p\pi)^3$$

or, more briefly, $KL(3s\sigma)^2\ (3p\sigma)^2(3p\pi)^3$.   The configuration

$$KL(3s\sigma)^2(3p\sigma)(3p\pi)^4,$$

corresponding to the state $^2\Sigma^+$, has also been observed, at a higher energy than the $^2\Pi$ ground state.

Diatomic hydrides, because of the small internuclear distance and the relatively small perturbation of the electric field around the heavier nucleus by the proton, are described quite accurately in many respects by the united-atom approximation.   Not only the ground state but also often the order and approximate spacing of excited electronic levels can be predicted from this model.   Molecules composed of larger atoms do not fit nearly as well.

2.233   SEPARATED-ATOM APPROXIMATION

A molecule may be considered to consist of an appropriate number of nuclei, arranged in space, to which are added electrons.   The electrons fill up the lowest-energy orbitals.   The problem that is not easily solved in a straightforward manner is to determine the nature of these orbitals. In the united-atom approximation the difficulty is circumvented by combining nuclei and adding the electrons to an "atomic" core.   The orbitals are then considered to be only slightly perturbed by the small separation of the two nuclear fragments.

An alternative device for determining the nature of the orbitals and the order in which they will be filled is to keep the two atoms well separated. The problem is again reduced to one of filling atomic orbitals, and it is again assumed that only small changes in the energy of the orbitals will be produced by the long-range interaction of the atoms.   This is called the separated-atom approximation.

Each atom contributes the same number of orbitals that it would if it were by itself.   They interact in pairs to form linear combinations that are symmetric and antisymmetric with respect to inversion if the nuclei are identical.   For unlike nuclei, the symmetry properties are similar, but approximate, as discussed below.   To show that the orbitals are written in the separated-atom approximation the projected angular momentum is specified first, followed by the atomic principal and orbital angular momentum quantum number designations.

Oxygen atoms exist in the ground state configuration $1s^2 2s^2 2p^4$, ^3P_g. Combination of two of these will produce the configuration

$$(\sigma_g 1s)^2 (\sigma_u 1s)^2 (\sigma_g 2s)^2 (\sigma_u 2s)^2 (\sigma_g 2p)^2 (\pi_u 2p)^4 (\pi_g 2p)^2$$

These orbitals are written in the order of increasing energy. It should be noted in particular that the $\sigma_u 2p$ orbital is of higher energy than the $\pi_u 2p$ or the $\pi_g 2p$ orbitals; also, the $\pi_u 2p$ orbital is of lower energy than the $\pi_g 2p$. The energies of these orbitals depend on their bonding-antibonding characteristics (Fig. VI-9).

In the configuration given above for the oxygen molecule, all orbitals are filled with the exception of the $\pi_g 2p$ orbital, which contains two electrons. The possible states of the oxygen molecule are therefore the possible states that can result from two equivalent π electrons, $^3\Sigma_g^-$, $^1\Delta_g$, and $^1\Sigma_g^+$. All three states have been observed, the last two lying 0.98 ev and 1.63 ev, respectively, above the ground state.

Carbon monoxide does not have a center of symmetry, but it is isoelectronic with the molecule N_2 and would be expected to have a very similar electronic configuration. Nitrogen molecules have a $^1\Sigma_g^+$ ground state with the configuration $(\sigma_g 1s)^2 (\sigma_u 1s)^2 (\sigma_g 2s)^2 (\sigma_u 2s)^2 (\sigma_g 2p)^2 (\pi_u 2p)^4$. The equivalent orbitals in CO would be written

$$(\sigma 1s)^2 (\sigma^* 1s)^2 (\sigma 2s)^2 (\sigma^* 2s)^2 (\sigma 2p)^2 (\pi 2p)^4$$

The starred orbitals are antibonding, as are the σ_u and π_g orbitals of the homonuclear molecules. In the limit of small differences in the two nuclei the bonding and antibonding orbitals coincide with the appropriate g or u orbitals; as the difference in nuclear charge increases, there will be a tendency for the bonding and antibonding orbitals to approach "ionic" orbitals, largely concentrated on one or the other of the nuclei.

The essential bonding and antibonding properties of electrons located in σ_g and σ_u orbitals is clearly shown in the calculated potential curves for the hydrogen molecule ion (Fig. X-12). This is confirmed also by the force constants of the bonds (Fig. VII-1). Nitrogen and carbon monoxide have six more bonding electrons than antibonding electrons and the force constant is consistent with the value for a triple bond. Oxygen has four more bonding electrons than antibonding and a force constant typical of double bonds. Molecules that are considered to have single bonds have an excess of two bonding electrons.

The inner electronic orbitals have been written as linear combinations, $\sigma_g 1s$ and $\sigma_u 1s$ or $\sigma 1s$ and $\sigma^* 1s$. The actual orbitals are not expected to be very different from those in the free atoms. It is, therefore, at least as satisfactory to indicate them by the notation KK, indicating that two K shells are filled, as to write the orbitals as if the mixing were complete.[1]

[1] See Kimball and Loebl, *J. Chem. Educ.* **36**, 233 (1959).

The justification for the familiar chemical rule-of-thumb that most stable molecules have an even number of electrons can be seen by examination of a molecule such as CN.   The configuration would be expected to be $KK(\sigma 2s)^2(\sigma^*2s)^2(\sigma 2p)^2(\pi 2p)^3$ or $KK(\sigma 2s)^2(\sigma^*2s)^2(\sigma 2p)(\pi 2p)^4$.   (These have nearly the same energy.)   Either the $\sigma 2p$ or the $\pi 2p$ orbital, both of which are bonding orbitals, is unfilled; addition of an electron, with or without a proton, should increase the bonding energy.   This is consistent with the existence of the CN^- ion, the metal cyanides, and the molecule HCN.   An extra electron added to N_2 or to CO would go into an antibonding orbital of higher energy than any occupied orbital.   It is not

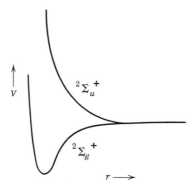

FIG. X-12.   Bonding and antibonding properties of H_2^+ orbitals.   The $^2\Sigma_g^+$ state is a bonding orbital because there is a minimum in the potential curve; the $^2\Sigma_u^+$ curve shows no minimum and is antibonding.   The curves for the $^1\Sigma_g^+$ and $^3\Sigma_u^+$ states of H_2 are essentially identical in nature with those above.

surprising, therefore, that N_2 forms only very weak bonds to metal surfaces and shows no tendency to pick up electrons.   Carbon monoxide, despite some asymmetry, also adds weakly to metal surfaces and is reasonably inert at room temperatures.   It is true in most cases, but not all, that the extra bonding energy acquired by adding an electron to a partially filled bonding orbital more than compensates for the repulsion energy arising from putting two electrons together in the same orbital.

2.234   INTERMEDIATE APPROXIMATIONS

Imagine two isolated atoms brought together slowly, with no forces acting except along the internuclear line.   The atomic orbitals of the individual atoms will go over to the separated-atom orbitals discussed in the previous section.   They will be continually modified in character as the distance is decreased until eventually they have become identical with the united-atom molecular orbitals and then with the atomic orbitals of the united atom.   Throughout this process the projection of angular momentum on the axis and the symmetry properties will be unchanged, even though the energies of the orbitals will change markedly.   If it can be assumed that the energies of the orbitals change monatonically, a unique correspondence can be drawn between the extreme states of equivalent symmetry.

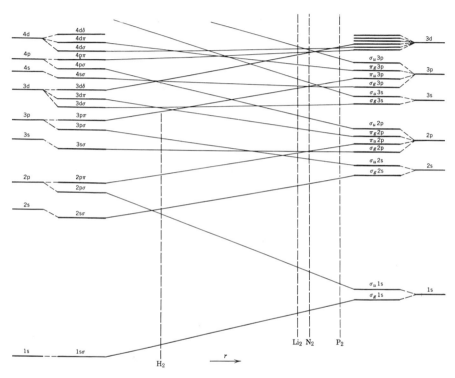

FIG. X-13.   Correlation chart for homonuclear diatomic molecules.   The united-atom orbitals at the left may be considered to go over to the separated-atom orbitals on the right as the interatomic distance is increased.   (From G. Herzberg, *Spectra of Diatomic Molecules*, Second Edition, copyright 1950, D. Van Nostrand, Company, Inc., Princeton, N.J.)

Figures X-13 and X-14 show the hydrogenic atomic orbitals at the left extreme.   Adjacent to these are the corresponding united-atom molecular orbitals, where the separation of the nuclei is assumed large enough to produce a field of axial symmetry but not large enough to cause a significant change in energy of the orbitals.   On the extreme right are the atomic orbitals and the corresponding separated-atom molecular orbitals, either for homonuclear or for heteronuclear molecules.   Since the number of states is unchanged by the process of molecule formation, there will be a one-to-one correspondence between states on the left and states on the right. Because of the higher symmetry for homonuclear molecules and the rule that states of the same symmetry cannot cross (a general rule of mechanics), the correlation table for like nuclei differs somewhat from that for unlike nuclei.

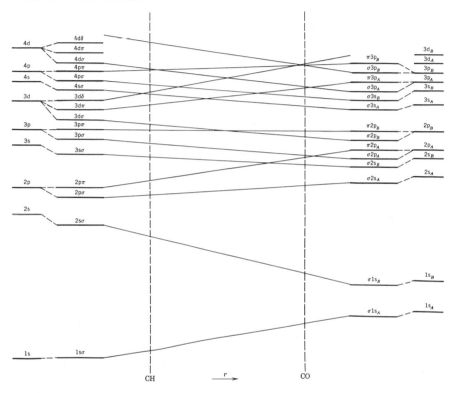

FIG. X-14. Correlation chart for heteronuclear diatomic molecules. The united-atom orbitals on the left are associated with separated-atom orbitals somewhat different from those in Fig. X-13 because of the lower symmetry and correspondingly greater prohibition of crossing here. (From G. Herzberg, *Spectra of Diatomic Molecules*, Second Edition, copyright 1950, D. Van Nostrand Company, Inc., Princeton, N.J.)

The figures can be constructed by means of the correlations given in Table X-XVIII. The parity of a molecular orbital formed in the united atom depends on the type of atomic orbital. In the separated-atom approximation, however, two atomic s orbitals can give both σ_g and σ_u molecular orbitals, atomic p orbitals can give σ_g, σ_u, π_u, and π_g orbitals, etc., as discussed in the previous section.

Any real molecule is expected to fall somewhere between the two extremes of the correlation diagrams; the smaller the nuclei, the closer they are to the left-hand side, the larger the nuclei, the closer to the right-hand side. Some examples are given in the figures. The cross-over of some of the orbitals—for example, the $\sigma2p$ and $\pi2p$ (or σ_g2p and π_u2p)—leads to no detectable change in the ground state of molecules such as N_2 or CO but will affect the excited states of these. The ground state of the CN molecule is $^2\Sigma^+$, rather than $^2\Pi$ (separation 9242 cm^{-1}, or 1.14 ev), as a consequence of this cross-over.

Two difficulties concerning such correlation tables should be kept in mind. Although it is rigorously true that states of the same symmetry cannot cross, "virtual" crossings are possible in which the two energy levels approach each other, "interact," and separate. Near the point of virtual crossing, the states are mixed but at any appreciable distance from the crossing the states are the same as if the levels had actually crossed. This apparently causes little difficulty in practice.[1] Also, the atomic levels are written for the hydrogen atom. As the nuclear charge and the number of electrons increase, these levels change relative positions. This will, of course, change the order of the united-atom and the separated-atom molecular orbitals.

Alternative notations have been introduced to accommodate the intermediate cases. One system[2] replaces the symbols $\sigma2s$, σ^*2s, $\sigma2p$, $\pi2p$, π^*2p, σ^*2p, ... by the more abbreviated symbols $z\sigma$, $y\sigma$, $x\sigma$, $w\pi$, $v\pi$, $u\sigma$, ..., the order corresponding to increasing energy in the separated-atom approximation. The abbreviated notation is more flexible, largely because it is less specific about the "origin" of the orbitals in the separated atoms. For small internuclear distances the $x\sigma$ and $w\pi$ orbitals are inverted; this is indicated by writing them in reversed order, but the designations x and w retain their original meaning. The inner shells are conveniently represented by the x-ray shell designations, K, L, M, ... to the approximation that these shells are undisturbed by the formation of the chemical bond. The molecules BO and SiO, written in this notation, have the configurations

$$KK(z\sigma)^2(y\sigma)^2(w\pi)^4x\sigma, \quad ^2\Sigma^+ \quad \text{and} \quad KKL(z\sigma)^2(y\sigma)^2(w\pi)^4(x\sigma)^2, \quad ^1\Sigma^+$$

respectively.

2.24 Electronic Spectra

For most molecules only a very few, if any, electronic transitions can be observed in the visible and near ultraviolet. Each transition appears, in

---

[1] An unsymmetrical double minimum arising from such a virtual crossing has been reported for the first excited state of the hydrogen molecule of symmetry $^1\Sigma_g^+$ by E. R. Davidson, *J. Chem. Phys.* **35**, 1189 (1961).

[2] R. S. Mulliken, *Revs. Mod. Phys.* **4**, 1 (1932).

the vapor phase, as a "band system," consisting of progressions of narrow bands that arise from a simultaneous change of vibrational and electronic states.

2.241 BAND SYSTEMS

At low temperatures, near or below room temperature, the absorption spectrum will be reasonably simple and may be approximately described by the formula

$$\nu = \nu_e + \mathbf{v}'\nu_v' \tag{X-45}$$

where ν_e is $\Delta E_e/h$, ν_v' is the vibrational frequency in the excited electronic state, and $\mathbf{v}'$ is an integer characterizing each of the bands in the progression, which may be identified with the vibrational quantum number in the upper state. Deviations from this simple formula are observed due to the convergence of the vibrational energy levels in the upper electronic state, which may be expected to be more rapid than the convergence in the ground state. A much better approximation will be given by a formula that assumes a constant increment of convergence, represented mathematically by a quadratic expression in the quantum number $\mathbf{v}'$. To this approximation, then, and still assuming that the initial state is unexcited vibrationally, the absorption frequencies for the members of a particular band system will be given by

$$\nu = \nu_e + \nu_v'\mathbf{v}' - \delta\mathbf{v}'^2 \tag{X-46}$$

The transitions that contribute to such a progression are indicated in Fig. X-15.

In emission, a given band system (corresponding to a single electronic transition) will consist of a number of progressions, since the initial state will, in general, be excited vibrationally as well as electronically. The formula for the resultant frequencies is obtained by subtracting from equation X-46 the term values of the final (excited vibrational) states of the transitions. Representing the vibrational quantum number and frequency for the upper state by $\mathbf{v}'$ and ν', respectively, and the vibrational quantum number and frequency in the lower state by $\mathbf{v}''$ and ν'', it should then be possible to represent all the bands of a given band system by the expression

$$\nu = \nu_e + (\nu_v'\mathbf{v}' - \delta'\mathbf{v}'^2) - (\nu_v''\mathbf{v}'' - \delta''\mathbf{v}''^2) \tag{X-47}$$

A band system may thus be considered as a number of progressions of the type given by equation X-46, but differing by the term representing the vibrational level in the lower state or, equally well, the system may be considered as a number of progressions in $\mathbf{v}''$ and ν'', which differ by the term representing the vibrational level in the upper electronic state.

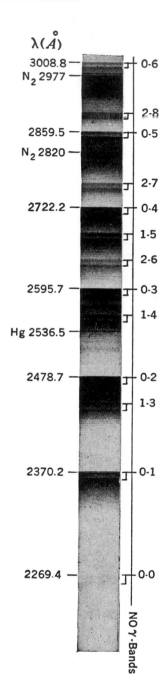

FIG. X-15. Emission spectrum of NO, showing transition from first excited state to ground state. Vibrational levels are indicated. (From G. Herzberg, *Spectra of Diatomic Molecules*, Second Edition, copyright 1950, D. Van Nostrand Company, Inc. Princeton, N.J.)

Relative intensities of the bands can be interpreted by means of the Franck-Condon principle (sections VI-2.4 and X-5.23).

2.242   BAND STRUCTURE

Each of the bands described by equation X-47 will consist of a very large number of closely spaced lines, which may not be resolved, that arise from the change in rotational state accompanying the electronic and vibrational transition.   These rotational lines will disappear completely, giving a continuous band of very roughly the same width as that formed by the large number of narrow lines, when the molecule is observed in the liquid state rather than as a gas.   The spectrum of the solid may resemble that of the liquid or may have several sharp bands in place of each single broad band.

As a first approximation, the rotational lines would be expected to be evenly spaced (section VII-4), but in general the lines show a strong convergence that arises because the moment of inertia in the upper state is different from that in the lower state.   If ν_0 is the frequency associated with the electronic plus vibrational change, the observed frequency for a rotational line should be given by

$$\nu = \nu_0 + B'J'(J' + 1) - B''J''(J'' + 1) \qquad \text{(X-48)}$$

The selection rule is $\Delta J = 0, \pm 1$, except that for Σ-Σ transitions $\Delta J = 0$ is forbidden.   Taking the case of $\Delta J = 1$, $J' = J'' + 1$,

$$\nu = \nu_0 + 2B' + J''(3B' - B'') + J''^2(B' - B'') \qquad \text{(X-49)}$$

Assuming B' and B'', the rotational constants in the upper and lower electronic states, respectively, to be constant (independent of the vibrational and rotational levels), the spacing between rotational lines should be

$$\Delta\nu = (4B' - 2B'') + 2(B' - B'')J'' \qquad \text{(X-50)}$$
$$(J'' + 1 \leftarrow J')$$

If $B' = B''$, this reduces to the spacing $2B$ found for rotation-vibration and pure rotation spectra.   The deviations from the expression above due to centrifugal distortion and interaction with vibrations will be comparatively small.

For most diatomic molecules the convergence is so marked that the second term of equation X-50 becomes equal to, and then larger than, the first for moderately large J'' values, causing the lines to reverse their direction.   Figure X-16 gives a plot of frequency *vs.* J'' value, with the appearance of the resultant spectrum.   The representation of such lines by a parabola is due to Fortrat.   For most molecules the binding in the excited electronic state is weaker than that in the ground state, leading to a larger internuclear distance and a larger value of the moment of inertia, or smaller value of B.   That is, $B' < B''$.   If this is the case, the "band head," formed by the convergence of the rotational lines, will fall in the R branch, on the high-frequency side, and the band will be shaded, or degraded, toward lower frequencies ("shaded toward the red").   For some molecules, however, this is just reversed, the band head lying in the

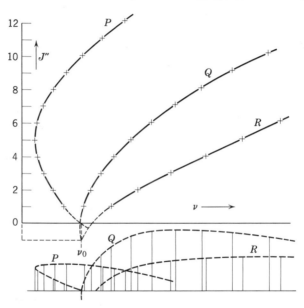

FIG. X-16.   Fortrat diagram for the $^1\Sigma \rightarrow {}^1\Pi$ (emission) band of CO.   (From Brode, ref. 2.)

P branch, causing the band to be degraded toward higher frequencies ("toward the violet").

For Σ-Σ transitions (parallel band), the transition $\Delta J = 0$ is forbidden and there will be a line missing (the zero line, null line, zero gap, or null line gap) between the P and R branches.   If $\Delta J = 0$ is allowed (perpendicular band), there will be a whole new set of lines which will form the Q branch.   The formula for the spacing of lines of the Q branch can be found from equation X-48 by setting $J' = J''$ and taking the difference between successive J values.   This gives

$$\Delta \nu = 2(B' - B'')J \qquad\qquad (X\text{-}51)$$

It will be observed that the convergence is identical with that for the P and R branches.   If $B' = B''$, the Q branch will degenerate to a single sharp, strong line. Ideally, one should choose the zero gap, or the head of the Q branch, for insertion into equation X-47, but in practice it is more convenient to measure the band heads. Since in most cases the difference $B' - B''$ will be essentially constant throughout a band system, this simply causes a uniform shift of frequencies, without appreciable loss of accuracy in determining the vibrational constants. For more accurate work, it is necessary to take into account also the deviations from the rigid-rotor approximation. In a few instances these are sufficiently important to produce qualitative changes in the spectrum, such as extra band heads, as well as shifts of position.

2.243 CLASSIFICATION OF TRANSITIONS

A convenient separation of observed transitions may be made on the basis of the direction in which the dipole moment changes or of the symmetry species of the upper state in transitions to or from a totally symmetric ground state. Σ-Σ transitions are allowed; since the change in dipole must be along the symmetry axis, these transitions are designated parallel bands. Σ-Π transitions are accompanied by a change in moment perpendicular to the axis and are called perpendicular bands. This does not, in itself, provide all the information that may be desired concerning the change in electron configuration; thus further description is required.

Three broad types of transitions may be considered, each starting from the normal ground state (N). If the electron that changes its state is both initially and finally in the valence shell (V), the transition is labeled V ← N.[1] If the electron moves from an atomic orbital (a non-bonding orbital, or an orbital of lower n than the valence shell) to the valence shell, a Q ← N transition results. Just as for atoms, the selection rules permit any integral value for Δn, so that Rydberg series might be expected, with frequencies given by a formula of the type

$$\nu = A - \frac{R}{(n + a)^2} \qquad \text{(X-52)}$$

where A and a are characteristic of the initial state, R is a universal constant, and n is the integral principal quantum number. Such series have been observed for some molecules, but with the exception of the loosely bound molecule He_2 they occur in the vacuum ultraviolet, above 50,000 cm^{-1} (below 2000 Å). The members of such a series are called R ← N transitions.

Further breakdown of these classifications may be possible in some cases. A V ← N transition in which the electron moves from a bonding

---

[1] By convention, the higher-energy state is written first in discussions of transitions. The arrow indicates whether emission or absorption is considered.

to the corresponding antibonding orbital will always be an allowed transition in a diatomic molecule, since it can be accomplished without a change in Λ (parallel transition) and will satisfy the requirements of parity.   An antibonding orbital may be closely correlated, for atoms of similar atomic number, with σ_u or π_g orbitals of homonuclear molecules.   The electron density (the probability of finding the electron at any given point) is symmetrical with respect to a plane bisecting the chemical bond, but the wave function has opposite signs on each side of this plane; this corresponds, in the wave picture, to a change of phase.   Each of these orbitals has associated with it an angular momentum component perpendicular to the nuclear axis (Table X-XVIII).   These properties are consistent with the classical picture of an electron revolving in an orbit containing the molecular axis as a diameter.   In this classical picture (which must not be taken too seriously since there is no way of confirming its validity), the electron oscillates between opposite sides of the molecule when it is in an antibonding orbital and remains more nearly localized in the interior of the molecule when it is in a bonding orbital.   The antibonding states should not be confused with ionic states, which have a distinctly higher probability of finding the electron at one end of the molecule than at the other.   On the other hand, as the asymmetry increases, certain of the antibonding orbitals will become highly asymmetric, leading to ionic states.   This classical picture of antibonding orbitals has given rise to the term "charge-transfer" spectra for transitions which take an electron between a bonding orbital and an antibonding orbital.   These transitions can also be labeled σ-σ or π-π (or σ-σ*, π-π*) if attention is fixed on electrons and orbitals rather than on the states involved.   n-π bands are examples of $Q \rightarrow N$ transitions in which an electron moves from a nonbonding orbital in the valence shell to a bonding π orbital.

2.3   Polyatomic Molecules

From the spectrum of a diatomic molecule, under high resolution, it is possible to determine the bond length and the vibrational frequency for each of the electronic states participating in the observed transitions. Dissociation, predissociation, variation of intensities attributable to the Franck-Condon principle, and band contours serve as important guides to the identification of the nature of the electronic transition.   In the spectra of polyatomic molecules all these aids are applied when possible, together with the information supplied by the relative intensities of the various vibrational modes.   Interpretation is, in general, much more difficult for polyatomic spectra, since there are more electrons of comparable energy that could take part in the jump and more possible states to which these electrons can move. There are also more parameters required to describe the nuclear positions, but generally less information is available since the rotational structure is seldom resolved.

Whereas the outer electrons of even heavy atoms move in a potential field that is roughly spherical, and the outer electrons in a diatomic molecule move in a field that is essentially axially symmetric, the electrons of a polyatomic molecule such as propane, benzene, or acetone cannot be assumed to fit any one simple, idealized structure. The hydrogen atom and hydrogen molecule ion, for which exact solutions can be calculated, have no good analog in the polyatomic molecules. Consequently a variety of approaches to the description and calculation of electronic states and properties can be found in the literature, with no one technique fully satisfactory for all types of molecules.

One of the earliest approximations was that initiated by Heitler and London and subsequently developed by Slater and by Pauling. Emphasis is placed on finding suitable atomic orbitals, by taking linear combinations of the hydrogen atom orbitals, that will give a maximum overlap between the hybridized orbitals located on adjacent atoms. It was found that even the best models calculated on this basis could not represent molecules such as benzene or butadiene, since the nature of the calculation fixes the valence electrons between two nuclei. Better agreement with experiment is obtained by constructing several of these possible structures, then taking linear combinations of the wave functions for them to find a superior wave function. There is no question of the mathematical validity of this procedure for finding wave functions that will approximate the true wave functions (although the number of functions required in the linear combinations is generally much greater than can be handled by normal means). The difficulties with the method are in large part conceptual. First, it is sometimes implied, or assumed through lack of understanding, that writing down a linear combination of terms to obtain a physically significant function gives some physical significance to the individual terms. Also, because emphasis is placed on the extent of overlap of orbitals, it is very often mistakenly assumed that it is the close approach of the electrons, rather than the localization of the electrons in the region between the nuclei, that is responsible for the chemical binding.

A significantly different approach, developed by Hund, Mulliken, and others at approximately the same period of time as the "valence bond" approach, has been called the "molecular orbital" method. This has been modified in many ways and may be said to include, in addition to the united-atom and separated-atom approximations discussed for diatomic molecules, the free-electron molecular-orbital method (section VIII-1.2) and many newer approximation techniques that have shown promise.

The description of electronic states depends largely on the approximate calculational method chosen.   In principle, any one of these methods, carried to a sufficiently high approximation, should yield exactly the same results as any other.   In practice, most calculations stop at an early stage so that quite different numerical values and physical interpretations can be obtained by the different approaches.   Specific techniques for calculating electronic wave functions are outside the intended scope of this work. Furthermore, the interpretation of electronic spectra depends heavily on the interactions of electronic and vibrational states.   The discussion of the electronic states and spectra of polyatomic molecules will therefore be largely postponed to section 5.2.

For certain purposes it is quite adequate to consider a polyatomic molecule, and particularly a linear polyatomic molecule, as a collection of bonds of the type found in diatomic molecules.   To this approximation it is possible to speak of σ bonds and π bonds, even though there is no true rotational symmetry about the bond.   Justification for this approximation is to be found in the nearly free rotation about single bonds and also in the chemical and spectroscopic evidence that saturated bonds are effectively insulated from each other.   For conjugated systems this is no longer a valid assumption, but even in these molecules it is often possible to partition the structure into isolated single bonds plus one or more conjugated regions and treat each bond separately or, as in aromatic molecules, to consider "π" orbitals to be superimposed on a framework of atomic kernels and σ bonds.

On theoretical grounds such an abrupt partition is not justified.   In methane, for example, if there were four identical C—H bonds, each with two electrons, there would be a four-fold degeneracy of the ground electronic state.   This is impossible on theoretical grounds (Jahn-Teller theorem, section 5.2) as well as from experimental observations.   Accurate descriptions of electronic orbitals in molecules must conform to the symmetry characteristics of the entire molecule.   The orbitals are labeled with the symbols of the appropriate irreducible representations in lower-case letters.   Orbitals of the same symmetry are numbered consecutively in the order of their energies.

The formaldehyde molecule[1] provides a simple illustration of the formation of molecular orbitals.   The task may be approached by writing down atomic orbitals, noting the symmetry of them (or of linear combinations where necessary), and then estimating the linear combinations of those of given symmetry that will give the lowest-energy states.   (The notation chosen is that now officially recommended, with the x axis perpendicular

[1] See Robinson and DiGiorgio, *Can. J. Chem.* **36**, 31 (1958), and references given there.

to the plane and the irreducible representation B_1 symmetric with respect to reflection in the xz plane.) Totally symmetric orbitals (species A_1) available are the following: $(1s_H + 1s_{H'})$, $1s_C$, $1s_O$, $2s_C$, $2s_O$, $2p_{zC}$, and $2p_{zO}$. There are no orbitals of species A_2. Orbitals of symmetry B_1 are: $2p_{xC}$ and $2p_{xO}$. The remaining orbitals are of symmetry B_2: $(1s_H - 1s_{H'})$, $2p_{yC}$, and $2p_{yO}$. Only from calculations is it possible to know how these atomic orbitals should be combined, but the qualitative nature of the molecular orbitals may be anticipated from simple valence considerations. The orbitals, with their symmetry characteristics and bonding characteristics, are listed in estimated order of energy in Table X-XIX. (No attempt has been made to estimate the magnitudes of coefficients in the linear sums; this applies particularly to the addition of various amounts of

TABLE X-XIX

Linear Combination	Number and Symmetry	Bonding Character
$1s_O$	a_1	Non-bonding
$1s_C$	a_1	Non-bonding
$2s_O$	$1a_1$	Non-bonding
$(1s_H + 1s_{H'} + 2s_C)$	$2a_1$	σ bonding (CH_2)
$(1s_H - 1s_{H'} - 2s_C)$	$1b_2$	σ bonding (CH_2)
$(2p_{zC} + 2p_{zO})$	$3a_1$	σ bonding (CO)
$(2p_{xC} + 2p_{xO})$	$1b_1$	π bonding (CO)
$2p_{yO}$	$2b_2$	Non-bonding (lone-pair)
$(2p_{xC} - 2p_{xO})$	$2b_1$	π antibonding
$(2p_{zC} - 2p_{zO})$	$4a_1$	σ antibonding

the $2s_C$ and $2s_O$ orbitals.)   The numbers preceding the symmetry designations simply order the valence orbitals of the same symmetry class.   The configuration of formaldehyde in its ground state should be, assuming the results of Table X-XIX, as follows.

$$(1a_1)^2(2a_1)^2(1b_2)^2(3a_1)^2(1b_1)^2(2b_2)^2, \quad {}^1A_1$$

The lowest unfilled orbitals are the antibonding orbitals $2b_1$ and $4a_1$. The lowest-frequency transition is a weak absorption band with its origin at 27,021 cm^{-1}. This should be an n-π transition from the non-bonding orbital on the oxygen ($2b_2$) to the antibonding CO π orbital. This reduces the strength of the carbon-oxygen bond by making it $1\frac{1}{2}$ bonds (3 electrons); it also destroys the stability of the planar form, so that the structure in which the CO is tilted about 20° out of the plane of the CH_2 group is the most stable by a small amount. The resulting state can then be described by the configuration $\ldots(2b_2)(2b_1)$, $^1A_2$. As would be expected, the transition to the state $(2b_2)(2b_1)$, $^3A_2$ also occurs, but much more weakly.

This system is observed on the low-frequency side of the singlet-singlet transition, with its origin at 25,200 cm^{-1}. There is very little difference in the characters of the singlet and triplet upper states.

Many transitions observed in the ultraviolet region violate the selection rules for dipole radiation. In most cases they appear because the symmetry of the molecule has been lowered by a non-totally-symmetric vibration and they have, in general, intensities much lower than do the allowed transitions. There is also the selection rule for total angular momentum, $\Delta J = 0, \pm 1$, but this can be satisfied by appropriate changes in the rotational energy. The rotational fine structure is very seldom resolved for polyatomic molecules.

3   Vibrational Spectra

The general characteristics of vibrational spectra have been considered in some detail in chapters VII and VIII. Very briefly, it was seen that for a non-linear molecule of N atoms there should be $3N - 6$ independent, or normal, modes of vibration ($3N - 5$ for linear molecules). Only certain vibrations will contribute to the infrared spectrum, since a necessary condition for the appearance of an absorption band is that the vibrational transition shall involve a change in dipole moment. The positions of these absorption bands may be calculated with moderate accuracy (roughly 1%) on the basis of classical equations of motion which assume the molecule to be a system of coupled harmonic oscillators. Unfortunately, however, we have no way of knowing *a priori* the values of the force constants, so that these must be obtained from the calculations and experimentally observed frequencies. It would be much more gratifying, of course, if the frequencies could be calculated independently of experiment. At present, those skilled in the art can often predict the positions of absorption bands from direct comparisons with frequencies observed in related molecules more closely than they can be calculated by transferring force constants. Some limited success has been achieved in calculating principal force constants, but interaction constants, relating changes of one bond length or angle to changes in another, have thus far been determined empirically. It is to be hoped that increased understanding of valence theory will someday permit vibrational frequencies to be calculated from a knowledge of the electronic structure of a molecule.

3.1   Normal Vibrations

To the extent that the anharmonicity can be neglected, all the vibrational motions of the molecules are resolvable into normal vibrations. It will be convenient to discuss the forms of the normal vibrations in terms of the approximate descriptions afforded by symmetry coordinates.

A symmetry coordinate is a linear combination of changes in bond lengths or bond angles that has the same symmetry properties as one of the irreducible representations of the point group to which the molecule belongs.   There are two reasons for choosing such a coordinate system. The normal vibrations will have symmetry properties corresponding to one or another of the irreducible representations (section 1.62) and it is helpful to work with coordinates that approximate the normal coordinates of the system.   Of even greater importance, the equations of motion in the symmetry-coordinate system will factor into sets of equations, each set containing only those vibrations belonging to a specific symmetry species.

The proof of this factorization is straight-forward for nondegenerate vibrations.   The kinetic and potential energies are quadratic expressions in the coordinates or their time derivatives.   If q_i and q_j are two coordinates belonging to different irreducible representations, then there must be some symmetry operation to which one coordinate will be symmetric and the other antisymmetric.   The product $q_i q_j$, under this symmetry operation, would go to $-q_i q_j$.   The kinetic and potential energies, however, must be invariant to any symmetry operation, regardless of the form of the vibration.   The coefficient of the $q_i q_j$ (or $\dot{q}_i \dot{q}_j$) term must accordingly be identically zero.   Since it is possible to find symmetry operations that produce a similar change in sign for the two components of degenerate vibrations, these must also factor out from each other.   The result is that the kinetic and potential energy matrices consist of submatrices along the diagonal, with all other elements zero.   There will be one submatrix for each irreducible representation, with dimensions equal to the number of normal vibrations belonging to that representation (zero in many cases). The doubly degenerate vibrations will give two identical submatrices, each with dimensions equal to the number of distinct frequencies belonging to the representation; triply degenerate vibrations will give three identical submatrices.

Symmetry coordinates can be written down by inspection, since they must be linear combinations of equivalent bond-length or bond-angle changes and must have specific symmetry properties.   The coordinates given in equations X-1 and X-2, if they represented displacements of the atoms, would be suitable, except that the coordinate q_2 would represent a pure rotation in the case of the ammonia molecule.   The degenerate coordinates are not unique.   As a further example, a set of symmetry coordinates applicable to the formaldehyde molecule are the following. $q_1(A_1) = (1/\sqrt{2})(r_1 + r_2)$; $q_2(A_1) = R$; $q_3(A_1) = (1/\sqrt{2})(\gamma_1 + \gamma_2)$; $q_4(B_1) = \beta$; $q_5(B_2) = (1/\sqrt{2})(r_1 - r_2)$; $q_6(B_2) = (1/\sqrt{2})(\gamma_1 - \gamma_2)$, where r_1 and r_2 are the *changes* in the two C—H bond lengths, R is the change in the carbonyl bond length, γ_1 and γ_2 are the changes in the two H—C—O angles, and β is the change in the H_2—C—O angle (initially 180°, assuming the planar structure).

The symmetry coordinates may be considered idealized forms of the vibrations. If there is no interaction, for example, between C—H stretching and bending motions or between them and the carbonyl stretching motion, the symmetry coordinates correctly represent the normal vibrations. This is sometimes a good approximation, but very often a normal vibration will contain two or three components in roughly equal amounts. The constancy of certain characteristic vibrational frequencies is an indication that the form of the vibration is constant, not that the vibration is localized in one bond. Simple considerations of invariance of the center of mass will show that some mixing must occur. Just how the normal coordinates will differ from the symmetry coordinates can only be determined by detailed calculations for each molecule.

One important restriction can be placed on the mixing of the symmetry coordinates. Only those belonging to the same irreducible representation can be mixed together (in the harmonic oscillator approximation) to give the true normal coordinates. In a particular case, therefore, 10% of the second symmetry coordinate might be combined with 90% of the first to give a normal vibration that is primarily a C—H stretch but also partially a carbonyl stretch, or the true normal vibration might include also a certain amount of CH_2 deformation. There cannot, however, be any out-of plane bending (β) contribution to the vibrations of species A_1, nor can there be any carbonyl stretch contribution to the B_1 or B_2 motions.

In all non-degenerate vibrations and in certain degenerate modes the atoms will move along straight lines, passing through their equilibrium positions simultaneously, with the frequency characteristic of the vibration. For degenerate vibrations it is only necessary that all atoms move with the same frequency during the vibration. For example, the degenerate bending mode of CO_2 may be described in terms of any linear combination of the linear displacements at right angles. This is equivalent to an elliptical motion of the oxygen atoms, the eccentricity of the ellipse depending on the relative coefficients and phases of the two orthogonal motions, and the direction of traversal of the ellipse depending on the relative phases of the motions. Similarly, it is possible to describe certain of the motions of the hydrogens in a methyl group in terms of elliptical paths.

An angular momentum can be associated with each degenerate vibration. If this is set equal to lh, where l is an integral quantum number, the vibrational mode is multiplied by a phase factor of the form $\exp(\pm il\phi)$. In a linear molecule the value of l represents the projection of the vibrational angular momentum on the symmetry axis; $l = 0$ for a Σ state, $l = 1$ for a Π vibrational state. In molecules belonging to other point groups, the vibrational angular momenta about any particular axis will not necessarily be integral, but they may be expressed in the form ζl, where $-1 \leqslant \zeta \leqslant 1$. This angular momentum can interact with the rotational angular momentum of the molecule, producing significant changes in rotation-vibration band contours.

3.2 Anharmonic Oscillator

In addition to the fundamental frequencies of vibration one commonly observes bands, of lower intensity, with frequencies that are very nearly multiples or sums of the fundamental frequencies and occasionally also bands that represent the difference in frequency between two normal vibrations.[1] Such bands occur because of the anharmonicity of the vibrations. For these, as for the fundamentals, there must be a change in dipole moment if they are to absorb infrared radiation, or a change in polarizability if they are to be active in the Raman effect. In section 1.61 it has been shown how these selection rules may be obtained in a straightforward manner with the assistance of group theory.

The problem of the simple harmonic oscillator is one that can be solved exactly by quantum mechanical methods. As in the case of the hydrogen atom, the form of the solution depends on the quantum number. The wave functions for the ground state and the first few excited states are given in Table X-XX. In Fig. V-6 and Fig. V-7 these functions were plotted against the displacement, or the internuclear distance. The square of the wave function, which is proportional to the probability of finding the particles at a particular distance, is also plotted.

The energy levels of the harmonic oscillator, it will be remembered, are given by $E = h\nu_0(v + \frac{1}{2})$, where ν_0 is the classical frequency of oscillation, v is the integral quantum number, and h is Planck's constant. This result assumes the potential energy to be of the form

$$V = \tfrac{1}{2}k(r - r_e)^2$$

where k is the classical force constant, r the internuclear distance (or for a polyatomic molecule the value of the normal coordinate), and r_e is the equilibrium distance. A better approximation to reality is the Morse curve,

$$V = hcD_e\{1 - \exp[-\beta(r - r_e)]\}^2 \qquad\qquad \text{(X-53)}$$

This function is shown in Fig. X-17. For large values of r, the potential energy approaches hcD_e, the dissociation energy. For $r = r_e$, the

---

[1] Strictly speaking, it is incorrect to refer to the observation of combination or overtone bands of normal vibrations, or to talk of the anharmonicity of a normal vibration, since a normal vibration is necessarily harmonic and cannot produce combination or overtone bands. The meaning, of course, is always "almost normal" vibrations.

TABLE X-XX

Wave Functions for a Harmonic Oscillator

$$\psi_0 = \left(\frac{\alpha}{\pi}\right)^{1/4} e^{-\xi^2/2}$$

$$\psi_1 = \sqrt{2}\left(\frac{\alpha}{\pi}\right)^{1/4} \xi e^{-\xi^2/2}$$

$$\psi_2 = \frac{1}{\sqrt{2}}\left(\frac{\alpha}{\pi}\right)^{1/4} (2\xi^2 - 1)e^{-\xi^2/2}$$

$$\psi_3 = \frac{1}{\sqrt{3}}\left(\frac{\alpha}{\pi}\right)^{1/4} (2\xi^3 - 3\xi)e^{-\xi^2/2}$$

$$\psi_4 = \frac{1}{2\sqrt{3}}\left(\frac{\alpha}{\pi}\right)^{1/4} (4\xi^4 - 12\xi^2 + 3)e^{-\xi^2/2}$$

$$\alpha \equiv \sqrt{km/\hbar}; \qquad \xi \equiv \sqrt{\alpha}\, x$$

potential energy is zero. This particular function not only fits the observed potential curve well but also makes the Schroedinger equation solvable, giving a convenient closed form for the energy.

$$E(v) = h\beta \sqrt{\frac{hcD_e}{2\pi^2\mu}} (v + \tfrac{1}{2}) - \frac{h^2\beta^2}{8\pi^2\mu} (v + \tfrac{1}{2})^2 \qquad (X\text{-}54)$$

Experimental results, on the other hand, have been successfully fitted to a power series of the form

$$E(v) = h\nu_e\{(v + \tfrac{1}{2}) - x_e(v + \tfrac{1}{2})^2 + y_e(v + \tfrac{1}{2})^3 + \cdots\} \qquad (X\text{-}55)$$

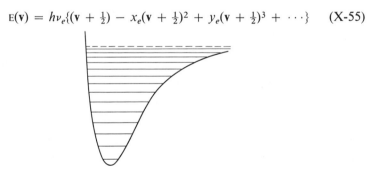

FIG. X-17.   Morse curve for the vibrational potential curve of a diatomic molecule.

If one assumes, as is most often the case, that the cubic and higher-order terms are negligible, the coefficients in equation X-54 may be set equal to those in equation X-55. Solving for β, one obtains

$$\beta = \sqrt{\frac{2\pi^2\mu}{D_e hc}} \nu_e \qquad (X\text{-}56)$$

The equation is written for a diatomic molecule, with a reduced mass μ. If D_e, β, and ν_e/c are expressed in cm^{-1} and μ_A in atomic weight units ($C^{12} = 12$), equation X-56 reduces to the form

$$\beta = 1.2179 \times 10^7 \sqrt{\frac{\mu_A}{D_e} \frac{\nu_e}{c}}$$

As may be seen from equation X-55, ν_e is the frequency that the system would have if the anharmonic terms could be neglected. The molecule will approach this frequency, classically, as the amplitude of the oscillation decreases. Quantum mechanically, the frequency absorbed, or the difference between adjacent energy levels, will approach the harmonic value as the quantum number v is decreased. Even in the ground state, however, the effects of anharmonicity will not disappear, since the expression $(v + \frac{1}{2})$ cannot go to zero. It becomes necessary, therefore, to distinguish between several closely related quantities—the "harmonic" frequency of the oscillator, which is given by $\nu = (1/2\pi)\sqrt{k/\mu}$ for a diatomic molecule; the frequency of the oscillator in its ground state, which will be slightly lower than the harmonic limit; and the observed frequency, which will depend on the difference in energy between two adjacent vibrational levels. To emphasize these differences we shall represent the vibrational frequency of the molecule by the symbol ω.[1] The frequency of the radiation absorbed will be represented by ν. Values which correspond to the minimum of the potential energy well, and hence to the harmonic limit, will be designated by the subscript e, and values which correspond to the ground state by the subscript 0. The frequency of the radiation absorbed is the difference in term values, which are given the symbol G for vibrational states. The notation is summarized in Table X-XXI.

TABLE X-XXI

ω_e = frequency of oscillation of the molecule in the limit of small amplitudes

ω_0 = frequency of oscillation of the molecule in the ground state

ν = frequency of radiation absorbed

$G(v) = \dfrac{E(v)}{h}$ = term value of the molecule in the vibrational state v

r_e = equilibrium internuclear distance (diatomic molecule), defined by the minimum of the potential energy curve

---

[1] Note that ω represents the quantity $2\pi\nu$ in most of the literature of physics. The notation given above has, however, become established in molecular spectroscopy.

The equations above may be written in this notation as follows.

$$G(v) = \beta \sqrt{\frac{D_e ch}{2\pi^2\mu}} (v + \tfrac{1}{2}) - \frac{h\beta^2}{8\pi^2\mu} (v + \tfrac{1}{2})^2 \qquad \text{(X-54')}$$

$$G(v) = \omega_e\{(v + \tfrac{1}{2}) - x_e(v + \tfrac{1}{2})^2 + y_e(v + \tfrac{1}{2})^3 + \cdots\} \quad \text{(X-55')}$$

Then

$$\nu = \Delta G = \omega_e\{1 - 2x_e v + 3y_e(v^2 + \tfrac{1}{12}) \mid \cdots\} \simeq \omega_e \qquad \text{(X-57)}$$

for the transition $v - 1 \rightarrow v$

$$\nu = \Delta G = \omega_e v\{1 - x_e(v + 1) + y_e(v^2 + \tfrac{3}{2}v + \tfrac{3}{4}) + \cdots\} \approx v\omega_e$$
$$\text{(X-58)}$$

for the transition $0 \rightarrow v$

The term value relative to the ground state may be written in the form

$$G_0(v) = G(v) - G(0) = \omega_e\{v(1 - x_e + \tfrac{3}{4}y_e) - v^2(x_e + \tfrac{3}{2}y_e) + v^3 y_e + \cdots\}$$

or

$$G_0(v) = \omega_0 v - \omega_0 x_0 v^2 + \omega_0 y_0 v^3 \qquad \text{(X-59)}$$

where

$$G(0) = \omega_e(\tfrac{1}{2} - \tfrac{1}{4}x_e + \tfrac{1}{8}y_e)$$
$$\omega_0 = \omega_e(1 - x_e + \tfrac{3}{4}y_e)$$
$$\omega_0 x_0 = \omega_e(x_e + \tfrac{3}{2}y_e) \qquad \text{(X-60)}$$
$$\omega_0 y_0 = \omega_e y_e$$

Diatomic molecules will, of course, have only one vibrational mode, and the observation of the fundamental and overtones will permit a determination of the best values of the constants ω_e, x_e, and y_e (in general, the cubic term is small enough to be neglected). For heteronuclear molecules these will all be allowed, by symmetry, in the infrared and also in the Raman spectrum. Homonuclear molecules will not show any absorption in the infrared region but can be observed in the Raman effect.

Polyatomic molecules will have a much larger number of vibrational modes, which will not be strictly independent. Very few molecules have been adequately treated in the anharmonic oscillator approximation because of the difficulties of obtaining a sufficient number of experimental frequencies, as well as the additional mathematical complexities. In the absence of unusual perturbations, such as Fermi resonance, one normally expects to find binary overtone or combination bands somewhere in the vicinity of 2 to 20 cm^{-1} below the sum or multiple of the appropriate fundamental frequencies, although much larger deviations are found in some molecules. Neglecting cubic terms, the same discrepancy will appear for each successive quantum step. HCl, which has a rather large anharmonicity, has the absorption bands in the infrared shown in Table

X-XXII. Note that in this case the deviation from the harmonic oscillator formula is very nearly linear, showing that third-order terms are very small, increasing slightly with v. Since one is observing differences between vibrational levels, which are characteristic of the molecule rather than the experimental apparatus, exactly the same values will be found whether the transitions are observed as infrared absorption bands or as Raman shifts. Because of the relative weakness of combination bands in the Raman effect and the greater experimental difficulties in observing weak bands, the infrared spectrum is more convenient for examining the effects of anharmonicity in heteronuclear diatomic molecules.

TABLE X-XXII[a]

v	$\dfrac{\nu}{c}$ obs	$\dfrac{1}{c}\Delta G_{obs}$	$\dfrac{1}{c}\Delta^2 G_{obs}$
0	—		
		2885.9_0	
1	2885.9_0		-103.7_5
		2782.1_5	
2	5668.0_5		-103.2_2
		2678.9_3	
3	8346.9_8		-102.80
		2576.1_3	
4	$10{,}923.1_1$		-102.69
		2473.4_4	
5	$13{,}396.5_5$		

[a] From Herzberg, ref. 43.

3.3 Intensities

The exact expressions relating molecular configurations to observed band intensities are rather complex and will not be given here.[1] A rather large amount of work has been carried out on this problem over recent years, but much remains to be done. The field promises to be fruitful, for theoretical studies as well as for analytical purposes, since quantitative information can be obtained on the change in dipole moment during the vibrational displacement (Fig. X-18).

[1] For an introduction to the problems of infrared intensities see Wilson and Wells, *J. Chem. Phys.* **14**, 578 (1946); D. A. Ramsay, *J. Am. Chem. Soc.* **74**, 72 (1952); Penner and Aroeste, *J. Chem. Phys.* **23**, 2244 (1955); Kaplan and Eggers, *ibid.* **25**, 876 (1956); Haas and Hornig, *ibid.* **26**, 707 (1957); R. N. Jones, ref. 55, p. 38; W. B. Person, *J. Chem. Phys.* **28**, 319 (1958); B. Crawford, Jr., *ibid.* **29**, 1042 (1958).

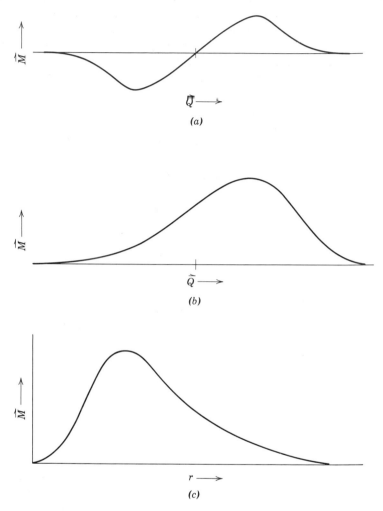

FIG. X-18. Schematic representation of variation of dipole moment with normal coordinate. (*a*) An infrared-active vibration of a symmetrical molecule, such as the 2350 cm^{-1} band of CO_2. (*b*) Stretching vibration of a non-symmetrical molecule, such as HCN. (*c*) Stretching of an individual bond, as in a diatomic molecule. Equilibrium bond distance in (*c*) may fall to the left or right of the maximum, or approximately at the maximum (as in HD). Intensity of the fundamental depends on the slope at the equilibrium position, $\partial M/\partial Q)_0$; intensity of the overtone depends on curvature at the equilibrium point, $\partial^2 M/\partial Q^2)_0$ (plus the effects of mechanical anharmonicity). In each example it is assumed that dissociation to neutral species occurs for large values of the coordinate.

Qualitatively we have already noted that such bonds as Si—O, C—Cl, or C—F tend to give very intense infrared bands, whereas C—C and C—H stretches tend to give weak bands, although C—H bending vibrations, such as the out-of-plane hydrogen motions in aromatic or olefinic compounds, may give rise to rather strong absorption bands. It is only reasonable to expect that essentially the same considerations would apply to such overtone and combination bands as may be observed in consequence of anharmonicity. Especially in the infrared region it is not too uncommon to find some binary combination bands which are more intense than some of the fundamentals. But combination bands would not be expected to be more intense than either of the fundamentals contributing to the combination band, assuming the fundamentals to be infrared active. For example, the C—F stretching vibrations tend to be very intense in the infrared but weak in the Raman effect. Combinations involving C—F stretching fundamentals may accordingly be expected to be strong in the infrared (whether that particular fundamental is allowed or forbidden by symmetry) but weak in the Raman effect. The reverse would be true for a double bond, which may be expected to give rise to strong scattering in the Raman effect and relatively strong scattering at a frequency corresponding to combination bands, whereas the fundamental and combination bands would be weak in the infrared spectrum.

The anharmonicity described in the previous section may be called "mechanical anharmonicity," since it is a deviation of the nuclear motion from that of the harmonic oscillator. If one considers very large displacements, leading to the dissociation of·the molecule, it will be clear that the effective charge on each atom must vary during this displacement, since the dissociation step must involve neutral atoms or atoms with an integral number of ionic charges. The variation of effective charge on the atoms during a vibration gives rise to an "electrical anharmonicity."

Both the mechanical and electrical anharmonicities contribute to the appearance of overtone and combination bands in the infrared spectrum. Electrical anharmonicity can also cause the appearance of overtone or combination bands in the Raman effect. Mechanical anharmonicity, however, will cause an overtone or combination band to appear in the Raman spectrum only when one of the contributing fundamental frequencies is Raman active.

3.4 Transitions from Excited States

To a first approximation it is possible to consider only transitions from the lowest vibrational state, since the number of molecules in a state of energy ΔE above the ground state will be limited by the Boltzmann factor.

$n_{\text{excited}}/n_{\text{ground state}} = \exp(-\Delta E/kt)$. At room temperature the factor kT/h is about 200 cm $^{-1}$, so the population of a non-degenerate state of this energy will be about one third that of the ground state, but the ratio drops off rapidly as ΔE increases, as shown in Fig. X-19. Beam intensities in op-

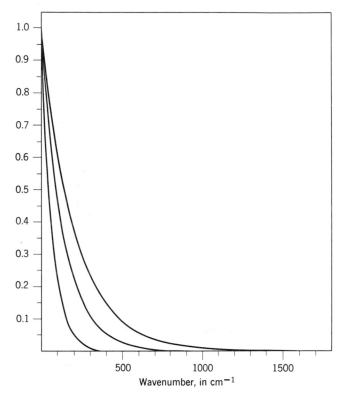

FIG. X-19. Boltzmann factor. The ordinate gives the relative probability of finding a molecule in a state of energy $hc\sigma$, at temperatures of 100°, 200°, and 300° K. If the state is degenerate, the ordinate should be multiplied by the degeneracy. Note that the absolute probability is smaller, since the relative probability is divided by the sum of these over all states.

tical spectroscopy are too low to produce any significant change in the normal distribution. For most purposes it is sufficient to consider transitions that might arise from excited states that are less than 600 cm^{-1} above the ground state and ignore the possibilities of transitions originating, at room temperature, from levels higher than this. The three types of transitions to be considered are Raman anti-Stokes bands, difference bands, and "upper stage" or "hot" bands.

Since the Raman effect is explained classically in terms of a beat fre-

quency between the frequencies of the imposed electromagnetic field and
the molecular vibrations, there should be an equal probability of observing
shifts toward higher and toward lower frequencies. The very great difference in intensities actually observed can only be explained by the quantum mechanical model. Shifts toward higher frequencies represent a
transfer of energy from a single molecule to a photon and are therefore
possible only when the molecule initially has the required excess energy
above its ground state. The number satisfying this requirement will be
determined by the Boltzmann factor.

The observed ratio of intensities of Raman bands at lower and higher
frequencies than the exciting line (Stokes and anti-Stokes lines, respectively) will be the product of the Boltzmann factor and the fourth power of
the emitted frequency,[1] but the former term will predominate.

$$\frac{I(\nu_i + \Delta\nu)}{I(\nu_i - \Delta\nu)} = \exp\left(-h\Delta\nu/kT\right)\left(\frac{\nu_i + \Delta\nu}{\nu_i - \Delta\nu}\right)^4 \approx \exp\left(-h\Delta\nu/kT\right) \quad \text{(X-61)}$$

Only those bands lying close to the exciting frequency, which arise from
low-frequency vibrations or rotations, will be observed as anti-Stokes
lines.

Combination bands, in either the infrared or Raman, tend to be quite
weak relative to the fundamental frequencies, but many of them are nevertheless observed. The probability of a transition from the ground state
to an upper state involving the simultaneous excitation of two vibrations,
Ψ_j and Ψ_k, will depend on an integral of the form $\int(\Psi_j\Psi_k)^*\mathbf{O}\Psi_g\,d\tau$,
where Ψ_g is the (totally symmetric) ground state wave function. If this
transition is allowed by symmetry, the "difference band" transition from
the state Ψ_j to the state Ψ_k, which depends on the integral $\int\Psi_k^*\mathbf{O}\Psi_j\,d\tau$,
must also be allowed by symmetry. The integrals need not have the same
value, but they have the same symmetry properties and involve approximately the same anharmonicities. It is the anharmonicity that makes the
integrals different from zero in each case. In the combination band,
$\Delta\mathbf{v}_j = \Delta\mathbf{v}_k = 1$, and in the difference band, $-\Delta\mathbf{v}_j = \Delta\mathbf{v}_k = 1$; neither
satisfies the selection rule requirement that $\Delta\mathbf{v}_j = 1$, $\Delta\mathbf{v}_k = 0$ or $\Delta\mathbf{v}_j = 0$,
$\Delta\mathbf{v}_k = 1$. The values will therefore be expected to be quite similar and

[1] The theory of Raman intensities has been given by G. Placzek, *Marx Handbuch der
Radiologie*, Second Edition, Vol. VI, Part II, pp. 209–374, 1934. Assuming that the
incident frequency is much larger than the vibrational frequency but much smaller than
the lowest electronic absorption frequency, the intensity is dependent on the number of
molecules in the initial state and on the fourth power of the emitted frequency. If the
incident frequency is comparable to the lowest electronic absorption frequency, changes
in the polarizability can become quite important, leading to significant changes in the
scattering probability. Certain parts of the theory have recently been questioned by
Kondilenko, Korotkov, and Strizhevskii, *Optics and Spectroscopy* **9**, 13 (1960).

for qualitative purposes, at least, may be taken to be the same. The intensity of the transition from the state Ψ_j to the state Ψ_k will be less than that of the corresponding sum band because of the small population of the initial state, Ψ_j. The observed frequency of a difference band must be exactly equal to the difference between the frequencies of the transitions from the ground state to the singly excited states (Fig. X-20).

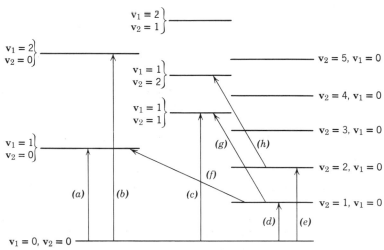

FIG. X-20. Combination and difference bands. Transitions (a) and (d) give the observed fundamental vibrational frequencies, ν_1 and ν_2, which differ only slightly from the harmonic values, $(\omega_e)_1$ and $(\omega_e)_2$. Transitions (b) and (e) correspond to overtones, of frequencies approximately (but generally somewhat less than) twice the observed fundamental frequencies, ν_1 and ν_2. Transition (c) gives a combination band, of frequency somewhat less than $\nu_1 + \nu_2$. Transition (f) corresponds to a difference band for which the observed frequency must be exactly $\nu_1 - \nu_2$. The transitions designated (g) and (h) give rise to "hot" bands. These are allowed but are seldom observed except under high resolution, since the frequencies will be nearly equal to ν_1 [transition (a)] and the intensities will be decreased by the Boltzmann factors for the initial states.

Among the many possible ternary combination bands will be those due to transitions starting from an excited state, Ψ_j, and ending in an excited state $\Psi_j\Psi_k$. The frequency for this transition will be approximately, but not exactly, $(\nu_j + \nu_k) - \nu_j = \nu_k$, since the level $\Psi_j\Psi_k$ does not lie precisely at the frequency $(\nu_j + \nu_k)$ above the ground state, but generally slightly lower than this because of the anharmonicity. The frequency associated with the "hot band" may therefore also be expected to be slightly lower than ν_k. In practice, such bands are seldom observed because they are inherently weak, as a consequence of the Boltzmann factor, and because they tend to be hidden by the stronger, nearby fundamental. However, these bands are allowed, since $\Delta \mathbf{v}_k = 1$, $\Delta \mathbf{v}_j = 0$. They are often apparent in the vapor phase under high resolution if there is a low-lying vibrational level.

3.5 Polarization of Raman Lines

An incident wave traveling along the x axis with electric vector in the xy plane will cause an oscillator at the origin to vibrate along the y axis. Scattered radiation will be restricted to the xz plane with electric vector parallel to the y axis (Fig. X-21).   An incident wave traveling along the x axis with electric vector in the xz plane will cause oscillations, at the origin, along the z axis.   Scattered radiation will then be restricted to the xy plane, with electric vector parallel to the z axis.

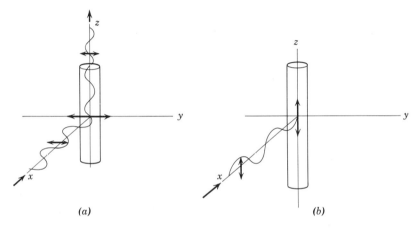

(a)   (b)

FIG. X-21.   Polarization of Raman emission.   (a) A wave traveling along the x axis with electric vector in the xy plane will give rise to radiation in the xz plane.   (b) A wave traveling in the xy plane with electric vector parallel to the z axis will not give rise to scattered radiation along the z axis unless the anisotropy, or "degree of depolarization," of the scattering center is non-zero.

Consider a Raman tube lying along the z axis, with the incident radiation in the xy plane.   If this radiation is polarized with electric vector parallel to the z axis, the scattered intensity observed along the z axis will be zero except as a consequence of asymmetry of the molecular vibration.   If the radiation is polarized in the xy plane, the appearance of scattered radiation along the z axis will not depend on asymmetry.   The "degree of depolarization." ρ, is defined as the ratio of the observed intensities of scattered radiation under these two conditions.   For a totally symmetric vibration of a molecule such as CCl_4, $\rho = 0$.   A non-totally symmetric vibration, of any molecule, will have the maximum value of ρ, which is $\frac{6}{7}$

under certain limiting experimental conditions. A totally symmetric vibration can have any value between these limits.

If the value of the polarizability is plotted on a coordinate system with origin at the center of mass of the molecule, an ellipsoid is obtained. If the molecule is a symmetric rotor, the ellipsoid will be a solid of revolution; if the molecule is a spherical rotor, the ellipsoid will be a sphere.

The induced dipole is related to the impressed field by the equation $\vec{\mu} = \alpha\vec{\mathscr{E}}$, or, more explicitly, remembering that the polarizability tensor is symmetric,

$$\begin{aligned}
\mu_x &= \alpha_{xx}\mathscr{E}_x + \alpha_{xy}\mathscr{E}_y + \alpha_{xz}\mathscr{E}_z \\
\mu_y &= \alpha_{xy}\mathscr{E}_x + \alpha_{yy}\mathscr{E}_y + \alpha_{yz}\mathscr{E}_z \\
\mu_z &= \alpha_{xz}\mathscr{E}_x + \alpha_{yz}\mathscr{E}_y + \alpha_{zz}\mathscr{E}_z
\end{aligned}$$ (X-62)

Now, if the incident electric vector is parallel to the z axis, $\mathscr{E}_x = \mathscr{E}_y = 0$. There will still be induced dipole moments along each of the three axes, of magnitudes

$$\begin{aligned}
\mu_x &= \alpha_{xz}\mathscr{E}_z \\
\mu_y &= \alpha_{yz}\mathscr{E}_z \\
\mu_z &= \alpha_{zz}\mathscr{E}_z
\end{aligned}$$ (X-63)

The induced dipole moment will be parallel to the impressed field only if the off-diagonal terms, α_{xz} and α_{yz}, are zero.

For random orientation of the scattering molecules, the ratios μ_x/μ_y and μ_x/μ_z must equal $\mathscr{E}_x/\mathscr{E}_y$ and $\mathscr{E}_x/\mathscr{E}_z$, respectively, if the scattered radiation is to be unchanged in its plane of polarization. This requires that $\alpha_{xx} = \alpha_{yy} = \alpha_{zz}$. That is, plane polarized incident radiation will have its plane of polarization altered by the scattering process unless the polarizability tensor is of the form

$$\alpha = \begin{bmatrix} \alpha_s & 0 & 0 \\ 0 & \alpha_s & 0 \\ 0 & 0 & \alpha_s \end{bmatrix}$$

This is equivalent to the condition that the polarizability ellipsoid should be a sphere, and must hold throughout the entire vibration. Accordingly, for the totally symmetric vibrations of a molecule belonging to one of the cubic point groups, there will be no tendency at all for the process of Raman scattering to change the plane of polarization of the incident radiation. For any vibration that is not totally symmetric, regardless of the point group to which the molecule belongs, the scattered radiation will be "completely" depolarized. A symmetric vibration of a molecule in a non-cubic point group may fall any place between these limits.

This provides an important means of identifying the origin of lines observed in the Raman effect.   If the depolarization is found to be $\frac{6}{7}$ (or a corresponding value when one takes into consideration the precise experimental conditions), one can only surmise that the band may arise from a transition allowed under a non-totally-symmetric species.   But, if the depolarization is observed to be less than $\frac{6}{7}$, in the gas phase and in the absence of extraneous perturbations such as strong Coriolis coupling, one may conclude definitely that the band corresponds to a totally symmetric vibration.   It is immaterial whether the vibration is a totally symmetric fundamental, an overtone, or a combination level; if, and only if, the transition has a component transforming according to the totally symmetric representation, the degree of depolarization can be less than the maximum value.

An additional characteristic that may be helpful in the recognition of totally symmetric Raman bands is the line width.[1]   In the gas phase, totally symmetric bands should be much sharper than non-totally-symmetric bands.   In this case, in contrast to the case of depolarization ratios, the observation of a broad line in the gas phase is strong evidence that the band is non-totally-symmetric; the observation that the line is sharp is only weak evidence as to symmetry since bands may be sharp for other reasons.   In the liquid state the argument is much less conclusive.

3.6 Fermi Resonance

It is well known that two oscillations of approximately the same frequency and of the same symmetry properties will appear to interact and split apart if they are mechanically coupled, giving two new modes of oscillation and two new frequencies, one higher than the original, the other lower.   A particular case, which was first recognized and explained by Fermi, is the interaction that may occur between a fundamental vibrational frequency and a combination or overtone vibration which happens to have nearly the same frequency.

The problem appeared first in a study of the infrared and Raman spectra of CO_2.   Two frequencies should appear in the infrared spectrum, corresponding to the antisymmetric stretch and the degenerate bending mode.   These are observed, at 2349.3 and 667.3 cm^{-1}.   The other fundamental mode should appear in the Raman effect, but two bands, of roughly equal intensity, were observed at 1285.5 and 1388.3 cm^{-1}, and both were polarized, as the fundamental should be.   The first overtone of the bending vibration (667.3) would be expected to occur at or very slightly below 1334 cm^{-1}.   This should consist of the components Σ_g^+, Σ_g^-, and Δ_g.

[1] See Herzberg, ref. 44, p. 444.

Of these the $\Sigma_g{}^+$ and Δ_g components should be Raman active but weak. Since the fundamental is also of symmetry $\Sigma_g{}^+$, the possibility for interaction between this and the totally symmetric component of the overtone exists. If one then assumes that the fundamental frequency should "naturally" occur at about 1334 cm^{-1}, the two observed totally symmetric bands in the Raman spectrum are readily interpreted as the two vibrations resulting from the mixing of the symmetric stretching and the overtone of the bending. The degenerate component of the bending vibration should still occur at about 1334 cm^{-1} as a depolarized line, but it is too weak to have been observed.

Fermi resonance, such as that described in the CO_2 molecule, is quite commonly observed, both in the infrared and the Raman spectrum. Two requirements must be met: the vibrational levels which are to interact must be of the same symmetry species, and the vibrations must be in the same or closely adjacent parts of the molecule so that the mechanical coupling between them will be significant. The amount of splitting observed will vary directly with the strength of the coupling and inversely with the separation of the unperturbed vibrational levels. In cases of strong mixing such as the CO_2 1285–1388 pair, the two resultant levels cannot be individually assigned to either mode of motion. The intensities of the two bands will then be comparable; if the levels are initially farther apart, the amount of mixing will be smaller and both the displacement and the extent of intensity sharing will be considerably smaller. The extent to which the coupled bands share intensity is dependent on the state of the sample. In condensed phases the bands will be more nearly equal in intensity, even though the splitting is comparable.[1] Fermi resonance can be readily demonstrated with molecular models, arising as in actual molecules through the inevitable anharmonicity of the vibrations.

3.7 Inversion Doubling

Exchange of two identical particles cannot change the energy of a molecule, but the process of moving them may require a large amount of energy, thus leading to a potential well with two or more minima and possibly a very high maximum between them. Other operations, such as the rotation of one part of a molecule against another or the reflection of the molecule in a plane, may give similar potential energy curves, if the same configuration cannot be achieved by a rotation of the molecule. Examples would be the exchange of nitrogen nuclei in N—N—O or of equivalent fluorine nuclei in F—PF_3—F, the rotation of one methyl group

---

[1] V. L. Strizhevskii, *Optics and Spectroscopy* **8**, 86 (1960); Abramowitz and Bauman, *Spectrochim. Acta* **17**, 125 (1961).

against the other in ethane or of the hydroxyl group against the methyl in methanol, and the reflection, in a plane parallel to the H_3 plane, of the NH_3 or $ClCH_3$ molecules. Exchange of oxygen atoms in CO_2 or of fluorine atoms in BF_3 will not give a configuration that could not also be achieved by a rotation, so the potential wells for these molecules will each have a single minimum.

In most cases the energy required to get from one equivalent form to the other is so large that the double minimum may conveniently be disregarded. There are a few instances, however, such as the ammonia molecule and molecules with weakly hindered internal rotation, in which the existence of the equivalent states has a marked influence on the observed spectrum.

The potential curve for the ν_2 vibration of ammonia (950 cm^{-1}) is shown in Fig. X-22a. If the barrier between the two forms were infinitely high, the vibrational levels would be those indicated by dotted lines. Classically the same result should be expected for a finite barrier as long as the energy of the molecule is less than the barrier height. But, if the problem is treated by quantum mechanics, one finds a calculable probability of the molecule passing from one form to the other even though the energy available is less than that required to surmount the barrier. This is an example of "tunneling," which is associated with the indeterminism of simultaneous momentum and position measurements (section V-2.1). If such interaction between the two states is possible, the degeneracy between positive and negative states will be split. This is actually observed, the true energy levels being those indicated by the solid lines.[1] The transition between the two levels of the ground vibrational state is allowed in absorption. It is observed in the microwave region.

The wave functions for the two ground states are shown in Fig. X-22b. The lower state is symmetrical to the reflection operation, the upper state is antisymmetric. The probability of finding the nitrogen atom on either side of the plane of the hydrogens depends only on $\Psi^*\Psi$ and is identical in the two states.

Tunneling is characteristic of small systems and is closely associated with the uncertainty principle. No strictly classical analog exists. A semiclassical model for the behavior of the ammonia molecule can be constructed on the following basis. The antisymmetric wave function differs in phase in the two mirror-image forms of the molecule. This correlates, in the wave picture, with the classical concept of an oscillatory motion of the nitrogen atom through the plane. The period of the motion

---

[1] The term "inversion doubling," introduced by Herzberg, is suitably descriptive. It should be noted, however, that the operation involved is not always that of inversion, or reflection through a center of symmetry, although it can always be written as the product of an improper rotation, such as the inversion operation, and a pure rotation.

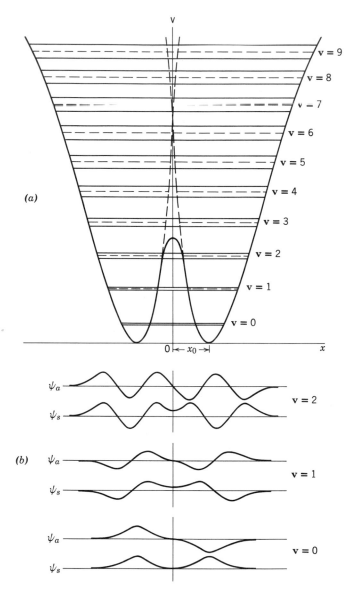

FIG. X-22. Inversion splitting in ammonia. (*a*) Splitting of vibrational energy levels (with splitting for **v** = 0 and **v** = 1 exaggerated). (*b*) The simple-harmonic-oscillator wave functions for the two equivalent states combine into symmetric and anti-symmetric functions for each value of the vibrational quantum number. (From G. Herzberg, *Infrared and Raman Spectra of Polyatomic Molecules*, copyright 1945, D. Van Nostrand Co., Inc., Princeton, N.J.).

is assumed to be the reciprocal of the frequency absorbed, which is the difference in energy between the symmetric and antisymmetric states divided by Planck's constant. If the barrier is infinitely high, the two states (symmetric and antisymmetric to the reflection operation) will have identical energy and the lifetime of either form will be infinite. In this limit the distinction between symmetric and antisymmetric states becomes meaningless. If the molecule exists in one form, the phase of the wave function in an inaccessible region cannot affect the observed properties.

As the height of the barrier is lowered or the energy of the system approaches the value required classically to surmount the barrier, the time required for the barrier penetration will decrease; hence the associated frequency will rise, and the two states (symmetric and antisymmetric) will become increasingly different in energy. For very high-energy values of the molecule the symmetric and antisymmetric states give two sets of evenly spaced levels.

The selection rules are most easily derived by consideration of the symmetry properties of the planar configuration. For a planar ammonia molecule, of symmetry D_{3h}, the bending mode leading to the pyramidal structure will be a vibration of symmetry A_2''. The vibrational levels for this mode will therefore be A_1' or A_2'' depending on whether the vibrational quantum number is even or odd. Thus the vibrational levels, reading from bottom to top, will be symmetric (ground state), antisymmetric (first excited state), symmetric (first "overtone" level), antisymmetric, etc., with respect to the plane. A distortion of the potential well to produce the barrier shown in Fig. X-22a will cause a convergence of certain of the levels, as shown, but will not change the symmetry properties. Under the point group C_{3v} they will all be of symmetry A_1 but will be alternately symmetric or antisymmetric.

The selection rules under D_{3h} allow transitions between A_1' and A_2'' but not between A_1' and A_1' for dipole radiation, whereas Raman transitions are allowed between A_1' and A_1' but not between A_1' and A_2''. Thus transitions from symmetric to antisymmetric levels are observed in the infrared, for which the observed splitting is the sum of the splittings of the two (dotted line) vibrational levels, but transitions in the Raman effect are symmetric to symmetric or antisymmetric to antisymmetric and only the difference of the two splittings is observed. For vibrational levels well above the barrier the vibrational frequency will appear to be only half as great in the Raman spectrum as in the infrared. For vibrational levels below the top of the barrier the splitting depends strongly on the area under the potential barrier above the vibrational energy level. As other vibrational modes will not cause the molecule to approach the planar configuration for reasonable values of the energy and quantum number, the splitting in all vibrational levels for these modes will be essentially that of the ground state of the vibration of Fig. X-22. This ground state splitting is only 0.67 cm^{-1}.

1 Rotational Spectra

The moment of inertia of any rigid body will depend on the axis of rotation but will be independent of direction of rotation about that axis. If the moment of inertia is plotted in a cartesian coordinate system centered in the molecule a momental ellipsoid, similar to the polarizability ellipsoid of section 3.5, is obtained. In the case of an asymmetric rotor, the ellipsoid will have three unique axes which will be maxima or minima; they define the principal axes of the molecule. Two of these axes will be equal if the molecule is a symmetric rotor, and the momental ellipsoid will be an ellipsoid of revolution. The two equal axes are not unique but may be taken as any mutually perpendicular diameters of the circular cross section through the center of mass. A linear molecule may be considered a special case of the symmetric top, for which the momental ellipsoid degenerates into a straight-line segment. A spherical rotor will have all three principal axes equal; they will be any three mutually perpendicular diameters of the spherical momental ellipsoid.

4.1 Rotational Energy Levels

The rotational energy levels and selection rules were derived on a semi-classical basis in sections V-2.5 and V-4.4. For the symmetric rotor, the total angular momentum is represented by $\mathbf{J}$, the quantum number corresponding to the vector $\vec{\mathbf{J}}$ of magnitude $\sqrt{\mathbf{J}(\mathbf{J}+1)}\,\hbar$ directed perpendicular to the plane of rotation; the projection of $\vec{\mathbf{J}}$ on the symmetry axis is exactly $\mathbf{K}\hbar$. The rotational term values, assuming no electronic angular momentum, are then

$$F(\mathbf{J}, \mathbf{K}) = \mathbf{J}(\mathbf{J}+1)B + \mathbf{K}^2(A-B) \qquad \text{(X-64)}$$

to the rigid rotor approximation.

For linear molecules the rotational constant A becomes very large, since I_A is essentially zero, and thus $\mathbf{K}$ must be zero. The term values are then simply

$$F(\mathbf{J}) = \mathbf{J}(\mathbf{J}+1)B \qquad \text{(X-65)}$$

Exactly the same formula will give the term values for spherical rotors, since in this case $A = B$ and the second expression in equation X-64 again drops out.

Actual molecules are not rigid, and consequently they become distorted during rotation due to the centrifugal force.   Classically the angular velocity is given by

$$\omega = \sqrt{2\text{E}/I} \qquad\qquad (\text{X-66})$$

and from the law of equipartition of energy the rotational energy of a molecule should be determined by the temperature.   Light molecules, with small moments of inertia, will have high angular velocities.   The centrifugal distortion term is nearly always small and is often neglected, but for light molecules in high rotational states it may become appreciable.   For any molecule this and other corrections will be important in fitting observed rotational levels to the theoretical calculations when the levels are measured to the high precision now possible.   For example, it has been found necessary to include as many as ten terms, most of which are very small, to fit the absorption lines observed in the inversion spectrum of ammonia.   Expressed in megacycles per second, the frequencies[1] are given by

$$\nu = 23{,}785.8 - 151.450J(J + 1) + 211.342K^2 + 0.503027J^2(J + 1)^2$$
$$- 1.38538J(J + 1)K^2 + 0.949155K^4 - 0.001259997J^3(J + 1)^3$$
$$+ 0.00518267J^2(J + 1)^2K^2 - 0.007088534J(J + 1)K^4$$
$$+ 0.003210437K^6$$

The general case of an asymmetric rotor is not readily treated.[2]   Qualitative solutions can be obtained by the following method.   The intermediate moment of inertia is set equal to the largest of the moments of inertia, thus giving a prolate symmetric rotor, for which the energy levels are readily calculated and plotted.   The intermediate moment of inertia is then set equal to the smallest of the moments of inertia, and the energy levels of the resultant oblate symmetric rotor are calculated and plotted. A correlation diagram, assuming a minimum amount of crossing of levels and smooth variation of energy as a function of the intermediate moment of inertia, can then be constructed and the energy levels for the intermediate case read from this diagram.   The levels can be calculated for specific values of the moments of inertia.   Formulas for this have been given by a number of investigators.   In addition, there are certain necessary relationships between levels, which give rise, for example, to "sum rules" relating energies of sublevels of a given J.   They provide

[1] Sharbaugh, Madison, and Bragg, *Phys. Rev.* **76**, 1529 (1949); see also C. C. Costain, *ibid.*, **82**, 108 (1951).

[2] See Herzberg, ref. 44, pp. 45–46, for a discussion and references.

convenient guide posts in assigning rotational quantum numbers to observed lines.

Interpretation of rotational spectra is too specialized to warrant comprehensive treatment here.[1]   Even without detailed assignments, however, it is often possible to draw important conclusions from the observed spectra.   They are related in part to the symmetry properties of the rotational levels.

4.2   Symmetry Classification of Rotational States and Selection Rules

Rotational wave functions must have symmetry properties consistent with the rotational subgroup[2] of the momental ellipsoid of the molecule. Moreover, certain other symmetry properties must be added if identical nuclei are present, because of the spin properties of the nuclei, and for planar or linear molecules or molecules that are sufficiently close to being planar that an "inversion" of the molecule (or any reflection operation giving a result not obtainable by rotations alone) is probable.

The momental ellipsoid of an asymmetric rotor has three distinct principal axes, designated a, b, and c in order of increasing moment of inertia. The rotational subgroup for such an ellipsoid is the group D_2 (or V). This has the elements I, $C_2{}^a$, $C_2{}^b$, $C_2{}^c$ and the irreducible representations[3] A, B_1, B_2, B_3 (p. 586).   The symmetry is related to the projection of angular momentum on the axis, in the sense that as the moments of inertia are varied to give a symmetric top, for which a quantum number K is defined, an even value of K will correspond to a wave function that is symmetric, an odd K to a wave function that is antisymmetric, with respect to the axis on which K is the projection.

The selection rules for rotational transitions of an asymmetric rotor are easily determined.   Absorption of radiation by a dipole mechanism requires that the direct product of the representations of initial and final states must contain (for the non-degenerate case, must be identical with)

---

[1] Interpretation of the rotational structure of rotation-vibration bands is treated in detail by Allen and Cross, ref. 65.

[2] The rotational subgroup of a point group is the group consisting of those elements which are proper rotations.   If, as is generally true, the original point group also contained improper rotations, the subgroup will contain fewer elements, fewer classes, and fewer representations.

[3] The nomenclature for rotational levels here is chosen to retain the maximum consistency with discussions of other applications of the same symmetry properties.   The states labeled A, B_1, B_2, B_3 are the $+ +$, $- +$, $- -$, $+ -$ states given by Herzberg (ref. 44, p. 51).   Note in particular that the letter designations here and in the remainder of this section are not the A, E, etc., states of Herzberg, which are based on properties of the nuclei.

the representation for one of the components of the dipole moment. In the absence of a symmetry axis of the molecule, the dipole moment will not fall along any one axis but will have a component along each, so that rotation about any of the three principal axes will cause a change in dipole moment. Then any transition of the form $A \leftrightarrow B_i$ or $B_i \leftrightarrow B_j$ will be allowed, but transitions with totally symmetric character will be forbidden ($A \leftrightarrow A$, $B_i \leftrightarrow B_i$).

An asymmetric rotor may have an axis of symmetry, in which case the dipole moment must lie along this unique axis. Only one type of transition will then be possible from a totally symmetric level. This will be to

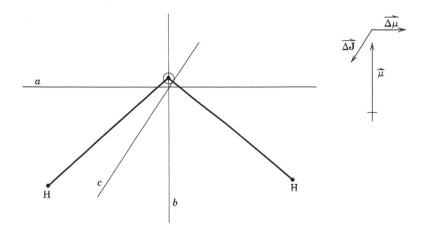

FIG. X-23. Rotational selection rule. A change in dipole moment due to a rotation must correspond to a rotation about an axis perpendicular to the symmetry axis. For example, if $\overrightarrow{\Delta \mu}$ is along the a axis of H_2O, $\overrightarrow{\Delta J}$ must be along the c axis (perpendicular to $\overrightarrow{\Delta \mu}$ and to $\overrightarrow{\mu}$). The rotational energy about the symmetry axis remains unchanged.

the state representing *no* change in angular momentum along the symmetry axis. For example, in the water molecule the two-fold axis lies along the intermediate axis, b (Fig. X-23). The electromagnetic field must change the direction of the dipole moment to cause rotation, producing an angular momentum represented by a vector, $\overrightarrow{\Delta J}$, perpendicular to the two-fold axis. The projection of $\overrightarrow{J}$ on the two-fold axis (essentially K) will be unchanged. The transition from a totally symmetric state (A) will therefore be to a state of that symmetry species which is symmetric to the two-fold axis of the water molecule but antisymmetric to the other principal axes (B_2). Since the normal distribution of rotational energy is such as to give significant populations in all the low-lying rotational states, transitions from excited non-totally-symmetric rotational states will be equally intense as the transitions from totally symmetric states. The rules may be written $A \leftrightarrow B_2$, $B_1 \leftrightarrow B_3$, but the subscripts will depend on whether the symmetry axis lies along the a, b, or c axis.

Rotational transitions are allowed in the Raman spectrum between all states for an asymmetric rotor without an axis of symmetry. If a symmetry axis is present, the momental ellipsoid will coincide with the polarizability ellipsoid.[1] The only transition possible from a totally symmetric state will then be to another totally symmetric state. More generally, a transition can take place from any state to another state of the same symmetry.

The momental ellipsoid of a symmetric rotor will be a figure of revolution with a center of symmetry and will thus belong to the point group $D_{\infty h}$. The rotational subgroup will have properties sufficiently similar to $C_{\infty v}$ or $D_{\infty h}$ that these tables may be employed. It will be convenient to designate the non-degenerate species by A (rather than Σ) and the degenerate species E_i (rather than Π, Δ, Φ, ...). To cause a change in rotational state the field must produce a change in dipole moment perpendicular to the symmetry axis. As for the asymmetric rotor with a symmetry axis, this cannot change the angular momentum along the symmetry axis ($\mathbf{K}$). The selection rule for a symmetric rotor, including linear molecules, is therefore $A \leftrightarrow A$, $E_i \leftrightarrow E_i$, $A \longleftrightarrow E_i$. These are also the Raman selection rules, for essentially the same reason as given above in the discussion of the asymmetric rotor with a symmetry axis.

A symmetric rotor which has no permanent dipole moment may still give a Raman rotational spectrum but cannot have a pure rotational spectrum in the infrared or microwave regions. A spherical rotor cannot undergo a change in either dipole moment or polarizability by means of a rotation, since both ellipsoids are spheres. Consequently a spherical rotor will not give a pure rotational spectrum in either the infrared or Raman.

If the vibrational or electronic states are not totally symmetric or if the transitions between electronic or vibrational (or "inversion") states occur simultaneously with the rotational transition, the selection rules must include additional considerations. Furthermore, the intensities of certain of the lines that are allowed by the selection rules given above are markedly

---

[1] This coincidence of axes is not to be expected in the absence of a symmetry axis. When the two sets of axes coincide, they may be chosen as the x, y, z axes. In this coordinate system both tensors are diagonalized, consisting only of the terms α_{xx}, α_{yy}, α_{zz}, or I_{xx}, I_{yy}, I_{zz}. The diagonal components of the polarizability matrix transform according to the totally symmetric representation, A, and the transition moment will vanish unless the product of initial and final rotational states transforms in the same fashion. This is possible only if the rotational states have the same symmetry.

affected by the nuclear spins.   Some of the rotational levels are actually missing for this reason.

4.3   Statistical Weights and Intensities

The intensity of a rotational line depends on the magnitude of the change in dipole moment or change in polarizability and also on the population of the initial rotational level.   The relative population of an energy level of a molecule is proportional to the statistical weight, which is equal to the number of independent states that contribute to that level, or equal to the degeneracy of the level.   Thus a molecule with angular momentum J will have (at least) $2J + 1$ states of equal energy, corresponding to the various possible orientations of J.

If the spins of the nuclei are taken into account there will be an additional factor in the statistical weight.   For example, in the well-known case of the hydrogen molecule, the probability of obtaining a state with parallel spins of the hydrogen nuclei (triplet state, *ortho*-hydrogen) is three times as great as the probability of a state with antiparallel spins (singlet state, *para*-hydrogen).   If two identical nuclei are interchanged, the wave function must be left unchanged if the nuclei follow Bose-Einstein statistics (even half-integral spin, resulting from even mass number) or it must change sign if the nuclei follow Fermi-Dirac statistics (odd half-integral spin, resulting from odd mass number).   If both types of nuclei are involved the sign change will be the product for each equivalent pair; hence Bose statistics will be applicable if an even number of pairs following Fermi statistics are present, otherwise Fermi statistics.

Consider first the case in which the identical nuclei that are exchanged by the inversion operation have zero spin.   The inversion operation must leave the total wave function of the molecule unchanged; thus only those rotational states that are symmetric to this operation can be present.   The other states will not exist.   In the case of the hydrogen molecule, the total wave function must be antisymmetric to the inversion operation.   For *ortho*-hydrogen the nuclear spin function is unchanged by inversion (Table X-XIV) and therefore only antisymmetric rotational states can exist, whereas for *para*-hydrogen the nuclear spin function is antisymmetric to inversion and only symmetrical rotational states can exist.   Since there should be three times as many ortho molecules as para, the statistical weight, due to nuclear spins, of the antisymmetric rotational levels is three times as great as for the symmetric levels.

The interaction of nuclear spins with their environment is much weaker than the interaction of electron spins, so that there exists a prohibition of intercombinations (similar to the rule $\Delta S = 0$) that is unusually strict, applying not only to absorption of radiation and Raman scattering but also to other processes such as collisions between molecules.[1] Accordingly, only transitions between two states that are symmetric in the nuclei or two states that are antisymmetric in the nuclei are observed. Pure *ortho*-hydrogen will show one set of rotational lines, pure *para*-hydrogen will show an entirely different set of rotational lines, and the equilibrium mixture at room temperature and above will show both sets with an intensity ratio of 3 to 1 (excluding differences in statistical weight due to different values of **J**). It should be noted that the classification discussed here is with respect to an inversion of the nuclei only, not with respect to inversion of the entire molecule. Thus the symmetric or antisymmetric character (designated *s* and *a*) is not the same as the parity property (designated + and −) discussed in section 3.7.

Since the statistical weights arising from considerations of nuclear spin depend on the actual value of the spin and on the symmetry of the molecule, no detailed discussion of individual cases will be given here. Most of the cases of interest are discussed in the literature. It should be noted, however, that this dependence often allows the determination of both molecular symmetries and nuclear spins from the observed spectra.

5   Superposition of Transitions and Perturbation Effects

To a first approximation the spectra observed in the microwave and very far infrared regions are pure rotational transitions, the spectra observed in the near infrared region are a superposition of rotational transitions on vibrational transitions, and the spectra observed in the ultraviolet and visible regions are a superposition of the rotation-vibration transitions on electronic transitions. The selection rules in each case are very nearly those of the primary (highest energy) transition, plus a restriction on change in total angular momentum, but the observation of the band contours and the intensity relationships within band systems can give important information on the structure of the molecule.

5.1   Rotation-Vibration Spectra

The selection rules for rotation-vibration spectra are those of the vibrational and rotational transitions, independently, except in cases of strong Coriolis coupling. The band contour is determined by the nature of the vibrational mode excited and can provide a clue to the assignment of observed bands to individual molecular vibrations. Rotational struc-

---

[1] The attainment of equilibrium between *ortho*- and *para*-hydrogen at room temperature may require weeks or months in the absence of a catalyst.

tures of electronic transitions of diatomic molecules are also of great importance, but such structure is not often resolved for polyatomic molecules.

5.11   Rotation-Vibration Band Contours

Vibrational transitions in asymmetric rotors are classified according to the axis along which the dipole moment changes.   Type A bands correspond to a change in dipole moment along the axis of smallest moment of inertia; type B bands to a change along the intermediate axis; type C to a change along the axis of largest moment.   These designations are completely independent of any symmetry properties or classifications.   Unless there is a symmetry axis, it is likely that most bands will not fall uniquely into any of these three classifications but will be hybrid bands, having properties relating to more than one type.

The structures of rotation-vibration bands of asymmetric rotors are very complex, with little regularity, except when the molecule is very nearly a symmetric rotor.   Even the band contours can vary appreciably.[1]   In most cases, however, a type A band will be expected to show a strong central maximum.   Type B bands should have a central minimum, usually flanked by two strong bands which are flanked, in turn, by broader side bands.   A type C band is more likely to resemble the type A band than type B.

Vibrational transitions in symmetric rotors are classified into parallel and perpendicular bands according to the direction of change of dipole moment with respect to the symmetry axis.   Parallel bands must accompany non-degenerate vibrations, whereas a perpendicular band is associated with a degenerate vibration.   For transitions between two excited degenerate levels the band can be either of the parallel or of the perpendicular type according to whether it is allowed by the M_z or the $M_{x,y}$ component of the dipole moment.

In a parallel transition the nuclei move parallel to the symmetry axis, corresponding to an angular momentum vector perpendicular to this axis. This leaves the quantum number $\mathbf{K}$ unchanged.   If $\vec{\mathbf{J}}$ was initially perpendicular to the axis ($\mathbf{K} = 0$), $\mathbf{J}$ can only change by ± 1; otherwise it can change by 0 or ± 1.

$$\Delta\mathbf{K} = 0$$
$$\Delta\mathbf{J} = 0, \pm 1 \qquad\qquad (\text{X-67})$$
$$\Delta\mathbf{J} \neq 0 \text{ for } \mathbf{K} = 0$$

The observed absorption band will therefore consist of a P branch, at frequencies less than the vibrational frequency, corresponding to $\Delta\mathbf{J} = -1$;

---

[1] Badger and Zumwalt, *J. Chem. Phys.* **6**, 711 (1938).

a Q branch, at the vibrational frequency, arising from transitions with $\Delta J = 0$; and an R branch, at higher frequencies, corresponding to $\Delta J = +1$. Since the spacing between levels increases with increasing J, the $\Delta J = \pm 1$ transitions between levels of higher J will correspond to larger energy differences and will fall farther away from the center of the band.

To a first approximation, the spacing between levels and therefore the positions of the lines shown in Fig. X-24a will be independent of K, so

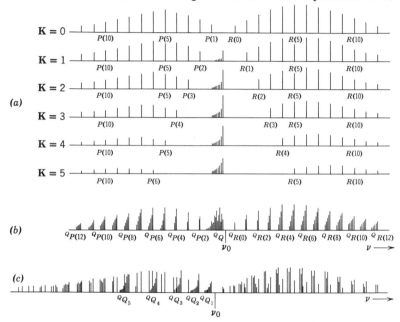

FIG. X-24.   Rotational structure of a parallel band of a symmetric rotor.   (a) Sub-bands for various values of K.   (b) Superposition of sub-bands from (a) assuming only a small change in rotational constants between vibrational states.   (c) Superposition of K sub-bands assuming a larger change in moments of inertia.   Intensities are calculated for $T = 144°$ K and $A = 5.25$, $B = 1.70$ cm^{-1} in lower state.   Sublevels with negative K values are included in (b) and (c).   (From G. Herzberg, *Infrared and Raman Spectra of Polyatomic Molecules*, copyright 1945, D. Van Nostrand Co., Inc., Princeton, N.J.)

that the identical sets of lines will be superimposed corresponding to the various values of K in the initial state of the molecule.   Since $J \geqslant K$, $K - 1$ lines will be missing from the center of each set.   In practice, the spacing will depend slightly on the value of K, causing the lines of identical J but different K to form a sharp sub-band, rather than a single line.   The effect of this on the over-all band contour is shown in Fig. X-24b.   Diatomic and linear polyatomic molecules will have only a single set, determined by the value of Λ, the electronic angular momentum along the axis, since $K = 0$ for all states.[1]   For a Σ^+ state the pattern will be that of Fig. X-24a except that the Q branch is missing; Π states will have a strong, sharp Q branch.

A perpendicular transition, since it moves the nuclei perpendicular to the symmetry axis, produces an angular momentum along the symmetry axis.   The selection rules are therefore

$$\Delta K = \pm 1$$
$$\Delta J = 0, \pm 1 \qquad \qquad \text{(X-68)}$$
$$J = 0 \leftrightarrow J = 0$$

The contours of perpendicular bands are completely unpredictable without some knowledge of the ratio of the two moments of inertia and the Coriolis coupling coefficients.[2]

Band contours are potentially as valuable in the Raman spectrum as in the infrared.   The contours to be expected are discussed in the literature, but very few molecules have been studied under sufficiently high resolution to display the rotational structure.

5.12 Coriolis Interactions

Motions of a body referred to a uniformly rotating coordinate system will not be properly represented unless two correction terms are added to the equations of motion.   The "centrifugal force",

$$\vec{f} = \vec{p_i} \times \vec{\omega} \qquad \qquad \text{(X-69)}$$

is an apparent radial force perpendicular to the angular velocity vector, $\vec{\omega}$, and to the linear momentum measured with respect to the inertial, or space-fixed, coordinate system.

The "Coriolis force,"

$$\vec{f} = 2\vec{p_r} \times \vec{\omega} \qquad \qquad \text{(X-70)}$$

is perpendicular to the angular velocity vector and to the linear momentum, $\vec{p_r}$, measured in the rotating coordinate system.   Like the centrifugal force, it is fictitious in the sense that it appears only to the rotating observer.

The centrifugal force has the effect of increasing the moment of inertia of the molecule as it rotates.   This may be considered as an interaction

---

[1] It should perhaps be emphasized that the moment of inertia about the symmetry axis of a linear molecule is vanishingly small for all states.   Electronic angular momentum is possible not because the moment of inertia is large but because the product $I\omega_e^2$ is made large by the rapid motions of the electrons.

[2] Expected contours for various values of Coriolis coupling constants and the ratio of the two moments of inertia of symmetric rotors have been calculated by Edgell and Moynihan.

between rotation and vibration since the distention of the molecule is governed by the vibrational force constants, which oppose the centrifugal forces. The effect is very small but sometimes is measurable.

Coriolis forces tend to be larger because the linear momentum associated with vibrations is much greater than that associated with rotations. The Coriolis forces acting on a molecule undergoing a totally symmetric vibration cause a coupling between the vibration and rotation (Fig. X-25). This is small and is often excluded from the class of Coriolis interactions. In a non-totally symmetric vibration the Coriolis forces often couple two normal modes of vibration of different symmetry. The strength of this coupling depends on the angular velocity, disappearing entirely for states

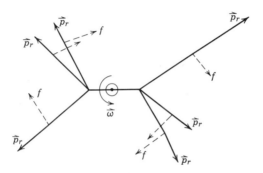

FIG. X-25.   Coriolis coupling for a totally symmetric vibration. The angular momentum, ω, points out of the paper, the linear momenta, p_r, lie in the planes of the bonds and the symmetry axis.   The Coriolis forces, $2p_r x\omega$, are perpendicular to ω and therefore in the plane of the paper.   These give a negative contribution to ω as drawn, or a positive contribution during the opposite phase of the vibration.

with $J = 0$ (thus not changing the band centers).   It also varies inversely with the frequency difference between the vibrations, since the mixing depends on the excitation of one oscillation at the frequency of the other. Jahn has shown that in order for two vibrations to be coupled the integral over the product of the two vibrational wave functions and the rotational wave function must not vanish.   This is satisfied only if the product of the two vibrational functions transforms according to a symmetry species to which a rotation belongs.

Coriolis perturbations, though stronger than centrifugal stretching effects, are generally small because the vibrations that are coupled have significantly different frequencies, even though these are approximately accidentally degenerate.   Degenerate vibrations, by contrast, may exhibit strong coupling between the two modes since the frequencies are identical. This coupling is described classically in terms of a Coriolis force opposing or supplementing the vibrational force constant, thus changing the vibrational frequency for excited rotational levels.   It may also be described quantum mechanically by requiring that the projection on the axis of the total angular momentum, including the vibrational component, shall be integral.   Since the vibrational contribution is generally between zero and one unit, the molecular rotational angular momentum must be correspondingly increased or decreased to keep the sum integral.

For a symmetric rotor the rotational levels are given by the expression

$$F(J, K) = BJ(J + 1) + (A - B)K^2 \mp 2A\zeta K$$

when the Coriolis splitting due to the excitation of one degenerate vibration is taken into account.   The value of zeta depends on the form of the vibration (section 3.1).   If the form of the vibration is such that the nuclei move perpendicular to the symmetry axis, the two components may be written as circular motion in clockwise and counterclockwise directions. This produces the maximum coupling, $\zeta = \pm 1$ (the sign depending on relative directions of vibrational and pure rotational motions).   If the form of the vibration is such that the nuclei move along the same straight line in both components, $\zeta = 0$.   In intermediate cases the nuclei will follow elliptical paths, the eccentricity of the ellipse and the value of ζ depending on the masses of the atoms, the size and shape of the molecule, and the force constants.   The sum of the zeta constants for any one symmetry species is independent of force constants, however, depending at most on the values of the moments of inertia.   If there is only one vibration in the degenerate species its constant is fixed; if there is more than one it may be possible to determine one constant from observation of another and the application of this sum rule.   Approximate values of the ζ_i can be estimated from a knowledge of the general form of the vibration.[1]

5.13 Doubling of Rotational Lines

To a first approximation each rotational level is $(2J + 1)^2$-fold degenerate.   This degeneracy is split (except in a spherical rotor) by the difference in energy corresponding to different values of the projection of $\overrightarrow{J}$ on the symmetry axis (or on other axes of an asymmetric rotor).   That is, levels of different K have different energy.   This leaves each level with K > 0 two-fold degenerate (neglecting nuclear spins), since the energy is the same for +K and −K, in addition to the $(2J + 1)$-fold degeneracy arising from the orientation of $\overrightarrow{J}$ in space.

The two-fold degeneracy can also be split if there is an angular momentum along the symmetry axis that can interact with this.   In diatomic

[1] See, for example, Herzberg, ref. 44, pp. 401–406; Lord and Merrifield, *J. Chem. Phys.* **20**, 1348 (1952); Meal and Polo, *ibid.*, **24**, 1119 (1956).

molecules with $\Lambda > 0$ the interaction between Λ and R, the molecular rotation, is ignored in first approximation [Hund's cases (a) and (b)]. The weak coupling between this electronic angular momentum and the molecular rotation can lead to a splitting that ranges from much less than 1 cm^{-1} to a maximum of several cm^{-1}, depending on the value of J and the strength of the coupling. This is called "Λ-type doubling."

A similar splitting, known as "l-type doubling," can arise from an interaction between vibrational angular momentum and molecular rotation. The label "K-type doubling" has been given to the splitting of rotational levels of an asymmetric rotor in the approximation that the molecule is nearly a symmetric rotor. It is also applied to the splitting of "accidentally degenerate" (in the sense of Table X-X) excited rotational levels by Coriolis interaction.

5.2   Vibronic Spectra

Vibrational-electronic, or vibronic, spectra of polyatomic molecules play an important part in the study of molecular structure. The vibrations of the molecule not only influence the nature of the spectrum but also serve as important guides to the properties of the individual electronic states.

5.21   Vibronic States

Certain of the important theorems concerning electronic states are independent of the conditions for transitions between states. The transitions, however, depend strongly on the properties governed by these theorems.

Assume for the present that two electronic states have the same symmetry of the nuclei. That is, the molecule belongs to the same point group in the two electronic states. It is still possible that the size of the molecule will be different. Most often, if there is a change in dimensions, the upper state will be larger because of the weaker bonding arising from change of electronic configuration. In such a case the vibrational potential curves for a totally symmetric vibrational mode will be displaced as shown at the left of Fig. X-26.

Each of the electronic states will have non-totally symmetric vibrations in addition to the totally symmetric vibrations. Assume that the form of a particular non-totally symmetric vibration is at least approximately constant in the two electronic states. Then, if the potential energy is plotted against this normal coordinate for the two states, the equilibrium position of the molecule in each electronic state—since it is to be totally symmetric with respect to the same point group—must correspond to the same value of the normal coordinate. The potential curves for all non-totally symmetric vibrational modes must therefore lie exactly above one another (as at the right in Fig. X-26).

Degeneracy of orbital electronic functions, as well as vibrational wave functions, arises because of molecular symmetry.   It might be expected that highly symmetric molecules would have a high probability of existing in degenerate electronic states.   Actually, orbital degeneracy is impossible for a symmetric molecule because interaction with vibrational motions can

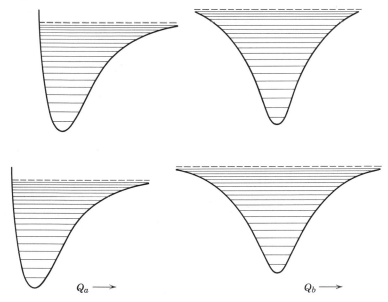

FIG. X-26.   Potential wells for totally symmetric and non-symmetric vibrations. If Q_a is the normal coordinate for a symmetric vibration, the equilibrium value of Q_a may be different in an excited electronic state and in the ground state.   If Q_b is a normal coordinate for a non-symmetric vibration, then the equilibrium value must be the same in all electronic states of the same nuclear symmetry.   The equilibrium point, $Q_a = Q_a{}^\circ$, $Q_b = Q_b{}^\circ$, which is the minimum of the vibrational wells, is a common point for any particular electronic state.

always split the degeneracy, leading to a more stable, non-symmetric configuration.   If a molecule exists in a symmetric form, therefore, it may be concluded that the electronic state is non-degenerate.   This does not apply to linear molecules.

The proof of this theorem is due to Jahn and Teller.   An example will illustrate the nature of the interaction.   Consider the vibrations of a planar four-membered ring.   The opposite phases of one vibrational mode are shown in Fig. X-27.   Assume the electronic state to be degenerate, with component states Ψ_x and Ψ_y.   The vibrational energy of the electronic state Ψ_x will depend on the phase of the vibration, since the vibration destroys the symmetry of the molecule. The curve of potential energy *vs.* vibrational displacement for this electronic state might be as

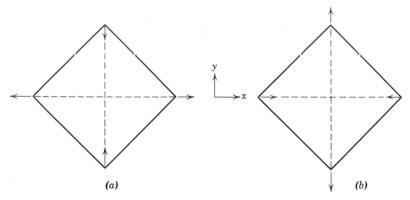

(a)   *(b)*

FIG. X-27. B_{1g} vibration of a planar ring. The displacements shown represent the two extremes of a single vibrational mode.

shown by the line labeled Ψ_x in Fig. X-28. The vibrational energy of the conjugate electronic state, Ψ_y, will also depend on the vibrational displacement, but the potential energy must vary 180° out of phase with that of

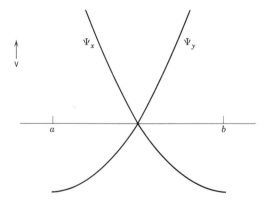

FIG. X-28. Variation of potential energy during a vibration of symmetry B_{1g} for the Ψ_x and Ψ_y components of a degenerate electronic state. [See Jahn and Teller, *Proc. Roy. Soc.* **A161**, 220 (1937); Clinton and Rice, *J. Chem. Phys.* **30**, 542 (1959).]

the first state. That is, Ψ_x must have the same energy at one extreme of the vibration that Ψ_y has at the other extreme. For either electronic state the potential energy has its minimum value for the asymmetric nuclear configuration.

Degenerate states of a linear molecule will not be split by degenerate vibrations. A degenerate vibration, perpendicular to the symmetry axis, will split the degeneracy, but the resultant states will be symmetric and antisymmetric to the plane of the vibrational motion. Each will have a minimum at the linear position.

5.22 Selection Rules

Transitions between vibronic states (disregarding rotations) depend on a transition moment that may be written $\int \Psi^*_f M \Psi_i \, d\tau$ or, to the Born-Oppenheimer approximation, $\int \Psi^*_{ef} M \Psi_{ei} \, d\tau \int \Psi_{vf}^* \Psi_{vi} \, d\tau$. The first integral of the product gives the selection rules for a pure electronic transition, which are those for any dipole-induced transition. The second integral will be unity if the initial and final vibrational states are identical states of a harmonic oscillator. It will be zero if they are different states of a harmonic oscillator or states of different symmetry of an anharmonic (or harmonic) oscillator. It will be small, but non-zero, if they are different states, of the same symmetry, of an anharmonic oscillator or if they are states corresponding to different vibrational quantum numbers of two different, but similar, harmonic oscillators. Consequently, unless the vibrational frequency differs significantly in the upper and lower electronic states, the strongest transitions should be those occurring without change of vibrational quantum number.

More generally, by expressing the vibrational levels of the initial state as linear combinations of the orthonormal vibrational functions of the final state, it is possible to show that the sum of the integrals taken from any initial vibrational state to all possible final vibrational states is unity. Thus any intensity appearing in a band corresponding to a change in vibrational quantum number may be considered to be "borrowed" from the fully allowed transition between identical vibrational states.

When the upper electronic state has a different symmetry in the nuclei from the lower state, the symmetry requirements are relaxed for vibrational transitions. Those transitions are permitted for which the product of initial and final vibrational functions is totally symmetric with respect to those symmetry elements common to both configurations (the "intersection" of the groups). For non-degenerate vibrations this requires that the initial and final wave functions both be totally symmetric or that the quantum number of any antisymmetric vibration change by an even number of units (Table X-X).

The selection rules for the electronic transition are those of the initial nuclear configuration, even though the final state may have a different symmetry. The electronic transition may be considered to occur without change of nuclear positions; the nuclei then oscillate about the new equilibrium position. A non-totally symmetric vibration excited in the initial electronic state can make an otherwise forbidden electronic transition weakly allowed. From the rigorous requirement that the transition moment for the total wave function must be totally symmetric, it follows that the non-totally symmetric vibration must change its vibrational quantum number by one unit (for harmonic vibrations).

To the extent that there is an interaction between vibrational and electronic states it is possible for a non-symmetric vibration of an excited electronic state to give this electronic state a component of the proper symmetry to combine with the initial electronic state. An analysis of this shows that the intensity of the transition depends on the proximity, to the upper electronic state, of a neighboring electronic level that has the proper symmetry to combine with the ground state; thus the non-symmetric vibration can be considered to mix the upper electronic state with the neighboring electronic state of different symmetry. The requirement is that the product of electronic and vibrational functions of the excited level be of the same symmetry as the neighboring level and that they be of proper symmetry to combine with the initial electronic state. The intensities arising by this mechanism are generally negligible except when the electronic transition is otherwise rigorously forbidden. Even then the transition to the allowed perturbing level may hide the forbidden transition.

5.23 Franck-Condon Principle

Not all transitions allowed by symmetry or by anharmonicity are observed. The intensities are strongly influenced by the Franck-Condon principle. This was discussed in section VI-2.4; more specific statements can be made on the basis of the conclusions drawn in the preceding sections.

For an allowed electronic transition, excitation of a totally symmetric vibration may occur with any number of quanta, but the transitions with $\Delta v = 0$ should be most intense. From the relative intensities of the various vibrational transitions it is possible to estimate the displacement of the minimum for the upper curve and thus the difference in size of the molecule. If there are no changes in dimensions the 0-0 transition will be by far the most intense, since the 1-1, 2-2, etc., transitions are weakened by the Boltzmann factor and the 0-1, 0-2, etc., transitions are weakened by the Franck-Condon principle (or, what amounts to the same thing, by the orthogonality of the normal modes).

A non-totally symmetric vibration will change by an even number of quanta, so that 0-0, 0-2, 0-4, . . . , 1-1, 1-3, 1-5, etc., transitions are possible. Those arising from excited vibrational states will usually be weak at room temperature, so the 0-0 band will be much stronger than the 1-1, 2-2, etc., bands.   Those involving a change of quantum number will be very much weakened by the Franck-Condon principle, since the vibrational minima lie one above the other.   The 0-0 band is therefore much more intense than the 0-2, 0-4, . . . bands.   If the vibrational frequency is low, the 1-3, 2-4, . . . transitions will appear with significant intensities relative to the 1-1, 2-2, . . . transitions.

Forbidden transitions that are made weakly allowed by vibration will have a structure similar to allowed transitions except that the frequency of the non-symmetric vibration of the upper or lower state (depending on the mechanism) will be added.   The 0-0 transition will be absent, but progressions of totally symmetric vibrations (0-0, 0-2, . . .) may appear, displaced by the value of the non-symmetric frequency.

5.24 Dissociation and Predissociation

Diatomic molecules have only one mode of dissociation, although this may occur in more than one electronic state.   If the dissociation occurs as part of the primary transition process, one should observe clearly defined vibrational levels converging to a dissociation limit, followed by a continuum; if the upper state has no potential minimum, only the continuum will be observed.   Predissociation can occur if two electronic states interact slightly, allowing a radiationless transition from a stable excited electronic state to another electronic state that is unstable with respect to dissociation (Fig. X-29a).   In some cases excited rotational states may exist at energies greater than the dissociation limit, so that the predissociation may occur by a conversion of rotational energy into vibrational energy within the same electronic state.   The diffuse appearance of the bands that results from such predissociation will generally have a sharp onset, at an energy equal to or greater than the corresponding dissociation limit.

Polyatomic molecules may have many unstable excited states and many modes of dissociation.   The dissociation energy in a symmetrical upper vibrational state will normally be quite high, since the nature of the motion would require the simultaneous rupture of all the equivalent bonds.   For this reason totally symmetric vibrations tend to be more nearly harmonic than strongly asymmetric vibrations.

Dissociation in polyatomic molecules is often a relatively complex phenomenon, depending on a concentration of vibrational motion in an upper state in a highly unsymmetric mode.   Since the necessary transfer of energy may depend in part on the anharmonicity of the vibrations, it may be relatively slow.

Predissociation is more likely in polyatomic molecules than in diatomic molecules because there are more excited electronic levels and many more vibrational levels for each electronic level.   The "selection rules" for predissociation are much the same as for absorption or emission, except that since the dipole operator does not appear in the transition probability the interacting levels must have the same symmetry. In contrast, however, to radiative transitions, the "forbidden" non-radiative transitions are more likely in predissociation. If the states have really equivalent symmetry, they will mix strongly and ordinary dissociation will occur, as shown in Fig X-29b.

An important example of dissociation arises in the spectra of tetrahedral molecules. Selection rules for these molecules permit transitions only to

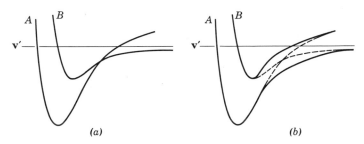

(a)   (b)

FIG. X-29. Conditions for predissociation. It may often happen that two electronic states can give rise to the same total energy for the same nuclear configuration. If these states do not interact (for example, because of different symmetries or multiplicities of the electronic wave functions), the curves will cross as in (a); if the states interact strongly, they will seem to repel each other as in (b). When the interaction is slight, a transition to the vibrational level v' of state A may be followed, after a small number of vibrational cycles, by a radiationless transition to state B. Since the energy is greater than the dissociation energy of B, the molecule flies apart. This shortened lifetime for the vibrational state v' causes the absorption line for the transition to this state to be broadened. When strong interaction is present, as in (b), a transition to the level v' results in ordinary dissociation.

states of symmetry F_1. An electronic state of this symmetry, however, is unstable as long as the molecule retains its cubic symmetry. Absorption of radiation therefore must lead to an unsymmetrical form and is most likely to cause dissociation.

5.25 Isotopic Substitution

Examination of the rotational levels of isotopically substituted molecules has shown that such substitution leaves equilibrium bond distances unchanged to an extremely good approximation. It might be expected, therefore, that the electronic spectrum would show no change upon isotopic substitution except in the spacing of vibrational and rotational levels.

Actually there may be a rather sizable change in the position of the 0-0 band of an electronic transition, accompanied by changes in appearance of the spectrum due to changes in relative intensities of the vibrational transitions. These effects can be traced to the zero-point vibrations and to the resultant changes in intensity caused by the Franck-Condon principle.

The vibronic energy may be written to a good approximation for the ground vibrational state of each electronic level as

$$E = E_{el} + E_{vib} = E_{el} + \sum_i \tfrac{1}{2}h\nu_i$$

The transition from one electronic state to another, without excitation of vibrations, is then

$$\nu_{0\cdot0} = T' - T'' = T_{el}' - T_{el}'' + \tfrac{1}{2}\sum_i(\nu_i' - \nu_i'')$$

Similarly, for the isotopically substituted molecule (indicated by a bar),

$$\bar{\nu}_{0\cdot0} = \bar{T}' - \bar{T}'' = \bar{T}_{el}' - \bar{T}_{el}'' + \tfrac{1}{2}\sum_i(\bar{\nu}_i' - \bar{\nu}_i'')$$

Assuming the electronic energies are unchanged, the shift in position of the 0-0 transition is

$$\Delta\nu_{0-0} = \nu_{0-0} - \bar{\nu}_{0-0} = \tfrac{1}{2}\sum_i(\nu_i' - \nu_i'') - \tfrac{1}{2}\sum_i(\bar{\nu}_i' - \bar{\nu}_i'')$$

$$\approx \tfrac{1}{2}(1 - \rho)\sum_i(\nu_i' - \nu_i'')$$

where the last sum is over those vibrational frequencies that are shifted by the isotopic substitution, and ρ is the weighted-average shift factor that can vary in principle between 1 and 0.707, depending on the relative masses of the two isotopes. Since the vibrational frequencies in upper and lower state will be roughly the same, and ρ will not be greatly different from one, the shift will be only a small part of the zero-point energy of the molecule, but it may still be of appreciable magnitude since the zero-point energy of a polyatomic molecule may be very large. This will be in addition to the shift in band position of a particular vibration relative to the frequency of the pure electronic transition.

The shape of the potential energy curve will be left unchanged by isotopic substitution, but the positions of the vibrational levels will, of course, vary. Classically, this corresponds to a smaller frequency of vibration for the same force constant as the mass is increased; quantum mechanically one can best say that the vibrational energy levels are closer together for the heavier molecule. Since the shape of the potential energy curve for the upper electronic state is, in general, not identical with the shape in the lower state, as they would be for harmonic vibrations if the force constants were identical in the two electronic states, and since the two potential energy curves will often tend to be displaced slightly from each other, the application of the Franck-Condon principle will show that the relative intensities of the various transitions may change, as well as the frequencies at which they will appear.

Problems

1. Construct a multiplication table for the point group C_{3v} analogous to Table X-II. Show by multiplication that the three representations given in Table X-IV actually satisfy the multiplication table for C_{3v}.

2. Show that the coordinates

$$q_3 = r_1 - r_2 - r_3 + r_4$$
$$q_4 = r_1 + r_2 - r_3 - r_4$$

form the basis for a representation of the point group D_{4h}, where r_1, r_2, r_3, and r_4 are vectors directed outward from the four corners of a square. Find the 2×2 matrices of the representation. Show that the character of the representation agrees with one of the degenerate representations of the table on p. 591.

3. Find the trace of the dipole moment operator and the polarizability operator for the point group C_{2v}. Reduce this representation to find the number of components belonging to each irreducible representation of the group. Show that the individual components belonging to each irreducible representation are those indicated on p. 586.

4. Find the representations of the dipole moment operator and polarizability operator for the point group D_{4h}. Reduce the representation and identify the behavior of individual components as in the previous problem.

5. Find the number of vibrations belonging to each symmetry species for the ethylene molecule. Find the number of C—H bond stretches and the number of CH_2 angle deformations belonging to each symmetry species.

6. Find the number of vibrations belonging to each symmetry species for the benzene molecule. Identify the approximate forms of each of the vibrations. (Remember that the actual vibrations may be mixtures of these simple forms falling within any symmetry species.)

7. What symmetry operations do the following molecules have? To what point group does each belong?

(a) o-dichlorobenzene
(b) trans-1,2-dichloroethene
(c) anthracene
(d) allene
(e) PCl_5 (assuming three equivalent Cl atoms in an equatorial plane; two equivalent Cl atoms in the polar positions)
(f) triborine-triamine, $B_3N_3H_6$ (planar ring, isoelectronic with benzene).

8. Find normalizing factors, $1/\sqrt{N}$, for $\Phi(\phi)$, $\Theta(\theta)$, and $R(r)$, such that, for example, $(1/N) \int_0^{2\pi} \Phi^* \Phi \, d\phi = 1$. Show that the product of these normalized functions agrees with those of Table X-XI.

9. Show that equation X-33 is a solution of equation X-32 if, and only if,

$$\alpha_{\mu+2} = \frac{(\mu + m)(\mu + m + 1) - \beta}{(\mu + m)(\mu + 1)} \, \alpha_\mu$$

(Collect coefficients of like powers of $\cos \theta$ after substitution.)   Note that, in order for $\alpha_{\hat{\mu}}$ to be the last term in the series,

$$\beta = (\hat{\mu} + m)(\hat{\mu} + m + 1)$$

10. The recursion formula of problem 9, together with equation X-33, defines the associated Legendre functions, $\Theta(\theta)$, subject to arbitrary assignment of two constants.

(a) Let $a_0 = 1$, $a_1 = 0$, and find the functions Θ_0, Θ_2, and Θ_4.
(b) Let $a_0 = 0$, $a_1 = 1$, and find the functions Θ_1, Θ_3, and Θ_5.

(Compare your results with those of Table X-XI.)

11. The functions $\Theta(\theta)$ are eigenfunctions of the operators

$$\mathbf{P}_z = -i\hbar \frac{\partial}{\partial \phi} \quad \text{and} \quad \mathbf{P}^2 = -\hbar^2 \left\{ \frac{1}{\sin \theta} \frac{\partial}{\partial \theta} \sin \theta \frac{\partial}{\partial \theta} + \frac{1}{\sin_2 \theta} \frac{\partial^2}{\partial \phi^2} \right\}$$

with eigenvalues $\mu + m$ and $(\mu + m)(\mu + m + 1)$, respectively.   Show this for three of the functions $\Theta(\theta)$.

12. The angular dependence of the states of the hydrogen atom of unit angular momentum can be written in either of the two forms

$$
\begin{aligned}
p_x &= \sin \theta \cos \phi & \qquad p_1 &= \sin \theta e^{i\theta} \\
p_y &= \sin \theta \sin \phi & \qquad p_0 &= \cos \theta \\
p_z &= \cos \theta & \qquad p_{-1} &= \sin \theta e^{-i\theta}
\end{aligned}
$$

(a) Which of the functions p_x, p_y, p_z and p_1, p_0, p_{-1} are eigenfunctions of $\mathbf{P}_z$?
(b) Which of the functions are eigenfunctions of $\mathbf{P}^2$?
(c) Find the expectation values, $\langle \mathbf{P}_z \rangle$ and $\langle \mathbf{P}^2 \rangle$, for each of the functions.

13. Using the united-atom approximation, give the probable electronic configuration of the molecule NH in its ground state.   Give the term symbol for this state.

14. Using the separated-atom approximation, give the probable electronic configuration of the molecule GeF in its ground state.   Give the term symbol for this state.

(a) What is the bond order?
(b) From the bond order and the reduced mass estimate the vibrational frequency to be expected.
(c) What causes the ground-state splitting in this molecule?   Why is the splitting several times as large as in NO?

15. A linear molecule, A—B—C, shows an electronic transition to a non-linear excited state.   Assume that the bending vibration has a frequency equivalent to 500 cm^{-1} in the ground electronic state and 600 cm^{-1} in the upper electronic state.   Sketch qualitatively the potential energy curves as a function of angle for the two states.   Show which transitions are most probable (according to your diagram).   Sketch the general appearance that might be expected for the ultraviolet absorption of the molecule (neglecting the effects of any other vibrations), including spacings and relative intensities as far as possible.

16. Sketch the motions and Coriolis forces for the ethane molecule in a vibration belonging to the species E_g and in a vibration belonging to the species E_u.   (Compare Fig. X-25.)

17. Select a molecule containing at least three atoms that has been studied spectroscopically. On the basis of information available in the literature, summarize what measurements have been made and what conclusions are possible concerning the structure of the molecule. Include microwave, infrared, and ultraviolet spectra in your considerations.

I

Matrix methods

Matrices provide a convenient and time-saving method for handling systems of linear equations whenever they arise. They are particularly valuable in problems in the mechanics of N particles, in the solution of analytical analyses in several unknowns, in group theory, and in virtually all fields of advanced physics and mathematics in which vector and tensor quantities or orthogonal sets of functions are to be manipulated. This treatment is intended only as an introduction to matrix methods, with some applications to problems of particular interest in the field of absorption spectroscopy.

I Determinants

It will be convenient to open the discussion of matrices by treating first the closely related subject of determinants. Although a determinant is written as a square array of numbers, it is defined in such a way that it has a unique numerical value. That is, it is simply a number, which is obtained from the square array by finding the sum of products of the "elements" in the array.

Determinants will be indicated by vertical lines. The elements of the determinant are given two subscripts, the first indicating the row in which the element occurs, the second indicating the column. Thus the general element, a_{ij}, represents a number in the ith row and the jth column, counting from the top and from the left, respectively. The element a_{34} is the element in the 3rd row and the 4th column.

1.1   Evaluation of Determinants

Small determinants can be evaluated directly from the definition. More efficient methods are available for larger determinants. According to the definition, the determinant $|a_{ij}|$ is given by a sum of $n!$ products of n numbers each.

$$\begin{vmatrix} a_{11} & a_{12} & a_{13} & \cdots & a_{1n} \\ a_{21} & a_{22} & a_{23} & \cdots & a_{2n} \\ \cdots\cdots\cdots\cdots\cdots\cdots\cdots \\ a_{n1} & a_{n2} & a_{n3} & \cdots & a_{nn} \end{vmatrix} \equiv \sum_j \text{sign}\,(j_1, j_2, \ldots, j_n)a_{1j_1}a_{2j_2}a_{3j_3}\cdots a_{nj_n}$$

(AI-1)

The sum is over all possible products of each number, or element, a_{ij}, with all other elements not in the same row or column, with the sign added according to the following convention. The n elements appearing in each product are arranged in order of ascending values of the first index. If an even number of transpositions of adjacent terms is then required to put the elements in order of ascending values of the second index, the expression sign $(j_1, j_2, \ldots, j_n)$ is just $+1$; if an odd number of transpositions is required, the expression is equal to -1. The summation is over all permutations of the subscript j.[1] For example, the determinant

$$\begin{vmatrix} a_{11} & a_{12} \\ a_{21} & a_{22} \end{vmatrix}$$

which is of *order*, or dimension, two, is identically equal to $(a_{11}a_{22} - a_{21}a_{12})$; the determinant

$$\begin{vmatrix} a_{11} & a_{12} & a_{13} \\ a_{21} & a_{22} & a_{23} \\ a_{31} & a_{32} & a_{33} \end{vmatrix}$$

is identically equal to

$$a_{11}a_{22}a_{33} - a_{11}a_{23}a_{32} + a_{12}a_{23}a_{31} - a_{12}a_{21}a_{33} + a_{13}a_{21}a_{32} - a_{13}a_{22}a_{31}$$

A determinant of order four requires 24 such products of 4 elements each.

---

[1] A permutation is an order, or arrangement, of objects. A set of n objects, or numbers, can be arranged in $n!$ arrangements or permutations. ($n!$ represents n factorial, the product of all integers from 1 to n. Thus $5! = 5 \times 4 \times 3 \times 2 \times 1 = 120$. It is convenient to define $0! = 1! = 1$.) If there is a standard order, such as the arrangement $1, 2, 3, \ldots, n$, then transposing any two adjacent numbers will change the permutation from even to odd, or from plus to minus. The sign of the permutation is therefore $(-1)^t$ where t is the number of transpositions, or interchanges, of adjacent numbers required to return the set to the standard order.

In practice it is a tedious process to write down all the products indicated and sum these (see Table AI-I).   Faster and more efficient methods have been found for evaluating determinants.   They are always preferable for determinants of order larger than 3.

I.II   Laplace Expansion

The best-known method for evaluating determinants is the Laplace expansion.   The *cofactor*, A_{ij}, of an element a_{ij} is the determinant obtained from the original by removing the ith row and jth column, with a plus or minus sign added depending on whether $(i + j)$ is even or odd.   The determinant $|a_{ij}|$ is then equal to the sum $\sum_i a_{ij}A_{ij}$, or also to the sum $\sum_j a_{ij}A_{ij}$.   The method involves selecting any row or column and adding together the elements of this row or column multiplied by the respective cofactors.   For example, the determinant

$$\begin{vmatrix} 2 & 1 & 4 \\ 5 & 3 & 0 \\ 3 & 1 & 2 \end{vmatrix}$$

is equal to

$$2(3 \times 2 - 1 \times 0) - 1(5 \times 2 - 3 \times 0) + 4(5 \times 1 - 3 \times 3) = -14$$

expanded in terms of the first row, or it is equal to

$$4(5 \times 1 - 3 \times 3) - 0(2 \times 1 - 3 \times 1) + 2(2 \times 3 - 5 \times 1) = -14$$

by expansion on the last column.   This method will obviously be very satisfactory if there is a large number of zero elements in any row or column.   A general determinant of order four may be expanded as follows:

$$\begin{aligned} &a_{11}\{a_{22}(a_{33}a_{44} - a_{43}a_{34}) - a_{23}(a_{32}a_{44} - a_{42}a_{34}) + a_{24}(a_{32}a_{43} - a_{42}a_{33})\} \\ &-a_{12}\{a_{21}(a_{33}a_{44} - a_{43}a_{34}) - a_{23}(a_{31}a_{44} - a_{41}a_{34}) + a_{24}(a_{31}a_{43} - a_{41}a_{33})\}. \\ &+a_{13}\{a_{21}(a_{32}a_{44} - a_{42}a_{34}) - a_{22}(a_{31}a_{44} - a_{41}a_{34}) + a_{24}(a_{31}a_{42} - a_{41}a_{32})\} \\ &-a_{14}\{a_{21}(a_{32}a_{43} - a_{42}a_{33}) - a_{22}(a_{31}a_{43} - a_{41}a_{33}) + a_{23}(a_{31}a_{42} - a_{41}a_{32})\} \end{aligned}$$

This is a stepwise process, in the sense that an n-dimensional determinant is reduced to the sum of n $(n - 1)$-dimensional determinants.   In evaluating each of the smaller determinants the signs of the cofactors are fixed on the basis of the position of the element in that smaller determinant, without regard for the position of the columns or rows in the original determinant.   The Laplace expansion becomes exceedingly cumbersome for larger determinants (Table AI-I), especially since it becomes difficult to maintain an orderly arrangement for the process on paper. Thus, although many terms are repeated during the evaluation, it might well require more time to find these terms than to re-evaluate them.

1.12   Triangularization

The shortest method of evaluation, though not necessarily the most convenient, is triangularization   Since the addition of a multiple of any one row of the determinant to another row does not change the value of the determinant (section AI-1.2) it is possible to add a multiple of the first row to each of the other rows such that the first term in each row (except the first) is a zero.   Multiples of the second row can then be added to each succeeding row to make the second element in each row (except the first and second) zero.   The process is continued till all elements below the diagonal are zeros.

For the general determinant $|a_{ij}|$, the first row is multiplied by a_{21}/a_{11} and subtracted from the second row.   This does not change the first row. The first row is then multiplied by a_{31}/a_{11} and subtracted from the third row, by a_{41}/a_{11} and subtracted from the fourth row, and so forth.   The second row is then multiplied by a_{32}'/a_{22}' and subtracted from the third. The determinant finally assumes the triangular form

$$\begin{vmatrix} a_{11} & a_{12} & a_{13} & \cdots & a_{1n} \\ 0 & a_{22}' & a_{23}' & \cdots & a_{2n}' \\ 0 & 0 & a_{33}'' & \cdots & a_{3n}'' \\ \cdots & \cdots & \cdots & \cdots & \cdots \\ 0 & 0 & 0 & \cdots & a_{nn}^{(n')} \end{vmatrix}$$

Evaluation of this by means of the Laplace expansion, starting with the first column and progressing to the right, shows that the determinant is just equal to the product of the diagonal elements in this triangular form. For example, the determinant

$$\begin{vmatrix} 1 & 3 & 4 \\ 2 & 4 & 6 \\ 3 & 0 & 2 \end{vmatrix}$$

is converted, by multiplying the first row by 2 and subtracting from the second, to the form

$$\begin{vmatrix} 1 & 3 & 4 \\ 0 & -2 & -2 \\ 3 & 0 & 2 \end{vmatrix}$$

and then, multiplying the first row by 3 and subtracting from the third row, to the form

$$\begin{vmatrix} 1 & 3 & 4 \\ 0 & -2 & -2 \\ 0 & -9 & -10 \end{vmatrix}$$

Multiplying the second row of the last form by $\frac{9}{2}$ and subtracting from the last row gives

$$\begin{vmatrix} 1 & 3 & 4 \\ 0 & -2 & -2 \\ 0 & 0 & -1 \end{vmatrix} = 2$$

If one of the diagonal elements is or becomes zero, the process can be continued by interchanging two rows or two columns to put a non-zero element on the diagonal. This simply changes the sign of the determinant.

I.13 Pivotal Condensation

A particularly convenient technique for the evaluation of determinants, especially when a desk calculator with "cumulative multiplication" and "negative multiplication" is available, is the process of pivotal condensation. It is particularly valuable in that small changes made in the determinant often require only a few additional steps to find the new value of the determinant. Also, symmetry properties of a determinant are retained and can greatly reduce the number of steps.

A determinant of dimension n is reduced to an $(n - 1)$-dimensional determinant. The new elements are the 2-dimensional determinants formed by the pivotal element, which will be assumed to be the a_{11} element, each other element not in the first row or column, and the elements in the first row and first column that fall in the column and row, respectively, of the second element. That is, the 2-dimensional determinants consist of the elements

$$\begin{vmatrix} a_{11} & a_{1j} \\ a_{i1} & a_{ij} \end{vmatrix}$$

These determinants, which are of course simply numbers, become the elements of the $(n - 1)$-dimensional determinant. This is divided by $(a_{11})^{n-2}$. Thus

$$\begin{vmatrix} a_{11} & a_{12} & a_{13} & \cdots & a_{1n} \\ a_{21} & a_{22} & a_{23} & \cdots & a_{2n} \\ \multicolumn{5}{c}{\cdots\cdots\cdots\cdots\cdots\cdots} \\ a_{n1} & a_{n2} & a_{n3} & \cdots & a_{nn} \end{vmatrix} = \frac{1}{(a_{11})^{n-2}} \begin{vmatrix} \begin{vmatrix} a_{11} & a_{12} \\ a_{21} & a_{22} \end{vmatrix} & \begin{vmatrix} a_{11} & a_{13} \\ a_{21} & a_{23} \end{vmatrix} & \begin{vmatrix} a_{11} & a_{14} \\ a_{21} & a_{24} \end{vmatrix} & \cdots \\ \begin{vmatrix} a_{11} & a_{12} \\ a_{31} & a_{32} \end{vmatrix} & \begin{vmatrix} a_{11} & a_{13} \\ a_{31} & a_{33} \end{vmatrix} & \begin{vmatrix} a_{11} & a_{14} \\ a_{31} & a_{34} \end{vmatrix} & \cdots \\ \multicolumn{4}{c}{\cdots\cdots\cdots\cdots\cdots\cdots} \end{vmatrix}$$

For example, evaluation of a 4×4 determinant proceeds by the following steps.

$$\begin{vmatrix} 2 & 1 & 3 & 1 \\ 3 & 3 & 7 & 2 \\ 5 & 4 & 9 & 6 \\ 2 & 0 & 1 & 4 \end{vmatrix} = \frac{1}{2^2} \begin{vmatrix} 3 & 5 & 1 \\ 3 & 3 & 7 \\ -2 & -4 & 6 \end{vmatrix} = \frac{1}{4 \times 3} \begin{vmatrix} -6 & 18 \\ -2 & 20 \end{vmatrix} = \frac{-120 + 36}{12} = -7$$

Table AI-I shows the number of operations required for the evaluation of determinants of various dimensions by each of the methods discussed.

TABLE AI-I

Number of Operations Required in Evaluation of Determinants of Order n

n	Definition	Laplace	Laplace[a]	Pivotal Condensation	Triangular- ization
			Multiplications		
2	2	2	2	2	3
3	12	9	9	11	10
4	72	40	28	31	23
5	480	205	75	66	44
10	32,659,200	6,235,300	5110	601	259
n	$n!(n-1)$	$n! \sum\limits_{p=1}^{n-1} \dfrac{1}{p!}$	$n! \sum\limits_{p=1}^{n-1} \dfrac{1}{(n-p-1)!p!}$	$\dfrac{4n^3 - 3n^2 - 7n + 6}{6}$	$\dfrac{n^3 + 2n - 3}{3}$
			Additions		
2	1	1	1	1	1
3	5	5	5	5	5
4	23	23	17	14	14
5	119	119	49	30	30
10	3,628,799	3,628,799	4097	285	285
n	$n! - 1$	$n! - 1$	$\sum\limits_{p=2}^{n} \dfrac{(p-1)n!}{(n-p)!p!}$	$\dfrac{n(2n^2 - 3n + 1)}{6}$	$\dfrac{n(2n^2 - 3n + 1)}{6}$

[a] Number of different operations. If a particular 2×2 (or larger) determinant appears more than once, it is counted only once in this column.

1.22 Properties of Determinants

The following properties are of importance in the manipulation of determinants.

(a) Interchanging any two rows, or columns, of a determinant will simply change the sign of the determinant. This follows directly from the definition (equation AI-1).

(*b*) Interchanging all the rows with the corresponding columns of a determinant will not change the value of the determinant.

(*c*) Multiplying one row, or column, of a determinant by a constant multiplies the determinant by that constant. This may be easily verified from the definition or from the Laplace expansion.

(*d*) If one row, or column, of a determinant consists entirely of zero elements, the determinant is zero. This follows from the definition or from a Laplace expansion in terms of the zero row or column.

(*e*) If any two rows, or columns, of a determinant are identical, the determinant will be zero, since interchanging identical rows or columns must make the determinant change sign (from the definition) but cannot change the value. The determinant is zero also if one row, or column, is a multiple of another.

(*f*) Adding a multiple of one row, or column, to another row, or column, of the same determinant will not change the value of the determinant. The resultant may be written as a sum of the original and another determinant which is zero because it has one row a multiple of another.

(*g*) Since a determinant is a number, determinants may be multiplied together as simple numbers. They may also be multiplied according to the rules of matrix multiplication (see below).

2 Matrices

A matrix is a rectangular array of numbers, of dimensions $m \times n$ (m rows by n columns). By suitably defining the operations of addition and multiplication, it is possible to handle matrices in almost exactly the same manner as ordinary numbers; the algebra of ordinary numbers (scalars) may be considered a special case of the algebra of matrices, since a scalar may be considered as a matrix of dimensions 1×1. We shall use bold-face capital letters to denote matrices, and small letters to represent scalars. The general element of a matrix **A** is written a_{ij}, where the first subscript denotes the number of the row and the second denotes the number of the column, as for determinants. Square brackets will enclose elements of a matrix. **A** $= [a_{ij}]$.

Two matrices are said to be equal only if they are identical, element for element. **A** $=$ **B** if and only if $a_{ij} = b_{ij}$ for all i and j.

2.1 Basic Operations

The following definitions serve for the basic manipulations of matrices.

Addition of two matrices is performed by the addition of corresponding elements. Thus, if $\mathbf{A} + \mathbf{B} = \mathbf{C}$, then

$$c_{ij} = a_{ij} + b_{ij} \tag{AI-2}$$

$$\begin{bmatrix} a_{11} & a_{12} & a_{13} & \cdots \\ a_{21} & a_{22} & a_{23} & \cdots \\ \cdots \cdots \cdots \cdots \end{bmatrix} + \begin{bmatrix} b_{11} & b_{12} & b_{13} & \cdots \\ b_{21} & b_{22} & b_{23} & \cdots \\ \cdots \cdots \cdots \cdots \end{bmatrix}$$

$$= \begin{bmatrix} (a_{11} + b_{11}) & (a_{12} + b_{12}) & \cdots \\ (a_{21} + b_{21}) & (a_{22} + b_{22}) & \cdots \\ \cdots \cdots \cdots \cdots \cdots \cdots \end{bmatrix}$$

Matrices can be added together only if they have the same dimensions. The resultant matrix will, of course, also have these dimensions.

A matrix is "augmented" by the addition of rows or columns to the matrix to increase its dimensions. For example, the matrix

$$\begin{bmatrix} 3 & 1 \\ 4 & 0 \\ 3 & 3 \end{bmatrix}$$

can be augmented by a column of zeros to form a square matrix. In contrast to the process of addition defined above, this process is of little practical significance.

Multiplication of two matrices, $\mathbf{A}$ and $\mathbf{B}$, is defined only if the number of columns in the left matrix, $\mathbf{A}$, is equal to the number of rows in the right matrix, $\mathbf{B}$. Then

$$\mathbf{AB} = \mathbf{C}$$

if

$$c_{ij} = \sum_k a_{ik} b_{kj} \tag{AI-3}$$

For example, taking the special case in which $\mathbf{A}$ is $1 \times n$ and $\mathbf{B}$ is $n \times 1$,

$$\mathbf{C} = c_{ij} = [a_{i1} \quad a_{i2} \quad a_{i3} \quad \cdots] \begin{bmatrix} b_{1j} \\ b_{2j} \\ b_{3j} \\ \vdots \end{bmatrix}$$

$$= (a_{i1} b_{1j} + a_{i2} b_{2j} + a_{i3} b_{3j} + \cdots)$$

More specifically,

$$[2 \quad 3 \quad 0] \begin{bmatrix} 5 \\ 3 \\ 7 \end{bmatrix} = (2 \times 5 + 3 \times 3 + 0 \times 7) = 19$$

Thus multiplication of a row times a column, in the order shown, gives a scalar. In the example above, the i and j subscripts are unnecessary and could be omitted.

The multiplication rule as applied to matrices of any dimensions may be readily visualized by considering the left matrix to consist of a number of row matrices, the right to consist of a number of column matrices. Each row and column may then be multiplied as above. The restriction still applies, however, that the number of elements in each row of the left matrix must equal the number of elements in each column of the right matrix. Two matrices which satisfy this condition are said to be conformable; A and B are conformable if A is $m \times p$ and B is $p \times n$. The product matrix, $C = AB$, will be of dimensions $m \times n$.

For example,

$$\begin{bmatrix} a_{11} & a_{12} \\ a_{21} & a_{22} \end{bmatrix} \begin{bmatrix} b_{11} & b_{12} \\ b_{21} & b_{22} \end{bmatrix} = \begin{bmatrix} (a_{11}b_{11} + a_{12}b_{21})(a_{11}b_{12} + a_{12}b_{22}) \\ (a_{21}b_{11} + a_{22}b_{21})(a_{21}b_{12} + a_{22}b_{22}) \end{bmatrix}$$

or

$$\begin{bmatrix} 2 & 3 & 0 \\ 1 & 4 & 6 \end{bmatrix} \begin{bmatrix} 5 & 1 & 3 & 2 \\ 3 & 4 & 1 & 0 \\ 7 & 2 & 3 & 6 \end{bmatrix}$$

$$= \begin{bmatrix} (10 + 9 + 0)(2 + 12 + 0)(6 + 3 + 0)(4 + 0 + 0) \\ (5 + 12 + 42)(1 + 16 + 12)(3 + 4 + 18)(2 + 0 + 36) \end{bmatrix}$$

$$= \begin{bmatrix} 19 & 14 & 9 & 4 \\ 59 & 29 & 25 & 38 \end{bmatrix}$$

Multiplication of a matrix by a constant (a scalar) is performed by multiplying each element of the matrix by that constant. Multiplication of a matrix by a number is to be contrasted with the method of multiplication of a determinant by a number.

The following special properties of matrix multiplication may be noted. A row times a column gives a scalar.[1] A column times a row gives a

---

[1] A row or column matrix is sometimes called a vector, since such matrices can serve to represent vector quantities in many (but not all) applications. The product of a row times a column is therefore analogous to the scalar, or dot, product of vectors.

square matrix of dimensions $n \times n$. Multiplication of any matrix by a square matrix will not change the dimensions of the other matrix (the product will have the same dimensions as the matrix being multiplied by the square matrix). If **A** and **B** are conformable such that **AB** = **C**, it does not necessarily follow that they will be conformable in reverse order; **BA** may not be defined. But, even if **AB** and **BA** are both defined, the two products will not, in general, be equal. In general, then, **AB** $\neq$ **BA**. If a set of matrices commute (**AB** = **BA** for all **A** and **B**) the set is called *abelian*.

2.2 Definitions

The principal diagonal of a square matrix is the succession of elements running from the upper left to the lower right corner. The term diagonal will always mean the principal diagonal.

The trace, or character, or spur, of a matrix is the sum of the elements along the principal diagonal.

A diagonal matrix is one with non-zero elements along the principal diagonal only; all other elements are zero. A diagonal matrix must be square.

The unit matrix, **I**, plays the role in matrix algebra of the unit, 1, in the algebra of scalars. It is defined as the diagonal matrix, of any appropriate dimension, with elements along the diagonal all equal to 1. It may be written **I** = $[\delta_{ij}]$, where δ_{ij} is the Kronecker delta. $\delta_{ij} = 1$ if $i = j$; $\delta_{ij} = 0$ if $i \neq j$. The unit matrix may be inserted or suppressed in matrix multiplication just as the scalar 1 may be in scalar algebra. Thus **AI** = **A**.

The role of a constant in matrix multiplication and addition is played by a constant matrix, which is any number, c, times the unit matrix. $[c] = c\mathbf{I} = [c\delta_{ij}]$.

The zero matrix, or null matrix, is a matrix of any dimensions that has only zero elements.

A submatrix is any portion of a matrix that forms a matrix of smaller dimensions. The relative positions of elements must be maintained in going from the matrix to a submatrix, but rows and/or columns may be omitted. Since the rules of matrix addition and multiplication are a generalization of those for scalars, the rules hold whether the elements of the matrices are scalars or are submatrices, provided the submatrices to be multiplied are conformable and are kept in proper sequence. It is often helpful to consider a matrix as composed of submatrices, which are then treated symbolically as simple elements.

The elements of a square matrix may be regarded as forming a determinant. The value of this determinant is said to be the determinant of

the matrix.   A determinant exists only for a square matrix; the determinant of a non-square matrix can be defined as the determinant of the
matrix augmented by sufficient rows or columns of zero elements to make
it square, but such a determinant is necessarily zero.   The product of the
determinants of two square matrices is equal to the determinant of the
product.   If $\mathbf{AB} = \mathbf{C}$, then $|\mathbf{A}||\mathbf{B}| = |\mathbf{C}|$.

A matrix is said to be "singular" if its determinant is zero.   The extension of the term singular to include non-square matrices is a matter of
preference.   A "non-singular" matrix is any matrix, necessarily square,
with a determinant different from zero.

The determinant of any square submatrix is called a minor of the matrix.
A principal minor is one that is symmetrically located about the principal
diagonal of the matrix.   Thus a principal minor consists of corresponding
sections of corresponding rows and columns.   For example, the first-order
principal minors of the matrix

$$\begin{bmatrix} a_{11} & a_{12} & a_{13} \\ a_{21} & a_{22} & a_{23} \\ a_{31} & a_{32} & a_{33} \end{bmatrix}$$

are the three diagonal elements, a_{11}, a_{22}, and a_{33}; the second-order principal minors are

$$\begin{bmatrix} a_{11} & a_{12} \\ a_{21} & a_{22} \end{bmatrix}, \quad \begin{bmatrix} a_{11} & a_{13} \\ a_{31} & a_{33} \end{bmatrix}, \quad \text{and} \quad \begin{bmatrix} a_{22} & a_{23} \\ a_{32} & a_{33} \end{bmatrix}$$

and the only third-order minor is the determinant of the matrix.

The order of a square matrix is its dimension.   The rank of a matrix is
the dimension of its largest non-zero minor.

The transpose of a matrix is obtained by interchanging the rows with
the corresponding columns.   For a square matrix this is equivalent to
rotating the matrix about the principal diagonal.   The transpose will be
indicated by a tilde, $\sim$. $\tilde{\mathbf{A}} = [\widetilde{a_{ij}}] = [a_{ji}]$.   The transpose of a column
matrix is a row matrix, and vice versa.

The conjugate of a matrix is obtained by replacing each element by its
complex conjugate, or by replacing i by $-i$ wherever it appears in the
matrix.   The conjugate will be denoted by a bar. $\overline{\mathbf{A}} = [\overline{a_{ij}}]$.   The
transposed conjugate appears so often in matrix equations that it will be
given a special symbol.

$$\tilde{\overline{\mathbf{A}}} \equiv \mathbf{A}^* \tag{AI-4}$$

It will be understood that $\mathbf{A}^*$ will be identical with $\overline{\mathbf{A}}$ for scalars and will
be identical with $\tilde{\mathbf{A}}$ for real matrices (no complex elements).   This permits

the notation in physical equations to be independent of the form of representation of the quantities and independent of whether the quantities are real or complex.

If the matrix $\mathbf{A}$ is non-singular, an inverse matrix, $\mathbf{A}^{-1}$, can be found such that $\mathbf{A}\mathbf{A}^{-1} = \mathbf{A}^{-1}\mathbf{A} = \mathbf{I}$. The inverse is found by replacing each element by its cofactor. Then the matrix is transposed and divided by the determinant of the original matrix.

$$\mathbf{A}^{-1} = \frac{1}{|\mathbf{A}|} \begin{bmatrix} A_{11} & A_{21} & A_{31} & \cdots \\ A_{12} & A_{22} & A_{32} & \cdots \\ A_{13} & A_{23} & A_{33} & \cdots \\ \cdot & \cdot & \cdot & \cdots \end{bmatrix} \tag{AI-5}$$

For example, the inverse of the matrix

$$\begin{bmatrix} a_{11} & a_{12} \\ a_{21} & a_{22} \end{bmatrix}$$

is

$$\frac{\begin{bmatrix} a_{22} & -a_{12} \\ -a_{21} & a_{11} \end{bmatrix}}{(a_{11}a_{22} - a_{12}a_{21})}$$

The inverse of the matrix

$$\begin{bmatrix} 2 & 3 & 1 \\ 0 & 4 & 2 \\ 1 & 5 & 3 \end{bmatrix}$$

is

$$\frac{1}{6} \begin{bmatrix} \begin{vmatrix} 4 & 2 \\ 5 & 3 \end{vmatrix} & -\begin{vmatrix} 0 & 2 \\ 1 & 3 \end{vmatrix} & \begin{vmatrix} 0 & 4 \\ 1 & 5 \end{vmatrix} \\ -\begin{vmatrix} 3 & 1 \\ 5 & 3 \end{vmatrix} & \begin{vmatrix} 2 & 1 \\ 1 & 3 \end{vmatrix} & -\begin{vmatrix} 2 & 3 \\ 1 & 5 \end{vmatrix} \\ \begin{vmatrix} 3 & 1 \\ 4 & 2 \end{vmatrix} & -\begin{vmatrix} 2 & 1 \\ 0 & 2 \end{vmatrix} & \begin{vmatrix} 2 & 3 \\ 0 & 4 \end{vmatrix} \end{bmatrix}^* = \frac{1}{6} \begin{bmatrix} 2 & -4 & 2 \\ 2 & 5 & -4 \\ -4 & -7 & 8 \end{bmatrix} = \begin{bmatrix} \frac{1}{3} & \frac{-2}{3} & \frac{1}{3} \\ \frac{1}{3} & \frac{5}{6} & \frac{-2}{3} \\ \frac{-2}{3} & \frac{-7}{6} & \frac{4}{3} \end{bmatrix}$$

The transpose, conjugate, and inverse properties are reflexive. That is, if $\tilde{\mathbf{A}} = \mathbf{B}$, then $\tilde{\mathbf{B}} = \mathbf{A}$ and $\tilde{\tilde{\mathbf{A}}} = \mathbf{A}$, with equivalent relations for the conjugate and inverse.   From the definitions the following important rules can be demonstrated.

$$\widetilde{(AB)} = \tilde{B}\tilde{A}$$
$$(AB)^{-1} = B^{-1}A^{-1}$$
$$\overline{(AB)} = \overline{A}\overline{B}$$
$$(AB)^* = B^*A^*$$

$$(\text{AI-6})$$

2.3   Special Matrices, Transformations, and Properties

The following special types of matrices are defined.

Type	Property
Symmetric	$A = \tilde{A}$
Real	$A = \overline{A}$
Involutory	$A = A^{-1}$
Hermitian	$A = A^*$
Orthogonal	$\tilde{A} = A^{-1}$
Unitary	$A^* = A^{-1}$

It should be noted that these relationships impose conditions on the determinants of the matrices.   In particular,

$$|A^{-1}| = |A|^{-1}$$
$$|\tilde{A}| = |A|$$
$$|A^*| = |A|^*$$

and therefore the determinant of an orthogonal matrix must be ± 1 and the determinant of a unitary matrix must be $\pm \sqrt{\pm 1}$.

In the product AB, the matrix A is said to "pre-multiply" B and B is said to "post-multiply" A.   Simultaneous pre-multiplication and post-multiplication of a matrix is called a "transformation."   (Transformations of column or row matrices involve only pre- or post-multiplication.   See section AI-2.6.)   If two matrices, A and B, are related by an equation of the type $PAQ = B$, where P and Q are non-singular, then B is the transform of A and the matrices A and B are said to be "equivalent."

Several special types of transformation, defined in terms of the relationship between P and Q, are of importance.

Type of transformation	Example
Similarity	$H^{-1}AH$
Congruent	$\tilde{H}AH$
Orthogonal	$H^{-1}AH, H^{-1} = \tilde{H}$
Unitary	$H^{-1}AH, H^{-1} = H^*$

The similarity transformation is also called collineatory; the congruent transformation is called correlatory. The congruent transformation is of little value in itself.

The similarity transformation, including the special cases of orthogonal and unitary transformations, is of very great importance. This is the mechanism for transformations of coordinates in physical problems, as well as the basis of innumerable applications in group theory and other branches of mathematics. The value of the similarity transformation is associated with the fact that such a transformation leaves all matrix equations unchanged. For example, if $\mathbf{A} + \mathbf{B} = \mathbf{C}$, then $\mathbf{A'} + \mathbf{B'} = \mathbf{C'}$ where $\mathbf{A'} = \mathbf{H^{-1}AH}$, $\mathbf{B'} = \mathbf{H^{-1}BH}$, and $\mathbf{C'} = \mathbf{H^{-1}CH}$. Also, if $\mathbf{AB} = \mathbf{C}$, then $\mathbf{A'B'} = \mathbf{C'}$ under the same transformation, since $\mathbf{H^{-1}AHH^{-1}BH} = \mathbf{H^{-1}ABH} = \mathbf{H^{-1}CH}$. The determinant and the trace are among the properties of a matrix that are invariant to a similarity transformation.

A product of the form $\mathbf{Y^*AX}$, where $\mathbf{A}$ is square and $\mathbf{X}$ and $\mathbf{Y}$ are column matrices, is called a bilinear form; $\mathbf{X^*AX}$ is called a quadratic form. If the matrix, $\mathbf{A}$, in a real quadratic form is not symmetric, it may be made so. The product $\mathbf{\tilde{X}AX}$ is a scalar and therefore equal to its own transpose. Thus

$$\mathbf{\tilde{X}AX} = \mathbf{\tilde{X}\tilde{A}X} = \mathbf{\tilde{X}[\tfrac{1}{2}(A + \tilde{A}]X}$$

If the product of a matrix, $\mathbf{A}$, and a non-zero matrix, $\mathbf{B}$, is the zero matrix, the matrix $\mathbf{A}$ must be singular. If this were not true, $\mathbf{A}$ would have an inverse. Then

$$\mathbf{AB} = \mathbf{O}$$
$$\mathbf{A^{-1}AB} = \mathbf{A^{-1}O} = \mathbf{O}$$
$$\mathbf{B} = \mathbf{O}$$

Since $\mathbf{B}$ was assumed non-zero, $\mathbf{A^{-1}}$ must not exist and therefore $\mathbf{A}$ must be singular. It follows also that $\mathbf{B}$ is singular if $\mathbf{A}$ is not zero.

The similarities and differences between matrix algebra and scalar, or ordinary, algebra can now be pointed out. The laws of addition, subtraction, and multiplication are the same with the following exceptions. Addition and subtraction are possible only if the matrices have the same dimensions; multiplication is possible only if the matrices are conformable. Matrix multiplication is in general non-commutative, whereas scalar algebra is always commutative.

Division is defined in terms of a multiplication process. $c/b = a$ if $ab = c$, but only if $b \neq 0$. The corresponding restriction in matrix algebra, which is clearly an extension of the impossibility of division by zero, is that "division," or multiplication by the inverse, is possible only if

$|\mathbf{B}| \neq 0$; that is, $\mathbf{CB}^{-1} = \mathbf{A}$ if $\mathbf{AB} = \mathbf{C}$, but only if $\mathbf{B}$ is non-singular. A non-zero number is clearly a special case of a non-singular matrix.

In scalar algebra the product of two numbers can be zero only if one of the numbers is zero. If $ab = 0$, then either $a = 0$ or $b = 0$. The corresponding rule in matrix algebra is as follows. If $\mathbf{AB} = \mathbf{O}$, then either $\mathbf{A} = \mathbf{O}$, or $\mathbf{B} = \mathbf{O}$, or $\mathbf{A}$ and $\mathbf{B}$ are *both* singular matrices, $|\mathbf{A}| = |\mathbf{B}| = 0$. The proof of this is contained in an earlier paragraph. The possibility that $\mathbf{A}$ and/or $\mathbf{B}$ may be singular because they are not square must be included.

2.4   The Characteristic Equation

A square matrix is characterized, to a large extent, by the latent roots, or characteristic values, or eigenvalues, λ_i, that satisfy the equation $|\mathbf{A} - \lambda\mathbf{I}| = 0$. For example, if $\mathbf{A}$ is the matrix

$$\begin{bmatrix} 2 & 3 & 1 \\ 0 & 4 & 2 \\ 1 & 5 & 3 \end{bmatrix}$$

then

$$|\mathbf{A} - \lambda\mathbf{I}| \equiv \begin{vmatrix} 2 - \lambda & 3 & 1 \\ 0 & 4 - \lambda & 2 \\ 1 & 5 & 3 - \lambda \end{vmatrix}$$

will be zero only for certain values of λ; in this case the values are approximately 0.6, 7.0, and 1.4. If $\mathbf{A}$ is of order n, the characteristic equation is equivalent to a set of n simultaneous linear equations, or to a polynomial of degree n.

Representing a principal minor of order p by the symbol ^pM, the polynomial in λ can be written out as follows:

$$|\mathbf{A} - \lambda\mathbf{I}| = (-1)^n\lambda^n + (-1)^{n-1}\sum_i {}^1M_i\lambda^{n-1} + (-1)^{n-2}\sum_i {}^2M_i\lambda^{n-2} + \ldots$$
$$+ (-1)^{n-p}\sum_i {}^pM_i\lambda^{n-p} + \ldots + (-1)\sum_i {}^{n-1}M_i\lambda + {}^nM$$

$$\text{(AI-7)}$$

The summation in each case is over the principal minors of the same dimension, starting with the first-order minors, ^1M_i (the sum of which is the trace), and ending with the nth order minor, ^nM, which is the determinant of $\mathbf{A}$.

For the matrix given above, the characteristic equation may be written

$-\lambda^3 + 9\lambda^2 - 15\lambda + 6 = 0$. The roots of such an equation are best found by successive approximation, employing synthetic division and rough graphing.

It can be easily shown, by expanding the product $\prod_i (\lambda - \lambda_i) = 0$ and comparing with equation AI-7, that the trace is the sum of the roots, or eigenvalues; the determinant is the product of the roots; and the sums of the pth-order principal minors are the sums of the products of the roots, taken p at a time.

A similarity transformation leaves all matrix equations unchanged, including the characteristic equation. Let $\mathbf{AX} = \lambda\mathbf{X}$. Then, since $\mathbf{AH^{-1}HX} = \mathbf{AX}$, $\mathbf{HAH^{-1}HX} = \lambda\mathbf{HX}$. But $(\mathbf{A} - \lambda\mathbf{I})\mathbf{X} = 0$ and therefore $|\mathbf{A} - \lambda\mathbf{I}| = 0$; also $(\mathbf{HAH^{-1}} - \lambda\mathbf{I})\mathbf{HX} = 0$ and therefore $|\mathbf{HAH^{-1}} - \lambda\mathbf{I}| = 0$ for the same values of λ. It follows that all the eigenvalues of a matrix are invariant to a similarity transformation. The invariance of the trace and determinant is a direct consequence.

A "positive definite" matrix has all its roots real and greater than zero. A singular matrix must have at least one zero root. The number of non-zero roots is equal to the rank.

If a matrix can be put into a diagonal form by a similarity transformation, the diagonal elements (of the diagonalized form) must be the eigenvalues of the matrix. A transforming matrix can always be found that will accomplish this if the original matrix is either hermitian or unitary (or real-symmetric or real-orthogonal) or if all the eigenvalues of the matrix are different. Diagonalization can generally be accomplished in a physical problem. The transforming matrix is constructed from the eigenvectors, which are the column matrices, $\mathbf{X}_i$, satisfying the equation $\mathbf{AX} = \lambda\mathbf{X}$ or $(\mathbf{A} - \lambda\mathbf{I})\mathbf{X} = 0$.

It can be shown that two matrices can be diagonalized by the same similarity transformation if, and only if, they commute. The physical significance of this is essentially the following. The eigenvectors describe the state, or state of motion, of the system. If two matrices are diagonalized by the same transformation, the columns, or rows, of the transforming matrix must be eigenvectors of both matrices. Thus the two matrices may be said to describe different properties of the same state of the system. The implications of this are especially important in the equations of quantum mechanics.

All diagonal matrices commute, but diagonal matrices do not, in general, commute with non-diagonal matrices. In fact, all matrices that commute with a diagonal matrix, all of whose eigenvalues are different, must be diagonal. Note that the zero matrix or a constant matrix will commute with all matrices, but their eigenvalues are not all different.

2.5   Eigenvectors and Complete Vector Sets

A vector consists of an ordered set of numbers (section V-3.1).   These numbers may be written as a column matrix or as a row matrix.   The matrix representation suffices for the addition of vectors, for the transformation from one coordinate system to another, and for evaluating the scalar product of two vectors.

In three-dimensional space two vectors are said to be perpendicular, or orthogonal, if their scalar product is zero.   Only three independent vectors can be found in three-dimensional space, although there is an infinite number of sets of three independent vectors, differing in length and, in the geometric interpretation, in angular orientation.   Orthogonal vectors are independent, although independent vectors need not be orthogonal.

In matrix notation two vectors, $\mathbf{X}$ and $\mathbf{Y}$, are orthogonal if $\mathbf{Y}^*\mathbf{X} = 0$. (For any two vectors, $|\mathbf{X}^*\mathbf{Y}| = |\mathbf{Y}^*\mathbf{X}|^*$.)   This is easily extended to n dimensions, or to column matrices of dimension n.   There will be just n independent vectors of dimension n.   If $\mathbf{X}^*\mathbf{X} = 1$, $\mathbf{X}$ is said to be normalized (to 1) and is called a unit vector, or a vector of unit length (regardless of the dimension of $\mathbf{X}$).   Two or more vectors that are normalized and orthogonal are said to be orthonormal.   If $\mathbf{X}_1$, $\mathbf{X}_2$, $\mathbf{X}_3$, ...,$\mathbf{X}_n$ satisfy the condition that $\mathbf{X}_i^*\mathbf{X}_j = \delta_{ij}$, the matrices $\mathbf{X}_i$ form an orthonormal set.   A set of orthogonal vectors is said to be complete if there is no other vector that is orthogonal to all vectors of the set.   Any set of n orthogonal vectors of dimension n must be a complete set.   Any other vector of dimension n can then be expressed as a linear combination of these n vectors and will not be orthogonal to one or more of them.

If a complete set of orthonormal vectors, say n vectors $\mathbf{U}_i$ of dimension n, is arranged to form a square matrix,

$$\mathbf{U} \equiv [\mathbf{U}_1, \mathbf{U}_2, \ldots, \mathbf{U}_n] \equiv \begin{bmatrix} u_{11} & u_{12} & u_{13} & \cdots & u_{1n} \\ u_{21} & u_{22} & u_{23} & \cdots & u_{2n} \\ \multicolumn{5}{c}{\cdots\cdots\cdots\cdots\cdots\cdots} \\ u_{n1} & u_{n2} & u_{n3} & \cdots & u_{nn} \end{bmatrix}$$

the matrix $\mathbf{U}$ will be unitary, since $\mathbf{U}^*\mathbf{U} = 1$.   If the elements are real, the matrix is orthogonal.

The vectors, $\mathbf{X}_i$, that satisfy the equation $\mathbf{A}\mathbf{X} = \lambda\mathbf{X}$ are called the eigenvectors (or poles) of the matrix $\mathbf{A}$.   If a vector $\mathbf{X}_i$ satisfies this equation, then $c\mathbf{X}_i$ will also satisfy the equation; the vectors $\mathbf{X}_i$ can therefore be assumed to be normalized without loss of generality.   In general, there will be a different eigenvector for each eigenvalue, λ, and therefore the n-dimensional square matrix $\mathbf{A}$ will have n eigenvectors. If $\mathbf{A}$ is hermitian, its eigenvectors will form a complete, orthonormal set.

Let $\mathbf{X}_i$ be the eigenvector corresponding to the eigenvalue λ_i and $\mathbf{X}_j$ the eigenvector corresponding to λ_j. Then, if $\mathbf{A}$ is hermitian, $\mathbf{X}_j^*(\mathbf{A}\mathbf{X}_i) = \mathbf{X}_j^*\lambda_i\mathbf{X}_i = (\mathbf{X}_j^*\mathbf{A})\mathbf{X}_i = (\mathbf{X}_j^*\mathbf{A}^*)\mathbf{X}_i = \mathbf{X}_j^*\lambda_j\mathbf{X}_i$. The constants, λ_i and λ_j, commute with the vectors. Therefore $\lambda_i\mathbf{X}_j^*\mathbf{X}_i = \lambda_j\mathbf{X}_j^*\mathbf{X}_i$ or $(\lambda_i - \lambda_j)\mathbf{X}_j^*\mathbf{X}_i = 0$. For a hermitian matrix, therefore, the eigenvectors belonging to different eigenvalues (non-degenerate states) must be orthogonal. If the eigenvalues are degenerate, the eigenvectors may still be chosen to be orthogonal.

Let $\mathbf{X} = (x_1, x_2, \ldots, x_n)$ be a square matrix, the columns of which are the eigenvectors of $\mathbf{A}$, and let Λ be the diagonal matrix of the eigenvalues of $\mathbf{A}$. Then

$$\mathbf{A}\mathbf{X} = \mathbf{X}\Lambda \tag{AI-8}$$

If $\mathbf{X}^{-1}$ exists, then $\mathbf{X}^{-1}\mathbf{A}\mathbf{X} = \Lambda$. $\mathbf{X}^{-1}$ will exist if the eigenvectors are independent, which will necessarily be true if the eigenvalues are all different but need not be true otherwise. $\mathbf{X}^{-1} = \mathbf{X}^*$ if $\mathbf{A} = \mathbf{A}^*$.

There is a general method for finding the eigenvectors of a matrix after the eigenvalues have been determined. The problem is to find a column matrix, $\mathbf{X}_i$, such that $(\mathbf{A} - \lambda_i\mathbf{I})\mathbf{X}_i = 0$. A column matrix is constructed consisting of the cofactors of the elements in the first row of the matrix $(\mathbf{A} - \lambda_i\mathbf{I})$. This column matrix, when multiplied by $(\mathbf{A} - \lambda\mathbf{I})$, will give the column matrix

$$\begin{bmatrix} |\mathbf{A} - \lambda_i\mathbf{I}| \\ 0 \\ 0 \\ \cdot \\ \cdot \\ \cdot \end{bmatrix}$$

which is just the zero matrix because the determinant itself is zero. If all the cofactors are found to be zero, then the cofactors of some other row will be non-zero and will give the same result.[1] Choosing different rows will give different column matrices, but they will differ from each other only by a constant factor and therefore represent the same normalized eigenvector.

---

[1] If the matrix has more than one eigenvalue of zero, but r eigenvalues different from zero (r is the rank), then all minors of the matrix of dimension larger than r will vanish. The r-dimensional minors will form the elements of the eigenvectors.

For example, the characteristic equation of the matrix

$$\begin{bmatrix} 7 & -\sqrt{3} & 0 \\ -\sqrt{3} & 5 & 0 \\ 0 & 0 & 12 \end{bmatrix}$$

can be written $-\lambda^3 + 24\lambda^2 - 176\lambda + 384 = 0$. The eigenvalues are 4, 8, and 12. The matrix $(\mathbf{A} - 4\mathbf{I})$ is

$$\begin{bmatrix} 3 & -\sqrt{3} & 0 \\ -\sqrt{3} & 1 & 0 \\ 0 & 0 & 8 \end{bmatrix}$$

The cofactors of the first row of this matrix, arranged in column form, are

$$\begin{bmatrix} 8 \\ 8\sqrt{3} \\ 0 \end{bmatrix}$$

The product of $(\mathbf{A} - 4\mathbf{I})$ and this vector is zero. The second row would have given the same column vector multiplied by a constant; the third row would have given the trivial result of a null vector.

The other eigenvalues will give the eigenvectors

$$\begin{bmatrix} -12 \\ 4\sqrt{3} \\ 0 \end{bmatrix} \quad \text{and} \quad \begin{bmatrix} 0 \\ 0 \\ 32 \end{bmatrix}$$

These are normalized by dividing each element of the vector by the square root of the sum of the squares of the elements. For example, the first vector is divided by $\sqrt{64 + 3 \times 64} = 16$, giving

$$\begin{bmatrix} 1/2 \\ \sqrt{3}/2 \\ 0 \end{bmatrix}$$

The three normalized vectors give the unitary (and orthogonal) matrix

$$\mathbf{X} = \begin{bmatrix} 1/2 & -\sqrt{3}/2 & 0 \\ \sqrt{3}/2 & 1/2 & 0 \\ 0 & 0 & 1 \end{bmatrix}$$

The product $\mathbf{X^*AX}$ is diagonal,

$$\mathbf{X^*AX} = \begin{bmatrix} 4 & 0 & 0 \\ 0 & 8 & 0 \\ 0 & 0 & 12 \end{bmatrix}$$

Often a matrix is encountered that is known to be singular. Such a matrix can be transformed, by an orthogonal matrix, to a form in which one row and one column (or as many rows and columns as the matrix has zero roots) consist of zeros and the remainder of the matrix is non-singular. The transforming matrix contains the eigenvector belonging to the eigenvalue zero.

Let $\mathbf{H}_1$ be an eigenvector of $\mathbf{G}$ such that $\mathbf{GH}_1 = 0\mathbf{H}_1 = \mathbf{O}$. Other columns, $\mathbf{H}_i$, can be chosen quite arbitrarily such that they are orthogonal to $\mathbf{H}_1$ and to each other. Then the matrix $\mathbf{H}$ will transform $\mathbf{G}$ as follows ($\mathbf{H^{-1}GH} = \mathbf{G'}$).

$$\begin{bmatrix} \mathbf{H}_1^* \\ \mathbf{H}_2^* \\ \mathbf{H}_3^* \\ \cdot \end{bmatrix} \begin{bmatrix} g_{11} & g_{12} & g_{13} & \cdots \\ g_{21} & g_{22} & g_{23} & \cdots \\ g_{31} & g_{32} & g_{33} & \cdots \\ \cdot & \cdot & \cdot & \cdots \end{bmatrix} [\mathbf{H}_1 \quad \mathbf{H}_2 \quad \mathbf{H}_3 \quad \cdots]$$

$$= \begin{bmatrix} 0 & 0 & 0 & \cdots \\ 0 & g_{11}' & g_{12}' & \cdots \\ 0 & g_{21}' & g_{22}' & \cdots \\ \cdot & \cdot & \cdot & \cdots \end{bmatrix}$$

2.6   Transformations of Coordinates

A cartesian coordinate system, in three dimensions, is defined by three orthogonal unit vectors.[1] They are often designated i, j, and k. Any point in space is then associated with a vector from the origin to the point. The projections of the vector $\vec{\rho}$, associated with the point P, on the axes are $\vec{\rho} \cdot i = x$, $\vec{\rho} \cdot j = y$, and $\vec{\rho} \cdot k = z$. These projections, x, y, and z, are called the coordinates of the point. They uniquely define the point in terms of the coordinate system i, j, k. The vector, $\vec{\rho}$, can be written $\vec{\rho} = xi + yj + zk$.

Assume that the origin and the point have some physical meaning. In

[1] These are unit vectors by definition, since they in turn define the unit of length along each axis independently. There can be no proof, mathematical or physical, that these three unit vectors have the same length.

any new coordinate system that describes the same portion of space the vector $\vec{\rho}$ must be unchanged. For example, let the unit vectors l, m, and n define a coordinate system such that the coordinates of P are u, v, w. Then

$$\vec{\rho} = xi + yj + zk \qquad \text{(AI-9)}$$
$$= ul + vm + wn$$

The coordinates, however, are not invariant to this change of coordinate systems. That is, $x \neq u$, $y \neq v$, $z \neq w$.

Another point, P', in the same region of space, will be specified by a vector $\vec{\rho}'$, or by the corresponding coordinates in any coordinate system.

$$\vec{\rho}' = x'i + y'j + z'k \qquad \text{(AI-10)}$$
$$= u'l + y'm + w'n$$

If the point P is considered to be transformed into the point P' by any process, a set of transformation coordinates can be written, in either coordinate system, as follows.

$$x' = t_{11}x + t_{12}y + t_{13}z$$
$$y' = t_{21}x + t_{22}y + t_{23}z$$
$$z' = t_{31}x + t_{32}y + t_{33}z$$

$$\qquad \text{(AI-11)}$$

$$u' = s_{11}u + s_{12}v + s_{13}w$$
$$v' = s_{21}u + s_{22}v + s_{23}w$$
$$w' = s_{31}u + s_{32}v + s_{33}w$$

These equations can be greatly condensed by writing them in matrix notation. The matrices will be defined as follows.

$$\mathbf{X} = \begin{bmatrix} x_1 \\ x_2 \\ x_3 \end{bmatrix} = \begin{bmatrix} x \\ y \\ z \end{bmatrix} \qquad \mathbf{X}' = \begin{bmatrix} x_1' \\ x_2' \\ x_3' \end{bmatrix} = \begin{bmatrix} x' \\ y' \\ z' \end{bmatrix}$$

$$\mathbf{U} = \begin{bmatrix} u_1 \\ u_2 \\ u_3 \end{bmatrix} = \begin{bmatrix} u \\ v \\ w \end{bmatrix} \qquad \mathbf{U}' = \begin{bmatrix} u_1' \\ u_2' \\ u_3' \end{bmatrix} = \begin{bmatrix} u' \\ v' \\ w' \end{bmatrix} \qquad \text{(AI-12)}$$

$$\mathbf{K} = \begin{bmatrix} k_1 \\ k_2 \\ k_3 \end{bmatrix} = \begin{bmatrix} i \\ j \\ k \end{bmatrix} \qquad \mathbf{L} = \begin{bmatrix} l_1 \\ l_2 \\ l_3 \end{bmatrix} = \begin{bmatrix} l \\ m \\ n \end{bmatrix}$$

$$\mathbf{T} = [t_{ij}] \quad \text{and} \quad \mathbf{S} = [s_{ij}]$$

from equations AI-11.

Then the point P is defined by the vector

$$\vec{\rho} = \mathbf{K*X} = \mathbf{X*K} = \mathbf{L*U} = \mathbf{U*L} \qquad \text{(AI-13)}$$

and the point P' by the vector

$$\vec{\rho'} = \mathbf{K*X'} = \mathbf{X'*K} = \mathbf{L*U'} = \mathbf{U'*L} \qquad \text{(AI-14)}$$

Also,

$$\mathbf{X'} = \mathbf{TX} \quad \text{and} \quad \mathbf{U'} = \mathbf{SU} \qquad \text{(AI-15)}$$

Define the matrix $\mathbf{R}$ as the product $\mathbf{KL*}$, a square matrix with the general term $r_{ij} = k_i \cdot l_j$. Then, since $\mathbf{KK*} = \mathbf{I}$,

$$\mathbf{X} = \mathbf{RU} \qquad \text{(AI-16)}$$
$$\mathbf{X'} = \mathbf{RU'}$$

from equations AI-13 and AI-14, respectively. Also from the same equations,

$$\mathbf{U} = \mathbf{R^{-1}X}$$
$$\mathbf{U'} = \mathbf{R^{-1}X'} \qquad \text{(AI-17)}$$

where[1] $\mathbf{R^{-1}} = \mathbf{LK*}$.

It follows, by direct substitution, that

$$\mathbf{U'} = \mathbf{SU} = \mathbf{R^{-1}X'} = \mathbf{R^{-1}TX} = \mathbf{R^{-1}TRU}$$

and therefore

$$\mathbf{S} = \mathbf{R^{-1}TR} \qquad \text{(AI-18)}$$
$$\mathbf{T} = \mathbf{RSR^{-1}}$$

This result is consistent with the earlier conclusion that a similarity transformation leaves the form of a matrix equation invariant. The geometrical interpretation of this rule is that a similarity transformation has the effect of changing the coordinate system (in this example, from the coordinate system defined by $\mathbf{K}$ to that defined by $\mathbf{L}$). The relationships between points in space are unaffected by the choice of cartesian coordinate systems and therefore equations involving such points (equations AI-9, AI-10, AI-15, for example) have identical forms in either coordinate system.

Since the length of the vectors defining the coordinate systems are

---

[1] The product of three or more vectors is not uniquely defined. For example, $(v_1 \cdot v_2)v_3 \neq v_1(v_2 \cdot v_3)$. Similarly, $(\mathbf{LK*})(\mathbf{KL*})$ is not the same as $\mathbf{L(K*K)L*}$. This causes no difficulty as long as $\mathbf{R^{-1}}$ is defined as $\mathbf{LK*}$ and the matrices $\mathbf{R}$ and $\mathbf{R^{-1}}$ are treated as entities.

assumed the same ($\mathbf{KK^*} = \mathbf{LL^*} = \mathbf{I}$), the lengths of all vectors in space are left unchanged.   Thus

$$\rho^2 = \vec{\rho} \cdot \vec{\rho} = (\mathbf{K^*X})^*(\mathbf{K^*X}) = \mathbf{X^*}(\mathbf{KK^*})\mathbf{X} = \mathbf{X^*X} \qquad \text{(AI-19)}$$
$$= (\mathbf{L^*U})^*(\mathbf{L^*U}) = \mathbf{U^*}(\mathbf{LL^*})\mathbf{U} = \mathbf{U^*U}$$

but

$$\mathbf{U^*U} = (\mathbf{R^{-1}X})^*(\mathbf{R^{-1}X}) = \mathbf{X^*RR^{-1}X} = \mathbf{X^*X}$$

since $\mathbf{R}$ is orthogonal ($\mathbf{R^{-1}} = \tilde{\mathbf{R}} = \mathbf{R^*}$).

The geometrical interpretation of a transformation of coordinates that leaves all lengths unchanged and leaves all equations invariant is quite clearly that the new coordinate system is identical with the original except for a rotation in space.   Orthogonal matrices are therefore often associated with rotations of axes.   For the special case of a rotation about the z axis by an angle ϕ, the transforming matrix is

$$\mathbf{R} = \begin{bmatrix} \cos\phi & \sin\phi & 0 \\ -\sin\phi & \cos\phi & 0 \\ 0 & 0 & 1 \end{bmatrix}$$

and the inverse, which is a rotation by $-\phi$, is

$$\mathbf{R^{-1}} = \begin{bmatrix} \cos\phi & -\sin\phi & 0 \\ \sin\phi & \cos\phi & 0 \\ 0 & 0 & 1 \end{bmatrix}$$

Finally, it should be mentioned that implicit in the equations given above are two types of transformations.   The equation $\mathbf{X} = \mathbf{RU}$ is considered to represent the change in coordinates of a single vector or point when the coordinate system is rotated.   The equation $\mathbf{X'} = \mathbf{TX}$ related two different points in the same coordinate system.   If $\mathbf{T}$ is an orthogonal matrix, then these two types of transformations are mathematically equivalent (except for the sign of ϕ).   It is necessary to decide, in any particular application, which interpretation is to be chosen.

The transformation equations have been discussed in terms of three-dimensional space.   There is, of course, no difficulty in applying the same equations with matrices of any dimension.

2.7   Direct Sums and Direct Products

Two ways of adding matrices have been defined, the customary addition, element by element (equation AI-2), and augmentation, in which rows or columns are added to increase the dimensions. For certain applications, especially in group theory, it is necessary to define another type of addition. The direct sum of two matrices, **A** and **B**, is the matrix

$$\begin{bmatrix} \mathbf{A} & 0 \\ 0 & \mathbf{B} \end{bmatrix}$$

The direct product of the matrices is obtained by multiplying each element of the first matrix by each element of the second. If **A** is $m \times n$ and **B** is $p \times q$, the direct product $\mathbf{A} \times \mathbf{B}$ will be of dimensions $(mp) \times (nq)$. It may be considered to consist of the submatrices $a_{ij}\mathbf{B}$, in the form

$$\begin{bmatrix} a_{11}\mathbf{B} & a_{12}\mathbf{B} & \ldots & a_{1n}\mathbf{B} \\ a_{21}\mathbf{B} & a_{22}\mathbf{B} & \ldots & a_{2n}\mathbf{B} \\ \ldots & \ldots & \ldots & \ldots \\ a_{m1}\mathbf{B} & a_{m2}\mathbf{B} & \ldots & a_{mn}\mathbf{B} \end{bmatrix}$$

or it may be written out in more detail as

$$\begin{bmatrix} a_{11}b_{11} & a_{11}b_{12} & \ldots & a_{11}b_{1q} & a_{12}b_{11} & a_{12}b_{12} & \ldots & & & & \\ & & & & & a_{12}b_{1q} & \ldots & a_{1n}b_{11} & \ldots & a_{1n}b_{1q} \\ a_{11}b_{21} & a_{11}b_{22} & \ldots & a_{11}b_{2q} & a_{12}b_{21} & a_{12}b_{22} & \ldots & & & \\ & & & & & a_{12}b_{2q} & \ldots & a_{1n}b_{21} & \ldots & a_{1n}b_{2q} \\ \ldots & \ldots & \ldots & \ldots & \ldots & & & & & \\ & & & & & \ldots & \ldots & \ldots & \ldots & \ldots \\ a_{m1}b_{p1} & a_{m1}b_{p2} & \ldots & a_{m1}b_{pq} & a_{m2}b_{p1} & a_{m2}b_{p2} & \ldots & & & \\ & & & & & a_{m2}b_{pq} & \ldots & a_{mn}b_{p1} & \ldots & a_{mn}b_{pq} \end{bmatrix}$$

The direct product $\mathbf{A} \times \mathbf{B}$ is not the same as the direct product $\mathbf{B} \times \mathbf{A}$, but each will have the same elements.

The trace of the direct sum of **A** and **B** is just the sum of the traces of **A** and **B**. The trace of the direct product of **A** and **B** is just the product of the traces of **A** and **B**. It is these conditions that allow a great simplification of the equations of group theory.

The ordinary product of the direct sums of matrices will be the direct sum of the ordinary matrix products. That is,

$$(\mathbf{A} + \mathbf{B})(\mathbf{A}' + \mathbf{B}') = \mathbf{A}\mathbf{A}' + \mathbf{B}\mathbf{B}'$$

or

$$\begin{bmatrix} \mathbf{A} & 0 \\ 0 & \mathbf{B} \end{bmatrix} \begin{bmatrix} \mathbf{A}' & 0 \\ 0 & \mathbf{B}' \end{bmatrix} = \begin{bmatrix} \mathbf{A}\mathbf{A}' & 0 \\ 0 & \mathbf{B}\mathbf{B}' \end{bmatrix}$$

2.8   Vectors, Tensors, and Matrices

The similarities between column matrices and vectors and between square matrices and certain tensors have been emphasized by representing the vectors or tensors by matrices.   It was also pointed out, however, that a vector is not identical with the physical quantity it often represents. Similar statements can be made concerning the relationships among tensors, physical quantities, and matrices.

A tensor is characterized by the manner in which the components transform under a change of coordinates.   Tensors are independent of the coordinate system (for certain "allowable" transformations) although the components will vary.   A tensor of zero rank is a scalar; a tensor of the first rank is a vector and may be represented for many purposes by a column (or row) matrix; a tensor of the second rank is often represented by a square matrix.

Tensor notation is somewhat more flexible than matrix notation, since the former considers the components individually.   Matrix notation, on the other hand, represents an appreciable simplification of notation when it is applicable.   It is therefore sometimes advisable to treat a problem in matrix notation to a certain point, to change to tensor notation temporarily, then revert to the same or to a different matrix notation for the remainder of the problem.   An example of this is given in the investigation of the transformation properties of the polarizability of a molecule (section X-1.612).   Another example is the expression of axial vectors, such as infinitesimal rotations, in matrix notation although the cross product, or vector product, of two vectors is not amenable to a matrix notation consistent with representing the vectors by column matrices.

3   Applications of Matrices

The following applications of matrices are of interest in absorption spectroscopy, either in the analytical procedures or in the determination of structures and bond strengths.   The discussion is not intended to be complete so much as suggestive of the possibilities.   Only matrices of finite dimension are considered.

3.1   Multicomponent Quantitative Analysis

Determination of the concentrations of several compounds present in the same mixture requires the solution of a set of simultaneous equations. If Beer's law is followed, these equations are linear.   For each component, at a concentration c_j, there will be a contribution A_{ij} to this observed absorbance, A_i, at the ith frequency given by the equation

$$A_{ij} = a_{ij}bc_j \tag{AI-20}$$
$$= k_{ij}c_j$$

where a_{ij} is the absorptivity of the compound j at the frequency i, b is the cell length, and k_{ij} is the product $a_{ij}b$. The total absorbance at this frequency, due to all compounds present, is the sum

$$A_i = \sum_j k_{ij}c_j \tag{AI-21}$$

Let **A** be a column matrix with the elements A_i, let **C** be a column matrix with elements c_j, and let **K** be a matrix of the k_{ij} values. The matrix **A** will have a number of elements equal to the number of frequencies at which absorbance measurements are made; **C** will have a number of elements equal to the number of compounds; **K** will have a number of rows equal to the number of frequencies and a number of columns equal to the number of compounds. Then

$$\mathbf{A} = \mathbf{KC} \tag{AI-22}$$

Assume for the present that the number of frequencies is just equal to the number of compounds. The equations then have a unique solution. If a large number of determinations are to be made on equivalent samples, it will be most expedient to evaluate the matrix $\mathbf{K}^{-1}$. The concentrations are then obtained by carrying out a matrix multiplication.

$$\mathbf{C} = \mathbf{K}^{-1}\mathbf{A} \tag{AI-23}$$

For less routine analyses it will often be faster to solve the equations by means of Cramer's rule. An unknown concentration, c_j, is found by replacing the jth column of the matrix **K** by the matrix **A**. The determinant of the new matrix is divided by the determinant of **K**.

$$c_1 = \frac{\begin{vmatrix} A_1 & k_{12} & k_{13} & \cdots \\ A_2 & k_{22} & k_{23} & \cdots \\ A_3 & k_{32} & k_{33} & \cdots \\ \cdots \cdots \cdots \cdots \end{vmatrix}}{|\mathbf{K}|} \qquad c_2 = \frac{\begin{vmatrix} k_{11} & A_1 & k_{13} & \cdots \\ k_{21} & A_2 & k_{23} & \cdots \\ k_{31} & A_3 & k_{33} & \cdots \\ \cdots \cdots \cdots \cdots \end{vmatrix}}{|\mathbf{K}|} \qquad \begin{matrix} \text{etc.} \\ \text{(AI-24)} \end{matrix}$$

3.2   Least-Squares Method

Occasionally one finds it advisable to admit that experimental measurements are not so accurate as might be desired but are subject to random errors.   An answer with higher probable accuracy can be obtained if excess experimental information is applied.   The equations will no longer have a solution, but if the general accuracy is high a set of values can be found that will almost satisfy the equations.   The best answer is that set of values for which the sum of the squares of the deviations is a minimum.

Consider first a linear equation of the form

$$y = mx + b \tag{AI-25}$$

The constants m and b are considered adjustable parameters, which are to be given values that make the sum of the squares of the deviations of the experimental values from the straight line a minimum.   The value of b that will meet this requirement is determined by the condition that the line should go through the "center of mass" of the points; that is, the sum of the deviations must be zero.

The optimum value of the constant m depends on the relative accuracies of the measurements of x and y.[1]   If y is known more accurately, the deviations are

$$\delta_i = y_i - mx_i - b \tag{AI-26}$$

If x is known more accurately, the deviations are defined as

$$\delta_i = x_i - \frac{1}{m} y_i + \frac{1}{m} b \tag{AI-27}$$

This can be expressed in matrix notation if a "unit vector" is defined, such that

$$\mathbf{I} = \begin{bmatrix} 1 \\ 1 \\ 1 \\ \vdots \end{bmatrix}$$

The values X_i, Y_i, and δ_i each form column matrices, $\mathbf{X}$, $\mathbf{Y}$, and $\mathbf{\Delta}$, of the same dimension.

Assuming the y_i are known more accurately,

$$\mathbf{\Delta} = \mathbf{Y} - m\mathbf{X} - b\mathbf{I} \tag{AI-28}$$

$$\mathbf{\Delta}^*\mathbf{\Delta} = \mathbf{Y}^*\mathbf{Y} - m\mathbf{Y}^*\mathbf{X} - b\mathbf{Y}^*\mathbf{I} - m\mathbf{X}^*\mathbf{Y} + m^2\mathbf{X}^*\mathbf{X} \\ + mb\mathbf{X}^*\mathbf{I} - b\mathbf{I}^*\mathbf{Y} + bm\mathbf{I}^*\mathbf{X} + b^2\mathbf{I}^*\mathbf{I} \tag{AI-29}$$

---

[1] The author is indebted to T. DeVries for pointing out the distinction between problems represented by equations 26 and 27, as well as the simplification achieved through introduction of center-of-mass coordinates.

This is differentiated with respect to m and expressed in terms of equivalent forms of the bilinear products. That is, $\mathbf{I}*\mathbf{X} = \mathbf{X}*\mathbf{I}$ and $\mathbf{I}*\mathbf{Y} = \mathbf{Y}*\mathbf{I}$, but if these are to be added the first form or the second form must be taken from each equation. Setting the derivative with respect to m equal to zero yields the result

$$m = \frac{(\mathbf{Y} - b\mathbf{I})*\mathbf{X}}{\mathbf{X}*\mathbf{X}} \tag{AI-30}$$

If the x_i were known more accurately, the corresponding expression would be

$$m = \frac{(\mathbf{Y} - b\mathbf{I})*(\mathbf{Y} - b\mathbf{I})}{(\mathbf{Y} - b\mathbf{I})*\mathbf{X}} \tag{AI-31}$$

These matrices are column matrices; hence the inverse matrices do not exist and the equations cannot be further simplified by "dividing out" matrices from top and bottom.

The expressions are greatly simplified if the average values of x and y are subtracted. Let $y_i' = y_i - \bar{y}$, $x_i' = x_i - \bar{x}$. Then

$$\mathbf{Y}' = m\mathbf{X}' \tag{AI-32}$$

and either

$$m = \mathbf{X}*'\mathbf{Y}'/\mathbf{X}*'\mathbf{X}' \tag{AI-33}$$

or

$$m = \mathbf{Y}*'\mathbf{Y}'/\mathbf{Y}*'\mathbf{X}' \tag{AI-34}$$

The last equations are easily remembered because they are obtained from equation (AI-32) by multiplying through by $\mathbf{Y}*'$ or by $\mathbf{X}*'$, whichever is known more accurately.

An entirely equivalent operation can be carried out on a system of linear equations of the form

$$\mathbf{A} = \mathbf{KC} \tag{AI-35}$$

such as occurs in multicomponent quantitative analyses. Assuming the k_{ij} and the A_i have been measured, the problem is to find the best value of the c_j.

If the number of elements in the matrix $\mathbf{A}$ is just equal to the number in the matrix $\mathbf{C}$, the equations have a unique solution. Any error in one of the A_i values forces an error into the $\mathbf{C}$ matrix. If the problem is over-determined, by measuring more A_i than the number of c_j to be found, the equations have no unique solution but a "best" solution can be found from the least-squares criterion. Let

$$\Delta = \mathbf{A} - \mathbf{KC} \tag{AI-36}$$

Differentiate the product $\Delta^*\Delta$ with respect to $\mathbf{C}$ to find the best value of $\mathbf{C}$.   This gives the equation

$$\mathbf{K^*A} = \mathbf{K^*KC} \tag{AI-37}$$

Letting $\mathbf{K^*A} = \mathbf{A'}$ and $\mathbf{K^*K} = \mathbf{K'}$, the equation becomes

$$\mathbf{A'} = \mathbf{K'C} \tag{AI-38}$$

This differs from the original in that $\mathbf{A'}$ and $\mathbf{C}$ now have the same dimension, which is the order of the square matrix, $\mathbf{K'}$.   Also, since the matrix $\mathbf{K'}$ is symmetric, evaluation of the determinant or inverse of $\mathbf{K'}$ will require less effort than for a non-symmetric matrix of the same size.   An example of the application of this to a quantitative analysis is given in section IX-4.12.

3.3   Equations of Motion

The displacement, velocity, and acceleration of a simple harmonic oscillator vary sinusoidally with time, differing only in phase.   If the displacement, x_i, is written (equation V-7)

$$x_i = x_i{}^\circ \cos(2\pi\nu t + c) \tag{AI-39}$$

then the acceleration is

$$\ddot{x}_i = -(2\pi\nu)^2 x_i{}^\circ \cos(2\pi\nu t + c) \tag{AI-40}$$

$$= -\lambda x_i$$

where $\lambda = (2\pi\nu)^2$.   This makes the equations of motion linear.

Let the kinetic and potential energies of a system of particles be given by

$$2\mathrm{T} = \sum_i m_i \dot{x}_i{}^2 = \dot{\mathbf{X}}^*\mathbf{M}\dot{\mathbf{X}}$$

$$= [\dot{x}_1, \dot{y}_1, \dot{z}_1, \dot{x}_2, \ldots, \dot{z}_n] \begin{bmatrix} m_1 & & & & & & 0 \\ & m_1 & & & & & \\ & & m_1 & & & & \\ & & & m_2 & & & \\ & & & & \ddots & & \\ & & & & & \ddots & \\ 0 & & & & & & m_n \end{bmatrix} \begin{bmatrix} \dot{x}_1 \\ \dot{y}_1 \\ \dot{z}_1 \\ \dot{x}_2 \\ \cdot \\ \cdot \\ \dot{z}_n \end{bmatrix} \tag{AI-41}$$

and[1]

$$2v = \sum_{i,j} k_{ij}x_ix_j = \mathbf{X}*\mathbf{KX} \qquad \text{(AI-42)}$$

where $\mathbf{K}$ is a square matrix that is, in general, not diagonal.

For the condition that force is mass times acceleration, the equations of motion can be written

$$-\mathbf{KX} = \mathbf{M\ddot{X}} \qquad \text{(AI-43)}$$

This equation can also be obtained in an equivalent manner from the Lagrangian formulation of the equations of motion. $\text{L} = \text{T} - \text{v}$ and

$$\frac{d}{dt} \frac{\partial \text{L}}{\partial \mathbf{\dot{X}}} - \frac{\partial \text{L}}{\partial \mathbf{X}} = 0$$

Therefore

$$\frac{1}{2} \frac{d}{dt} \frac{\partial}{\partial \mathbf{\dot{X}}} (\mathbf{\dot{X}}*\mathbf{M\dot{X}} - \mathbf{X}*\mathbf{KX}) - \frac{1}{2} \frac{\partial}{\partial \mathbf{X}} (\mathbf{\dot{X}}*\mathbf{M\dot{X}} - \mathbf{X}*\mathbf{KX}) = 0 \quad \text{(AI-44)}$$

and

$$\mathbf{M\ddot{X}} + \mathbf{KX} = 0$$

Since the accelerations are proportional to the displacements,

$$\mathbf{\ddot{X}} = -\lambda \mathbf{X} \qquad \text{(AI-45)}$$

and

$$-\mathbf{KX} = -\lambda \mathbf{MX}$$

or

$$\qquad \text{(AI-46)}$$

$$(\mathbf{M^{-1}K})\mathbf{X} = \lambda \mathbf{X}$$

since the matrix $\mathbf{M}$ is non-singular.   The solutions to this equation are those for which the determinant is zero.

$$|\mathbf{M^{-1}K} \quad -\lambda \mathbf{I}| = 0 \qquad \text{(AI-47)}$$

[1] A general expression for potential energy, considering this to be a function only of the positions of the particles, could be written $2v = k_1x_1 + k_2x_2 + \cdots + k_{11}x_1^2 + k_{12}x_1x_2 + k_{22}x_2^2 + \cdots + k_{111}x_1^3 + k_{112}x_1^2x_2 + \cdots$.   To have small oscillations about an equilibrium position two requirements are imposed.   The forces on the system, given by the terms $\partial v/\partial x_i$, must go to zero as the displacements go to zero.   This means that the coefficients of the linear terms in the displacements must be zero.   Also, in order that there shall be forces acting for small displacements, the derivative of the forces, $\partial^2 v/\partial x_i x_j$, must be non-zero when the displacements are zero.   This is not true for the cubic and higher terms.   For small oscillations the homogeneous quadratic expression given may therefore be considered completely general.   In certain systems, but not all, the cross terms, $k_{ij}x_ix_j$, will drop out.

Problems

1. Complete the following matrix equations:

(a) $[3 \quad 5 \quad 1]\begin{bmatrix} 1 \\ 0 \\ 4 \end{bmatrix} = $ ———

(b) $[1 \quad 2 \quad 3]\begin{bmatrix} 1 \\ 2 \\ 3 \end{bmatrix} = $ ———

(c) $\begin{bmatrix} 1 \\ 0 \\ 4 \end{bmatrix}[3 \quad 5 \quad 1] = \begin{bmatrix} & & \\ & & \\ & & \end{bmatrix}$

(d) $\begin{bmatrix} 1 \\ 2 \\ 3 \end{bmatrix}[1 \quad 2 \quad 3] = \begin{bmatrix} & & \\ & & \\ & & \end{bmatrix}$

(e) $\begin{bmatrix} 1 & 0 & 0 \\ 0 & 1 & 0 \\ 0 & 0 & 1 \end{bmatrix}\begin{bmatrix} 1 & 2 & 3 \\ 4 & 5 & 6 \\ 7 & 8 & 9 \end{bmatrix} = \begin{bmatrix} & & \\ & & \\ & & \end{bmatrix}$

(f) $\begin{bmatrix} 1 & 2 & 3 \\ 4 & 5 & 6 \\ 7 & 8 & 9 \end{bmatrix}\begin{bmatrix} 1 & 0 & 0 \\ 0 & 1 & 0 \\ 0 & 0 & 1 \end{bmatrix} = \begin{bmatrix} & & \\ & & \\ & & \end{bmatrix}$

(g) $\begin{bmatrix} 1 & 0 & 0 \\ 0 & 0 & 1 \\ 0 & 1 & 0 \end{bmatrix}\begin{bmatrix} 1 & 2 & 3 \\ 4 & 5 & 6 \\ 7 & 8 & 9 \end{bmatrix} = \begin{bmatrix} & & \\ & & \\ & & \end{bmatrix}$

(h) $\begin{bmatrix} 1 & 2 & 3 \\ 4 & 5 & 6 \\ 7 & 8 & 9 \end{bmatrix}\begin{bmatrix} 1 & 0 & 0 \\ 0 & 0 & 1 \\ 0 & 1 & 0 \end{bmatrix} = \begin{bmatrix} & & \\ & & \\ & & \end{bmatrix}$

(i) $\begin{bmatrix} 1 & 0 & 1 \\ 0 & 1 & 0 \\ 0 & 0 & 1 \end{bmatrix}\begin{bmatrix} 1 & 2 & 3 \\ 4 & 5 & 6 \\ 7 & 8 & 9 \end{bmatrix} = \begin{bmatrix} & & \\ & & \\ & & \end{bmatrix}$

(j) $\begin{bmatrix} 1 & 2 & 3 \\ 4 & 5 & 6 \\ 7 & 8 & 9 \end{bmatrix}\begin{bmatrix} 1 & 0 & 1 \\ 0 & 1 & 0 \\ 0 & 0 & 1 \end{bmatrix} = \begin{bmatrix} & & \\ & & \\ & & \end{bmatrix}$

(k) $\begin{bmatrix} 1 & 0 & 0 \\ 0 & 3 & 0 \\ 0 & 0 & 1 \end{bmatrix}\begin{bmatrix} 1 & 2 & 3 \\ 4 & 5 & 6 \\ 7 & 8 & 9 \end{bmatrix} = \begin{bmatrix} & & \\ & & \\ & & \end{bmatrix}$

(l) $\begin{bmatrix} 1 & 2 & 3 \\ 4 & 5 & 6 \\ 7 & 8 & 9 \end{bmatrix}\begin{bmatrix} 1 & 0 & 0 \\ 0 & 3 & 0 \\ 0 & 0 & 1 \end{bmatrix} = \begin{bmatrix} & & \\ & & \\ & & \end{bmatrix}$

2. (a) In order to transpose or multiply certain columns of a matrix, would you pre-multiply or post-multiply? How could you transpose or multiply certain rows of a matrix?

(b) Evaluate the determinants of the pre-multipliers in (e), (g), (i), and (k) of problem 1.

3. Evaluate the following determinants by the Laplace expansion.

(a) $\begin{vmatrix} 1 & 3 \\ -1 & 2 \end{vmatrix}$

(b) $\begin{vmatrix} 1 & -3 \\ -1 & -2 \end{vmatrix}$

(c) $\begin{vmatrix} 3 & 2 & 1 \\ 1 & 3 & 3 \\ -1 & 2 & 4 \end{vmatrix}$

(d) $\begin{vmatrix} 3 & 1 & -1 \\ 2 & 3 & 2 \\ 1 & 3 & 4 \end{vmatrix}$

(e) $\begin{vmatrix} 2 & 0 & -4 & 1 \\ 1 & 2 & -1 & 0 \\ -6 & 3 & 9 & -5 \\ -2 & 1 & 1 & 0 \end{vmatrix}$

(f) $\begin{vmatrix} 1 & 3 & 0 & 0 & 0 \\ -1 & 2 & 0 & 0 & 0 \\ 0 & 0 & 3 & 2 & 1 \\ 0 & 0 & 1 & 3 & 3 \\ 0 & 0 & -1 & 2 & 4 \end{vmatrix}$

4. Put each of the following matrices in triangular form by systematically adding multiples of the first row to the lower rows until the first column contains only one element, then adding multiples of the second row to the lower rows, etc.   How can the determinant of the original matrix be found from the triangular form?

(a) $\begin{bmatrix} 1 & 3 \\ -1 & 2 \end{bmatrix}$

(b) $\begin{bmatrix} 3 & 2 & 1 \\ 1 & 3 & 3 \\ -1 & 2 & 4 \end{bmatrix}$

(c) $\begin{bmatrix} 2 & 0 & -4 & 1 \\ 1 & 2 & -1 & 0 \\ -6 & 3 & 9 & -5 \\ -2 & 1 & 1 & 0 \end{bmatrix}$

5. Evaluate the determinants of the matrices (a), (b), and (c) in problem 4 by pivotal condensation.

6. Find the inverse of each matrix in problem 4.   Prove, by pre- and post-multiplication, that the matrix found is the correct inverse.

7. By means of earlier results, find the solutions of the following systems of linear equations.

(a) $x_1 + 3x_2 = 6$
      $-x_1 + 2x_2 = 1$

$\left(\text{or} \begin{bmatrix} 1 & 3 \\ -1 & 2 \end{bmatrix} \begin{bmatrix} x_1 \\ x_2 \end{bmatrix} = \begin{bmatrix} 6 \\ 1 \end{bmatrix} \right)$

(b) $x_1 + 3x_2 = 2$
      $-x_1 + 2x_2 = 7$

(c) $3x_1 + 2x_2 + x_3 = 4$
      $x_1 + 3x_2 + 3x_3 = 1$
      $-x_1 + 2x_2 + 4x_3 = 0$

(d) $2x_1 \qquad - 4x_3 + x_4 = 1$
      $x_1 + 2x_2 - x_3 \qquad = 2$
      $-6x_1 + 3x_2 + 9x_3 - 5x_4 = 3$
      $-2x_1 + x_2 + x_3 \qquad = 4$

8. Solve equation (c) in problem 7 by means of Cramer's Rule.

9. From the information given below, calculate the concentrations of compounds A and B in the mixture, according to the least-squares method (absorbance $= \Sigma$ absorptivity times concentration).

	ν_1	ν_2	ν_3
Absorptivity (A)	0.880	0.203	0.731
Absorptivity (B)	0.132	1.260	0.008
Absorbance (mixture)	0.640	0.490	0.502

10. (a) Find the eigenvalues of the matrix

$$\begin{bmatrix} 2.083 & -0.118 & -0.433 \\ -0.118 & 2.167 & 0.612 \\ -0.433 & 0.612 & 2.250 \end{bmatrix}$$

(b) Write out explicitly the equivalent polynominal form of the characteristic equation of the matrix above.   Show that this is the product $(\lambda - \lambda_1) \cdot (\lambda - \lambda_2) \cdot (\lambda - \lambda_3)$.

11. Find the eigenvectors corresponding to each eigenvalue of the matrix in problem 10.   Show that, when these are normalized, they form an orthonormal set.

12. Diagonalize the matrix of problem 10 by means of the orthogonal matrix composed of the normalized eigenvectors found in problem 11.

13. Find the eigenvalues of the matrix

$$\begin{bmatrix} 2 & 0 & 0 \\ 4 & 5 & 2 \\ 3 & -1 & 2 \end{bmatrix}$$

making use of the relationships suggested by problem 10b.   (Find $\lambda_1\lambda_2\lambda_3$, $\lambda_1\lambda_2 + \lambda_2\lambda_3 + \lambda_1\lambda_3$, and $\lambda_1 + \lambda_2 + \lambda_3$.)   Show that each of these satisfies the condition $|\mathbf{A} - \lambda\mathbf{I}| = 0$.

14. Prove the following.

(a) $\mathbf{A}\mathbf{X}_i = (\mathbf{X}_i^*\mathbf{A}^*)^*$.   (Use summation notation.)

(b) If $\mathbf{A} = \mathbf{A}^*$ and $\mathbf{A}\mathbf{X}_i = \lambda_i\mathbf{X}_i$, then λ_i is real.   (Use the quadratic form, $\mathbf{X}_i^*\mathbf{A}\mathbf{X}_i$.)

II

Nomenclature

The great variety of nomenclature in the field of spectroscopy is indicative of the broad applicability of the methods and the results of spectral measurements. Early notations were based on specific experimental techniques that are now almost forgotten, but the symbols have remained in the literature and still appear in current writings. One set of quantities may be of greater practicality for those who are interested in chemical analysis, a different set may be better for theoreticians who wish to determine molecular structures, and a third set may be preferred by the specialist who concentrates on optical qualities of filters and related devices.

The difficulties inherent in multiple notation are particularly unfortunate in that many times the same symbol is applied to physical quantities of different dimensions or the same name and symbol may be applied to quantities differing by the arbitrary choice of common or natural logarithms. Appreciable progress has been made in recent years toward acceptance of ground rules for spectroscopic notation and even toward the acceptance of terms and symbols for specific quantities. It will require a much greater period of time before the difficulties of conflicting notations are effectively eliminated.

An early attempt at standardization, aimed primarily if not exclusively at achieving a form of internal consistency in the publications coming from the National Bureau of Standards, was published in 1947.[1] Other committees have established a comprehensive system of nomenclature in the area of color specification and measurement.[2] The SUN Commission (Commission on Symbols, Units and Nomenclature) of IUPAP and the

---

[1] *NBS Letter Circular* LC-857, 1947. See chap. 5 of ref. 38 for a review of most of this discussion.

[2] See *J. Opt. Soc. Am.*, **33**, 552 (1943); Evans, ref. 58.

Joint Commission for Spectroscopy have been active in achieving cooperation on the international level.   The Joint Committee on Nomenclature
in Applied Spectroscopy, established by the Society for Applied Spectroscopy and the American Society for Testing Materials (Committee E-2),
has produced an important report[1] that has served as a set of working rules
for applied spectroscopy since that date.   Attention is called in particular
to the discussion of the requirements for a satisfactory system of notation
appearing in Report No. 6 of the Joint Committee.   A portion of that
material has been incorporated here.

I   General Criteria

It is important that the nomenclature of spectroscopy be in accord with
the accepted language of physics and chemistry.   This provides several
broad rules for evaluating alternative notations.   For example, the name
of a physical quantity should be independent of the units in which it is
expressed.   In so far as possible, however, a given name should always
refer to quantities of the same dimensions.   Thus the name force is
applied whether the unit is the dyne (gm-cm/sec^2) or the newton
(kg-m/sec^2), both of which have dimensions of mass times length divided
by time squared.   The symbol should also be independent of units in
order that the form of an equation may be independent of the choice of
(self-consistent) units.

The name of a unit is generally written without capitalization (gram,
newton, debye); the symbol is capitalized, or not, depending on the agreement for the specific unit (gm, nt, D).   Since the letter or letters representing the unit are considered properly defined symbols, rather than
abbreviations, they are written without periods or plural forms, except
where possible confusion makes this inappropriate (cm, not cm. or cms.;
but in. for inch).

A device is to be given a name ending with "-or," except for certain
cases in which "-er" is more appropriate.   Thus capacitor, transistor,
monochromator, meter, and filter are examples of the correct application
of this rule.   A process receives the ending "-ation" or sometimes "-sion,"
as in radiation, calibration, reflection, and transmission.   The application
of terms such as radiation and calibration to represent the result of the process (radiant energy or calibration data) may be less proper but is common
and often convenient.   A property of a specific body or device is given
the ending "-ance."   Thus the conductance and absorbance depend on the

[1] Report No. 6; see *Anal. Chem.* **24**, 1349 (1952).

size and shape of a body as well as on the material of which it is made. The corresponding intensive property would be given the ending "-ity," as in conductivity or absorptivity, which are independent of size and shape.

2 Intensity Units

The units for the intensity of radiant energy will depend on the exact quantity intended, which might be energy/steradian-time, energy/area-time, energy/volume, number of photons rather than the energy of the photons, or a function weighted according to visual sensitivity. For each of these, however, the units may be chosen consistent with mks or cgs systems or may be a standard modification of one of them such as calories/cm²-sec. Such absolute intensities are important in measuring the quality of a detector and in certain problems of low-frequency spectroscopy in which saturation effects must be considered.

Most often a spectroscopic measurement will find the ratio of two intensities or some function of this ratio. The ratio of intensities will depend on the form of the specific substance. The ratio of intensity transmitted to the incident intensity is therefore the transmittance; the ratio of reflected to incident intensities is the reflectance; the (common) logarithm of the ratio of incident to transmitted intensities is the absorbance. These ratios are given the respective symbols T, R, and A. Each is a pure number[1] and therefore has no dimensions or units. A unit for absorbance would often be helpful, but none has been adopted.[2]

For precise measurements it is necessary to take into consideration the several processes that occur simultaneously, including reflection at each interface between dissimilar materials, absorption by each substance through which the beam passes, and scattering associated with any inhomogeneities in the system. From the measured value one would normally wish to determine either the absorbing properties of a pure material or the absorbing properties of a solute present in a more or less transparent solvent. Terms such as "internal transmittance" and "external transmittance," as well as transmittancy and absorbancy, have been coined to

[1] The transmittance is a number less than or equal to 1 and is therefore often expressed as a percentage. For example, $T = 0.40 = 40\% = 40$ per cent transmittance.

[2] Actually the bel is an appropriate unit for absorbance. Unfortunately, however, the common subunit, the decibel, is quite generally employed as a measure of absolute intensity by assuming an implicit value for a reference level of absolute intensity. Any attempt to rehabilitate the bel for its original meaning might encounter difficulty because of confusion with this other usage.

distinguish between these properties under certain conditions of measurement and with certain applied corrections.   For nearly all spectroscopic applications the simple terms are to be preferred; certainly one should not employ a special term such as transmittancy without having made any and all corrections to the measured value that are implied in the term.   If corrections are applied to measured values, it is of great importance that the exact nature of such corrections be included in the report with the raw and corrected values.   There is occasional need for a term that will apply to the logarithm of the total decrease in intensity of a beam, not necessarily due entirely to absorption.   A term such as "attenuance" would seem appropriate; any symbol adopted should be easily distinguishable from the symbol A for absorbance.

In the earliest spectroscopic measurements the strength of absorption was determined by finding the thickness at which the light passing through the sample was effectively extinguished.   The quantity now known as absorbance was then called the "extinction."   This term and the symbol E are sometimes found.   Somewhat later spectroscopic measurements were made photographically and the density of the image in the emulsion was the important quantity.   It is probably from this source that the unfortunate term "optical density" was adopted.   This terminology conflicts with another meaning of optical density (an alternate name for refractive index), but, more important, it is misleading because it implies the quantity is an intrinsic property of the substance.   The difficulty is further increased by the inevitable tendency for the term to be shortened to "density."   The term absorbance is now replacing these earlier names.

Specification of the intrinsic absorbing power of a substance is nearly always based on the assumption that Bouguer's law or Beer's law is applicable. $I = I_0 e^{-\mu x}$ or $I = I_0 10^{-abc}$.   The choice of natural or common logarithms is quite arbitrary and is not easily revealed by the names or magnitudes of the quantities appearing in the exponent.   Other variations are quite common, such as the insertion of a factor of 2 or a factor of 2π into the exponent.   It is imperative, therefore, that the quantities appearing in the exponent be fully defined.

Measurements on solutions are the most common and can be readily specified by a notation consistent with the general rules given above.   It is assumed that the common logarithm (base 10) is employed unless otherwise stated.   (Absolute intensities, of importance for molecular structure studies, are often quoted in units based on the natural logarithm.   Even within the context of such a discussion it should be explicitly stated that such a choice has been made and terms reserved for common logarithms should be avoided.)   The exponent is then the product of three terms, the absorptivity, a, the cell length (or "breadth"), b, and the concentration, c.

The absorptivity has units which are the reciprocal of those of cell length times concentration—for example, liter/mole-cm or L/gm-cm, which may equally well be expressed as cm²/mole or cm²/gm. (It will be noted that cm²/molecule is an equally good unit, displaying the equivalence of the absorptivity to a collision cross section.)   Other names and symbols that have been applied to the quantity now called absorptivity include "extinction coefficient," k, K, ϵ, and the "molar extinction coefficient," ϵ_M The mixed symbol, $E_{1cm}^{1\%}$, the "extinction coefficient, 1%, 1 cm," represents the absorptivity for a solution containing 1 gm per 100 ml of solution (not 1% by weight or by volume).   These terms offer no advantages over the absorptivity in cm²/mole or cm²/gm.

3   Quality of Radiation

The symbols λ, ν, and c, for the wavelength, frequency, and speed in vacuum of radiant energy, respectively, have long been accepted nearly universally and are included in recent international conventions.   The symbol recommended for the wavenumber is σ, but the alternate symbol $\tilde{\nu}$ is listed as acceptable in the context of spectroscopic discussions because it has been established over many years.   Unfortunately, the symbols ν and $\tilde{\nu}$ have been interchanged in some spectroscopic writings, so that it is no longer possible to be sure what is meant by $\tilde{\nu}$.   It is because of this present ambiguity that the symbol σ has been employed in the present work to represent the wavenumber.

The wavenumber offers important advantages over each of the other quantities, to which it is related.   It can be determined as accurately as the wavelength.   A correction from wavenumber in air to vacuum is generally necessary, but this is often implicit in the measurement of the wavelength itself.   Recent measurements have substantiated the equation of Edlen for the refractive index of air, so that corrections can be calculated accurately when this is required.   Unlike the wavelength, however, the wavenumber is directly proportional to the frequency and energy, which are the quantitites of interest.

The disadvantages of the wavenumber are more subtle.   The concept of frequency is so firmly implanted in the literature and thinking of spectroscopy that the wavenumber has not displaced it but has only become scrambled with it.   (For example, a wavenumber of 1000 reciprocal centimeters is often refered to as a frequency of 1000 wavenumbers; this is about as appropriate as speaking of a lifetime of 10 wavelengths.)   Vibrations of molecules are labeled, quite appropriately, ν_1, ν_2, etc., since the wavenumber has no direct significance with respect to the molecule but only with respect to radiant energy that the molecule may absorb. The values given for the vibrational frequencies are, however, really wave-number values in reciprocal centimeters. The confusion is augmented by the fact that microwave spectroscopy deals directly with frequencies, so that term symbols and rotational constants do often have the dimensions of frequencies in microwave applications.

One obvious reason for the current mixed nomenclature lies in the awkwardness of the term "reciprocal centimeter" or equivalent expressions such as "centimeter minus one" or "waves per centimeter." To alleviate this difficulty, as well as the inconvenience of typing the symbol cm^{-1}, the name "kayser," with symbol K, was proposed for the unit cm^{-1}. Objections to this were raised; some objected to the symbol, others to duplicate symbols (K and cm^{-1}) for the same quantity, others to the implied necessity to replace the symbol ν with the symbol σ. Each seems to be a valid argument. The recommendation to adopt the unit of the kayser was therefore officially rescinded, but the unit has proved to be valuable in specifying separations of fine-structure components and has remained in limited use. (The millikayser, mK, is simpler and less ambiguous than 10^{-3} cm^{-1}; the kayser would also be valuable for electronic spectra since the kilokayser, kK, is more convenient than 10^3 cm^{-1}.)

Most, if not all, of the objections to a unit such as the kayser would be removed by the formal device of defining a frequency unit such that radiant energy with a vacuum wavelength of 1 cm would have a frequency of 1 unit. It would then be appropriate to apply these frequency units to radiation or to molecules, with the common symbol ν, and if an appropriate symbol were chosen the milli- and kilo- variations would be available for convenience in specifying small or large frequencies. The most appropriate name and symbol would have to be chosen by international agreement.

It should be noted that such a spectroscopic frequency unit would give values identically equal to those now familiar. Thus radiant energy with a (vacuum) wavelength of 10 μ would have a frequency of exactly 1000 of these units; light with a vacuum wavelength of 5000 Å would have a frequency of exactly 20,000 of these units. The potential ambiguity between vacuum wavenumber and wavenumber in air or other medium would disappear for the pure frequency.

Other frequency units or names have been proposed. An international agreement to call the unit of 1 cycle per second the "hertz," Hz, seems to have had little effect on current literature, in part because of the same question of duplicate symbols raised against the kayser as a unit equivalent to one reciprocal centimeter. The fresnel, equal to 10^{12} cycles/sec, was proposed some years ago but gave rise to unfamiliar numbers and did not gain wide acceptance.

Angular frequency, $2\pi\nu$, is quite universally denoted by the symbol ω. The quantity $2\pi\sigma$, which may be called angular wavenumber by analogy, is often indicated by κ or k. In certain calculations it is convenient to express the wavenumber in units of $1/3 \times 10^{10}$ cm. The reciprocal inch seems to have had a short scientific lifetime,[1] but the "permicron" is occasionally seen as a unit of wavenumber.

TABLE AII-I

Terms and Symbols of Absorption Spectroscopy

Notation of This Work	Other Current Variations	Older Notation
T = transmittance = percentage transmittance	T_i = internal transmittance T_s = transmittancy $\approx \dfrac{T_i \text{ solution}}{T_i \text{ solvent}}$	T = transmission = percentage transmission
A = absorbance = $\log_{10}(1/T)$	A = absorbancy = $\log_{10}(1/T_s)$	E = extinction O.D., D, d = optical density
a = absorptivity = A/bc	a_M = molar absorptivity = molar absorbancy index a_s = absorbancy index k, K = specific extinction coefficient $\epsilon, \epsilon_M, E_M$ = molar extinction coefficient	$E_{1cm}^{1\%}$ = "extinction coefficient, 1%, 1 cm"
ν = frequency σ = wavenumber λ = wavelength cm^{-1} = reciprocal centimeter	$\tilde{\nu}$ = wavenumber K = kayser = 1 cm^{-1}	

[1] See ref. 16, p. xli.

appendix

Character tables

Characters of the irreducible representations of the most important point groups are given, with the infrared and Raman selection rules indicated by means of the transformation properties of the translation vectors, T_x, T_y, and T_z, and of the polarizability components, α_{ij}. Parentheses indicate a conjugate pair (cf. Table X-IX).

Point groups are listed according to the order of the group (number of elements), according to increasing degeneracy, and according to increasing order of the highest axis or increasing selection rules. Recommendations of the Joint Commission on Spectroscopy [R. S. Mulliken, *J. Chem. Phys.* **23**, 1997 (1955)] have been noted below certain of the point groups. It is important that the choice of axes be specified whenever an arbitrary choice is possible.

C_s	I	σ^{xy}		
A'	1	1	$T_x, T_y; R_z$	$\alpha_{xx}, \alpha_{yy}, \alpha_{zz}, \alpha_{xy}$
A''	1	-1	$T_z; R_x, R_y$	α_{yz}, α_{xz}

C_2	I	$C_2{}^z$		
A	1	1	$T_z; R_z$	$\alpha_{xx}, \alpha_{yy}, \alpha_{zz}, \alpha_{xy}$
B	1	-1	$T_x, T_y; R_x, R_y$	α_{yz}, α_{xz}

C_i	I	i		
A_g	1	1	R	α
A_u	1	-1	T	

This point group is sometimes called S_2.

C_3	I	C_3	$C_3{}^2$		
A	1	1	1	T_z; R_z	$\alpha_{xx} + \alpha_{yy}$, α_{zz}
E $\begin{cases}(\Gamma_2) \\ (\Gamma_3)\end{cases}$	1 1	ω ω^2	ω^2 ω	$T_x + iT_y$; $R_x + iR_y$ $T_x - iT_y$; $R_x - iR_y$	$(\alpha_{xx} - \alpha_{yy}, \alpha_{xy})$, $(\alpha_{yz}, \alpha_{xz})$

The second and third representations are "separably degenerate."

The characters are the cube roots of 1: 1, $-\frac{1}{2} + i\sqrt{3}/2$, $-\frac{1}{2} - i\sqrt{3}/2$.

Such complex representations can also be used for the rotations of C_{3v} (Table X-IV), but they are mixed by the reflection operations. The symbol E in place of Γ_2 and Γ_3 is a reminder of the necessary degeneracy implied.

C_{2v}	I	$C_2{}^z$	$\sigma_v{}^{xz}$	$\sigma_v{}^{yz}$		
A_1	1	1	1	1	T_z	α_{xx}, α_{yy}, α_{zz}
A_2	1	1	-1	-1	R_z	α_{xy}
B_1	1	-1	1	-1	T_x; R_y	α_{xz}
B_2	1	-1	-1	1	T_y; R_x	α_{yz}

For planar C_{2v} molecules the x axis should be chosen perpendicular to the plane.

D_2	I	$C_2{}^z$	$C_2{}^y$	$C_2{}^x$		
A	1	1	1	1	—	α_{xx}, α_{yy}, α_{zz}
B_1	1	1	-1	-1	T_z; R_z	α_{xy}
B_2	1	-1	1	-1	T_y; R_y	α_{xz}
B_3	1	-1	-1	1	T_x; R_x	α_{yz}

This point group is often called V.

Note that for certain purposes such as finding direct products, it is more convenient to rename these representations mentally A_1, A_2, B_1, B_2, respectively.

C_{2h}	I	$C_2{}^z$	i	σ_h		
A_g	1	1	1	1	R_z	$\alpha_{xx}, \alpha_{yy}, \alpha_{zz}, \alpha_{xy}$
A_u	1	1	-1	-1	T_z	
B_g	1	-1	1	-1	$R_x; R_y$	α_{yz}, α_{xz}
B_u	1	-1	-1	1	$T_x; T_y$	

C_4	I	C_4	$C_4{}^3$	C_2		
A	1	1	1	1	$T_z; R_z$	$\alpha_{xx} + \alpha_{yy}, \alpha_{zz}$
B	1	-1	-1	1	—	$\alpha_{xx} - \alpha_{yy}, \alpha_{xy}$
E	$\begin{cases}1 \\ 1\end{cases}$	$\begin{matrix}i \\ -i\end{matrix}$	$\begin{matrix}-i \\ i\end{matrix}$	$\begin{matrix}-1 \\ -1\end{matrix}$	(T_x, T_y) (R_x, R_y)	$(\alpha_{yz}, \alpha_{xz})$

The species E is separably degenerate. See C_3 table above.

Note that the characters for any group C_p are identical with those of the rotational subgroup of C_{pv} (neglect reflections and subscripts of non-degenerate species), except that E species can be divided into two representations with characters $\sqrt[p]{1}$.

S_4	I	S_4	$S_4{}^3$	C_2		
A	1	1	1	1	R_z	$\alpha_{xx} + \alpha_{yy}, \alpha_{zz}$
B	1	-1	-1	1	T_z	$\alpha_{xx} - \alpha_{yy}, \alpha_{xy}$
E	$\begin{cases}1 \\ 1\end{cases}$	$\begin{matrix}i \\ -i\end{matrix}$	$\begin{matrix}-i \\ i\end{matrix}$	$\begin{matrix}-1 \\ -1\end{matrix}$	(T_x, T_y) (R_x, R_y)	$(\alpha_{yz}, \alpha_{xz})$

C_{3h}	I	C_3	$C_3{}^2$	σ_h	S_3	$S_3{}^5$		
A'	1	1	1	1	1	1	R_z	$\alpha_{xx} + \alpha_{yy}, \alpha_{zz}$
A''	1	1	1	-1	-1	-1	T_z	
E'	$\begin{cases}1 \\ 1\end{cases}$	$\begin{matrix}\omega \\ \omega^2\end{matrix}$	$\begin{matrix}\omega^2 \\ \omega\end{matrix}$	$\begin{matrix}1 \\ 1\end{matrix}$	$\begin{matrix}\omega \\ \omega^2\end{matrix}$	$\begin{matrix}\omega^2 \\ \omega\end{matrix}$	(T_x, T_y)	$(\alpha_{xx} - \alpha_{yy}, \alpha_{xy})$
E''	$\begin{cases}1 \\ 1\end{cases}$	$\begin{matrix}\omega \\ \omega^2\end{matrix}$	$\begin{matrix}\omega^2 \\ \omega\end{matrix}$	$\begin{matrix}-1 \\ -1\end{matrix}$	$\begin{matrix}-\omega \\ -\omega^2\end{matrix}$	$\begin{matrix}-\omega^2 \\ -\omega\end{matrix}$	(R_x, R_y)	$(\alpha_{yz}, \alpha_{xz})$

S_6	I	C_3	$C_3{}^2$	i	S_6	$S_6{}^5$		
A_g	1	1	1	1	1	1	R_z	$\alpha_{xx} + \alpha_{yy},\ \alpha_{zz}$
A_u	1	1	1	-1	-1	-1	T_z	
E_g	$\left\{\begin{matrix}1\\1\end{matrix}\right.$	$\begin{matrix}\omega\\\omega^2\end{matrix}$	$\begin{matrix}\omega^2\\\omega\end{matrix}$	$\begin{matrix}1\\1\end{matrix}$	$\begin{matrix}\omega^2\\\omega\end{matrix}$	$\left.\begin{matrix}\omega\\\omega^2\end{matrix}\right\}$	(R_x, R_y)	$(\alpha_{xx} - \alpha_{yy}, \alpha_{xy})$; $(\alpha_{yz}, \alpha_{xz})$
E_u	$\left\{\begin{matrix}1\\1\end{matrix}\right.$	$\begin{matrix}\omega\\\omega^2\end{matrix}$	$\begin{matrix}\omega^2\\\omega\end{matrix}$	$\begin{matrix}-1\\-1\end{matrix}$	$\begin{matrix}-\omega^2\\-\omega\end{matrix}$	$\left.\begin{matrix}-\omega\\-\omega^2\end{matrix}\right\}$	(T_x, T_y)	

C_{3v}	I	$2C_3$	$3\sigma_v$		
A_1	1	1	1	T_z	$\alpha_{xx} + \alpha_{yy},\ \alpha_{zz}$
A_2	1	1	-1	R_z	
E	2	-1	0	$(T_x, T_y);\ (R_x, R_y)$	$(\alpha_{xx} - \alpha_{yy}, \alpha_{xy})$, $(\alpha_{yz}, \alpha_{xz})$

D_3	I	$2C_3{}^z$	$3C_2$		
A_1	1	1	1		$\alpha_{xx} + \alpha_{yy},\ \alpha_{zz}$
A_2	1	1	-1	$T_z;\ R_z$	
E	2	-1	0	$(T_x, T_y);\ (R_x, R_y)$	$(\alpha_{xx} - \alpha_{yy}, \alpha_{xy})$, $(\alpha_{yz}, \alpha_{xz})$

D_{2h}	I	$C_2{}^z$	$C_2{}^y$	$C_2{}^x$	i	σ^{xy}	σ^{xz}	σ^{yz}		
A_g	1	1	1	1	1	1	1	1		$\alpha_{xx}, \alpha_{yy}, \alpha_{zz}$
A_u	1	1	1	1	-1	-1	-1	-1		
B_{1g}	1	1	-1	-1	1	1	-1	-1	R_z	α_{xy}
B_{1u}	1	1	-1	-1	-1	-1	1	1	T_z	
B_{2g}	1	-1	1	-1	1	-1	1	-1	R_y	α_{xz}
B_{2u}	1	-1	1	-1	-1	1	-1	1	T_y	
B_{3g}	1	-1	-1	1	1	-1	-1	1	R_x	α_{yz}
B_{3u}	1	-1	-1	1	-1	1	1	-1	T_x	

This group is sometimes called V_h. See point group D_2 concerning naming of representations. For planar D_{2h} molecules the x axis should be taken perpendicular to the plane. The z axis should pass through the largest possible number of atoms or, if this is not decisive, through the largest possible number of bonds.

C_{4h}	I	C_4	C_4^3	C_2^z	i	S_4	S_4^3	σ_h		
A_g	1	1	1	1	1	1	1	1	R_z	$\alpha_{xx} + \alpha_{yy},\ \alpha_{zz}$
A_u	1	1	1	1	-1	-1	-1	-1	T_z	
B_g	1	-1	-1	1	1	-1	-1	1		$\alpha_{xx} - \alpha_{yy},\ \alpha_{xy}$
B_u	1	-1	-1	1	-1	1	1	-1		
E_g	$\begin{cases}1\\1\end{cases}$	$\begin{matrix}i\\-i\end{matrix}$	$\begin{matrix}-i\\i\end{matrix}$	$\begin{matrix}-1\\-1\end{matrix}$	$\begin{matrix}1\\1\end{matrix}$	$\begin{matrix}-i\\i\end{matrix}$	$\begin{matrix}i\\-i\end{matrix}$	$\left.\begin{matrix}-1\\-1\end{matrix}\right\}$	(R_x, R_y)	$(\alpha_{yz}, \alpha_{xz})$
E_u	$\begin{cases}1\\1\end{cases}$	$\begin{matrix}i\\-i\end{matrix}$	$\begin{matrix}-i\\i\end{matrix}$	$\begin{matrix}-1\\-1\end{matrix}$	$\begin{matrix}-1\\-1\end{matrix}$	$\begin{matrix}i\\-i\end{matrix}$	$\begin{matrix}-i\\i\end{matrix}$	$\left.\begin{matrix}1\\1\end{matrix}\right\}$	(T_x, T_y)	

D_{2d}	I	$2S_4^z$	C_2^z	$2C_2$	$2\sigma_d$		
A_1	1	1	1	1	1		$\alpha_{xx} + \alpha_{yy},\ \alpha_{zz}$
A_2	1	1	1	-1	-1	R_z	
B_1	1	-1	1	1	-1		$\alpha_{xx} - \alpha_{yy}$
B_2	1	-1	1	-1	1	T_z	α_{xy}
E	2	0	-2	0	0	$(T_x, T_y);\ (R_x, R_y)$	$(\alpha_{yz}, \alpha_{xz})$

This group is sometimes called V_d.

C_{4v}	I	$2C_4^z$	C_2^z	$2\sigma_v$	$2\sigma_d$		
A_1	1	1	1	1	1	T_z	$\alpha_{xx} + \alpha_{yy},\ \alpha_{zz}$
A_2	1	1	1	-1	-1	R_z	
B_1	1	-1	1	1	-1		$\alpha_{xx} - \alpha_{yy}$
B_2	1	-1	1	-1	1		α_{xy}
E	2	0	-2	0	0	$(T_x, T_y);\ (R_x, R_y)$	$(\alpha_{yz}, \alpha_{xz})$

When a C_{4v} molecule contains a square array of atoms, the σ_v planes should pass through the larger number of atoms of the square array; if this is not decisive, then these planes should intersect the largest possible number of bonds in this array.

D_4	I	$2C_4^z$	C_2^z	$2C_2$	$2C_2'$		
A_1	1	1	1	1	1		
A_2	1	1	1	-1	-1	$T_z;\ R_z$	$\alpha_{xx} + \alpha_{yy},\ \alpha_{zz}$
B_1	1	-1	1	1	-1		$\alpha_{xx} - \alpha_{yy}$
B_2	1	-1	1	-1	1		α_{xy}
E	2	0	-2	0	0	$(T_x, T_y);\ (R_x, R_y)$	$(\alpha_{yz}, \alpha_{xz})$

D_{3h}	I	$2C_3$	$3C_2$	σ_h	$2S_3$	$3\sigma_v$		
A_1'	1	1	1	1	1	1		$\alpha_{xx} + \alpha_{yy}, \alpha_{zz}$
A_1''	1	1	1	-1	-1	-1		
A_2'	1	1	-1	1	1	-1	R_z	
A_2''	1	1	-1	-1	-1	1	T_z	
E'	2	-1	0	2	-1	0	(T_x, T_y)	$(\alpha_{xx} - \alpha_{yy}, \alpha_{xy})$
E''	2	-1	0	-2	1	0	(R_x, R_y)	$(\alpha_{yz}, \alpha_{xz})$

D_{3d}	I	$2C_3$	$3C_2$	i	$2S_6$	$3\sigma_d$		
A_{1g}	1	1	1	1	1	1		$\alpha_{xx} + \alpha_{yy}, \alpha_{zz}$
A_{1u}	1	1	1	-1	-1	-1		
A_{2g}	1	1	-1	1	1	-1	R_z	
A_{2u}	1	1	-1	-1	-1	1	T_z	
E_g	2	-1	0	2	-1	0	(R_x, R_y)	$(\alpha_{xx} - \alpha_{yy}, \alpha_{xy})$, $(\alpha_{yz}, \alpha_{xz})$
E_u	2	-1	0	-2	1	0	(T_x, T_y)	

C_{6v}	I	$2C_6$	$2C_3$	C_2	$3\sigma_v$	$3\sigma_d$		
A_1	1	1	1	1	1	1	T_z	$\alpha_{xx} + \alpha_{yy}, \alpha_{zz}$
A_2	1	1	1	1	-1	-1	R_z	
B_1	1	-1	1	-1	1	-1		
B_2	1	-1	1	-1	-1	1		
E_1	2	1	-1	-2	0	0	$(T_x, T_y); (R_x, R_y)$	$(\alpha_{yz}, \alpha_{xz})$
E_2	2	-1	-1	2	0	0		$(\alpha_{xx} - \alpha_{yy}, \alpha_{xz})$

In this conventional notation the numerical subscripts have a different significance for the degenerate and non-degenerate representations. An alternative notation, such as E_A and E_B (instead of E_2 and E_1, respectively) would be preferable for some purposes. See C_{4v} for choice of σ_v and σ_d.

T	I	4C₃	4C₃²	3C₂		
A	1	1	1	1		$\alpha_{xx} + \alpha_{yy} + \alpha_{zz}$
E	$\left\{\begin{array}{l}1 \\ 1\end{array}\right.$	$\begin{array}{c}\omega \\ \omega^2\end{array}$	$\begin{array}{c}\omega^2 \\ \omega\end{array}$	$\left.\begin{array}{l}1 \\ 1\end{array}\right\}$		$(\alpha_{xx} + \alpha_{yy} - 2\alpha_{zz}, \alpha_{xx} - \alpha_{yy}),$ $(\alpha_{xy}, \alpha_{xz}, \alpha_{yz})$
F	3	0	0	-1	T, R	

The triply degenerate representation is designated **T** in discussions of crystals.

D_{4h}	I	2C₄	C₂ᶻ	2C₂	2C₂′	i	2S₄	σₕ	2σᵥ	2σ_d		
A_{1g}	1	1	1	1	1	1	1	1	1	1		$\alpha_{xx} + \alpha_{yy}, \alpha_{zz}$
A_{1u}	1	1	1	1	1	-1	-1	-1	-1	-1		
A_{2g}	1	1	1	-1	-1	1	1	1	-1	-1	R_z	
A_{2u}	1	1	1	-1	-1	-1	-1	-1	1	1	T_z	
B_{1g}	1	-1	1	1	-1	1	-1	1	1	-1		$\alpha_{xx} - \alpha_{yy}$
B_{1u}	1	-1	1	1	-1	-1	1	-1	-1	1		
B_{2g}	1	-1	1	-1	1	1	-1	1	-1	1		α_{xy}
B_{2u}	1	-1	1	-1	1	-1	1	-1	1	-1		
E_g	2	0	-2	0	0	2	0	-2	0	0	(R_x, R_y)	$(\alpha_{yz}, \alpha_{xz})$
E_u	2	0	-2	0	0	-2	0	2	0	0	(T_x, T_y)	

C₂ should pass through largest number of atoms of planar configuration or, if this is not decisive, through largest number of bonds.

D_{6h}	I	2C₆ᶻ	2C₃	C₂ᶻ	3C₂	3C₂′	i	2S₃	2S₆	σₕ	3σ_d	3σᵥ		
A_{1g}	1	1	1	1	1	1	1	1	1	1	1	1		$\alpha_{xx} + \alpha_{yy},$ α_{zz}
A_{1u}	1	1	1	1	1	1	-1	-1	-1	-1	-1	-1		
A_{2g}	1	1	1	1	-1	-1	1	1	1	1	-1	-1	R_z	
A_{2u}	1	1	1	1	-1	-1	-1	-1	-1	-1	1	1	T_z	
B_{1g}	1	-1	1	-1	1	-1	1	-1	1	-1	1	-1		
B_{1u}	1	-1	1	-1	1	-1	-1	1	-1	1	-1	1		
B_{2g}	1	-1	1	-1	-1	1	1	-1	1	-1	-1	1		
B_{2u}	1	-1	1	-1	-1	1	-1	1	-1	1	1	-1		
E_{1g}	2	1	-1	-2	0	0	2	1	-1	-2	0	0	(R_x, R_y)	$(\alpha_{yz}, \alpha_{xz})$
E_{1u}	2	1	-1	-2	0	0	-2	-1	1	2	0	0	(T_x, T_y)	
E_{2g}	2	-1	-1	2	0	0	2	-1	-1	2	0	0		$(\alpha_{xx} - \alpha_{yy},$ $\alpha_{xy})$
E_{2u}	2	-1	-1	2	0	0	-2	1	1	-2	0	0		

It would be preferable for some purposes, such as finding direct products, to relabel the degenerate representations E_{Bg}, E_{Bu}, E_{Ag}, E_{Au} (cf. C_{6v}). See D_{4h} for choice of **C₂** and **C₂′** (and hence σ_v and σ_d).

T_d	I	$6S_4$	$3C_2$	$8C_3$	$6\sigma_d$		
A_1	1	1	1	1	1		$\alpha_{xx} + \alpha_{yy} + \alpha_{zz}$
A_2	1	-1	1	1	-1		
E	2	0	2	-1	0		$(\alpha_{xx} + \alpha_{yy} - 2\alpha_{zz},$
							$\alpha_{xx} - \alpha_{yy})$
F_1	3	1	-1	0	1	R	
F_2	3	-1	-1	0	1	T	$(\alpha_{xy}, \alpha_{yz}, \alpha_{xz})$

O	I	$6C_4$	$3C_4{}^2$	$8C_3$	$6C_2$		
A_1	1	1	1	1	1		$\alpha_{xx} + \alpha_{yy} + \alpha_{zz}$
A_2	1	-1	1	1	-1		
E	2	0	2	-1	0		$(\alpha_{xx} + \alpha_{yy} - 2\alpha_{zz},$
							$\alpha_{xx} - \alpha_{yy})$
F_1	3	1	-1	0	-1	R, T	
F_2	3	-1	-1	0	1		$(\alpha_{xy}, \alpha_{yz}, \alpha_{xz})$

O_h	I	$6C_4$	$3C_4{}^2$	$8C_3$	$6C_2$	i	$6S_4$	$3\sigma_h$	$8S_6$	$6\sigma_d$		
A_{1g}	1	1	1	1	1	1	1	1	1	1		$\alpha_{xx} + \alpha_{yy} + \alpha_{zz}$
A_{1u}	1	1	1	1	1	-1	-1	-1	-1	-1		
A_{2g}	1	-1	1	1	-1	1	-1	1	1	-1		
A_{2u}	1	-1	1	1	-1	-1	1	-1	-1	1		
E_g	2	0	2	-1	0	2	0	2	-1	0		$(\alpha_{xx} + \alpha_{yy} - 2\alpha_{zz}, \alpha_{xx} - \alpha_{yy})$
E_u	2	0	2	-1	0	-2	0	-2	1	0		
F_{1g}	3	1	-1	0	-1	3	1	-1	0	-1	R	
F_{1u}	3	1	-1	0	-1	-3	-1	1	0	1	T	
F_{2g}	3	-1	-1	0	1	3	-1	-1	0	1		$(\alpha_{xy}, \alpha_{yz}, \alpha_{xz})$
F_{2u}	3	-1	-1	0	1	-3	1	1	0	-1		

$C_{\infty v}$	I	$\cdots 2C^{(z)}_{2\pi/\phi} \cdots$	$C_2^{(z)}$	$\infty\sigma_v$		
Σ^+	1	1	1	1	T_z	$\alpha_{xx}+\alpha_{yy},\ \alpha_{zz}$
Σ^-	1	1	1	-1	R_z	
Π	2	$2\cos\ \phi$	-2	0	$\begin{cases}(T_x, T_y)\\(R_x, R_y)\end{cases}$	$(\alpha_{xz}, \alpha_{yz})$
Δ	2	$2\cos 2\phi$	2	0		$(\alpha_{xx}-\alpha_{yy},\ \alpha_{xy})$
Φ	2	$2\cos 3\phi$	-2	0		

$D_{\infty h}$	I	$\cdots 2C^{(z)}_{2\pi/\phi}\cdots$	$C_2^{(z)}$	$\infty\sigma_v$	i	$\cdots 2S_{2\pi/\phi}\cdots$	σ_h	∞C_2		
Σ_g^+	1	1	1	1	1	1	1	1	T_z	$\alpha_{xx}+\alpha_{yy},\ \alpha_{zz}$
Σ_u^+	1	1	1	1	-1	-1	-1	-1		
Σ_g^-	1	1	1	-1	1	1	1	-1	R_z	
Σ_u^-	1	1	1	-1	-1	-1	-1	1		
Π_g	2	$2\cos\phi$	-2	0	2	$-2\cos\phi$	-2	0	(R_x, R_y)	$(\alpha_{xz}, \alpha_{yz})$
Π_u	2	$2\cos\phi$	-2	0	-2	$2\cos\phi$	2	0	(T_x, T_y)	
Δ_g	2	$2\cos 2\phi$	2	0	2	$2\cos 2\phi$	2	0		$(\alpha_{xx}-\alpha_{yy},\ \alpha_{xy})$
Δ_u	2	$2\cos 2\phi$	2	0	-2	$-2\cos 2\phi$	-2	0		
Φ_g	2	$2\cos 3\phi$	-2	0	2	$-2\cos 3\phi$	-2	0		
Φ_u	2	$2\cos 3\phi$	-2	0	-2	$2\cos 3\phi$	2	0		

IV

Greek alphabet

Greek		English Equivalent	Common Pronunciations
Symbols	Name		
A, α	alpha	a	ăl′fȧ
B, β	beta	b	bā′tȧ, bē′tȧ
Γ, γ	gamma	g	găm′ȧ
Δ, δ	delta	d	dĕl′tȧ
E, ε,ϵ	epsilon	e	ĕp′sĭ·lŏn
Z, ζ	zeta	z	zā′tȧ, zē′tȧ
H, η	eta	e, a	ā′tȧ, ē′tȧ
Θ, θ	theta	th, t	thā′tȧ, thē′tȧ
I, ι	iota	i, e	ī·ō′tȧ
K, κ	kappa	k	kăp′ȧ
Λ, λ	lambda	l	lăm(b)′dȧ
M, μ	mu	m	mū
N, ν	nu	n	noo
Ξ, ξ	xi	x (ks)	(k)zē, (k)zī
O, o	omicron	o	ŏm′ĭ·krŏn
Π, π	pi	p	pī
P, ρ	rho	r	rō
Σ, $\sigma, (s)$	sigma	s	sĭg′mȧ
T, τ	tau	t	tô (as in "tall"), tou (as in "now")
Υ, υ	upsilon	y, u	ŭp′sĭ·lŏn, ūp′sĭ·lŏn
Φ, ϕ	phi	ph, p	fī, fē
X, χ	chi	ch, k	kī
Ψ, ψ	psi	ps	(p)sī, (p)sē
Ω, ω	omega	o	ȯ·mĕg′ȧ, ōm′ė·gȧ, ō·mēg′ȧ

bibliography

General

1. E. C. C. Baly, *Spectroscopy*, Third Edition, Longmans, Green, and Co., London, Vol. 1, 1924; Vol. II, 1927.
2. W. R. Brode, *Chemical Spectroscopy*, Second Edition, John Wiley & Sons, Inc., New York, 1943.
3. W. Brugel, *Einfuhrung in die Ultrarotspektroskopie*, Steinkopff, Darmstadt, 1954.
4. G. L. Clark, *Encyclopedia of Spectroscopy*, Reinhold Publishing Corp., New York, 1960.
5. W. W. Coblentz, "Investigations of Infrared Spectra," Carnegie Inst. *Tech. Bull.* **35**, 1905; **65**, 1906; **97**, 1908; *Nat. Bur. Standards Bull.* **11**, 131 (1914).
6. A. D. Cross, *An Introduction to Practical Infrared Spectroscopy*, Butterworths, London, 1960.
7. G. R. Harrison, R. C. Lord, and J. R. Loofbourow, *Practical Spectroscopy*, Prentice-Hall Inc., Englewood Cliffs, N.J., 1948.
8. G. F. Lothian, *Absorption Spectrophotometry*, Second Edition, Hilger & Watts, Ltd., London, 1958.
9. F. A. Miller, *Applications of Infrared and Ultraviolet Spectra to Organic Chemistry*, in H. Gilman *et al.*, eds., *Organic Chemistry*, Vol. III, John Wiley & Sons, Inc., New York, 1953.
10. R. A. Sawyer, *Experimental Spectroscopy*, Second Edition, Prentice-Hall, Inc., Englewood Cliffs, N.J., 1951.
11. H. W. Thompson, editor, *Advances in Spectroscopy*, Vol. I, Interscience Publishers, Inc., New York, 1959.
12. V. Z. Williams, "Infrared Instrumentation and Techniques," *Rev. Sci. Instr.* **19**, 135–178 (1948).

Optics

13. A. E. Conrady, *Applied Optics and Optical Design*, Dover Publications, Inc., New York, 1957.
14. R. W. Ditchburn, *Light*, Interscience Publishers, Inc., New York, 1953.
15. F. A. Jenkins and H. E. White, *Fundamentals of Optics*, Third Edition, McGraw-Hill Book Co., Inc., New York, 1957.
16. I. Newton, *Opticks* (Fourth Edition, London, 1730), Dover Publications, Inc., New York, 1952.
17. J. K. Robertson, *Introduction to Physical Optics*, Third Edition, D. Van Nostrand Co., Inc., Princeton, N.J., 1941.
18. R. W. Wood, *Physical Optics*, Third Edition, Macmillan, New York, 1934.

Instrumentation

19. C. G. Cannon, editor, *Electronics for Spectroscopists*, Hilger & Watts, Ltd., London, 1960.
20. G. K. T. Conn and D. G. Avery, "Infrared Methods: Principles and Applications," *Physical Chemistry*, Vol. 7, Academic Press, New York, 1960.
21. H. L. Hackforth, *Infrared Radiation*, McGraw-Hill Book Company, Inc., New York, 1960.
22. L. R. Koller, *Ultraviolet Radiation*, John Wiley & Sons, Inc., New York, 1952.
23. *Proceedings of the London Conference on Optical Instruments*—1950, John Wiley & Sons, Inc., New York, 1952.
24. R. A. Smith, F. E. Jones, and R. P. Chasmar, *Detection and Measurement of Infrared Radiation*, Oxford University Press, London, 1957.

Classical Mechanics

25. H. C. Corben and P. Stehle, *Classical Mechanics*, John Wiley & Sons, Inc., New York, 1950.
26. H. Goldstein, *Classical Mechanics*, Addison-Wesley Press, Inc., Cambridge, Mass., 1950.
27. D. Halliday and R. Resnick, *Physics for Students of Science and Engineering*, John Wiley & Sons, Inc., New York, 1960.
28. J. W. Strutt, Baron Rayleigh, *The Theory of Sound* (Second Edition revised and enlarged, 1894), Dover Publications, New York, 1945.

Quantum Mechanics

29. D. Bohm, *Quantum Theory*, Prentice-Hall, Inc., Englewood Cliffs, N.J., 1951.
30. W. Heisenberg, *The Physical Principles of the Quantum Theory*, Dover Publications, Inc., New York, 1930.
31. W. Kauzmann, *Quantum Chemistry*, Academic Press, Inc., New York, 1957.
32. L. Pauling and E. B. Wilson, Jr., *Introduction to Quantum Mechanics*, McGraw-Hill Book Co., Inc., New York, 1935.
33. L. I. Schiff, *Quantum Mechanics*, Second Edition, McGraw-Hill Book Co., Inc., New York, 1955.

Analytical

34. L. J. Bellamy, *The Infrared Spectra of Complex Molecules*, Second Edition, Methuen & Co., Ltd., London, 1958.
35. A. E. Gillam and E. S. Stern, *An Introduction to Electronic Absorption Spectroscopy in Organic Chemistry*, Second Edition, Edward Arnold, Ltd., London, 1957.
36. R. N. Jones and C. Sandorfy, "The Application of Infrared and Raman Spectrometry to the Elucidation of Molecular Structure," chapter IV of ref. 47.
37. L. Meites and H. C. Thomas, *Advanced Analytical Chemistry*, McGraw-Hill Book Co., Inc., New York, 1958.
38. M. G. Mellon, editor, *Analytical Absorption Spectroscopy*, John Wiley & Sons, Inc., New York, 1950.
39. E. Muller, editor, *Houben-Weyl, Methoden der Organischen Chemie*, Band III, Teil 2, "Physikalische Forschungsmethoden," George Thieme Verlag, Stuttgart, 1955.

Atomic and Molecular Spectroscopy

40. S. Bhagavantam, *Scattering of Light and the Raman Effect*, Chemical Publishing Co., Inc., Brooklyn, N.Y., 1942.
41. J. C. D. Brand and J. C. Speakman, *Molecular Structure, the Physical Approach*, St. Martin's Press, New York, 1960.
42. G. Herzberg, *Atomic Spectra and Atomic Structure*, Second Edition, Dover Publications, Inc., New York, 1944.
43. G. Herzberg, *Molecular Spectra and Molecular Structure. I. Spectra of Diatomic Molecules*, Second Edition, D. Van Nostrand Co., Inc., Princeton, N.J., 1950.
44. G. Herzberg, *Molecular Spectra and Molecular Structure. II. Infrared and Raman Spectra of Polyatomic Molecules*, D. Van Nostrand Co., Inc., Princeton, N.J., 1945.
45. L. Kasha and M. Kasha, *Molecular Electronic Bibliography*, Vol. I, Publishers Press, Inc., Tallahassee, Fla., 1960.
46. H. E. White, *Introduction to Atomic Spectra*, McGraw-Hill Book Co., Inc., New York, 1934.
47. A. Weissberger, editor, *Technique of Organic Chemistry*, Vol. IX, "Chemical Applications of Spectroscopy," W. West, editor, Interscience Publishers, Inc., New York, 1956.
48. E. B. Wilson, Jr., J. C. Decius, and P. C. Cross, *Molecular Vibrations*, McGraw-Hill Book Co., Inc., New York, 1955.

Matrices and Group Theory

49. S. Bhagavantam and T. Venkatarayudu, *Theory of Groups and Its Application to Physical Problems*, Second Edition, Andhra University, Waltair, India, 1951.
50. M. Bocher, *Introduction to Higher Algebra*, Macmillan, New York, 1907.
51. R. A. Frazer, W. J. Duncan, and A. R. Collar, *Elementary Matrices*, Cambridge University Press, 1938.
52. B. Higman, *Applied Group-Theoretic and Matrix Methods*, Oxford University Press, 1955.
53. H. Margenau and G. M. Murphy, *The Mathematics of Physics and Chemistry*, Second Edition, D. Van Nostrand Co., Inc., Princeton, N.J., 1956.
54. E. P. Wigner, *Group Theory and Its Application to the Quantum Mechanics of Atomic Spectra*, Academic Press, New York, 1959.

Other References

55. R. P. Bauman, consulting editor, "Biological Applications of Infrared Spectroscopy," *Ann. N.Y. Acad. Sci.*, **69**, 1–254 (1957).
56. E. J. Bowen, *The Chemical Aspects of Light*, Second Edition, Revised, Oxford University Press, 1949.
57. C. D. Coleman, W. R. Bozman, and W. F. Meggers, *Table of Wavenumbers*, National Bureau of Standards Monograph 3, 1960.
58. R. M. Evans, *An Introduction to Color*, John Wiley & Sons, Inc., New York, 1948.
59. G. R. Harrison, *M.I.T. Wavelength Tables*, John Wiley & Sons, Inc., New York, 1939.
60. S. S. Penner, *Quantitative Molecular Spectroscopy and Gas Emissivities*, Addison-Wesley Publishing Co., Inc., Reading, Mass., 1959.
61. J. Strong, *Procedures in Experimental Physics*, Prentice-Hall, Inc., Englewood Cliffs, N.J., 1938.

62. S. Krimm, "Infrared Spectra of High Polymers," *Advances in Polymer Science*, Vol. 2, pp. 51–172, 1960.

63. I.U.P.A.C. Commission on Molecular Structure and Spectroscopy, *Tables of Wavenumbers for the Calibration of Infrared Spectrometers*, Butterworths, Washington, D.C., 1961.

64. S. Flügge, editor, *Handbuch der Physik*, Springer-Verlag, Berlin.   Vol. XXVI (1958); Vol. XXVIII (1957); and others.

65. H. Allen and P. C. Cross, *Vibrational-Rotational Spectra*, John Wiley and Sons, Inc., New York, in press.

Also see section 3, "Bibliographies and Indices," on pp. 347–351.

Answers to selected problems

Chapter I

1. (*a*) 1.5×10^{15} sec^{-1}; 2000 Å. (*c*) 3×10^{13} sec^{-1}; 10 μ.
2. (*a*) 25,000 cm^{-1}; 7.5×10^{14} sec^{-1}. (*c*) 2000 cm^{-1}; 6×10^{13} sec^{-1}.
3. (*a*) 7.95×10^{-12} erg/molecule; 4.8×10^{12} erg/mole; 2.0×10^{6} cal/mole.
   (*c*) 6.0×10^{-13}; 3.6×10^{11}; 1.5×10^{5}.
4. (*a*) 9.55×10^{-5} watt/cm^2. (*b*) 0.955 watt/steradian. (*c*) 3.18×10^{-8} erg/cm^3.
   (*d*) 4.05×10^{3} photon/cm^3.
5. (*a*) 0.17 Å. (*c*) 1.52 μ.
6. (*a*) 3.33 μ. (*b*) 5012 Å. (*c*) 4606 Å.
7. (*a*) Red. (*b*) Yellow (caused by overlap of band into violet). (*c*) Green (malachite green).
8. (*a*) 4359.57 Å. (*b*) 22,938.0. (*c*) 3268.9 Å.
9. 2472 Å. 10. 32.8 gm/L. 11. 0.78M.
12. (*a*) 86.6%. (*b*) 92.1%. (*c*) 79.7%.

Chapter II

1. (*a*) 1500°K: $a/b/c = 24.6/5.46/1$; 2000°K: 72.5/8.8/1.
2. (*a*) 4.83×10^{-5}. (*b*) 2.20×10^{-5}.
5. Variation of dispersion with frequency differs for two prism materials.
7. 0.041 mm. 8. 1 mm. 9. 25 cm^{-1}.
11. (*a*) 12, 6, 4, 3, and 2.4 μ. (*b*) 833, 1667, 2500, 3333, and 4167 cm^{-1}; 45th or 46th order.
12. 0.0046 μ, 0.0007 μ; 6 cm^{-1}.

Chapter III

3. (*a*) 43.8°. (*b*) 37.3°. (*c*) 48.5°. (*d*) $\sin^{-1}(1/n)$. All; all.
4. (*a*) Constant. (*b*) $(\sin \theta + \sin i)/\cos \theta$. (*c*) $1/\lambda$, or σ. (*d*) As (*b*). (*e*) $1/\sigma$, or λ. (*f*) As (*b*).
6. 1.5 cm^{-1}. (*b*) 5.1 cm^{-1}.

7. (a) 10/1; 1/1.   (b) 10/1; 100/1.

8. (a) 0.004346. (c) 0.4771.

9. (a) 0.004346. (c) 0.04347.

12. 1.29 cm^{-1} from eq. III-11; 0.54 as modified in footnote.

Chapter V

3. (a) 2.41 × 10^{10} erg; 1.21 × 10^4 cm^{-1}; 8.25 × 10^3 Å. (b) 2.74 × 10^{-40} erg; 1.38 × 10^{-24} cm^{-1}; 7.25 × 10^{33} Å (multiplied by 1, 4, or 9).

7. 3.03 × 10^{13} sec^{-1}; 1.66 × 10^{13} sec^{-1}.

13. 0.36.   14. 6.1 D; 0.17 e.

15. $f = \dfrac{2.3mc^2 \times 10^3}{\pi e^2 N_A} \int a\, d\sigma = 4.3 \times 10^{-9} \int a\, d\sigma.$

17. (a) 30%. (b) 16%.

Chapter VI

1. $(1 - \delta)m$; $(1 - \delta)R_\infty$. $\delta = 1.37 \times 10^{-5}, 3.43 \times 10^{-6}, 2.3 \times 10^{-7}$. $\delta R_\infty = 1.504$, 0.376, 0.025 cm^{-1}.

3. $2n^2$; minimum at $n = (hcR/kT)^{1/2}$.

5. 0.042. "Forbidden," but not strongly.

8. $\bar{T}_e = -(E_e + \frac{3}{2}E_v)$.

Chapter VII

1. (a) 4.7 × 10^5 dynes/cm. (b) 2.14 cm^{-1}. (c) 0.11 Å, 8.6%; 0.19 Å, 15%.

3. 3.4 cm^{-1}.   4. 2018, 2083, 2085, 2160.   5. 3.8%.

6. CH: 849–661, 1178–867; 3047–2264; 3062–2292. CC: 606–577; 992–945; 1596–1559.

8.

	IR	R		IR	R		IR	R
(a)	ia	a	(b)	a	a	(c)	ia	a
(d)	a	a	(e)	ia	a	(f)	ia	a

9. (a) 16,712 cm^{-1}, 5984 Å; 14,655 cm^{-1}, 6824 Å; 14,551 cm^{-1}, 6872 Å. (b) Orange, red, red.

10. (b), (d), and (e) will show pure rotation spectra in microwave. All except (c) will show pure rotation spectrum in Raman; all will show rotation-vibration spectrum in infrared and Raman.

13. (a) $q_1 = A \cos(\omega t + \phi)$

$q_2 = \dfrac{\mu}{\mu'} A \cos(\omega t + \phi) + vt + q_2°; \dfrac{1}{\mu} = \dfrac{1}{m_1} + \dfrac{1}{m_2}, \dfrac{1}{\mu'} = \dfrac{1}{m_1} - \dfrac{1}{m_2}.$

Center of mass moves uniformly but q_2 is not referred to center of mass. Thus q_2, describing midpoint of bond, has oscillatory character.

(b) $\ddot{q}_2 = 0$, since q_2 describes center of mass, which moves uniformly.

$q_1 = A \cos(\omega t + \phi)$ + function of force constant, masses, and time.

16. $P - R = 4B(1 - \zeta)(kT/hcB)^{1/2}$ for spherical rotor with Coriolis constant ζ. (For significance of this extra factor see chapter X.)

Chapter VIII

2. (a) UV (or IR). (b) UV (or IR). (c) IR (or UV). (d) IR. (e) IR. (f) UV or IR.

4. C=O (not conjugated), monosubstituted benzene, aromatic and aliphatic C—H. ϕ—CH$_2$—CO—CH$_3$.

5. Urea.   6. Teflon.

7. Monosubstituted benzene; monosubstituted ethylene. Styrene.

8. 1-Butanol.   9. Nylon.   10. Methyl ethyl ketone.

11. ϕ—CH$_2$—CN.   12. NaNO$_2$.   13. ϕOH.

14. Pentanal.   15. p-Toluidine.   16. Calcium sulfate hydrate (crystalline).

17. Mylar (terephthalate).   18. Substituted benzene (bromobenzene).

19. Aniline.   20. Cinnamaldehyde.   21. 1-Naphthylamine.

Chapter IX

3. $A = (1/2.3)(1 - T)/T = (1/2.3)(1 - T)$ for $1 - T \ll 1$.

4. Slope $= \bar{a}bc$, where $\bar{a} = \int_{\nu_1}^{\nu_2} a\, d\nu \Big/ \int_{\nu_1}^{\nu_2} d\nu$.

5. (a) 1.4%   (a) 0.73%
   (b) 0.54%   (b) 0.55%
   (c) 2.2%   (c) 0.51%
   (d) 0.24%   (d) 0.24%

6. (a) 0.58(3) para; 0.15(4) ethylbenzene; 0.0008 ortho; 0.004 meta.
   (b) 0.58(2) para; 0.16(2) ethylbenzene. Synthesis: 0.574 para; 0.169 ethylbenzene.

8. $\dfrac{\pi}{2}\hat{a}\,\Delta\sigma_{1/2} = 11$ cm$^{-1}/bc$.

Chapter X

5. $3A_{1g} + A_{1u} + A_{2g} + 2A_{2u} + 3B_{1g} + B_{1u} + 2B_{2g} + 3B_{2u} + 3E_g + 4E_u$;
   $A_{1g} + A_{2u} + B_{1g} + B_{2u} + E_g + E_u$; $A_{1g} + B_{1g} + E_u$.

7. (a) C$_{2v}$. (b) C$_{2h}$. (c) D$_{2h}$. (d) D$_{2d}$. (e) D$_{3h}$. (f) D$_{3h}$.

12. (a) p_1, p_0, p_{-1}; p_z. (b) All. (c) $\langle p_z \rangle = 0, 0, 0$; $\hbar, 0, -\hbar$; $\langle p_z^2 \rangle = 2\hbar$.

13. $(1s\sigma)^2(2s\sigma)^2(2p\sigma)^2(2p\pi)^2$, $^3\Sigma^-$.

Appendix I

1. (a) 7. (b) 14.

   (c) $\begin{bmatrix} 3 & 5 & 1 \\ 0 & 0 & 0 \\ 12 & 20 & 4 \end{bmatrix}$ (g) $\begin{bmatrix} 1 & 2 & 3 \\ 7 & 8 & 9 \\ 4 & 5 & 6 \end{bmatrix}$ (j) $\begin{bmatrix} 1 & 2 & 4 \\ 4 & 5 & 10 \\ 7 & 8 & 16 \end{bmatrix}$

3. (a) 5. (b) -5. (c) 9. (d) 9. (e) -40. (f) 45.

6. (a) $\dfrac{1}{5}\begin{bmatrix} 2 & -3 \\ 1 & 1 \end{bmatrix}$ (b) $\dfrac{1}{9}\begin{bmatrix} 6 & -6 & 3 \\ -7 & 13 & -8 \\ 5 & -8 & 7 \end{bmatrix}$ (c) $\dfrac{1}{40}\begin{bmatrix} 15 & 14 & -3 & -19 \\ -5 & 18 & -1 & 7 \\ -25 & 10 & -5 & -5 \\ -30 & 12 & -14 & 18 \end{bmatrix}$

9. 0.68(5); 0.27(9).

11. $\begin{bmatrix} -2/\sqrt{6} & 1/\sqrt{6} & 1/\sqrt{6} \\ 1/\sqrt{3} & -1/\sqrt{3} & -1/\sqrt{3} \\ 0 & -2/\sqrt{8} & 2/\sqrt{8} \end{bmatrix}$

Index

Symbols are given in the alphabetical listing, with Greek letters following the English counterparts. In general, only pages on which the symbol is introduced or defined are listed. Quantum numbers are in ordinary boldface; operators and matrices are in sans serif bold; energy quantities are in small capitals; and states, term symbols, representations, and point groups are in sans serif light.

a, absorptivity, 15, 242, 368, 581
a, principal axis (smallest moment), 524
a_0, Bohr radius, 8, 246
a_{ij}, general element of matrix or determinant, 545
A, absorbance, 15, 368, 580
A, rotational constant (largest), 226, 309, 522
A, irreducible representation, 451
A, Platt symbol, 277
A, absorbance matrix, 405, 570
A, matrix $[a_{ij}]$, 551
Ã, transpose matrix, 555
Ā, complex conjugate matrix, 555
A*, transpose conjugate of **A**, 555
A^{-1}, inverse matrix, 556
Å, ångstrom, 5
α, **α**, polarizability, 238, 243, 301, 456, 516, 585
Abelian, 439, 554
Aberration, 95, 162, 171
  chromatic, 68
  spherical, 70
Abney mount, 102
Absorbance, 15, 368, 580
Absorptivity, 15, 242, 368, 581
Acetone, 294, 329
Acetophenone, 283, 324
Achromatic, 68

Adiabatic theorem, 262
Allowed transition, 243
Ammonia, inversion, 519
Ammonium phosphate, dihydrogen-, IR spectrum, 346
Amplitude, 38, 205, 209; *see also* Intensity
Angular frequency (velocity), 224, 230
Angular momentum, 224, 227, 230, 245, 304, 478, 482
Anharmonicity, 206, 244, 279, 505
Aniline, spectra, 337, 361
Antibonding orbital, 273, 288, 488
Anti-Stokes line, 303, 513
Aperture, 97
Applied Physics Corporation, *see* Cary *entries*
Applied Research Laboratories spectrometer, 144
Aspheric mirrors, 98
Astigmatism, 97, 99
Asymmetric rotor, 225, 523, 524, 529
Atomic units, 467
Attenuated total reflection, 184, 425
Augment, 552
Axial point groups, 441, 444
Axial vector, 233
Azimuthal quantum number, 252

603